CHOLESTEROL

Je nommerai *cholesterine*, de χολη, bile, et ςερεος, solide, la substance cristallisée des calculs biliaires humains,

The naming of Cholesterol (facsimile) — CHEVREUL, 1816

CHOLESTEROL

Chemistry, Biochemistry, and Pathology

Edited by

ROBERT P. COOK

University of St. Andrews,
Queen's College,
Dundee, Scotland

 1958

ACADEMIC PRESS INC • PUBLISHERS • NEW YORK

PREFACE

In these days of specialization the singling out of a particular topic, or in this case of a single chemical entity, for detailed consideration is no novelty. The potential buyer will ask, does cholesterol justify a complete volume? The editor, in answering yes, can point out the universal distribution of cholesterol in all animal tissues and, it would appear, in all parts of their cells. But this is no novelty, water and numerous other chemical compounds are also universal components of cells. Cholesterol, however, has an additional interest; it has been implicated as a pathogen *sui generis*. It is a favored candidate in the etiology of atherosclerosis, that major affection of our arteries. It has also been suggested as one of the factors concerned in the causation of cancer and it is certainly found in a large number of human gallstones.

Since it is present in all cells and yet a possible cause of disease, we may well ask in the words of the title of one of the lectures given by the late Harry Deuel: "Cholesterol—Friend or Foe?"

The compound is, above all, an interesting chemical species. Why has Nature singled out this particular shape of molecule for cholesterol and the related steroid hormones whose actions are a constant source of wonder? Its biosynthesis also poses the problems of how and why a compound is cyclized instead of, as it were, remaining straight.

From the chemical point of view it is used *inter alia* as a model for studying stereochemical problems and as the chemist remarks it will be a "happy hunting ground" for years to come. This attitude has much to commend it—we study a subject because we are interested in it and if this leads to useful practical applications in the field of medicine then our time has been well spent.

We have tried to make the book of use to scientific workers, not only those dealing directly with cholesterol but to all concerned with the wider aspects of biology, chemistry, and medicine. For example, the metabolic transformations of this compound (and of other sterols) by a great variety of organisms are therefore discussed, and wherever possible this information is given in a tabular or diagrammatic form for ease of reference. To emphasize the practical intention of the book we have included an appendix of commonly used laboratory methods.

There will be found, undoubtedly, overlaps and omissions. To have been encyclopedic would have meant a multivolume treatise and the value of such a work is debatable.

v

The general plan in each chapter has been to cover representative work and to include references, particularly those of a review nature, from which the reader, if he be so minded, may accumulate even more knowledge on the specialized aspects of the subject.

The references are listed at the end of each chapter with the names of the first cited authors arranged in alphabetical order. A chronological order is followed when several publications under the same name are quoted. In Chapter 1 the full titles of all the journal articles are given because of their historical interest. In other chapter titles of articles (or an indication of their subject) are given only when they are of a review nature, such references being marked with an asterisk. The abbreviations used for journals are in general conformity with the "List of Periodicals Abstracted by Chemical Abstracts, 1956," published by the American Chemical Society, Ohio State University, Columbus 10, Ohio.

The contributors are all experienced in their particular fields of study and have cooperated willingly in this project. To them I owe my sincere thanks and any success the book may have is due to their help.

The editor would like to thank the Staff of Academic Press for their kind assistance in the various stages of publication. They have made it possible to include much recent work. The book may therefore be regarded as reasonably "up to date" to the end of 1957.

ROBERT COOK

Dundee, Scotland
January, 1958

LIST OF CONTRIBUTORS

DAVID ADLERSBERG, *The Mount Sinai Hospital, New York, New York*

WERNER BERGMANN, *Sterling Chemistry Laboratory, Yale University, New Haven, Connecticut*

PETER BLADON, *Department of Chemistry, The Royal College of Science and Technology, Glasgow, Scotland*

GEOFFREY H. BOURNE, *Department of Anatomy, Emory University, Emory University, Georgia*

GEORGE S. BOYD, *Department of Biochemistry, University of Edinburgh, Edinburgh, Scotland*

ROBERT P. COOK, *University of St. Andrews, Queen's College, Dundee, Scotland*

HENRIK DAM, *Department of Biochemistry and Nutrition, Polytechnic Institute, Copenhagen, Denmark*

R. GORDON GOULD, *University of California, Los Alamos Scientific Laboratory, Los Alamos, New Mexico*

OSCAR HECHTER, *The Worcester Foundation for Experimental Biology, Shrewsbury, Massachusetts*

MARJORIE G. HORNING, *Laboratory of Cellular Physiology and Metabolism, National Heart Institute, National Institutes of Health, Bethesda, Maryland*

MICHAEL F. OLIVER, *Department of Cardiology, Royal Infirmary, Edinburgh, Scotland*

IRVINE H. PAGE, *Research Division, Cleveland Clinic Foundation and Frank E. Bunts Educational Institute, Cleveland, Ohio*

JAMES B. M. RATTRAY, *Department of Biochemistry, Queen's University, Kingston, Ontario, Canada*

HARRY SOBOTKA, *The Mount Sinai Hospital, New York, New York*

THRESSA C. STADTMAN, *Laboratory of Cellular Physiology and Metabolism, National Heart Institute, National Institutes of Health, Bethesda, Maryland*

vii

CONTENTS

Chapter 1

HISTORICAL INTRODUCTION

Henrik Dam

"Weite Welt und breites Leben,
Langer Jahre redlich Streben,
Stets geforscht und stets gegründet,
Nie geschlossen, oft geründet
Ältestes bewahrt mit Treue,
Freundlich aufgefasstes Neue.
Heitern Sinn und reine Zwecke,
Nun, man kommt wohl eine Strecke."

GOETHE

I. The Discovery and Occurrence of Cholesterol

The compound now known as cholesterol was described for the first time in the latter half of the 18th century. De Fourcroy (1789) mentions that more than 20 years earlier Poulletier de la Salle had obtained from the alcohol-soluble part of human gallstones "une substance feuilleté, lamelleuse, brillante, assez semblable à l'acide boracique." Fourcroy prepared a larger quantity of the substance, which he believed was the same as "blanc de baleine" i.e. spermaceti. He also believed that the crystalline substance from gallstones was related to what he called "adipocire" ("fatty wax"), a matter obtained by treating grave wax with acids.* During the time between Poulletier's observation and Fourcroy's publication other workers, e.g. Conradi (1775; see also Gren, 1789), had

---

* Grave wax is a substance formed in cemeteries, particularly in moist places, during decomposition of the bodies.

1

extracted the substance from gallstones and made observations regarding its solubility.

Chevreul (1815) showed that the substance remained unchanged after boiling with potassium hydroxide, and thereby as well as by its melting point differed from spermaceti and "adipocire." In 1816 Chevreul introduced the designation *cholesterine* from Greek: chole, bile; and steros, solid.* Cholesterine was found by Chevreul (1824) in human and animal bile, by Lecanu (1838) in human blood, and by Couerbe (1834) in brain. Lecanu is credited by Gobley (1846) with its discovery in hens' eggs. Gobley's analyses of egg yolk are models of clarity. It was thereafter gradually recognized as a normal constituent of all animal cells and several secretions, as well as a component of certain pathological deposits. Vogel (1843) found it in atheromatous arteries, and Müller (1838) in the type of tumors which he called cholesteatomes.

Berthelot (1859) showed that "cholestérine" was an alcohol and prepared esters of it. Cholesterol oleate and palmitate were isolated from serum by Hürthle (1896). The palmitate and stearate were found in normal adrenals in 1909 by Rosenheim and Tebb. Windaus (1910b) showed that the cholesterol desposit in atheromatous aorta is present chiefly as esters, his work on this problem being taken up on Aschoff's suggestion.

II. Early Chemistry

Reinitzer (1888) published the correct summation formula of cholesterol, and Diels and Abderhalden (1904) showed that the alcohol group is secondary in that they converted cholesterol into cholestenone. The presence of a double bond was shown in 1868 by Wislicenus and Moldenhauer.

The elucidation of the constitution is mainly due to the arduous work of Windaus and his associates. Aided by parallel studies by Wieland on the chemically related bile acids and earlier studies of Mauthner and Suida on derivatives of cholesterol, Windaus (1919) arrived at a tentative formula which was changed in 1932 to the one now accepted (see Chapter 2).

The new formula was based on X-ray studies by Bernal (1932a) and by the finding of chrysene by catalytic dehydrogenation (Diels and Gädke, 1927), thoroughly discussed by Rosenheim and King (1932a, b) and by Bernal (1932b). Windaus (1932) and Wieland and Dane (1932)

---

* See Frontispiece; the term cholesterol was introduced in English and French literature in the beginning of the 20th century, cholesterin is still used in the German literature.

decided on the final formulation. Windaus (1919, 1932) has given reviews of the various stages of this research.

III. Related Compounds

A. ANIMAL STEROLS

Coprosterol (Greek: copros, dung)* the saturated derivative to which cholesterol is usually transformed in the large intestine, was apparently first observed by Marcet (1857, 1860) as crystals separating by cooling of an alcoholic extract of human feces treated with lime. The pictures he gave of the crystals and the description of their solubility and melting point (given as 92–96° C.) seem to indicate the identity with coprosterol. Marcet believed that the substance which he called "excretine" contained sulfur. A substance "stercorine" from feces mentioned by Flint (1862) may have been impure coprosterol (melting point given as 96.8° F.).

Coprostanol was independently discovered and exactly described by Bondzynski (1896) who gave it the designation "Koprosterin." Bondzynski and Humnicki (1896) examined it further and correctly attributed its formation to bacterial reduction of cholesterol, although the imitation of the process by bacteria *in vitro* without the presence of intestinal content or feces was not carried out until later (cf. Snog-Kjaer *et al.*, 1955, 1956).

The chemical relationship between coprostanol and cholesterol was elucidated by Windaus and Uibrig (1915) and Windaus (1916). They carried out the first transformation of cholesterol into coprostanol by chemical means *in vitro* and cleared up the difference between coprostanol and the isomeric compound obtained by catalytic hydrogenation of cholesterol: *dihydrocholesterol*† (then called β-cholestanol, now *cholestanol*) as being due to differences in the steric arrangement of a hydrogen atom.

Windaus and Neukirchen (1919) converted the hydrocarbon corresponding to coprostanol into cholanic acid and thus definitely proved the relationship between coprostanol and the bile acids.

Other animal sterols but containing 30 carbon atoms, namely, *lanosterol* and *agnosterol* from wool fat, were found by Windaus and Tschesche (1930).

Δ⁷-Cholestenol was found by Fieser (1951) in commercial cholesterol and called by him "lathosterol" (Greek: latho, undetected). It was also found by Baumann and associates (e.g. Miller and Baumann, 1952) in

---

* Named now *coprostanol*: systematic nomenclature 5β-cholestan-3β-ol (see Chapter 2).

† Cholestanol (dihydrocholesterol) is in systematic nomenclature 5α-cholestan-3β-ol (see Chapter 2).

rodent skin as a sterol which gives a rapid reaction ("fast acting") with the Liebermann-Burchard reagent. Later it was shown to be widely distributed.

B. PLANT STEROLS

Sterols were found in plants, namely, in peas by Beneke (1862) and differentiated from cholesterol by Hesse (1878) who introduced the name *phytosterin* for a sterol isolated from Calabar beans. Thoms (1897) proposed to use the term phytosterol for all plant sterols.

Sitosterol (Greek: sitos, grain) from cereal germs was isolated by Burián (1897), *stigmasterol* from Calabar beans (*Phytostigma venenosum*, wherefrom the name was derived) by Windaus and Hauth (1906). Anderson and Shriner (1926) showed the existence of several isomeric forms of sitosterol.

Ergosterol was found in ergot by Tanret (1889) and called by him *ergostérine*. Ergosterol was prepared in impure form from yeast by Gérard (1895), and in pure form by Smedley-MacLean and Thomas (1920).

C. RELATION TO VITAMIN D[*]

"Activation of cholesterol" by irradiation to antirachitic substances was described in 1925 by Hess *et al.* and by Steenbock and Black, and in 1926 by Rosenheim and Webster. The work of Rosenheim and Webster (1926, 1927a, b), Heilbron *et al.* (1926, 1927), Pohl (1927), and Windaus and Hess (1927) proved that the phenomenon was due to the activation of a contaminant of ordinary cholesterol with a substance closely related to ergosterol, which latter substance became active on irradiation.

7-Dehydrocholesterol was synthesized from cholesterol in 1935 by Windaus *et al.* The following year Boer and associates (1936) isolated this substance from samples of cholesterol and proved it to be the provitamin accompanying cholesterol.

Bills and McDonald (1926) activated cholesterol to an antirachitic substance without irradiation, namely, by heating it in an organic solvent with floridin. The vitamin obtained by this procedure was later identified by Raoul and co-workers (1954).

D. RELATION TO STEROID HORMONES

The structural relation of cholesterol to certain *hormones* was disclosed when ovarian, testicular, and adrenal cortical hormones were isolated and their chemistry studied in the thirties of this century.

---

[*] For a more detailed account of the early history of the relation between cholesterol and the D vitamins reference is made to the review article by Bills (1935).

For the comprehensive literature concerning the relationship of cholesterol to hormones the reader is referred to Chapter 8 of this book and to monographs, such as that of Fieser and Fieser (1949). Here it may suffice to mention that Ruzicka and co-workers (1934) prepared androsterone from epicholestanol (cholestan-3α-ol) and that Fernholz (1934) converted stigmasterol into progesterone.

IV. Analytical Methods

Among the methods for detection and estimation of cholesterol the qualitative estimation was published in 1872.

The *Salkowski* color reaction with chloroform and sulfuric acid for qualitative estimation was published in 1872.

The *Liebermann-Burchard* reaction evolved in two stages. First, Liebermann (1885) described the color changes taking place when sulfuric acid is added to a concentrated solution of cholesterol in acetic anhydride (color shift through red to blue). Thereafter Burchard (1889) applied the reaction to a solution of cholesterol in chloroform or certain other water-free solvents and noted that a green color developed, the red and blue stages being bypassed when the solution of cholesterol is dilute.

The more sensitive reaction with acetyl chloride and zinc chloride in glacial acetic acid was described 1909 by Tschugaeff and Gasteff.

Windaus (1909, 1910a) introduced the *gravimetric digitonin method* which was a revolutionizing step not only in the quantitative determination but also in the isolation of sterols. Windaus' discovery was based on the observation by Ransom (1901) that cholesterol neutralizes the hemolyzing effect of saponin. Windaus, who was then working in the Institute of Chemistry, University of Freiburg, Germany, tested several saponins for their ability to precipitate cholesterol and found digitonin to be particularly suited for the purpose. The circumstance that the head of the Institute was the well-known investigator of saponins, Kiliani, probably favored this highly important study. Windaus also found that saponins react only with free sterols, not with sterol esters. Later (1916), he showed that the epi (3α-ol) forms of sterols are not precipitable with digitonin.

A micromethod combining digitonin precipitation with the Liebermann-Burchard reaction was developed by Schoenheimer and Sperry (1934) and revised by Brun (1939) and Sperry and Webb (1950).

Schoenheimer (1930) modified the original digitonin method for the purpose of determining saturated sterols in the presence of unsaturated, by adding bromine to the double bond of the unsaturated sterol. The bromine addition product did not precipitate with digitonin.

Windaus found that it is possible to extract the sterol from the digitonin addition compound by prolonged treatment with boiling xylene.

Another method, namely solution of the digitonide in pyridine in which it is dissociated, and subsequent precipitation of the digitonin with ether was introduced by Schoenheimer and Dam (1933).

V. Metabolism

Synthesis. Dezani (1913) and Dezani and Cattoretti (1914) were the first to show that cholesterol is synthesized in rats reared on a cholesterol-free diet. Their findings were confirmed for the same and other species, e.g. with infants by Gamble and Blackfan (1920), with human adults by Gardner and Fox (1921), with young dogs by Beumer and Lehmann (1923), with rats by Channon (1925) and Randles and Knudson (1925), with chicks by Dam (1929), and with laying hens by Schoenheimer (1929b).

The fact that cholesterol is an essential nutrient for certain insects was first established by Hobson (1935) in studies with blowflies.

Breakdown. The fact that the animal organism can also catabolize cholesterol was shown by Dam (1931) with chicks during the first two weeks after hatching, by Page and Menschick (1932) with rabbits fed cholesterol, and by Schoenheimer and Breusch (1933) with mice. Cook (1938) showed that feeding of cholesterol to rats resulted in an increase of acids in the feces in amount equal to the cholesterol broken down.

State and concentration in blood. Originally the interest centered mostly around the concentration of cholesterol and its esters in blood and particularly in plasma or serum. This was studied in relation to meals of varying composition with respect to fat and cholesterol and in relation to menstrual cycle, pregnancy, and to diseases such as atherosclerosis, lipidoses, xanthoma, and diseases of the liver and thyroid.

Of the enormous number of older studies on this subject mention may be made to those of Gardner and co-workers, e.g. Gardner and Gainsborough (1928), Bloor and Knudson (1917), Okey and Boyden (1927), and by Thannhauser and his colleagues. Thannhauser and Schaber (1926) studied particularly the so-called "Ester-sturz," namely, the pronounced fall in the ratio of ester to total cholesterol found in cases of liver disease.

More recently the interest, mostly in relation to atherosclerosis, has focused on the presence of cholesterol in lipoproteins and chylomicra. Of the rich literature on this subject the works of Gofman and his colleagues (e.g. Gofman *et al.*, 1950) shall be mentioned. However, the total cholesterol concentration in blood plasma is still receiving attention, particularly through the work of Keys and associates (e.g. Keys and Keys, 1954). This controversial subject is discussed in other chapters.

Absorption. The absorption of cholesterol from the intestine was demonstrated by Pribram (1906). J. H. Mueller (1915) showed that (in dogs) absorbed cholesterol is transported via the thoracic duct,— and in 1916 he reported that pancreatic juice and bile further the absorption. Russian workers had already shown that cholesterol feeding in rabbits causes deposition of the substance in the arterial wall (Anitschkow and Chalatow, 1913). The same was shown later for other species, e.g. for chicks (Dauber and Katz, 1942). The importance of fat for the ready absorption of cholesterol was pointed out by Cook (1936).

Schoenheimer (1929a) demonstrated the marked difference in absorbability between cholesterol which is easily absorbed and plant sterols which are much more difficultly absorbed from the intestine of rabbits. Von Behring and Schoenheimer (1930) showed that saturated sterols (stanols) such as cholestanol and coprostanol behave like plant sterols in this respect. That rats may absorb some cholestanol when fed this substance was shown by Dam and Brun (1935).

Peterson (1951) first reported that plant sterols interfere with the absorption of cholesterol in chickens. A similar effect exerted by cholestanol was found by Siperstein *et al.* (1953), and had been observed in man by Dam (1934).

The study of the influence of various sterols on blood and tissue cholesterol, and on atherosclerosis, led to further information of their absorbability and convertibility to cholesterol; for example Cook and associates (1954) showed that rabbits absorb Δ^7-cholestenol (lathosterol), 7-dehydrocholesterol, and also cholestanol, and that all of these are potentially atherogenic. Nichols *et al.* (1955) found that prolonged feeding of cholestanol to chickens resulted in deposition of the substance in the vascular wall.

Excretion. Since Chevreul (1824) found cholesterol in normal bile it has been known that bile is one of the excretion paths. In 1926 Sperry showed with bile fistula dogs that a considerable amount of cholesterol is excreted through the intestinal wall.

Conversion to other sterols. Conversion of a small part of the body's cholesterol into cholestanol was reported by Schoenheimer and co-workers (1930), who found that a small amount of cholestanol usually accompanies cholesterol and is excreted into the intestine. A considerable amount of cholestanol was found in the sterile content of an intestinal loop of 14 years duration in a surgical patient by Boehm (1911).

Schoenheimer and associates suggested that the formation of cholestanol from cholesterol in the body was accompanied by desaturation of other cholesterol molecules.

The formation of 7-dehydrocholesterol from cholesterol in the intestinal wall of guinea pigs was later demonstrated by Glover *et al.* (1952).

With the *era of isotopes* an unforeseen development in the study of cholesterol metabolism began. Rittenberg and Schoenheimer (1937) undertook studies of cholesterol formation using deuterium oxide and suggested that the formation of cholesterol in the animal body involved the coupling of a number of small molecules.

After the tragic death of Schoenheimer in 1941, Bloch and Rittenberg (1942) began their now classical work on the formation of cholesterol from deuterium containing acetic acid which was followed by a large number of studies on similar lines by these and other investigators, especially after carbon-labeled acetate was introduced (Rittenberg and Bloch, 1945).

The detailed discussion of these studies belongs under special chapters of this book, but it shall be mentioned here that the new technique made it possible to demonstrate synthesis of cholesterol in individual tissues *in vitro*, such as liver, intestine, and arteries. Further, it was shown that feeding of cholesterol depresses cholesterol synthesis in, for example, the liver (see Gould *et al.*, 1953; Tomkins *et al.*, 1953), and the relation of squalene to cholesterol synthesis was attacked (Tomkins *et al.*, 1953).

Through the work of Wüersch and associates (1952) (the side chain), and Cornforth *et al.* (1953) (the ring structure) it became possible to map the cholesterol molecule according to which of the carbon atoms originate from the CH_3 and which from the $COOH$ group of acetic acid. The complexity of the conversion is shown by the presence of "high counting companions" by Schwenk and his associates (e.g. Schwenk *et al.*, 1955).

Other workers began the study of the conversion of cholesterol into bile acids and hormones. Thus, Bloch *et al.* (1943) showed that deuterium-labeled cholesterol is converted into cholic acid, and other workers, especially Bergström (1952), have greatly extended the research on this subject.

Conversion to pregnandiol and probably to progesterone was reported by Bloch (1945). The formation of adrenal cortical hormones from cholesterol was demonstrated by Zaffaroni and associates (1951).

The conversion of cholesterol into coprostanol has also been taken up using the isotope technique. By suitable labeling of cholesterol, Rosenfeld and co-workers (1954) found that cholesterol can be converted into coprostanol without cholestenone as an intermediate, such as it had been suggested previously by Rosenheim and Webster (1935) and by Schoenheimer *et al.* (1935).

This very schematic outline of the history of cholesterol research could for the sake of briefness touch only some of the major points, whereby others have been bypassed. It will be seen that from a few sporadic observations dating back to the time before the French revolution an enormous amount of investigation has branched out, penetrating deeply into the realms of bile acids, hormones and vitamins. Many problems have been solved, many are being studied, and still more are approaching.

REFERENCES

Anderson, R. J., and Shriner, R. L. (1926). The phytosterols of corn oil. *J. Am. Chem. Soc.* **48**, 2976-2986.

Anitschkow, N., and Chalatow, S. (1913). Ueber experimentelle Cholesterinsteatose und ihre Bedeutung für die Entstehung einiger pathologischer Prozesse. *Zentr. allgem. Pathol. u. pathol. Anat.* **24**, 1-9.

Beneke, G. M. R. (1862). Cholesterin im Pflanzenreich aufgefunden. *Ann.* **122**, 249-255.

Bergström, S. (1952). The formation of bile acids from cholesterol in the rat. *Kgl. Fysiograf. Sällskap. i Lund, Förh.* **22**, 91-96.

Bernal, J. D. (1932a). Crystal structures of vitamin D and related compounds. *Nature* **129**, 277-278.

Bernal, J. D. (1932b). Carbon skeleton of the sterols. *Chem. & Ind.* (*London*) **51**, p. 466.

Berthelot, M. (1859). Sur plusieurs alcools nouveaux. *Ann. chim. et phys.* [3] **56**, 51-98, especially p. 54-69.

Beumer, H., and Lehmann, F. (1923). Über die Cholesterinbildung im Tierkörper. *Z. ges. exptl. Med.* **37**, 274-280.

Bills, C. E., and McDonald, F. G. (1926). The catalytic formation of an antirachitic cholesterol derivative. *J. Biol. Chem.* **67**, 753-758.

Bills, C. E. (1935). Physiology of the sterols, including vitamin D. *Physiol. Revs.* **15**, 1-97.

Bloch, K. (1945). The biological conversion of cholesterol to pregnanediol. *J. Biol. Chem.* **157**, 661-666.

Bloch, K., and Rittenberg, D. (1942). The biological formation of cholesterol from acetic acid. *J. Biol. Chem.* **143**, 297-298.

Bloch, K., Berg, B. N., and Rittenberg, D. (1943). The biological conversion of cholesterol to cholic acid. *J. Biol. Chem.* **149**, 511-517.

Bloor, W. R., and Knudson, A. (1917). Cholesterol and cholesterol esters in human blood. *J. Biol. Chem.* **29**, 7-13.

Boehm, R. (1911). Ein Beitrag zur Chemie des Darminhaltes. *Biochem. Z.* **33**, 474-479.

Boer, A. G., Reerink, E. H., Van Wijk, A., and Van Niekerk, J. (1936). A naturally occurring chicken provitamin D. *Proc. Acad. Sci. Amsterdam* **39**, 622-632.

Bondzynski, S. (1896). Ueber das Cholesterin der menschlichen Faeces. *Ber.* **29**, 476-478.

Bondzynski, S., and Humnicki, V. (1896). Ueber das Schicksal des Cholesterins im tierischen Organismus. *Z. physiol. Chem.* **22**, 396-410.

Brun, G. C. (1939). "Cholesterol Content of the Red Blood Cells in Man." Nyt Nordisk Forlag, Copenhagen, and Lewis, London.

Burchard, H. (1889). Dissertation, 26 pp., Rostock, Germany. Beiträge zur Kenntniss der Cholesterine.

Burián, R. (1897). Über Sitosterin (Ein Beitrag zur Kenntniss der Phytosterine). *Sitzber. Akad. Wiss. Wien, Math. naturw. Kl. Abt. IIb* **106**, 549-572.

Channon, H. J. (1925). Cholesterol synthesis in the animal body. *Biochem. J.* **19**, 424-432.

Chevreul, M. E. (1815). Recherches chimiques sur plusieurs corps gras, et particulièrement sur leurs combinations avec les alcalis. Cinquième Mémoire. Des corps qu'on a appelés adipocire, c'est-à-dire, de la substance cristallisée des calculs biliaires humains, du spermacéti et de la substance grasse des cadavres. *Ann. chim.* **95**, 5-50, especially p. 7-10.

Chevreul, M. E. (1816). Sixième Mémoire. Examen des graisses d'homme, de mouton, de boeuf, de jaguar et d'oie. *Ann. chim. et phys.* **2**, 339-372, especially p. 346.

Chevreul, M. E. (1824). Note sur la présence de la cholesterine dans la bile de l'homme. *Mém. Musée Hist. nat. Paris* **11**, 239-240.

Conradi, B. G. F. (1775). Dissertatio sistens experimenta nonnulla cum calculis vesiculae felleae humana instituta. Jena. Reprinted in: Thesaurus Dissertationum Medicarum Rariorum **1**, 191-211. Heidelbergae (1784).

Cook, R. P. (1936). Cholesterol feeding and fat metabolism. *Biochem. J.* **30**, 1630-1636.

Cook, R. P. (1938). Cholesterol metabolism. I. Acids apparently concerned in the metabolism of cholesterol. *Biochem. J.* **32**, 1191-1199.

Cook, R. P., Kliman, A., and Fieser, L. F. (1954). The absorption and metabolism of cholesterol and its main companions in the rabbit. *Arch. Biochem. Biophys.* **52**, 439-450.

Cornforth, J. W., Hunter, G. D., and Popják, G. (1953). Distribution of acetate carbon in the ring-system of cholesterol. *Biochem. J.* **53**, proc. xxiv-xxv.

Couerbe, J. P. (1834). Du cerveau, considéré sous le point de vue chimique et physiologique, pp. 181-184: De la cholesterine. *Ann. chim. et phys.* **56**, 160-193.

Dam, H. (1929). Cholesterinstoffwechsel in Hühnereiern und Hühnchen. *Biochem. Z.* **215**, 475-492.

Dam, H. (1931). Cholesterinbilanz des Hühnchens in den ersten zwei Lebenswochen. *Biochem. Z.* **232**, 269-273.

Dam, H. (1934). The formation of coprosterol in the intestine. I. Possible role of dihydrocholesterol, and a method of determining dihydrocholesterol in presence of coprosterol. *Biochem. J.* **28**, 815-819, especially p. 818.

Dam, H., and Brun, G. C. (1935). Ein Dihydrocholesterinbilanzversuch an der Ratte. *Biochem. Z.* **276**, 274-276.

Dauber, D. V., and Katz, L. N. (1942). Experimental cholesterol atheromatosis in an omnivorous animal, the chick. *A.M.A. Arch. Pathol.* **34**, 937-950.

De Fourcroy (1789). De la substance feuilletée et cristalline contenue dans les calculs biliaires, et de la nature des concrétions cystiques cristalisées. *Ann. chim.* **3**, 242-252.

Dezani, S. (1913). Ricerche sulla genesi della colesterina. Nota II. *Arch. farmacol. sper.* **16**, 3-11.

Dezani, S., and Cattoretti, F. (1914). Nuove ricerche sulla genesi delle colesterine. *Arch. farmacol. sper.* **18**, 3-11.

Diels, O., and Abderhalden, E. (1904). Zur Kenntniss des Cholesterins. *Ber.* **37**, 3092-3103.

Diels, O., and Gädke, W. (1927). Über die Bildung von Chrysen bei der Dehydrierung des Cholesterins. *Ber.* **60**, 140-147.

Fernholz, E. (1934). Die Darstellung des Corpus-luteum-Hormons aus Stigmasterin. *Ber.* **67**, 2027-2031.

Fieser, L. F. (1951). A companion of cholesterol. *J. Am. Chem. Soc.* **73**, 5007.

Fieser, L. F., and Fieser, M. (1949). "Natural Products Related to Phenanthrene," 3rd ed. Reinhold, New York.

Flint, A. (1862). Experimental researches into a new excretory function of the liver; consisting in the removal of cholesterine from the blood, and its discharge from the body in the form of stercorine. *Am. J. Med. Sci.* [N.S.] **44**, 305-365, especially pp. 337-348.

Gamble, J. L., and Blackfan, K. D. (1920). Evidence indicating a synthesis of cholesterol by infants. *J. Biol. Chem.* **42**, 401-409.

Gardner, J. A., and Fox, F. W. (1921). On the origin and destiny of cholesterol in the animal organism. Part XII. On the excretion of sterols in man. *Proc. Roy. Soc.* **B92**, 358-367.

Gardner, J. A., and Gainsborough, H. (1928). Studies on the cholesterol content of normal human plasma. III. On the so-called alimentary hypercholesterolaemia. *Biochem. J.* **22**, 1048-1056.

Gérard, E. (1895). Sur les cholésterines des cryptogames. *J. pharm. chim.* [6] **1**, 601-608.

Glover, M., Glover, J., and Morton, R. A. (1952). Provitamin D_3 in tissues and the conversion of cholesterol to 7-dehydrocholesterol *in vivo*. *Biochem. J.* **51**, 1-9.

Gobley (1846). Recherches chimiques sur le jaune d'oeuf. *J. pharm. chem.* [3] **9**, 81-91.

Gofman, J. W., Lindgren, F. T., Elliott, H. A., Mantz, W., Hewitt, J., Strisower, B., Herring, V., and Lyon, T. P. (1950). The role of lipids and lipoproteins in atherosclerosis. *Science* **111**, 166-171, 186.

Gould, R. G., Taylor, C. B., Hagerman, J. S., Warner, I., and Campbell, D. J. (1953). Cholesterol metabolism. I. Effect of dietary cholesterol on the synthesis of cholesterol in dog tissue *in vitro*. *J. Biol. Chem.* **201**, 519-528.

Gren (1789). Zerlegung eines Gallensteins. Beyträge zu den chemischen Annalen von Lorenz Crell. Helmstädt und Leipzig, pp. 19-26, especially p. 24.

Heilbron, I. M., Kamm, E. D., and Morton, R. A. (1926). The absorption spectra of cholesterol and its possible biological significance with reference to vitamin D. *J. Soc. Chem. Ind.* (*London*) **45**, 932.

Heilbron, I. M., Kamm, E. D., and Morton, R. A. (1927). The absorption spectra of oils and oil constituents with special reference to provitamin D. *Biochem. J.* **21**, 1279-1283.

Hess, A. F., Weinstock, M., and Helman, F. D. (1925). The antirachitic value of irradiated phytosterol and cholesterol. I. *J. Biol. Chem.* **63**, 303-308.

Hesse, O. (1878). Ueber Phytosterin und Cholesterin. *Ann.* **192**, 175-179.

Hobson, R. P. (1935). On a fat-soluble growth factor required by blow-fly larvae. II. Identity of the growth factor with cholesterol. *Biochem. J.* **29**, 2023-2026.

Hürthle, K. (1896). Ueber die Fettsäure-Cholesterin-Ester des Blutserums. *Z. physiol. Chem.* **21**, 331-359.

Keys, A., and Keys, M. H. (1954). Serum cholesterol and the diet in clinically healthy men at Slough near London. *Brit. J. Nutrition* **8**, 138-147.

Lecanu, L. R. (1838). Etudes chimiques sur le sang humain. *Ann. chim. et phys.* **67**, 54-70.

Liebermann, C. (1885). Ueber das Oxychinoterpen. *Ber.* **18**, 1803-1809.

Marcet, W. (1857). On the immediate principles of human excrements in the healthy state. *Phil. Trans. Roy. Soc. London* **147**, 403-413.

Marcet, W. (1860). Memoire sur l'excrétine. Nouveau principe immédiat des excrément humains. *Ann. chim. et. phys.* [3] **59**, 91-98.

Miller, W. L., Jr., and Baumann, C. A. (1952). Studies on Δ^{-7} cholestenol in skin. *Federation Proc.* **11**, 261.

Müller, J. (1838). "Ueber den feineren Bau und die Formen der krankhaften Geschwülste," pp. 39-60, especially pp. 49-54. Gedruckt und verlegt bei G. Reimer, Berlin.

Mueller, J. H. (1915). The assimilation of cholesterol and its esters. *J. Biol. Chem.* **22**, 1-9.

Mueller, J. H. (1916). The mechanism of cholesterol absorption. *J. Biol. Chem.* **27**, 463-480.

Nichols, C. W., Jr., Lindsay, S., and Chaikoff, I. L. (1955). Production of arteriosclerosis in birds by the prolonged feeding of dihydrocholesterol. *Proc. Soc. Exptl. Biol. Med.* **89**, 609-613.

Okey, R., and Boyden, R. E. (1927). Variations in the lipid content of blood in relation to the menstrual cycle. *J. Biol. Chem.* **72**, 261-281.

Page, I. H., and Menschick, W. (1932). The destruction of cholesterol by the animal organism. *J. Biol. Chem.* **97**, 359-368.

Peterson, D. W. (1951). Effect of soybean sterols in the diet on plasma and liver cholesterol in chicks. *Proc. Soc. Exptl. Biol. Med.* **78**, 143-147.

Pohl, R. (1927). Ueber das Absorptionsspektrum des antirachitisch wirksamen Cholesterins. *Nachr. Ges. Wiss. Göttingen. Math.-physik. Kl.* pp. 142-145.

Pribram, H. (1906). Beitrag zur Kenntnis des Schicksals des Cholesterins und der Cholesterinester im tierischen Organismus. *Biochem. Z.* **1**, 413-424.

Randles, F. S., and Knudson, A. (1925). Synthesis of cholesterol in the animal body. *J. Biol. Chem.* **66**, 459-466.

Ransom, F. (1901). Saponin und sein Gegengift. *Deut. med. Wochschr.* **27**, 194-196.

Raoul, Y., Le Boulch, N., Baron, C., Chopin, J., and Guérillot-Vinet, A. (1954). Isolement du composé anti-rachitique formé au cours de l'áction de la floridine sur le cholesterol. *Bull. soc. chim. biol.* **36**, 1265-1271.

Reinitzer, F. (1888). Beiträge zur Kenntniss des Cholesterins. *Sitzber. Akad. Wiss. Wien, Math.-naturw. Kl. Abt. I.* **97**, 167-187.

Rittenberg, D., and Bloch, K. (1945). The utilization of acetic acid for the synthesis of fatty acids. *J. Biol. Chem.* **160**, 417-424.

Rittenberg, D., and Schoenheimer, R. (1937). Further studies on the biological uptake of deuterium into organic substances with special reference to fat and cholesterol formation.. *J. Biol. Chem.* **121**, 235-253.

Rosenfeld, R. S., Fukushima, D. K., Hellman, L., and Gallagher, T. F. (1954). The transformation of cholesterol to coprosterol. *J. Biol. Chem.* **211**, 301-311.

Rosenheim, O., and King, H. (1932a). The ring system of sterols and bile acids. *Chem. & Ind. (London)* **51**, 464-466.

Rosenheim, O., and King, H. (1932b). The ring system of sterols and bile acids. *Nature* **130**, 315.

Rosenheim, O., and Tebb, M. C. (1909). On the lipoids of the adrenals. *J. Physiol.* (*London*) **38**, proc. Liv.

Rosenheim, O., and Webster, T. A. (1926). The antirachitic properties of irradiated sterols. *Biochem. J.* **20**, 537-544.

Rosenheim, O., and Webster, T. A. (1927a). The relation of cholesterol to vitamin D. *Biochem. J.* **21**, 127-129.

Rosenheim, O., and Webster, T. A. (1927b). The parent substance of vitamin D; pp. 395-396: Ergosterol as provitamin D. *Biochem. J.* **21**, 389-397.

Rosenheim, O., and Webster, T. A. (1935). Precursors of coprosterol and the bile acids in the animal organism. *Nature* **136**, 474.

Ruzicka, L., Goldberg, M. W., Meyer, J., Brüngger, H., and Eichenberger, E. (1934). Zur Kenntniss der Sexualhormone. II. Über die Synthese des Testikelhormons (Androsterons) und Stereoisomerer desselben durch Abbau hydrierter Sterine. *Helv. Chim. Acta* **17**, 1395-1406.

Salkowski, E. (1872). Kleinere Mittheilungen physiologisch-chemischen Inhalts (II). *Pflüger's Arch. ges. Physiol.* **6**, 207-222.

Schoenheimer, R. (1929a). Über die Bedeutung der Pflanzensterine für den tierischen Organismus. *Z. physiol. Chem.* **180**, 1-37.

Schoenheimer, R. (1929b). Versuch einer Sterinbilanz an der legenden Henne. *Z. physiol. Chem.* **185**, 119-122.

Schoenheimer, R. (1930). Methodik zur quantitativen Trennung von ungesättigten und gesättigten Sterinen. *Z. physiol. Chem.* **192**, 77-86.

Schoenheimer, R., and Breusch, F. (1933). Synthesis and destruction of cholesterol in the organism. *J. Biol. Chem.* **103**, 439-448.

Schoenheimer, R., and Dam, H. (1933). Über die Spaltbarkeit und Löslichkeit von Sterindigitoniden. *Z. physiol. Chem.* **215**, 59-63.

Schoenheimer, R., and Sperry, W. M. (1934). A micromethod for the determination of free and combined cholesterol. *J. Biol. Chem.* **106**, 745-760.

Schoenheimer, R., von Behring, H., Hummel, R., and Schindel, L. (1930). Über die Bedeutung gesättigter Sterine im Organismus. *Z. physiol. Chem.* **192**, 73-111.

Schoenheimer, R., Rittenberg, D., and Graff, M. (1935). The mechanism of coprosterol formation. *J. Biol. Chem.* **111**, 183-192.

Schwenk, E., Alexander, G. J., Fish, C. A., and Stoudt, T. H. (1955). Biosynthesis of substances which accompany cholesterol. *Federation Proc.* **14**, 752-756.

Siperstein, M. D., Nichols, C. W., Jr., and Chaikoff, I. L. (1953). Prevention of plasma cholesterol elevation and atheromatosis in the cholesterol-fed bird by the administration of dihydrocholesterol. *Circulation* **7**, 37-41.

Smedley-MacLean, I., and Thomas, E. M. (1920). The nature of yeast fat. *Biochem. J.* **14**, 483-493.

Snog-Kjaer, A., Prange, I., and Dam, H. (1955). On the formation of coprosterol in the intestine. *Experientia* **11**, 316.

Snog-Kjaer, A., Prange, I., and Dam, H. (1956). Conversion of cholesterol into coprosterol by bacteria *in vitro*. *J. Gen. Microbiol.* **14**, 256-260.

Sperry, W. M. (1926-1927). A study of the relationship of the bile to the fecal lipids with special reference to certain problems of sterol metabolism. *J. Biol. Chem.* **71**, 351-378.

Sperry, W. M., and Webb, M. (1950). A revision of the Schönheimer-Sperry method for cholesterol determination. *J. Biol. Chem.* **187**, 97-106.

Steenbock, H., and Black, A. (1925). The induction of growth-promoting and calcifying properties in fats and their unsaponifiable constituents by exposure to light. *J. Biol. Chem.* **64**, 263-298.

Tanret, C. (1889). Sur un nouveau principe immediat de l'ergot de seigle, l'ergosterine. *Compt. rend.* **108**, 98-100.

Thannhauser, S. J., and Schaber, H. (1926). Ueber die Beziehungen des Gleichgewichtes Cholesterin und Cholesterinester im Blut und Serum zur Leberfunktion. *Klin. Wochschr.* **5** (1), 252-253.

Thoms, H. (1897). Über Phytosterine. *Arch. Pharm.* **235**, 39-43.

Tomkins, G. M., Sheppard, H., and Chaikoff, I. L. (1953). Cholesterol synthesis by liver. III. Its regulation by ingested cholesterol. *J. Biol. Chem.* **201**, 137-141.

Tschugaeff, L., and Gasteff, A. (1909). Zur Kenntnis der Cholesterins. I. *Ber.* **42**, 4631-4634.

Vogel, J. (1843). Icones histologiae pathologiae. Erläuterungstafeln zur pathologischen Histologie, plate xi, Fig. 1, page 52; plate xxii, Fig. 7, pages 101-102. Leopold Voss, Leipzig.

Von Behring, H., and Schoenheimer, R. (1930). Sind gesättigte Sterine resorbierbar? *Z. physiol. Chem.* **192**, 97-102.

Wieland, H., and Dane, E. (1932). Untersuchungen über die Konstitution der Gallensäuren. 39. Mitteilung. Zur Kenntnis der 12-Oxy-cholansäure. *Z. physiol. Chem.* **210**, 268-281.

Windaus, A. (1909). Über die Entgiftung der Saponine durch Cholesterin. *Ber.* **42**, 238-246.

Windaus, A. (1910a). Über die quantitative Bestimmung des Cholesterins und der Cholesterinester in einigen normalen und pathologischen Nieren. *Z. physiol. Chem.* **65**, 110-117.

Windaus, A. (1910b). Über den Gehalt normaler und atheromatöser Aorten an Cholesterin und Cholesterinestern. *Z. physiol. Chem.* **67**, 174-176.

Windaus, A. (1916). 24. Mitteilung zur Kenntnis des Cholesterins. Überführung des Cholesterins in Koprosterin. *Ber.* **49**, 1724-1734.

Windaus, A. (1919). Die Konstitution des Cholesterins. *Nachr. kgl. Ges. Wiss. Göttingen, Math.-physik. Kl.* pp. 237-254.

Windaus, A. (1932). Über die Konstitution des Cholesterins und der Gallensäuren. *Z. physiol. Chem.* **213**, 147-187.

Windaus, A., and Hauth, A. (1906). Ueber Stigmasterin, ein neues Phytosterin aus Calabar-Bohnen. *Ber.* **39**, 4378-4384.

Windaus, A., and Hess, A. (1927). Sterine und antirachitisches Vitamin. *Nachr. Ges. Wiss. Göttingen, Math.-physik. Kl.* pp. 175-184.

Windaus, A., and Neukirchen, K. (1919). Die Umwandlung des Cholesterins in Cholansäure. *Ber.* **52**, 1915-1919.

Windaus, A., and Tschesche, R. (1930). Über das sogenannte "Isocholesterin" des Wollfettes. *Z. physiol. Chem.* **190**, 51-61.

Windaus, A., and Uibrig, C. (1915). 21. Mitteilung zur Kenntnis des Cholesterins. Über Koprosterin. *Ber.* **48**, 857-863.

Windaus, A., Lettré, H., and Schenck, F. (1935). Über das 7-Dehydro-cholesterin. *Ann.* **520**, 98-106.

Wislicenus, J., and Moldenhauer, W. (1868). Ueber das Cholesterindibromür. *Ann.* **146**, 175-180.

Wüersch, J., Huang, R. L., and Bloch, K. (1952). The origin of the isooctyl side chain of cholesterol. *J. Biol. Chem.* **195**, 439-446.

Zaffaroni, A., Hechter, O., and Pincus, G. (1951). Adrenal conversion of C^{14}-labeled cholesterol and acetate to adrenal cortical hormones. *J. Am. Chem. Soc.* **73**, 1390-1391.

CHEMISTRY

Peter Bladon

I. Introduction

The survey of the chemistry of cholesterol presented in this chapter is necessarily incomplete; the same subject in Elsevier's Encyclopedia occupies several hundred pages. The writer has felt obliged to curtail those sections of the subject that are of mainly historical interest and those that have been discussed in detail elsewhere. Thus, the degradations on which the structure of cholesterol is based have scanty treatment. Discussions of the method of molecular rotation differences applied to steroids, and of ultraviolet and infrared spectra are also largely omitted.

Instead, a fairly detailed account of the chemical reactions of cholesterol and related sterols is presented, largely by means of charts in Section VI. The inclusion of many reactions of "academic interest" is amply justified by the frequent isolation in Nature of steroid derivatives of unusual structure (e.g. helvolic acid; Cram and Allinger, 1956). Also, besides its intrinsic biological importance, cholesterol has played the part of an easily accessible substance, on which organic chemists have in the past tried and tested many theories of stereochemistry and re-action mechanisms. It will undoubtedly remain their "Happy Hunting Ground" for several years to come.

The chemistry of the whole field of steroids is covered by several monographs: Fieser and Fieser (1949), Lettré and Tschesche (1954), Shoppee and Shoppee (1953), Shoppee (1958), Klyne (1957), and Nazarov and Bergel'son (1955); and by the appropriate volumes of "Elsevier's Encyclopaedia of Organic Chemistry" (Josephy and Radt, 1940; Georg, 1954, 1956).

II. Nomenclature

The general recommendations of the Ciba Conference on Steroid Nomenclature are followed (Ciba Conference, 1951). Some of the more important aspects of the subject which are encountered in this book are discussed below.

(I)   (II)

The formula (I) shows the skeleton of cholesterol numbered in the generally accepted manner. The formula (II) shows the additional numbering adopted when one, or two extra carbon atoms are present at C-24 in the side chain, and when extra methyl groups are present at C-4 and C-14. The usual conventions are adopted in naming stereo-isomers. Substituents below the plane of the ring are α-substituents; and are joined to the ring by broken lines. Substituents above the plane of the ring are β-substituents and are joined to the ring by solid lines. Substituents of uncertain configuration are denoted by the Greek letter ξ (Xi) in names, and by wavy lines in formulas.

In the formulas above, each angle of the structures represents a carbon atom and a sufficient number of hydrogen atoms to fill all the unused valencies of the carbon atom. Also, the terminations of the side chains and the strokes in the angular positions (C-10, C-13, and C-14) represent methyl groups. Consequently, when it is necessary to show the configuration of hydrogen atoms at the angular positions C-5, C-8, and C-9, etc., such atoms are indicated by the usual letter symbol "H."

In the tables of physical constants (Section X), both hydroxyl and ketone groups are indicated as suffixes (-ol, -one) when they occur in the same molecule (contrary to *Chemical Abstracts* practice). This leads to the use of unfamiliar names for certain compounds (e.g. 7-keto-cholesterol is cholest-5-en-3β-ol-7-one). Halogen substituents and epoxide rings, etc., are indicated by prefixes.

The names of the nine steroid hydrocarbons which are the basis of steroid nomenclature are shown in Table I. (See page 20.)

Table II
NATURAL STEROLS

No. of C atoms	Name	Formula	Substituents C-5a	Substituents C-24	Double bonds Δ	Free sterol m.p. °C	Free sterol [α]_D degrees	Acetate m.p. °C	Acetate [α]_D degrees	Benzoate m.p. °C	Benzoate [α]_D degrees	Occurrence	References
27	Cholestanol (dihydrocholesterol)	$C_{27}H_{48}O$	H	—	—	142	+24	111	+13.5	135	+20	Companion of cholesterol	1, 3
	Coprostanol (coprosterol)	$C_{27}H_{48}O$	βH	—	—	101	+28	90	—	125	+31	In feces	42, 43, 44
	Cholesterol	$C_{27}H_{46}O$		—	5	148	−40	115	−48	146	−14	In animal cells	1, 9
	Δ7-Cholestenol (lathosterol)	$C_{27}H_{46}O$	H	—	7	126	+6	119	+2	157	+7	Companion of cholesterol	
	Δ7-Coprostenol	$C_{27}H_{46}O$	βH	—	7	106	+54	91	+48	129	+56	Rat feces	53
	7-Dehydrocholesterol	$C_{27}H_{44}O$		—	5,7	147	−114	130	−85	140	−52	In egg yolk cholesterol	2
	Zymosterol	$C_{27}H_{44}O$	H	—	8,24	110	+49	108	+35	127	+38	In yeast	4, 5, 6, 19
	Cerebrosterol	$C_{27}H_{46}O_2$		ξOH	5	176	−48	97	+28	181 (dibenzoate)	−16	Horse brain, human brain	7, 8
	Cholestanetriol	$C_{27}H_{48}O_3$	OH	—a	—	245	+3	165 (diacetate)	−46	—	—	Companion of cholesterol	9
	Cholesta-5,24-dienol (desmosterol)	$C_{27}H_{44}O$		—	5,24	121	−40	—	—	168 (p-iodobenzoate)	—	Chick embryo	33
	Unnamed companion of "desmosterol"	$C_{27}H_{46}O?$		—	24?	—	—	—	—	144 (p-iodobenzoate)	—	Chick embryo	33
28	Ergostanol	$C_{28}H_{50}O$	H	bMe	—	144	+15	145	+6	165	—	Synthetic	10, 11, 12, 14, 15
	Fungisterol	$C_{28}H_{48}O$	H	bMe	7	150	−4	160	+3	179	0	Companion of ergosterol in ergot	14, 15
	5-Dihydroergosterol	$C_{28}H_{46}O$	H	bMe	7,22	178	−23	181	−23	198	−6	Companion of ergosterol	13, 14, 15
	Ergosterol	$C_{28}H_{44}O$		bMe	5,7,22	165	−130	181	−90	169	−71	In yeast and ergot	16
	14-Dehydroergosterol	$C_{28}H_{42}O$		bMe	5,7,14,22	201	−396	167	−322	212	−260	In strain of Aspergillus niger	17, 18
	Brassicasterol	$C_{28}H_{46}O$		bMe	5,22	148	−64	159	−65	167	—	Oil from Brassica rapa	24, 25
	Cerevisterol	$C_{28}H_{46}O_3$	OH	bMeb	7,22	265	−79	171 (diacetate)	−149	138	—	Minor component in yeast	
	24-Methylenecholesterol (chalinasterol, ostreasterol)	$C_{28}H_{46}O$		=CH₂	5,24(28)	146	−42	136	−47	152	−14	Molluscs	29, 30, 31, 48, 52
	Ascosterol	$C_{28}H_{46}O$	H	Me	8,23	142	+45	152	+21	136	+39	Minor component of yeast	20, 21, 23
	Fecosterol	$C_{28}H_{46}O$	H	=CH₂	8,24(28)	162	+42	161	+20	146	+34	Minor component of yeast	20, 21, 23
	Episterol	$C_{28}H_{46}O$	H	=CH₂	7,24(28?)	151	+5	162	+4	163	+12	Minor component of yeast	22, 23
	Campestanol	$C_{28}H_{50}O$	H	aMe		147	+31	144	+18	—	—		26, 27, 28
	Campesterol	$C_{28}H_{48}O$		aMe	5	158	−33	138	−35	160	−9	Oil of Brassica campestris	26, 27, 28
	Stellastanol and stellastenol mixture	$C_{28}H_{46,48}O$	H	aMe	7 and 7, 22	129-159	+6	137-181	+2	159-197	+9	Starfish Asterias forbesi	32
	8(14)-Stellastenol	$C_{28}H_{48}O$	H	aMe	8(14)	125	+20	106	+13	—	—	Synthetic	32

TABLE II (continued)

No. of C atoms	Name	Formula	Substituents C-5	Substituents C-24	Double bonds Δ	Free sterol m.p. °C	Free sterol [α]_D degrees	Acetate m.p. °C	Acetate [α]_D degrees	Benzoate m.p. °C	Benzoate [α]_D degrees	Occurrence	References
29	Stigmastanol	$C_{29}H_{52}O$	H	bEt	—	145	+ 25	138	+ 14	137	+ 20	Minor component in plants	45
	"β"-Sitosterol	$C_{29}H_{50}O$	—	bEt	5	140	− 36	127	− 42	147	− 14	In many plant cells as a mixture	46
	Stigmasterol	$C_{29}H_{48}O$	—	bEt	5, 22	170	− 49	144	− 56	160	− 25	Calabar bean or soya bean oil	47
	"α"-Spinasterol	$C_{29}H_{48}O$	H	bEt	7, 22	172	− 4	187	− 5	201	+ 2	Spinach and senega root	34, 15
	Fucosterol	$C_{29}H_{48}O$	—	=CHMe	5, 24(28)	124	− 38	119	− 46	120	− 16	Marine algae and seaweeds	35, 36
	Poriferastanol	$C_{29}H_{52}O$	H	aEt	—	143	+ 25	141	+ 16	—	—	Synthetic	37
	"γ"-Sitosterol Clionasterol	$C_{29}H_{50}O$	—	aEt	5	138	− 42	137	− 40	140	− 16	Sponges, soya bean oil	37, 38, 39
	Poriferasterol	$C_{29}H_{48}O$	—	aEt	5, 22	156	− 49	147	− 53	142	− 22	Sponges	37, 40
	Chondrillasterol	$C_{29}H_{48}O$	H	aEt	7, 22	169	− 1	175	− 1	195	+ 4	Sponges	41
30	Dihydrolanosterol	$C_{30}H_{52}O$	4,4,14α-Trimethyl 5α-H		8(9)	150	+ 61	120	+ 60	—	—	Constituent of "isocholesterol" in wool wax	49, 50
	Dihydroagnosterol γ-Lanosterol	$C_{30}H_{50}O$	4,4,14α-Trimethyl 5α-H		7, 9	159	+ 67	168	+ 86	—	—	Constituent of "isocholesterol" in wool wax	49, 50
	Lanosterol	$C_{30}H_{50}O$	4,4,14α-Trimethyl 5α-H		8(9), 24	140	+ 58	130	+ 57	194	+ 70	Constituent of "isocholesterol" in wool wax	49, 50, 51
	Agnosterol	$C_{30}H_{48}O$	4,4,14α-Trimethyl 5α-H		7, 9, 24	169	+ 69	187	+ 92	—	—	Constituent of "isocholesterol" in wool wax	49, 50

[a] α-substituents unless otherwise stated.
[b] 6β-OH.

REFERENCES

1. Fieser (1953a).
2. Windaus and Stange (1936).
3. Schoenheimer (1930).
4. Smedley-Maclean (1928).
5. Wieland and Asano (1929).
6. Wieland and Gough (1930).
7. Ercoli et al. (1953).
8. Ercoli and de Ruggieri (1953).
9. Fieser and Bhattacharyya (1953).
10. Tanret (1908).
11. Wieland and Coutelle (1941).
12. Wieland and Benend (1943).
13. Callow (1931).
14. Bladon et al. (1951)

15. Barton and Cox (1948a).
16. Barton and Bruun (1951).
17. Windaus and Welsch (1909).
18. Smedley-Maclean (1928).
19. Fernholz and Staveley (1939, 1940).
19. Heath-Brown et al. (1940).
20. Heilbron (1942).
21. Jones et al. (1942).
22. Carter et al. (1939).
23. Fieser and Fieser (1949, p. 292).
24. Bills and Honeywell (1928).
25. Alt and Barton (1952).
26. Fernholz and MacPhillamy (1941).
27. Bergmann and Ottke (1949).
28. Fernholz and Ruigh (1941).

29. Bergmann (1934a,b).
30. Bergmann et al. (1945).
31. Tsujimoto and Koyanagi (1934, 1935).
32. Bergmann and Stansbury (1944).
33. Stokes et al. (1956).
34. Fieser et al. (1949).
35. MacPhillamy (1942).
36. Hey et al. (1950).
37. Valentine and Bergmann (1941).
38. Kind and Bergmann (1942).
39. Mazur (1941).
40. Lyon and Bergmann (1942).
41. Bergmann and McTigue (1948).

42. Bondzynski (1896).
43. Hummicki (1897).
44. Dorée and Gardner (1908).
45. Sandqvist and Bengtsson (1931).
46. Wallis and Chakravorty (1937).
47. Steiger and Reichstein (1937).
48. Fagerlund and Idler (1956);
    Idler and Fagerlund (1955, 1957).
49. Lewis and McChie (1956).
50. Jones and Halsall (1955).
51. Johnston et al. (1957).
52. Bergmann and Dusza (1957).
53. Coleman and Baumann (1957).

In addition the names ergostane (24b-Me), campestane (24a-Me), stigmastane (24b-Et) poriferastane (24a-Et), and lanostane (4,4,14-trimethyl) are used for the alkylated cholestanes.

TABLE I

NAMES OF STEROID HYDROCARBONS[a]

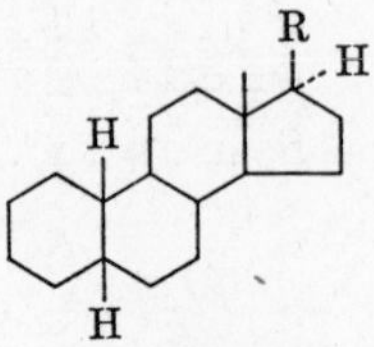

(III) 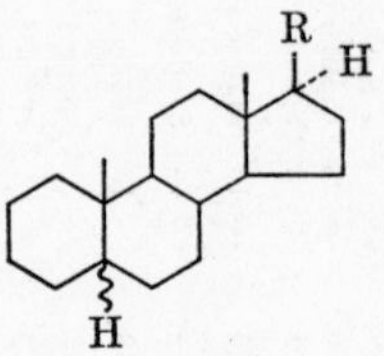   (IV)

		5α-H-Series	5β-H-Series
(III)	R = H		Estrane
(IV)	R = H	*Androstane*	Testane
(IV)	R = C$_2$H$_5$	Allopregnane	*Pregnane*
(IV)	R = CHMe.CH$_2$.CH$_2$.CH$_3$	Allocholane	*Cholane*
(IV)	R = CHMe.(CH$_2$)$_3$.CH(CH$_3$)$_2$	*Cholestane*	Coprostane

[a] When there is no asymmetry at C-5 the names printed in italics are used.

III. Table of Natural Sterols

The table (Table II) lists the more important natural sterols only. Sterols of questionable homogeneity are omitted. (See pp. 18 and 19.)

The sterols listed fall into three groups, according to the number of carbon atoms: 27, 28, 29. Those containing 28 and 29 carbon atoms have the extra atom(s) as a methyl or ethyl group at C-24 in the side chain. They are further subdivided according to the configuration ("a" or "b") of this extra group (sometimes there is a double bond between C-24 and C-28, e.g. in fucosterol and 24-methylenecholesterol).

The melting point and specific rotation (in chloroform) of the free sterol, its acetate, and its benzoate are listed. In the absence of constants for these derivatives, sometimes constants for other derivatives are given. For a review on the natural sterols see Bergmann (1952). The members of the trimethylcholestane series ("isocholesterol") which contain 30 carbon atoms are also listed.

IV. Occurrence and Large-Scale Isolation of Cholesterol

The distribution of cholesterol in tissues is considered in Chapter 4 and the methods used for its isolation on a small scale and determination in Chapter 3. In this section are considered the relatively large-scale preparation of cholesterol from natural sources, the nature of, and methods for the removal of the common impurities, and criteria of purity.

A. ISOLATION

The cholesterol of commerce is prepared by solvent (ethylene dichloride) extraction of the spinal cord and brain of cattle, available, as slaughter house residues. Cholesterol present in the free state is then obtained by direct crystallization. Alternatively a preliminary saponification with 40% aqueous sodium hydroxide solution can be used, followed by extraction. This liberates the esterified cholesterol. Since the sodium soaps formed can give troublesome emulsions, saponification with slaked lime (Porsche and Solms, 1940; Porsche, 1945) has been also used, when the calcium soaps formed are insoluble. A similar effect was obtained by precipitating the fatty acids obtained by a normal sodium hydroxide saponification as barium salts by adding barium chloride (Prelog et al., 1943).

Another source of cholesterol is wool fat. Here the isolation is complicated by the presence of lanosterol and similar compounds. After an initial saponification and isolation of the mixed sterols in a solvent, oxalic acid is added, when the cholesterol is preferentially precipitated as the complex $(C_{27}H_{46}O)_2 C_2H_2O_4$. The complex can be obtained pure by recrystallization from ethyl acetate, alcohol, or acetone as the complexes formed with lanosterol, etc., are more soluble. Simply adding water to the complex regenerates pure cholesterol (Yoder et al., 1945; Pickard and Seymour, 1945; Miescher and Kägi, 1941).

Fieser and Bhattacharyya (1953) describe laboratory methods for the preparation of cholesterol from gall stones and from brain, and also from various animal skins (Nakanishi et al., 1953).

In the separation of cholesterol from the unsaponifiable fraction of wool fat, Hackmann (1950) made use of complex formation with metallic salts, e.g. $CaCl_2.6H_2O$ and $MnCl_2.4H_2O$.

B. IMPURITIES IN CHOLESTEROL AND THEIR REMOVAL

As usually prepared, cholesterol is contaminated by cholestanol (0.2%), Δ^7-cholestenol or lathosterol (see below) (0.5–3%), and 7-dehydrocholesterol (traces) (Fieser, 1953a, 1954b). Wool fat "sterol" contains appreciable amounts of lanosterol as well as cholesterol, their separation being discussed above.

These contaminants can be removed by treatment with bromine in ether when cholesterol is converted to the insoluble 5α,6β-dibromide (see Section VI, J) (Fieser, 1953b). Regeneration of the sterol is easily effected by treatment of the pure dibromide with either zinc and acetic acid (Fieser, 1953b), sodium iodide (Schoenheimer, 1930, 1935), ferrous chloride (Bretschneider and Ajtai, 1943), or chromous chloride (Julian et al., 1945). By this means the cholestanol is left in the mother liquors of the sparingly soluble dibromide and the Δ^7-cholestenol and 7-dehydro-cholesterol are converted to more unsaturated derivatives (cf. Anderson et al., 1952).

An alternative method of purification (Fieser, 1953a) involves crystallization of cholesterol from acetic acid. This also serves to remove cholestanol and Δ^7-cholestenol very effectively. According to Fieser, cholesterol is stirred with boiling acetic acid (8 ml./gm.) until dissolved and then rapidly cooled in ice. The cholesterol separates as a complex $C_{27}H_{46}O.CH_3CO_2H$ (Hoppe-Seyler, 1863) which loses acetic acid on drying at 90° C. A mixture of cholesterol with 6% added cholestanol treated in this way gave a product in which cholestanol could not be detected by melting point or rotation. The method works well on amounts of cholesterol in the region of 150 gm. but on a large-scale extensive acetylation occurs. The sterol acetates however do not contaminate the recrystallized product but remain behind in the mother liquors. The oxalic acid complex (see above) can also be used similarly to purify cholesterol.

The presence of cholestanol in crude cholesterol had been inferred by Schoenheimer (1930) who had isolated it from gallstone cholesterol which has been treated with sodium in a solvent at high temperature. As the cholestanol might conceivably be an artifact of these conditions, its direct isolation by Fieser (1953a) constituted a final proof. He isolated it from the mother liquors of cholesterol that had been crystallized from acetic acid. The remaining cholesteryl acetate was removed as the dibromide, when cholestanyl acetate could be isolated from the mother liquors.

Δ^7-Cholestenol (Lathosterol: Greek, lathos—undetected) (Fieser, 1951, 1953a; Fieser and Bhattacharyya, 1953) was isolated from the acetylated material from the mother liquors of the acetic acid crystallization of cholesterol, and by fractional crystallization of the sterol-oxalic acid complex. The presence of lathosterol in cholesterol can be easily shown by the very sensitive selenium dioxide test due to Fieser, which has been developed into a quantitative method for the microdetermination of Δ^7-sterols (Nakanishi *et al.*, 1953). The test depends on the rapid reduction of selenium dioxide by Δ^7-stenols at room temperature in acetic acid–benzene, to give a yellow color or red precipitate. In the quantitative method, the selenium is retained as a colloidal solution in benzene, and is oxidized back to selenium dioxide with nitric acid. The selenium dioxide then liberates iodine from potassium iodide which is estimated spectrophotometrically. Under the conditions of the test Δ^5-stenols (e.g. cholesterol) do not react.

7-Dehydrocholesterol (provitamin D_3) was first isolated by Windaus and Stange (1936) by chromatography of egg yolk cholesterol. Recently Idler and Baumann (1952) have shown that the sterols extracted from the skins of certain animals contain relatively large amounts of 7-dehydrocholesterol and Δ^7-cholesterol.

The presence of the so-called "Ketone 104 precursor" in cholesterol was inferred from the isolation of "Ketone 104" in experiments in which cholesterol was destructively oxidized by sodium dichromate and acetic acid (Fieser 1953a; Fieser and Bhattacharyya, 1953). By this means the cholesterol is largely converted to acidic products and cholest-4-en-3,6-dione which can be removed by extraction with Claisen's alkali (aqueous methanolic potassium hydroxide, Fieser, 1955a). The neutral steroid ketones remaining consist of cholestanone and "Ketone 104" which can be separated by selective reaction with Girard's reagent. Cholesterol that has been purified by crystallization from acetic acid or *via* the dibromide yields Ketone 104 substantially free from cholestanone, from which it was originally inferred that "Ketone 104" precursor" (i.e. the corresponding alcohol) was very similar to cholesterol and was precipitated as a dibromide.

(V)   (Va)

Ketone 104 has the composition $C_{27}H_{44}O_3$ which was confirmed by analysis of several derivatives. Subsequently Fieser (1954b) proposed the structure (V) both for "Ketone 104" (m.p, 123.5–124.5° C., $[\alpha]_D$ —37.1° (CHCl$_3$), IR λ_{max} CHCl$_3$ 5.78 μ) and a product of the dichromate oxidation of cholesterol [presumably the compound $C_{27}H_{42}O_3$ described as having m.p. 120-121° C., $[\alpha]_D$ —41° (CHCl$_3$) IR λ_{max} CHCl$_3$ 5.85 μ

(Fieser, 1953c)]. It is now clear that "Ketone 104" is derived from cholesterol itself (Fieser *et al.*, 1957) and the alternative formula (Va) has been advanced (Fieser, 1957).

Other higher oxygenated cholesterol derivatives occur in cholesterol isolated from certain organs of animals. Human brain extracted with acetone yields cholesterol containing 0.5% of cholestane-3β,5α,6β-triol (Fieser and Bhattacharyya, 1953). This is also present in gall stone cholesterol. Caution is needed in accepting other reports of sterol fractions containing this substance, as it is very readily formed by oxidation of cholesterol and may be an artifact in some cases. This is almost certainly true in the case of 25-hydroxycholesterol which is found in only old samples of cholesterol and is presumably formed by aerial oxidation (Fieser, 1953b).

Cerebrosterol (24-ξ-hydroxycholesterol) was found in horse brain cholesterol (Ercoli and de Ruggiere, 1953) to the extent of $\sim$0.002%, it appears that this is not an artifact. In general all the hydroxylated cholesterols can be removed by chromatography on alumina on which they are more strongly absorbed than cholesterol.

C. Criteria of Purity

Fieser (1953a) records the following constants for cholesterol, purified by recrystallization from acetic acid: m.p. 149.5-150.0° C. (remelting 150.0-150.5°) (evacuated capillary see p. 78); $[\alpha]_D$ —39.6° —39.9° (c, 1.49, 1.73 in chloroform) —35.0°, —35.0° (c, 1.11, 1.52 in dioxane). The rotations are similar to those quoted by Barton (1946), who also gives $[\alpha]_D$ —30° (in alcohol or acetone). The molecular rotation of cholesterol [M] is given at various wavelengths from 300 to 650 mμ by:

$$[M] = -48.2/(\lambda^2 -0.0387) + 4{\cdot}37/\lambda^2$$

where λ is the wavelength in microns (Djerassi *et al.*, 1955c).

Cholesterol purified either by acetic acid crystallization or via the dibromide gives no color in the selenium dioxide test of Fieser (1953a) (absence of Δ^7-cholestenol, etc).

The constants quoted above refer to anhydrous cholesterol which is obtained by crystallization from dry solvents. It then forms triclinic needles. From moist solvents, it separates as the monohydrate, rhomb-shaped triclinic plates, which lose water at 70–80° C. Similar loose addition compounds are formed with the lower aliphatic alcohols, and with acetic acid (m.p. 110° C. dec.) and oxalic acid (m.p. 160° C. dec.).

V. The Structure of Cholesterol

As befits a compound of such profound biological importance, cholesterol has occupied the attention of organic chemists for a great number

of years. The structural relationship of the sterols and the bile acids
was realized quite early, and to a large extent the structures assigned
to the two classes of compounds are based on interrelated evidence.
This evidence and the arguments used have been summarized elsewhere
(Fieser and Fieser, 1949; Shoppee and Shoppee, 1953; Georg, 1954) and
only a very brief account is warranted here. The progress of steroid research has recently been reviewed by Shoppee (1956).

A. The Determination of the Structure of Cholesterol

The work of Mauthner, Diels, Windaus, and Wieland in the first
quarter of the century on the purely chemical degradation of cholesterol
had led to the promulgation in 1928 of the first (incorrect) formula
for cholesterol. The inadequacy of this formula was soon realized by
Wieland and Vocke (1930) who showed that there was no ethyl group
present in the molecule. The reappraisal of the earlier work of Diels
et al. (1927) on the selenium dehydrogenation of cholesterol, whereby
chrysene (VI) and the so-called Diels hydrocarbon (VII) are formed,
led to the suggestion of the presently accepted ring skeleton of the steroid
nucleus (Rosenheim and King, 1932). The results of X-ray crystallography (Bernal, 1932; for a review see Crowfoot, 1944) and surface film
measurements (Adam and Rosenheim, 1929; for a review see Adam,
1941) had shown that the steroid molecule was thinner (dimensions
7.2 × 5 × 20Å) than would be expected for the old formula [8.5 × 7
× 18Å]. The newer formulas of Rosenheim and King [7.2 × 4.5 × 20Å]
fitted these results better.

(VI)   (VII)

(VIII)

The formula (VIII) of cholesterol contains 8 asymmetric centers and
so it represents one of 256 possible isomers. The stereochemistry was

established during the second quarter of this century. Again the evidence and arguments are interrelated with the chemistry of other steroids. The remainder of this section is devoted to a discussion of the chemistry of cholesterol (and steroids in general) in terms of modern ideas of stereochemistry, rather than a historical survey of this problem.

B. The Implications of the Formula of Cholesterol

The conventional projection formula (VIII) does not give the best picture of the cholesterol molecule. Such a system of fused cyclohexane rings does not have all the carbon atoms in one plane, consequently consideration of stereochemical problems is facilitated by the use of perspective formulas.

Two models can be constructed for cyclohexane itself; the so-called *boat* form and the thermodynamically more stable *chair* form (shown in perspective formulas IX and X, respectively). Only the chair form need be considered here since models of the two principal types of steroids can be constructed which consist of only fused chair-form cyclohexane rings, for rings A, B, and C. These are the steroids with *trans-* fused rings A and B (*e.g.* cholestanol) (perspective formula XI) and those with *cis-* fusion of rings A and B (e.g. coprostanol) (XII). These models are consistent with the dimensions of the molecules found by X-ray crystallography. The C_{17} side chain in the sterols continues in the general line of the ring system, resulting in a lath-shaped molecule.

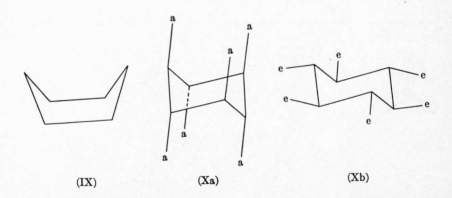

(IX)   (Xa)   (Xb)

In the chair form of cyclohexane it is possible to distinguish two types of hydrogen atoms: those joined to the ring by equatorial (e) bonds (i.e. those in the general plane of the ring) (Xb) and those joined by axial (a) bonds (i.e. at right angles to the general plane of the ring) (Xa).

The two types of atoms and bonds differ considerably in their degree of steric interference. Between alternate (*meta*) axial bonds there is considerable interference or hindrance, but between the various equatorial bonds there is no such interference. Consequently in simple substituted cyclohexanes (where the molecule is free to attain the most stable conformation*), the conformation taken up is that in which the largest number of the most bulky substituents have equatorial bonds.

In fused ring systems (where the molecules are much more rigidly held), that individual of a pair (or series) of isomers is thermodynamically most stable, which has the largest number of bulky groups in equatorial configurations. In this connection each ring is considered in turn and the bulky groups include carbon atoms of adjacent rings.

The original concept of equatorial and axial** bonds is due to Hassel (1943; Hassel and Ottar, 1947) and Pitzer (Beckett *et al.*, 1947) and was first applied to the steroid nucleus by Barton (1950). Subsequent discussion is here restricted to the steroid series but the whole subject of the conformation of six-membered rings is reviewed by Klyne (1954), Barton (1953), and Barton and Cookson (1956).

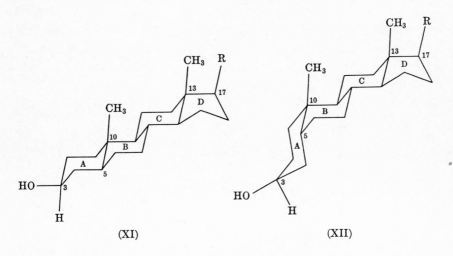

(XI)   (XII)

---

* The word "conformation" is used to denote differing strainless arrangements in space of a set of bonded atoms. These arrangements represent only one molecular species (Barton, 1950).

** In the literature prior to 1953 the word "polar" is used instead of "axial." The use of the former word was discontinued following the recommendation of Barton *et al.* (1953b) to avoid confusion with its use in the electrochemical sense.

It is seen from the perspective formulas of the two saturated derivatives of cholesterol: cholestanol (rings A and B *trans-* fused) (XI),
and coprostanol (rings A and B *cis-* fused((XII) that in both cases it
is possible to construct strainless ring systems containing only chair
conformations in the individual cyclohexane rings. The bonds joining
atoms or groups to the nucleus are then classified into equatorial and
axial bonds as in Table III.

TABLE III

CONFORMATIONS OF SUBSTITUENTS IN STEROID NUCLEI

Configuration position	A/B *trans*		A/B *cis*	
	α	β	α	β
1	a	e	e	a
2	e	a	a	e
3	a	e	e	a
4	e	a	a	e
5*	a	—	e (B ring)† a (A ring)	
6	e	a	e	a
7	a	e	a	e
8*	—	a	—	a
9*	a	—	a	—
10*	—	a		e (A ring)† a (B ring)
11	e	a	e	a
12	a	e	a	e
13*	—	a	—	a
14*	a	—	a	—
15‡	e	a	e	a
17‡	a	e	a	e

* Angular position, only one substituent.

† Note that in the A/B *cis* series, at the two angular positions between rings A
and B, the substituents are axial with respect to one ring and equatorial with respect
to the other.

‡ These carbon atoms are in five-membered ring D, the designations a and e
are relative to ring C.

In cholestanol (A/B *trans*) the 3β-OH group is equatorial and is
largely unhindered. In coprostanol (A/B *cis*) the 3β-OH is in the less
stable axial configuration.

With the introduction of a 5(6) double bond (as in cholesterol) it
might be expected that the conformation of the molecule would resemble
either that in cholestanol or in coprostanol. In actual fact the conformation closely resembles that of cholestanol, i.e. the 3β-OH group is equatorial.

A large number of reactions of the steroid nucleus can be the better understood when considered in terms of the nature (equatorial or axial) of the bonds involved.

A second factor which is of importance in considering the reactions of steroids is the over-all masking of the front (β-face) of the molecule (as usually drawn) by the two angular methyl groups at C-10 and C-13 and the β side chain at C-17. While these do not entirely prevent the approach of a reagent molecule to the front face at all of the carbon atoms, they do seriously impede it particularly in their immediate vicinity (carbons atoms 11, 1, 12, 17). Hence the preferred direction of approach of a reagent is from the rear (Fieser, 1950).

In discussing the reactions of steroids, references are not cited for individual examples, for which the reviews by Barton (1950, 1953) and Klyne (1954) should be consulted. Examples of most of the reactions discussed are contained in Section VI.

1. Esterification and Hydrolysis of Esters

In both these processes, the rate of reaction is higher with the equatorial isomer, than with the axial isomer (Barton, 1953). An exception to the rule is provided by the cholestane and coprostane-3,5-diols. (Henbest and Lovell, 1957) where the hydrolysis of the axial -3-acetates proceed at a greater rate due to the influence of the neighboring axial hydroxyl group.

2. Equilibration of Secondary Alcohols

When a steroid alcohol is heated with sodium alkoxide at a high temperature, equilibration occurs and a mixture of epimers results in which the more stable equatorial isomer predominates. This is in fact a special case of the Oppenauer-Meerwein-Pondorf oxidation-reduction reaction, and aluminum alkoxides can be used to effect equilibration (Barnett et al., 1940). Probably a trace of ketone is necessary for the equilibration to take place (Doering and Aschner, 1949).

3. Oxidation of Alcohols

The oxidation of alcohols by chromic acid or hypobromous acid to yield ketones proceeds faster with axial epimers than with the corresponding equatorial epimers. Until recently it was thought that this was because the rate-determining step involved attack not upon the hydroxyl group, but upon the C-H bond which, with an axial hydroxyl group, is necessarily equatorial (Barton, 1953). This has been disputed by Schreiber and Eschenmoser (1955) who suggest that the greater reaction rate of axial alcohols is due to the greater decrease in non-bonded interaction energy on oxidation.

4. Reductions of Ketones

The reduction of a steroid ketone in the Meerwein-Pondorf reaction leads to a mixture of alcohols in which the equatorial epimer predominates (often to the exclusion of the axial epimer). Reduction with sodium and alcohols gives a similar mixture of epimers and the same probably applies to Birch reduction with sodium in liquid ammonia. Reduction of ketones with lithium aluminum hydride and sodium borohydride is a more complex problem and has been discussed by Dauben *et al.* (1956). They conclude that unhindered ketones (e.g. C-3) give largely the equatorial alcohol, while hindered ketones (e.g. C-11) give the axial alcohol. With partly hindered ketones (e.g. C-7) a mixture of epimers results.

Catalytic hydrogenation of ketones gives almost always the β-epimeric alcohol. Here steric hindrance of the angular methyl groups is the overriding factor; the steroid molecule can only be adsorbed into the catalyst from the rear. Addition of hydrogen from the rear (α) side then gives the β-alcohol (for a table of results see Dauben *et al.*, 1956). Exceptions to this rule are C-3 and C-7 ketones.

5. Reactions of Double Bonds in Steroids

The two angular methyl groups effectively prevent approach by a reagent to the front (β face) of the steroid nucleus at those double bonds in their immediate vicinity (1, 2, 3, 9(11), 11). Thus attack by peracids gives 1α,2α; 2α,3α; 9α,11α; and 11α,12α epoxides almost exclusively. Hindrance is not so marked with double bonds in the 4 and 5 positions. Thus cholesterol gives with peracids a mixture of α- and β-epoxides; with cholesteryl esters the proportion of α-oxide is increased, possible due to the extra hindrance of the ester grouping. The reaction of cholest-4-en-3-one with alkaline hydrogen peroxide gives largely the β-epoxide.

Reactions with more bulky reagents (bromine, osmium tetroxide, etc.) and hydrogenation, where it is necessary for the steroid molecule to be adsorbed onto a catalyst surface, almost always proceed with attack from

(XIII)   (XIV)

the rear. The reaction of a double bond with halogens (e.g. bromine) gives first an unstable cyclic bromonium ion (XIII) analogous to an epoxide; ring opening then proceeds to give the diaxial dibromide (XIV) (see below for the analogous reactions of epoxides).

With the cholesterol 5,6-dibromides, the diaxial 5α,6β-dibromide is unstable and changes slowly in the presence of acid to the diequatorial
5β,6α-dibromide (see Section VI, J).

6. Opening of 1,2-epoxide Rings

Ring opening of a steroid epoxide gives a compound in which both the
resulting groups have axial configurations (Barton, 1953). No exceptions have been found to this rule so far. Attack of an ionic reagent
(e.g. H^+OH^-, H^+H^-, $Li^+(AlH_4)^-$, H^+Br^-) involves, first coordina-
tion of the positive ion with the epoxide to give the conjugate acid (XV),

and then attack of the negative ion from the opposite side of the molecule
in such a way that the resulting two groups both have axial configurations (XVI).

7. Polar Elimination Reactions

Barton (1953) states "For relatively ready 1:2-elimination reactions
of the ionic type the necessary geometric condition is that the four
centers of importance should lie in one plane. This condition is satisfied
in cyclohexane derivatives by 1:2-trans substituents both being in the
axial conformation (or being free to adopt this conformation)." Thus
cholesterol 5α, 6β-dibromide readily reacts with sodium iodide to yield
cholesterol, because both bromine atoms have axial configurations (see
Section VI, J). Similar criteria apply to elimination reactions in which
the product is an epoxide, thus cholesterol 2β,3β-epoxide is formed by
alkali treatment of 3α-mesyl,2β-hydroxycholestane (see Section VI, F).
The intermediate states in the two reactions can be compared. (The
plane of the ring is perpendicular to that of the paper and the
bond joining the carbon atoms involved is horizontal and in the plane
of the paper.)

Formation of Double Bond

Formation of Epoxide

8. Thermal Elimination Reactions

Examples of this type of reaction are the pyrolyses of carboxylic esters (e.g. 3β-acetoxycholestan-7α-yl benzoate, Barton and Rosenfelder, 1949). Here elimination of benzoic acid gives a double bond only in the 6(7) position (and not the 7(8) position); i.e. *cis* elimination occurs. Of

necessity one or other of the two groups involved (benzoate or hydrogen) must be equatorial, the other axial. It is thought that a cyclic intermediate transition state is involved. (For a discussion of the mechanism of such thermal elimination reactions, see Barton, 1949.)

VI.   Reactions of Cholesterol

A. Esterification and Other Reactions of the Hydroxyl Group

Cholesterol readily forms esters. The simplest carboxylic esters (acetate, propionate, etc.) are made by treating the sterol in pyridine with the appropriate acid anhydride. The benzoate is made similarly using benzoyl chloride and pyridine. The higher carboxylic esters (oleate, palmitate, etc.) are conveniently made by heating cholesterol with the carboxylic acid itself (Page and Rudy, 1930). Gray (1956) has prepared a series of the aliphatic carboxylic esters of cholesterol from the acid chlorides and pyridine, and has studied their mesomorphic behavior (see also Swell and Treadwell, 1955).

Sulfonic esters (methanesulfonate, *p*-toluenesulfonate) are made using the corresponding acid chloride and pyridine.

A reagent used by Fieser and his co-workers (1952) for the selective protection of hydroxyl groups is ethyl chloroformate. In the presence of pyridine it forms esters (carbethoxyl or "cathyl" derivatives) only with equatorial hydroxyl groups (such as that in cholesterol).

Hydroxyl groups in steroids can often be protected by treatment with dihydropyran and a trace of a Lewis acid. The resulting tetrahydro-pyranyl ethers are stable to reagents such as lithium aluminum hydride and Grignard reagents. Free hydroxyl groups are readily regenerated with aqueous acids (Dauben and Bradlow, 1952; Ott *et al.*, 1952).

B. ARRANGEMENT OF THE CHARTS AND ABBREVIATIONS USED IN C–Z

The reactions of cholesterol and its derivatives are outlined in the following sections, in the form of charts, and the following explanations will be of help in understanding them. Details of all reagents, conditions of chemical processes, and references are contained in footnotes to the charts. In general, a reference applies to the information given in preceding footnotes, up to the previous reference cited. Exceptions are in those charts where nearly all the information is given in one reference.

A number of the reactions mentioned have only been carried out in the ergosterol series. These are indicated in the references by the sign: [E] placed after the date. The inclusion of such reactions is justified, as many of them would undoubtedly be applicable to the cholesterol series.

When the nature of the reaction demands it, the hydroxyl groups present are assumed to be suitably protected by esterification. The necessary esterification and hydrolysis steps are not shown, unless they are of especial interest. The notation —OR is used to denote the alternatives of a free and esterified hydroxyl group.

Formulas are used extensively in the notes for the reagents, solvents, and catalysts, and in addition the following abbreviations are used.

Ac	Acetyl	NBA	N-Bromoacetamide
b.p.	Boiling point	NBP	N-Bromophthalimide
Bu	Butyl	NBS	N-Bromosuccinimide
Bz	Benzoyl	Ph	Phenyl
DMF	Dimethylformamide	Pr	Propyl
Et	Ethyl	Py	Pyridine
i	Iso- (not always abbreviated)	r.t.	Room temperature
IPA	Isopropenyl acetate	rx.	Reflux (under reflux)
Me	Methyl	*sec*	Secondary
Ms	Methanesulfonyl (Mesyl)	*tert*	Tertiary
m.p.	Melting point	THF	Tetrahydrofuran
n	normal	Ts	p-Toluenesulfonyl (tosyl)

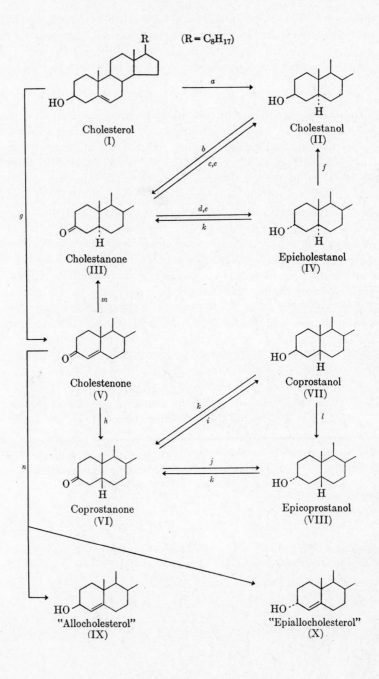

$(R = C_8H_{17})$

Cholesterol
(I)

Cholestanol
(II)

Cholestanone
(III)

Epicholestanol
(IV)

Cholestenone
(V)

Coprostanol
(VII)

Coprostanone
(VI)

Epicoprostanol
(VIII)

"Allocholesterol"
(IX)

"Epiallocholesterol"
(X)

C. Saturated Derivatives

(a) H_2-Pt. This is usually slow unless promoters are added. Hershberg et al. (1951) describe a method using EtOAc as solvent and a trace of $HClO_4$ as promoter. If AcOH is used as solvent the product must be saponified (Nace, 1951).

(b) CrO_3-AcOH (Barton and Cox, 1948a).

(c) Na-C_5H_{11}OH or H_2-Pt-neutral solvent (Diels and Abderhalden, 1906).

(d) H_2-Pt-acidic solvent (HCl added) (Vavon and Jakubowicz, 1933).

(e) $LiAlH_4$ (Shoppee and Summers, 1950) gives cholestanol (91%) and epi-cholestanol (9%).

(f) Equilibration with Na alkoxides, at 180°. The equilibrium is in favor of the equatorial isomer (cholestanol 90%), but the reaction has been used in the reverse sense to prepare epicholestanol (Windaus and Uibrig, 1914).

(g) See Section VI, H.

(h) Partial hydrogenation in a neutral or alkaline solvent with Pd catalysts (Grasshof, 1934a). This is quite a general reaction and has been used in other series (Barton et al., 1949, Pt catalyst).

(i) H_2-Pt-AcOH (Grasshof, 1934b).

(j) H_2-Pt-Et_2O (Ruzicka et al., 1934b) or Na-n-PrOH (Barton et al., 1949).

(k) CrO_3 (e.g. method of Barton and Cox, 1948a).

(l) Equilibration with Na alkoxides, at 180° (cf. footnote f). Again the equilibrium is in favor of the equatorial isomer (epicoprostanol) (Windaus and Uibrig, 1915; Windaus, 1916).

(m) Li-NH_3 (Barton et al., 1953a).

(n) Al(OPr^i)$_3$-i-PrOH-rx. The isomers were separated using digitonin (Schoenheimer and Evans, 1936). The systematic names cholest-4-en-3β-(and 3α-)ols are to be preferred to the trivial names "allocholesterol" and "epiallocholesterol" for (IX) and (X).

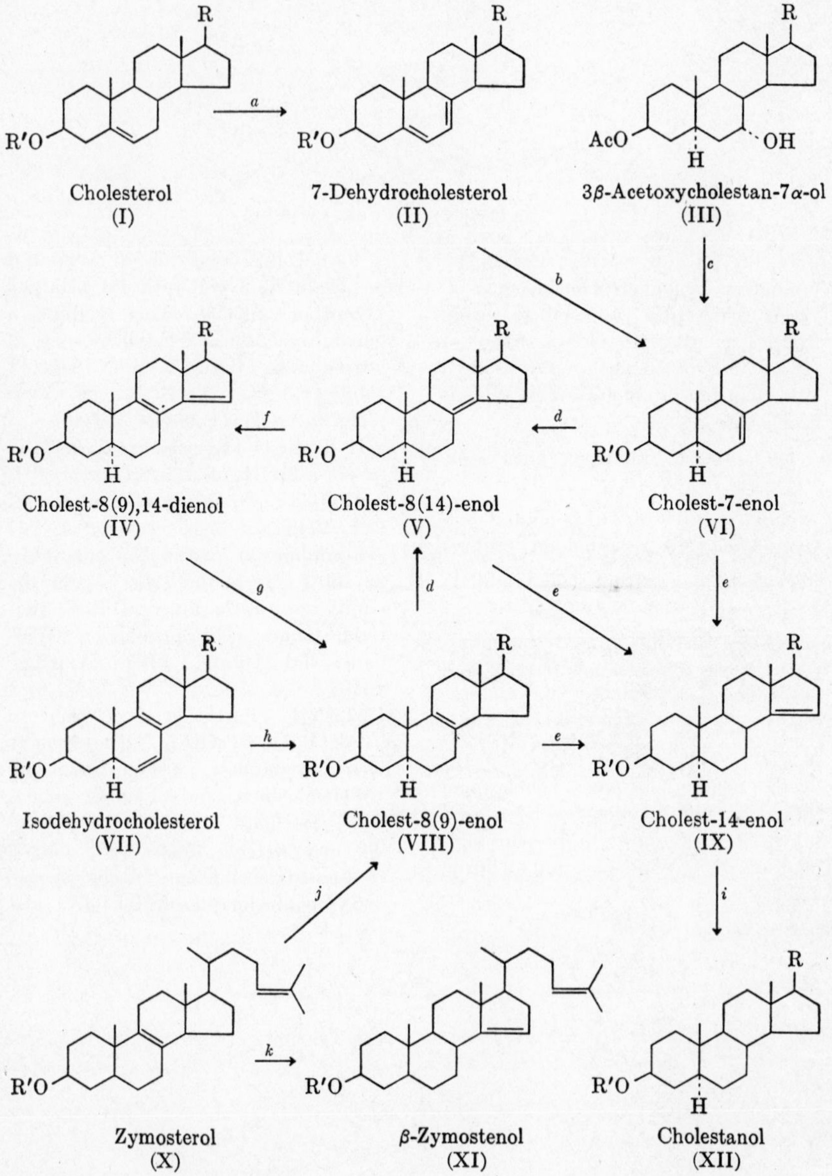

Cholesterol
(I)

7-Dehydrocholesterol
(II)

3β-Acetoxycholestan-7α-ol
(III)

Cholest-8(9),14-dienol
(IV)

Cholest-8(14)-enol
(V)

Cholest-7-enol
(VI)

Isodehydrocholesterol
(VII)

Cholest-8(9)-enol
(VIII)

Cholest-14-enol
(IX)

Zymosterol
(X)

β-Zymostenol
(XI)

Cholestanol
(XII)

R = C$_8$H$_{17}$, R' = H, Ac, or Bz

D. DOUBLE-BOND ISOMERS OF CHOLESTEROL

(a) See Section VI, E, notes a and b.

(b) H_2-Pt-EtOAc (i.e., neutral conditions) (Barton and Cox, 1948b), or Na-EtOH (Schenck et al., 1936) or H_2-Raney Ni-C_6H_6 (Anderson et al., 1952).

(c) $POCl_3$-Py (Buser, 1947, see also Section VI, O).

(d) H_2-Pt-AcOH or H_2-Pd-neutral or acidic solvent (Wieland and Benend, 1943). The migration of the double bond occurs only if the catalyst is kept saturated with hydrogen (Stavely and Bollenback, 1943). Bond migration also occurs when hydrogenations are carried out with Raney Ni catalysts at 100° but not at room temperature (Bladon et al., 1951; Mancera et al., 1952), or when copper chromite catalysts are used (Nes and Mosettig, 1953). These last authors also showed that isomerization also occurs with platinum catalysts under neutral conditions (EtOAc).

(e) HCl-$CHCl_3$ (Schenck et al., 1936; Heilbron and Wilkinson, 1932; Wieland and Görnhardt, 1947; Cornforth, et al., 1957).

(f) H_2O_2-$H \cdot CO_2H$-$CHCl_3$ ($H \cdot CO_3H$) (Barton and Cox, 1949 [E]).

(g) H_2-Raney Ni-EtOH (Barton and Cox, 1949 [E]). Besides the $\Delta^{8(9)}$ compound some $\Delta^{8(14)}$ compound is also formed and is separated by crystallization.

(h) H_2-PtO_2-EtOAc (Barton and Cox, 1949; cf. Wieland and Benend, 1943). A mixture of (VI) and (VIII) is formed and is separable by chromatography. Na-i-PrOH (Windaus et al., 1938).

(i) H_2-Pt-Et_2O-AcOH (Schenck et al., 1936; Heilbron and Wilkinson, 1932).

(j) H_2-Pt-EtOAc (Wieland et al., 1941).

(k) HCl-$CHCl_3$, KOH (to dehydrochlorinate the hydrochloride formed) (Wieland and Benend, 1942).

$R = C_8H_{17}$, $R' = H$, Ac, or Bz

E. Cholestadien- and Trien-ols

(*a*) NBS or NBP in a solvent (CCl$_4$ or petrol) rx. with illumination with visible light. The product (II) is probably the 7α-bromo compound (X = Br).

(*b*) Tertiary amine (PhNMe$_2$, Py, or collidine) rx. with or without a solvent (PhMe) (Bide *et al.*, 1948a, and Bernstein *et al.*, 1949, are leading references). Usually process *b* is carried out without isolating the product from *a*. R′ = Ac, Bz, or 3,4-dinitrobenzoyl, etc. Best results are obtained with the benzoates (Nes *et al.*, 1956). (V) is formed as a by-product in process *b* when 2,6-lutidine is used (Bernstein *et al.*, 1949; Bide *et al.* (1948a). (VI) is formed as a byproduct when collidine is used (Nes *et al.*, 1956; Hunziker *et al.*, 1955).

(*c*) Treatment with Py at 100° or collidine, picolines, or Py at r.t. (Tsuda *et al.*, 1954).

(*d*) Hg(OAc)$_2$ in a solvent (EtOH, CCl$_4$, CHCl$_3$) containing AcOH with or without rx. (Windaus and Linsert, 1928 [E]; Bergmann and Stevens, 1948 [E]; Antonucci *et al.*, 1951; Nes *et al.*, 1956).

(*e*) H$_2$-Raney Ni-C$_6$H$_6$ (Anderson *et al.*, 1952 [E]; Heusser *et al.*, 1951, footnotes p. 2132 [E]).

(*f*) HCl-CHCl$_3$ at —30° (Barton and Brooks, 1951 [E]; Barton and Laws, 1954 [E]; Woodward *et al.*, 1954). The cholesterol analog has been made in an impure state (Barton *et al.*, 1954b; Woodward *et al.*, 1957).

(*g*) Hg(OAc)$_2$-CHCl$_3$-AcOH (Heusser *et al.*, 1951 [E]; Anderson *et al.*, 1952 [E]; Ruyle *et al.*, 1953 [E]). The preferred method for this transformation involves two steps: (1) Br$_2$-AcOH-Et$_2$O at —66°; (2) Zn dust-C$_6$H$_6$ Anderson *et al.*, 1952 [E]). In the ergosterol series the side chain double bond adds on bromine in (1) (see also Cornforth *et al.*, 1957).

(*h*) HCl-CHCl$_3$ (Nes *et al.*, 1956 and earlier papers cited there). Burgstahler (1957) has shown that in 'X' the double bond is between C-14 and C-15.

(*i*) SO$_2$Py-C$_6$H$_6$ at 100° (Laubach *et al.*, 1953; 1956 [E]).

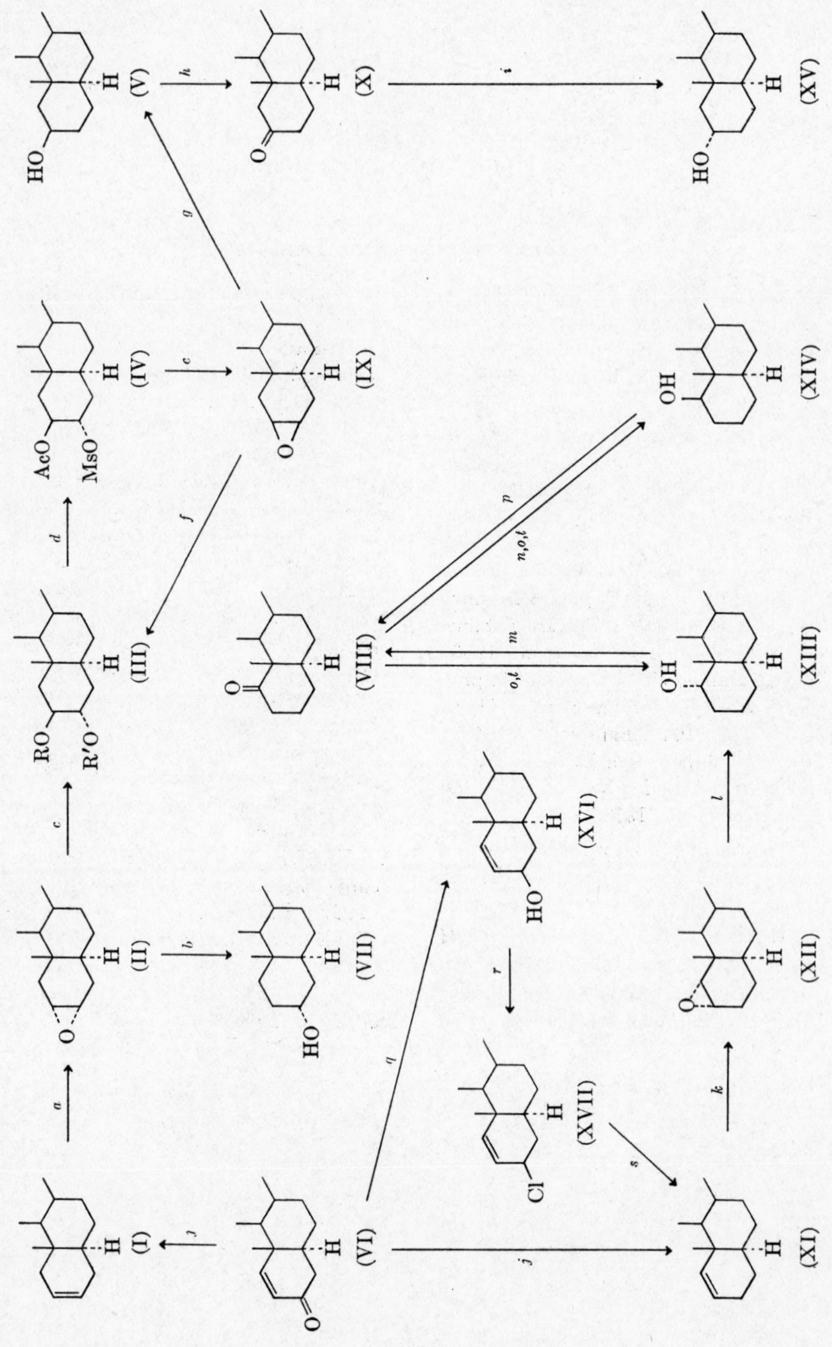
(I)
(II)
(III)
(IV)
(V)
(VI)
(VII)
(VIII)
(IX)
(X)
(XI)
(XII)
(XIII)
(XIV)
(XV)
(XVI)
(XVII)
RO
R'O
AcO
MsO
HO
OH
Cl

F. 1- AND 2-FUNCTIONS

(a) $PhCO_3H$-$CHCl_3$.

(b) H_2-PtO_2-AcOH (or EtOH) or $LiAlH_4$-Et_2O.

(c) 0.2 N H_2SO_4-Me_2CO (R = R' = H) AcOH at 100° (R = Ac, R' = H).

(d) MsCl-Py.

(e) KOH-MeOH.

(f) 0.2 N H_2SO_4-Me_2CO (R = R' = H).

(g) H_2-PtO_2-AcOH or $LiAlH_4$-Et_2O,

(h) CrO_3-AcOH.

(i) Na-EtOH (Fürst and Plattner, 1949).

(j) Two steps: (1) $(CH_2 \cdot SH)_2$ or $Ph \cdot CH_2 \cdot SH$-Et_2O-HCl (the products are of uncertain structure); (2) Raney Ni-Me_2CO-rx. The product was a mixture of (I) and (XI) which were not separated.

(k) $PhCO_3H$-Et_2O The product was an inseparable mixture of (II) and (XII).

(l) $LiAlH_4$-THF. The product was a mixture of (VII) and (XIII) which were separated at this stage.

(m) CrO_3-AcOH (Plattner et al., 1954).

(n) H_2-PtO_2-AcOH.

(o) Na-n-PrOH.

(p) CrO_3-AcOH (Striebel and Tamm, 1954).

(q) $LiAlH_4$-Et_2O at —40°.

(r) $SOCl_2$-C_6H_6.

(s) $LiAlH_4$-Et_2O rx. (Henbest and Wilson, 1956). These authors prepared, in this way, for the first time, pure cholest-1-ene. The subsequent conversions via the pure α-epoxide (XII) to cholestan-1α-ol and the β-epimer and cholestan-1-one were carried out by methods similar to those of Striebel and Tamm (1954).

(t) Reduction of cholestan-1-one with $LiAlH_4$-Et_2O gave 1α- and 1β-alcohols in the ratio 2:1. Reduction with Na-EtOH gave the products in the ratio 1:2 (Henbest and Wilson, 1956).

Several alternative ways of preparing 1-oxygenated cholestane derivatives were described by Striebel and Tamm (1954).

The acetate of 1α-hydroxycholestane is difficult to hydrolyze, and can best be converted to the hydroxy compound with $LiAlH_4$ (Plattner et al., 1954).

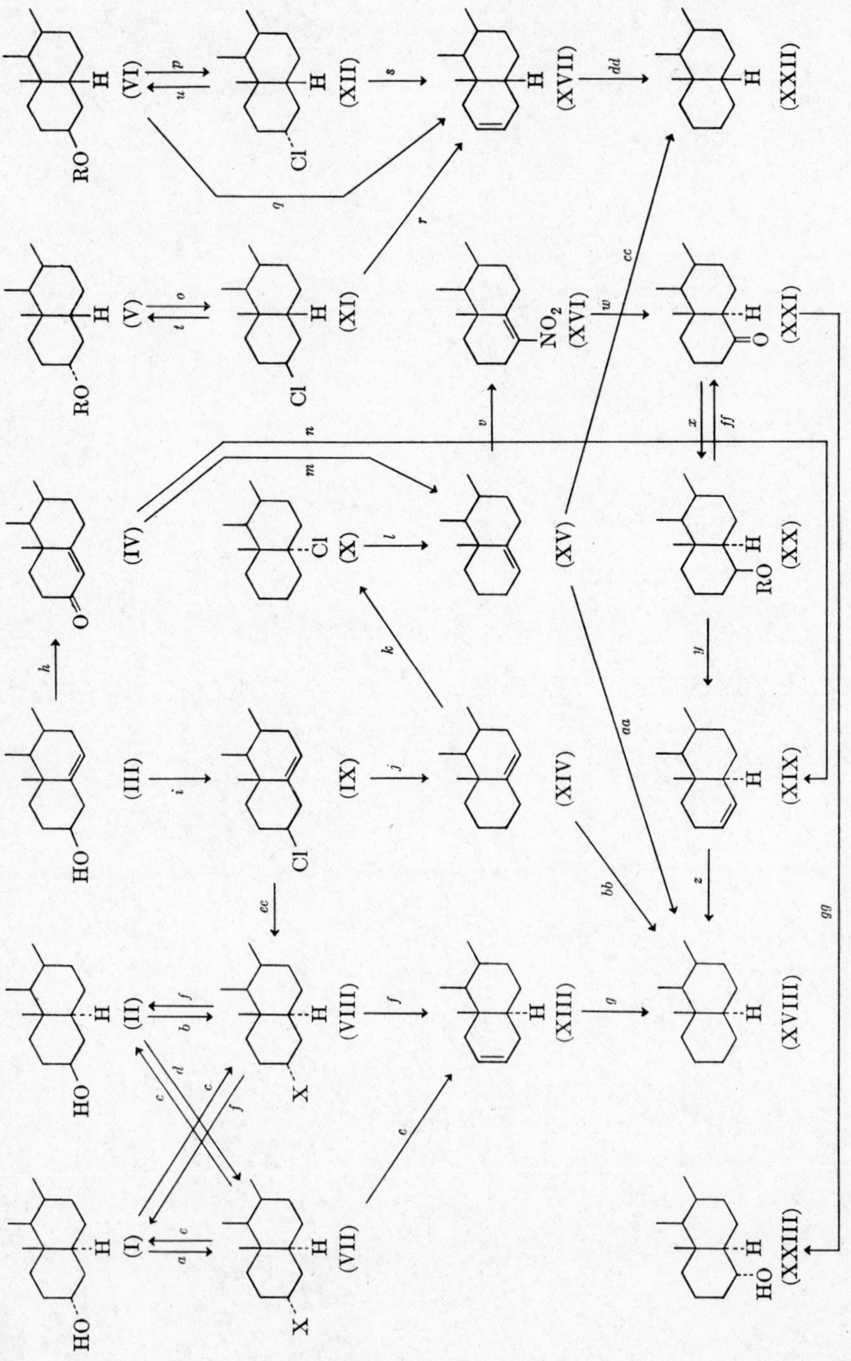
(I)
(II)
(III)
(IV)
(V)
(VI)
(VII)
(VIII)
(IX)
(X)
(XI)
(XII)
(XIII)
(XIV)
(XV)
(XVI)
(XVII)
(XVIII)
(XIX)
(XX)
(XXI)
(XXII)
(XXIII)

G. 3-Halides and Ring-A Unsaturated Hydrocarbons

(a, b) X = Cl, $SOCl_2$ (Marker et al., 1935; Shoppee, 1946a).

(b) X = $O.SO_2OK$, two steps; (1) SO_3-Py; (2) aq. KCl (Sobel and Spoerri, 1941).

(c) X = Cl, PCl_5 (Ruzicka et al., 1934a; Marker et al., 1935; Shoppee, 1946a).

(d) X = Cl, PCl_5 (Ruzicka et al., 1934a; Shoppee, 1946a).

(e, f) X = Cl, $KOAc$-n-$C_4H_9CO_2H$ rx. and hydrolysis (Shoppee, 1946a).

(f) X = $O.SO_2OK$, Na-caproxide-capryl alcohol at 180° yields (XIII) (Sobel and Rosen, 1941).

(g) H_2-Pt-Et_2O (Mauthner, 1909).

(h) See Section VI, H.

(i) PCl_5 (Loebisch, 1872; Mauthner, 1894). $SOCl_2$ (Diels and Blumberg, 1911). $SOCl_2$-Py (Daughenbaugh and Allison, 1929).

(j) Na-$C_5H_{11}OH$ (Mauthner and Suida, 1894).

(k) HCl-$CHCl_3$.

(l) Quinoline rx. or KOAc-EtOH rx. (Mauthner, 1907).

(m) Wolff Kishner reduction (Lettré, 1933) or two steps: (1) $Ph.CH_2SH$-$ZnCl_2$-Na_2SO_4; (2) Raney Ni-aq. dioxane (Hauptmann, 1947).

(n) Wolff Kishner reduction N_2H_4, H_2O-EtOH-NaOEt at 220° gives a small yield of (XIX) mixed with (XV), cf., m (Lardelli and Jeger, 1949).

(o, p) R = H, PCl_5-$CHCl_3$-$CaCO_3$.

(q) $SOCl_2$-Et_2O-$CaCO_3$ (R = H), or pyrolysis² (R = Bz).

(r, s, t, u) KOAc-AcOH rx.

(r, s) Quinoline rx. (Bridgewater and Shoppee, 1953).

(v) HNO_3 (fuming)-AcOH (Windaus, 1920; Barton and Rosenfelder, 1951).

(w) Zn-AcOH (Windaus, 1920; Barton and Rosenfelder, 1951).

(x) H_2-Pt-AcOH (Tschesche and Hagedorn, 1935; Barton and Rosenfelder, 1951).

(y) Pyrolysis at 400°/1 mm. (Barton and Rosenfelder, 1951).

(z) H_2-Pt-AcOH-EtOAc (Lardelli and Jeger, 1949).

(aa) H_2-Pt-AcOH (Windaus, 1919).

(bb) H_2-Pt-Et_2O (Mauthner, 1906).

(cc) H_2-Pt (or Pd)-Et_2O (i.e. neutral solution) (Mauthner, 1907; Windaus, 1919).

(dd) Not reported in the literature but would probably take place with H_2-Pt-AcOH.

(ee) X = Cl, H_2-Pt-EtOAc-AcOH (Shoppee, 1946b); Marker et al., 1935).

(ff) CrO_3 (Tschesche and Hagedorn, 1935).

(gg) Na-EtOH (Barton and Rosenfelder, 1951).

The hydrocarbons which have double bonds in rings B, C, and D, i.e. Δ^7, $\Delta^{8(9)}$, $\Delta^{8(14)}$, $\Delta^{9(11)}$, and Δ^{14}-cholestenes, can be made from the corresponding 3-alcohols by a two-stage process: (1) oxidation (CrO_3-AcOH); (2) Wolff Kishner reduction. See for example Barton and Cox (1948a) and Bladon et al. (1951).

NOTE: In (VIII), the bond joining the atom X to C-3 should be β (a full stroke).

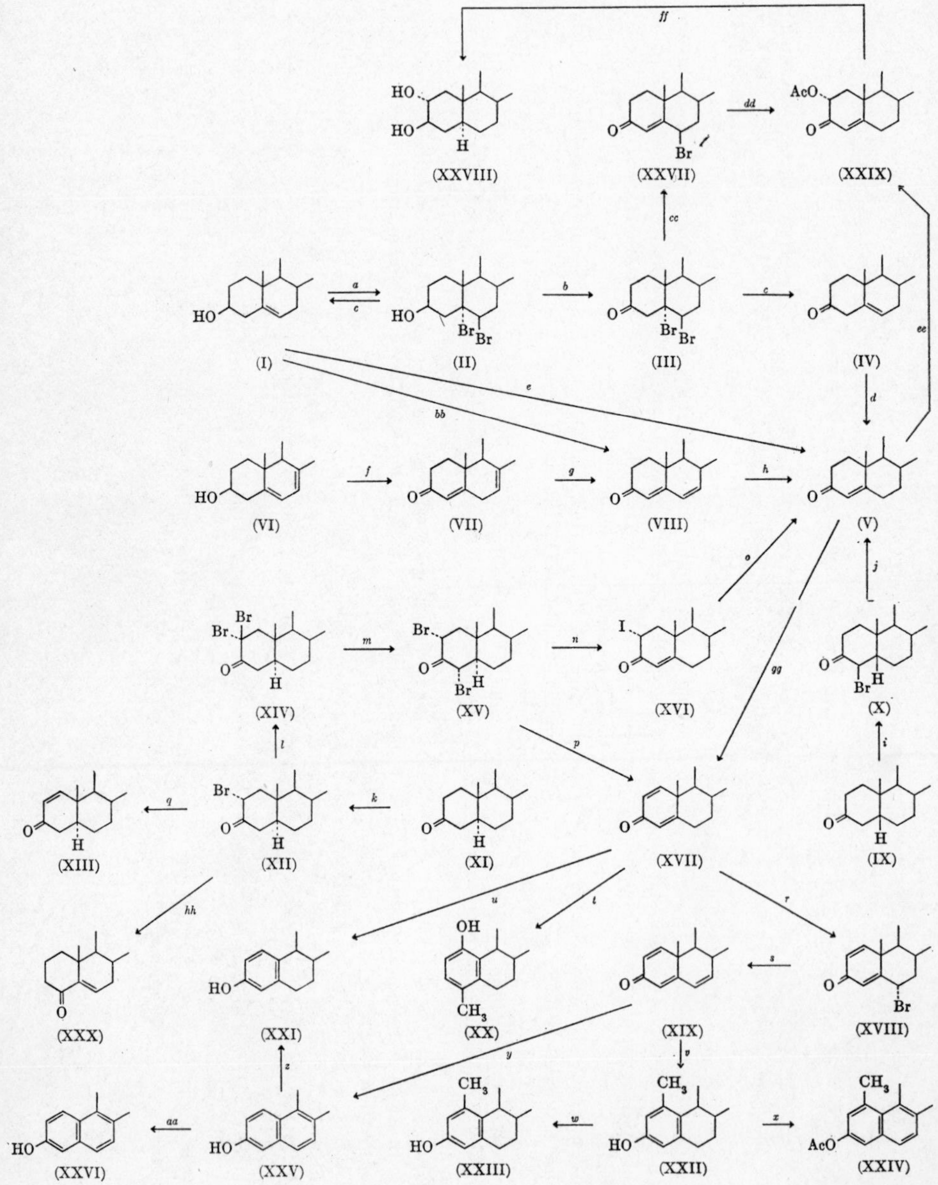
(XXVIII)
(XXVII)
(XXIX)
(I)
(II)
(III)
(IV)
(VI)
(VII)
(VIII)
(V)
(XIV)
(XV)
(XVI)
(X)
(XIII)
(XII)
(XI)
(XVII)
(IX)
(XXX)
(XXI)
(XX)
(XIX)
(XVIII)
(XXVI)
(XXV)
(XXIII)
(XXII)
(XXIV)

H. 3-Ketones: Bromination, Etc.

(a) Br_2-Et_2O at 25°.

(b) $Na_2Cr_2O_7$-AcOH.

(c) Zn-AcOH.

(d) Acidic or basic catalysts. $(CO_2H)_2$ is best. The development of this series or reactions for oxidation of cholesterol to cholestenone is due to Fieser (1953b, 1955b).

(e) Me_2CO-Al(OBu^{tert})$_3$-C_6H_6 rx. (Oppenauer, 1941) or cyclohexanone-Al(OPr^{iso})$_3$-PhMe (Eastham and Teranishi, 1955).

(f) Cyclohexanone - Al(OPr^{iso})$_3$ - PhMe (Daglish et al., 1953, Johnson et al., 1954).

(g) Acidic catalysts, e.g. HCl-MeOH (Johnson et al., 1954) or via the $\Delta^{3,5,7}$-enol acetate and subsequent hydrolysis (Heilbron et al., 1938c).

(h) H_2-Pd/C in alkaline solution (Slomp et al., 1955; Shepherd et al., 1955).

(i) Br_2-AcOH (Butenandt and Wolff, 1935; Butenandt et al., 1936) or NBS-CCl_4 (Djerassi and Scholz, 1947b).

(j) Hot Py (Djerassi and Scholz, 1947b).

(k, l) Br_2-AcOH or NBS-CCl_4 (Schwenk and Whitman, 1937; Inhoffen et al., 1940); Butenandt and Wolff, 1935; Djerassi and Scholz, 1947a, 1947b).

(m) HBr-AcOH (anhydrous) (Inhoffen and Huang, 1938); Inhoffen and Zühlsdorf, 1943); Wilds and Djerassi, 1946b; Dorée, 1909); Djerassi and Scholz, 1947a).

(n) NaI-Me_2CO (prolonged treatment).

(o) Reduction of the 2α-iodo-Δ^4-3-ketone (XVI) with either $CrCl_2$, or by collidine rx. (Rosenkranz et al., 1950a, 1950b).

(p. q) Collidine rx. (Butenandt et al., 1939).

(r) NBS-CCl_4-Bz_2O_2 in strong light.

(s) Collidine rx. (Romo et al., 1950a).

(t) Ac_2O-H_2SO_4 (Inhoffen and Zühlsdorf, 1941); Woodward et al., 1953).

(u) This reaction has not been successfully carried out in the cholesterol series (Inhoffen and Zühlsdorf, 1941; Wilds and Djerassi, 1946a) but can be carried out in the 1,4-androstadien-17-ol-3-one series (Inhoffen, 1947; Wilds and Djerassi, 1946a; FIAT, 1947) and in the 3-ketoetiochola-1,4-dienic acid series (Djerassi and Scholz, 1949). The method involves pyrolysis in 9,10-dihydrophenanthrene at 380–390°.

(v) Ac_2O-TsOH at 90°.

(w) H_2-Pd/BaSO$_4$-EtOAc.

(x) SeO_2-AcOH rx. on the 3-acetate (Romo et al., 1950a).

(y) Pyrolysis in tetralin at 600–700°.

(z) H_2-Pd/C-EtOAc (Romo et al., 1950b).

(aa) This reaction does not appear to have been done in the cholesterol series. The conversion of 6-dehydro-estradiol 3,17-diacetate to 17-dihydro-equilenin diacetate proceeds with SeO_2-AcOH rx. (Djerassi et al., 1950).

(bb) Modified Oppenauer oxidation: p-benzoquinone-Al(OBu^{tert})$_3$ PhMe (Wettstein, 1940; Wilds and Djerassi, 1946b; Djerassi, 1951; Ushakov and Kosheleva, 1944), or MnO_2-C_6H_6 rx. (Sondheimer et al. 1953).

(cc) KOAc-H_2O-C_6H_6 rx. (Ruzicka et. al., 1936); Dane et al., 1936; cf. Rivett and Wallis, 1950).

(dd) KOAc-AcOH rx. (Fieser and Romero, 1953; Rivett and Wallis, 1950).

(ee) Pb(OAc)$_4$-AcOH (or Ac_2O) (Fieser and Romero, 1953; Seeback and Reichstein, 1944).

(ff) H_2-PtO$_2$-AcOH, KOH-MeOH (Seeback and Reichstein, 1944).

(gg) SeO_2-tert BuOH-AcOH (Meystre et al., 1956; cf. Ringold et al., 1956; Szpilfogel et al., 1956). This reaction has not been reported in the cholesterol series.

(hh) KOAc-AcOH at 200° (Butenandt and Wolff, 1935).

Note: In (XXII), there should be a double bond between C-6 and C-7; in (XXV), there should be a single bond between C-8 and C-9.

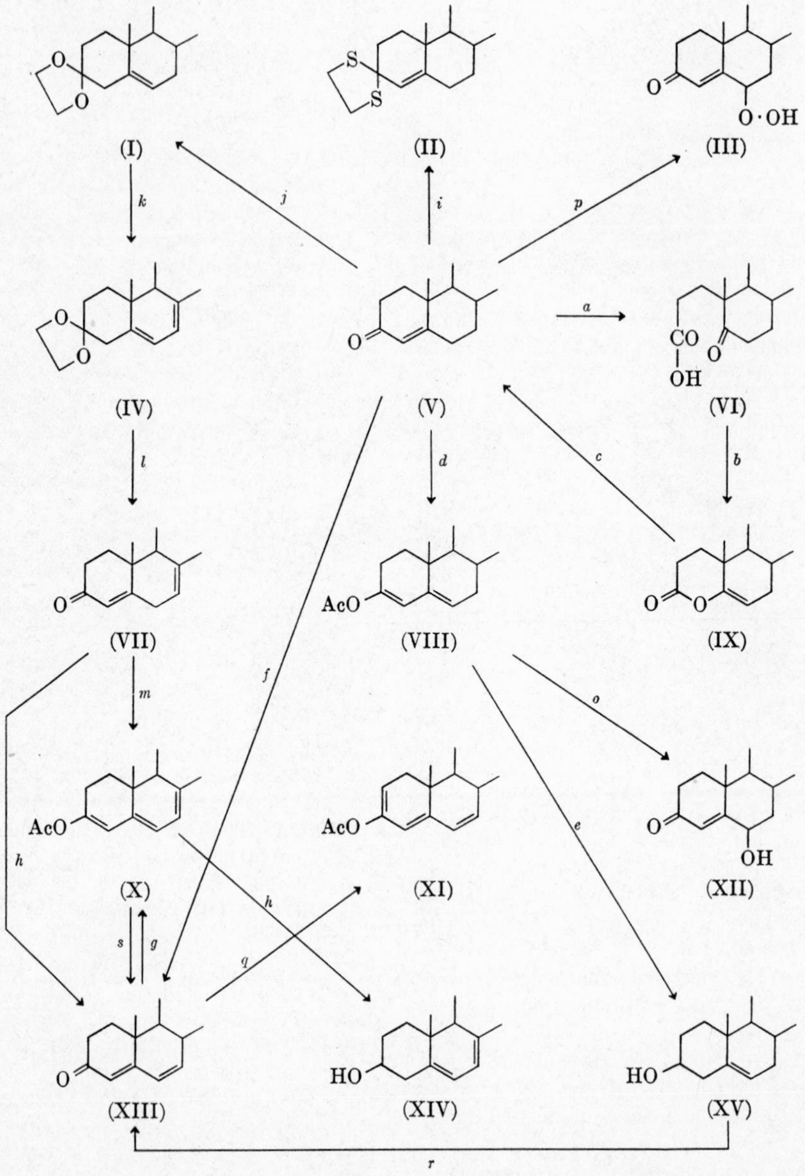

(I)
(II)
(III)
(IV)
(V)
(VI)
(VII)
(VIII)
(IX)
(X)
(XI)
(XII)
(XIII)
(XIV)
(XV)
O·OH
CO
OH
AcO
HO
OH
a
b
c
d
e
f
g
h
i
j
k
l
m
o
p
q
r
s

I. 3-KETONES

This chart is particularly designed to show the transformations that are possible with cholestenone (V), into which it is possible to introduce labeled carbon atoms (radioactive C^{14} or the stable isotope C^{13}) by reactions a, b, and c.

(a) O_3-EtOAc at —10°.

(b) Ac_2O rx. or AcCl rx. (Turner, 1950).

(c) MeMgI-Et_2O (Fujimoto, 1951); using labeled MeMgI this gives cholestenone-4-C^{14}. The earlier method (Turner, 1950) using PhOAc (labeled either in the methyl or the carboxyl group) and NaH gives lower yields of cholestenone (labeled, respectively, at C-4 and C-3).

(d) IPA-H_2SO_4 (Dauben and Eastham, 1951a).

(e) LiAlH$_4$-THF (Dauben and Eastham, 1951a) or NaBH$_4$ (Dauben and Eastham, 1951b) or two stages: (1) KNH$_2$-NH$_3$; (2) reduction of the cholest-5-enone with LiAlH$_4$ (Birch, 1950).

(f) Two steps: (1) NBS; (2) collidine (Meystre and Wettstein, 1946); Inhoffen and Stoeck, 1949).

(g) AcCl-Ac_2O rx. The product (X) is mixed with (XI).

(h) NaBH$_4$ (Dauben et al., 1951).

(i) $(CH_2SH)_2$ with either BF$_3$·Et_2O (Fieser, 1954a) or ZnCl$_2$-Na$_2$SO$_4$ (Antonucci et al., 1952).

(j) $(CH_2OH)_2$-C_6H_6-TsOH rx. (Antonucci et al., 1952).

(k) Two steps: (1) NBS; (2) collidine (Antonucci et al., 1952).

(l) Aq. AcOH (Antonucci et al., 1952).

(m) Ac_2O-Py rx. (Heilbron et al., 1938c).

(n) Section VI, H.

(o) Monoperphthalic acid (Romo et al., 1954).

(p) O_2-C_6H_{14} at 25° on Δ^5 compound. Compound (III) is a carcinogen (Fieser et al., 1955; Gollnick and Neumüller, 1957).

(q) AcCl-Ac_2O rx. (Heilbron et al., 1938c) (cf., g) or IPA-H_4SO_4, or AcCl-PhNMe$_2$, or Ac_2O-Py (Dauben et al., 1951).

(r) See Section VI, H.

(s) KOH-MeOH (Heilbron et al., 1938c).

NOTE: Beside the arrow at the extreme left-hand side, for h, read n.

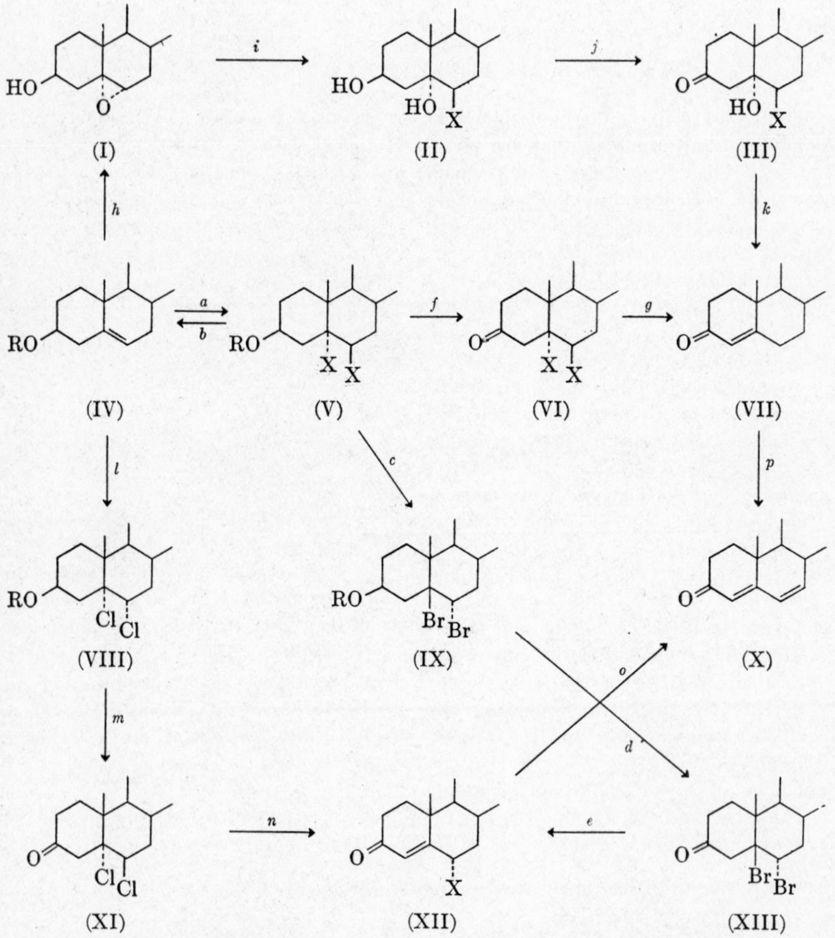

(I)

(II)

(III)

(IV)

(V)

(VI)

(VII)

(VIII)

(IX)

(X)

(XI)

(XII)

(XIII)

R = H, Ac or Bz   X = Cl or Br

J. CHOLESTEROL DIHALIDES

The structures of the cholesterol dihalides rests largely on the work of Barton and Miller. Their two papers deal with respectively the dichloro (1950a) and the dibromo compounds (1950b). The structures for the dihalides proposed by Rivett and Wallis (1950) are erroneous.

(a) X = Cl, Cl_2-$SbCl_3$-$CHCl_3$ at —20° (Barton and Miller, 1950a). X = Br, Br_2-Et_2O (Windaus, 1906; Fieser, 1953b, 1955b).

(b) Zn-AcOH (Fieser, 1953b, 1955b; see also p. 22).

(c) Standing in $CHCl_3$ for 3 days. (Barton and Miller, 1950b).

(d) CrO_3-AcOH (Barton and Miller, 1950b; Inhoffen, 1936).

(e) NaOEt-EtOH rx. (Barton and Miller, 1950b).

(f) CrO_3-AcOH.

(g) NaOEt-EtOH rx. (X = Cl, Barton and Miller, 1950a, b; X = Br, Ruzicka et al., 1936).

(h) See Section VI, M.

(i) HX-$CHCl_3$.

(j) CrO_3-AcOH.

(k) $SOCl_2$-Py (Barton and Miller, 1950a, b).

(l) $PhICl_2$-$CHCl_3$ (dry) (Berg and Wallis, 1946; Barton and Miller, 1950a).

(m) CrO_3-AcOH.

(n) NaOEt-EtOH rx. (Barton and Miller, 1950a).

(o, p) 2,4-Dinitrophenylhydrazine hydrochloride gives on heating the 2,4-dinitrophenylhydrazone of (X) (Barton and Miller, 1950a, b).

NOTE: In (VII), a β-oriented atom X should be present at C-6; in (XI), the chlorine atom at C-6 should be α-orientated.

(I) →a→ (II) →b→ (III)

(III) →d→ (IV) →e→ (V) →c→

(V) →f→ (VI)

(VII) →g→ (VI)

(VII) →h→ (VIII) →i→ (VI)

(VIII) →k→ (X)

(VIII) →j→ (XI)

(VIII) →o→ (IX)

(IX) →p→ (XII)

(XI) →k→ (X)

(XII) →s→ (XIII)

(X) →m→ (XIV)

(XIV) ⇌ m / l ⇌ (XV)

(XV) →n→ (XVI)

(XVII) →t→ (XVIII) →u→ (XIX)

K. Cholestadienes and Bischolestadienyl

The structures of the products derived from cholesta-2,4-diene are those proposed by Conca and Bergmann (1953). For the proof of the configurations of the hydroxyl groups in (XVIII), see Bladon *et al.* (1958). For the formation of (XIX) in the Salkowski reaction see p. 87.

For a review of the methods of formation of cholesta-3,5-diene see Stavely and Bergmann (1937a).

(*a*) CrO_3-AcOH (Windaus, 1920).

(*b*) Al(OPr^{iso})$_3$-*i*-PrOH (Dimroth and Trautmann, 1936).

(*c*) Ac$_2$O rx. (Dimroth and Trautmann, 1936; Eck and Hollingsworth, 1941).

(*d*) Pyrolysis of the benzoate at 125° (Dimroth and Trautmann, 1936).

(*e*) Heating (Dimroth and Trautmann, 1936).

(*f*) HCl-CHCl$_3$ (Eck and Hollingsworth, 1941).

(*g*) R = H, heat with CuSO$_4$; R = CS·SMe, heat (Eck *et al.*, 1939). R = SO$_2$·OK, Na-caproxide-capryl alcohol rx. (Sobel and Rosen, 1941).

(*h*) Al$_2$O$_3$ heat (Skau and Bergmann, 1938).

(*i*) HCl-EtOH rx. (Stavely and Bergmann, 1937b).

(*j*) O$_2$-eosin-EtOH-artificial light (Skau and Bergmann, 1938).

(*k*) EtOH-eosin-sunlight (Skau and Bergmann, 1938).

(*l*) Heat to 230° *in vacuo* or Ac$_2$O rx. (Bergmann *et al.*, 1939).

(*m*) KOH-MeOH-rx. (Bergmann *et al.*, 1939).

(*n*) TsOH-C$_6$H$_6$ rx. (Conca and Bergmann, 1953).

(*o*) H$_2$-Pt-EtOAc (Skau and Bergmann, 1938) or LiAlH$_4$-Et$_2$O rx. (Conca and Bergmann, 1953).

(*p*) CrO$_3$-AcOH.

(*q*) H$_2$-Pt black-EtOAc.

(*r*) H$_2$-PtO$_2$-EtOAc.

(*s*) N$_2$H$_4$·H$_2$O-KOH-MeOH-O(C$_2$H$_4$-OH)$_2$ at 195° (Conca and Bergmann, 1953).

(*t*) Na/Hg-*n*-PrOH-AcOH (S q u i r e , 1951) or electrolytic reduction (Bladon *et al.*, 1958).

(*u*) AcOH-Ac$_2$O-CHCl$_3$ rx. (Squire, 1951).

(VI)   (VII)   (VIII)

(I)   (II)   (IX)

(III)   (IV)   (V)   (X)

L. 4-Oxygen Functions

(a) H_2O_2-Et_2O-OsO_4 (Butenandt and Wolz, 1938). Despite a statement in this paper, the reaction does not go to completion in the presence of less than 1 mole of OsO_4.

(b) SeO_2-AcOH-C_6H_6 at 90° (Rosenheim and Starling, 1937).

(c) SeO_2-Ac_2O-AcOH rx. (Butenandt and Hausmann, 1937).

(d) HCl-EtOH or heating. (Rosenheim and Starling, 1937).

(e) $Pb(OAc)_4$-AcOH-C_6H_6.

(f) HCl-EtOH (Fieser and Stevenson, 1954).

(g) $(CH_2SH)_2$-BF_3.Et_2O.

(h) Raney Ni-EtOH.

(i) HCl-MeOH (Stevenson and Fieser, 1956).

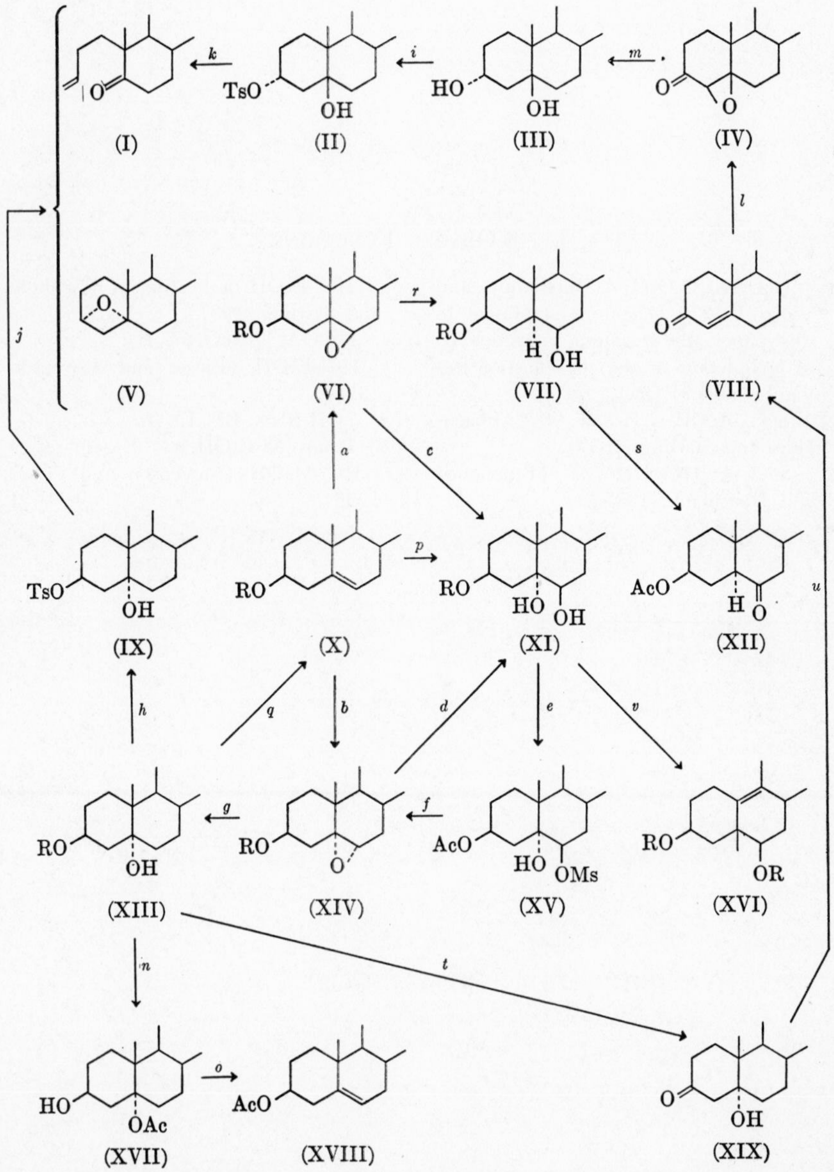

(I)
(II)
(III)
(IV)
(V)
(VI)
(VII)
(VIII)
(IX)
(X)
(XI)
(XII)
(XIII)
(XIV)
(XV)
(XVI)
(XVII)
(XVIII)
(XIX)
TsO
OH
HO
RO
AcO
OMs
OR
OAc
H
O
a
b
c
d
e
f
g
h
i
j
k
l
m
n
o
p
q
r
s
t
u
v

M. 5-Oxygen Functions

(a, b) PhCO$_3$H or monoperphthalic acid. When R = H the product formed is largely the α-oxide (XIV) (Ruzicka and Bosshard, 1937). When R = Ac or Bz, the product is a 1:1 molecular compound of the α- and β-oxides (acetates or benzoates) (XIV + VI) (Hattori, 1940; Baxter and Spring, 1943; Chakravorty and Levin, 1942). The compound can be separated into its components by chromatography (Plattner et al., 1944).

(c, d) H$_2$O at 160° (R = Ac) (Plattner and Lang, 1944) or aq. H$_2$SO$_4$ (Fürst and Koller, 1947).

(e) TsCl-Py.

(f) KOH-MeOH (Fürst and Koller, 1947).

(g) H$_2$-PtO$_2$-AcOH (Plattner et al., 1944) or LiAlH$_4$-THF (Bladon, Clayton, and Henbest, unpublished observations). Quite crude α-epoxide can be used for this last method, and the 3β:5α-diol purified as the monoacetate by chromatography.

(h, i) TsCl-Py.

(j, k) Tert-NaOBu in tert BuOH rx. (Clayton et al., 1957). Note that the cholestane derivative (IX) gives a mixture of the 3:5-epoxide (V) and the unsaturated ketone (I), while the coprostane derivative (II) yields only the latter product. (For details of the mechanism of this reaction, see the original paper.)

(l) H$_2$O$_2$-MeOH-NaOH.

(m) H$_2$-PtO$_2$-AcOH (Plattner et al., 1948).

(n) Two steps: (1) complete acetylation AcCl-PhNMe$_2$-CHCl$_3$ rx. (Plattner et al., 1944); (2) Partial hydrolysis KOH-MeOH r.t.

(o) TsCl-Py-rx. (Plattner and Lang, 1944).

(p) AcO$_2$H (H$_2$O$_2$-AcOH) (Petrow, 1937).

(q) Ac$_2$O-HClO$_4$-CCl$_4$ (Bladon et al., 1954).

(r) H$_2$-Pt-AcOH.

(s) R = Ac, CrO$_3$-AcOH (Plattner and Lang, 1944).

(t) CrO$_3$-AcOH.

(u) Ac$_2$O rx. (Plattner et al., 1944).

(v) Ac$_2$O-H$_2$SO$_4$ (Westphalen, 1915) For a discussion on the assignment of the structure, see Bladon et al. (1952b).

NOTE: In (XVIII), the 3-acetoxy group should be α-orientated.

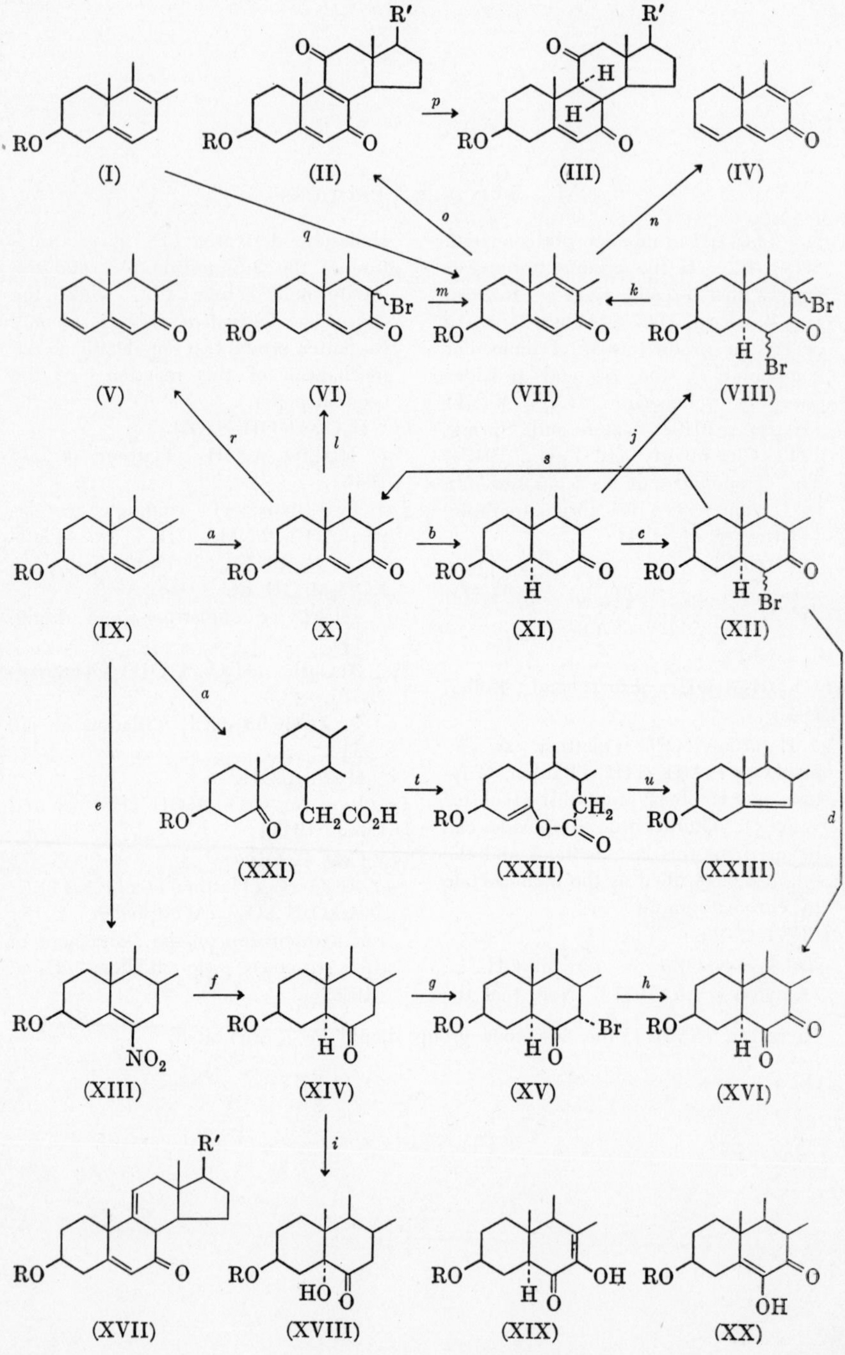
(I)
(II)
(III)
(IV)
(V)
(VI)
(VII)
(VIII)
(IX)
(X)
(XI)
(XII)
(XIII)
(XIV)
(XV)
(XVI)
(XVII)
(XVIII)
(XIX)
(XX)
(XXI)
(XXII)
(XXIII)

N. 6- AND 7-KETONES

(a) CrO₃-AcOH (Fieser *et al.*, 1949). The keto acid (XXI) is a by-product (Šorm, 1947; Šorm and Dyková, 1948; Dauben and Fonken, 1956).

(b) H₂-PtO₂-EtOAc (Wintersteiner and Moore, 1943).

(c) Bromination with Br₂-AcOH gives the 6β- and 6α-bromo compounds. The former is converted into the latter by HBr (Barr *et al.*, 1938; Corey, 1954; James and Shoppee, 1956).

(d) Treatment of the 6α-bromoketone with AgNO₃-Py (Barr *et al.*, 1938). Compound (XVI) exists in a monoenol form: either (XIX) or (XX).

(e) 96% HNO₃-AcOH (Heilbron *et al.*, 1938a; Mauthner and Suida, 1903).

(f) Zn dust-aq. AcOH (Heilbron *et al.*, 1938a).

(g) Br₂-AcOH rx. (Heilbron *et al.*, 1937). The 5α-bromo compound is formed first and converted unto the 7α-compound by the HBr present (Corey, 1954).

(h) AgNO₃-Py rx. (Heilbron *et al.*, 1937).

(i) SeO₂-AcOH (Hodinář and Pelc, 1956).

(j) NBS-CCl₄-Bz₂O₂-IR radiation (Tsuda and Hayatsu, 1955a). Br₂-AcOH gives a different dibromo compound (Barr *et al.*, 1938).

(k) Py rx. (Tsuda and Hayatsu, 1955a). The structure (VII) may be incorrect for the compound formed, as it has already been assigned to a different isomeric compound (Inhoffen and Mengel, 1954). The alternative structure (XVII) is a possibility for one or other of these two substances.

(l) NBS-CCl₄-Bz₂O₂-IR radiation (Tsuda and Hayatsu, 1955a, b).

(m) Py rx. (Tsuda and Hayatsu, 1955a, b).

(n) Occurs in processes k and m; i.e. (IV) is a by-product of (VII). It is also formed by refluxing the tosyl derivative of (VII) with PhNMe₂ (Tsuda and Hayatsu, 1955a).

(o) H₂-PtO₂-EtOAc (Tsuda and Hayatsu, 1955b).

(p) Zn-AcOH (Tsuda and Hayatsu, 1955b). Hydrogenation of (III) yields cholestane-3β-ol-7,11-dione (cf. Section VI, Q).

(q) CrO₃-AcOH (Tsuda *et al.*, 1954).

(r) KOH-EtOH (Mauthner and Suida, 1896) or HCl-EtOH (Stavely and Bergmann, 1937a, b).

(s) Py rx. Both the 6α and 6β-bromo compounds react (Barr *et al.*, 1938).

(t) BzCl-Py.

(u) Heat at 170° (Šorm, 1947; Šorm and Dyková, 1948; Dauben and Fonken, 1956).

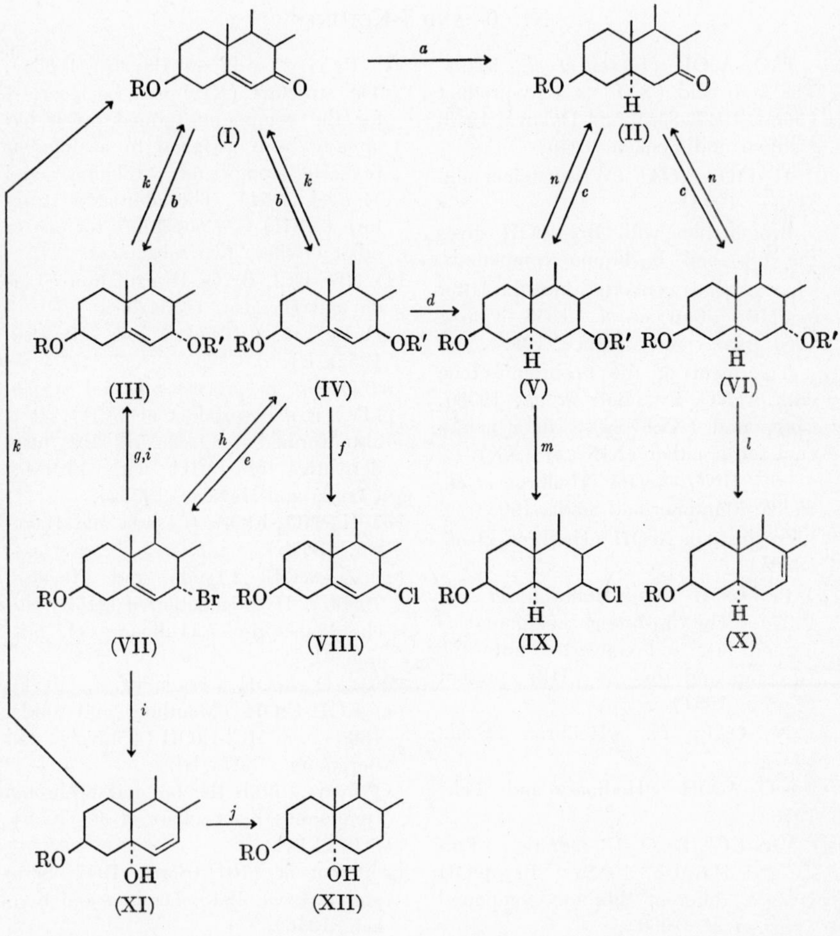
RO
O
(I)
a
RO
H
O
(II)
k
b
b
k
n
c
c
n
RO
OR′
(III)
RO
OR′
(IV)
d
RO
H
OR′
(V)
RO
H
OR′
(VI)
g,i
h
e
f
m
l
k
RO
Br
(VII)
RO
Cl
(VIII)
RO
H
Cl
(IX)
RO
H
(X)
i
RO
OH
(XI)
j
RO
OH
(XII)

O. 7-Hydroxyl Compounds

(a) H_2-PtO$_2$-EtOAc (Wintersteiner and Moore, 1943).

(b) Al(OPr^{iso})$_3$-i-PrOH rx. (Wintersteiner and Ruigh, 1942). This gives largely the β-isomer and a small amount of the α-isomer. LiAlH$_4$-Et$_2$O (Fieser et al., 1949) gives 59% β- and 5% α-hydroxy compounds as the benzoates (R = R' = Bz).

(c) H_2-PtO$_2$-AcOH (Wintersteiner and Moore, 1943). This gives the 7α- and 7β-hydroxy compounds in the ratio 3:1 as monoacetates (R = Ac). LiAlH$_4$-Et$_2$O gives approximately equal amounts of the 7α- and 7β-compounds (Fieser et al., 1949).

(d) H_2-Pd/C-EtOAc (Heymann and Fieser, 1952).

(e) PBr$_3$-Et$_2$O.

(f) SOCl$_2$-Py (Bide et al., 1948b).

(g) KOAc-AcOH (R' = Ac) or NaO· CO·H-H·CO$_2$H (R' = formyl).

(h) AgOAc-Py (R' = Ac).

(i) KHCO$_3$-aq. dioxane r.t. (R' = H).

(j) H_2-PtO$_2$-EtOH.

(k) CrO$_3$-AcOH (R = Ac, R' = H) (Henbest and Jones, 1948).

(l) POCl$_3$-Py (Fieser et al., 1949; Buser, 1947).

(m) POCl$_3$-Py (Fieser et al., 1949).

(n) CrO$_3$-AcOH (R = Ac, R' = H) (Wintersteiner and Moore, 1943).

In literature prior to 1949 (and in some subsequent papers) epimeric compounds containing hydroxyl and other groups at C-7 were distinguished by the trivial indices "α" and "β". When it became possible to correlate configurations at C-7 with those at other centers, it was found that a reversal of the indices was needed. Thus 7 "β"-hydroxy-cholesterol (pre-1949 nomenclature) is in fact cholest-5-ene-3β, 7α-diol. This apparent reversal of configuration should be born in mind when consulting the early literature.

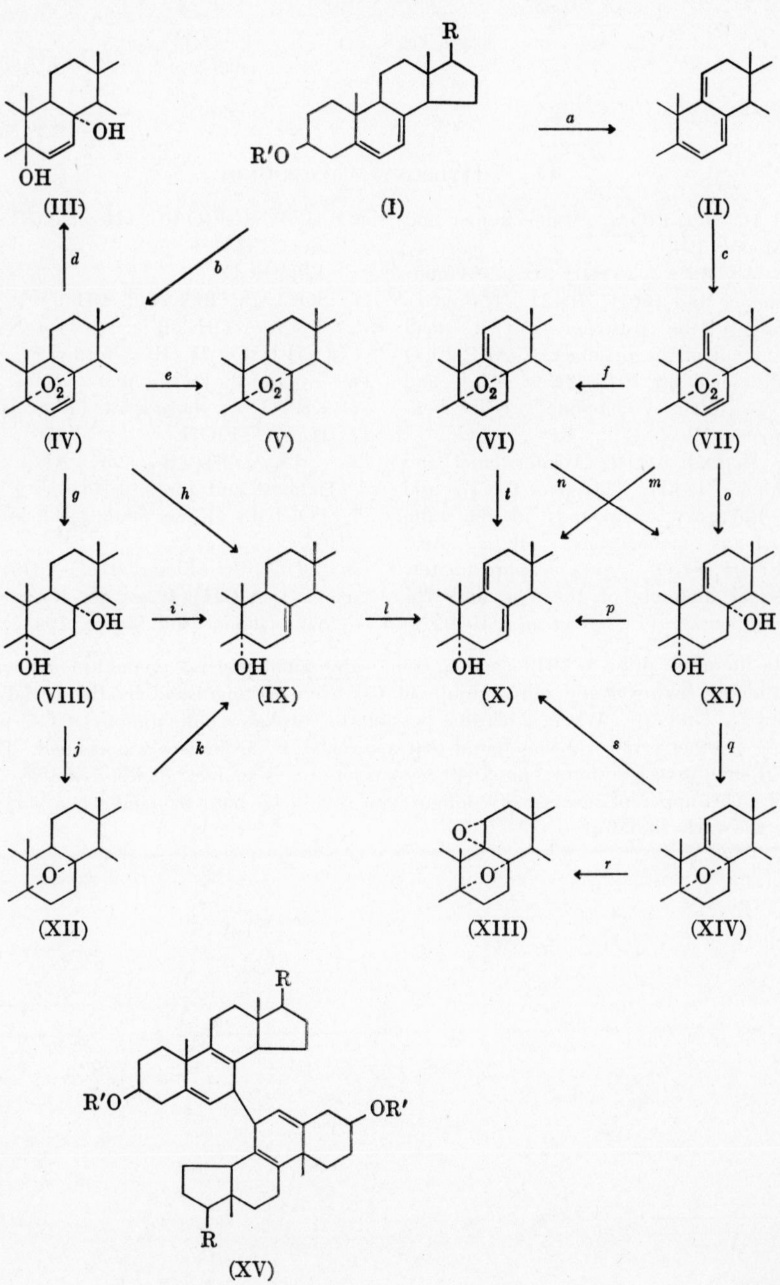
R
OH
OH
R′O
(III)
(I)
(II)
a
b
c
d
O2
e
f
(IV)
(V)
(VI)
(VII)
g
h
t
n
m
o
OH
OH
i
l
p
(VIII)
(IX)
(X)
(XI)
j
k
s
q
O
r
(XII)
(XIII)
(XIV)
R
R′O
OR′
R
(XV)

P. 5,8-Peroxides (Epidioxides)

The greater part of the work on 5,8-peroxides has been done with compounds of the ergosterol and 22-dihydroergosterol series (R = C_9H_{17}, C_9H_{19}, respectively), but most of the reactions are applicable to the cholesterol series (R = C_8H_{17}).

(a) $Hg(OAc)_2$-AcOH-CCl_4 (Inhoffen and Mengel, 1954; see also Section VI, E).

(b) O_2-eosin-EtOH with illumination (Windaus and Brunken, 1928 [E]; Clayton et al., 1953b [E]; Schenck et al., 1936) In the absence of oxygen the so-called "Pinacol" (XV) is formed (e.g. Mosettig and Scheer, 1952).

(c) O_2-eosin-EtOH with illumination (Inhoffen and Mengel, 1954; Windaus and Linsert, 1928 [E]; Bladon et al., 1952a [E]). Pinacol formation occurs in the absence of oxygen.

(d) Zn-EtOH-KOH (Schenck et al., 1936; Windaus and Linsert, 1928 [E]).

(e) H_2-Pt-EtOAc or AcOH (Clayton et al., 1953b [E]).

(f) H_2-Pt-EtOAc (Bladon et al., 1952a [E]).

(g) H_2-Pt-EtOAc.

(h) H_2-Pd-EtOH (Clayton et al., 1953b [E]) or $LiAlH_4$-Et_2O (Laws, 1953).

(i) HCl-MeOH.

(j) AcOH-Me_2CO rx.

(k) HCl-MeOH (Clayton et al., 1953b [E]).

(l) $Hg(OAc)_2$-$CHCl_3$-AcOH (Laws, 1953 [E]).

(m) Zn-KOH-EtOH (Windaus et al., 1930 [E]) or Raney Ni-H_2-EtOAc (Bladon et al., 1952a [E]).

(n) H_2-Pt-EtOAc (Bladon et al., 1952a [E]).

(o) H_2-Pt-Et_2O.

(p) AcOH rx. (Inhoffen and Mengel, 1954).

(q) AcOH-Me_2CO rx.

(r) Monoperphthalic acid-Et_2O.

(s) HCl-MeOH (Clayton et al., 1953a [E]).

(t) Zn-AcOH Bladon et al., 1952a [E].

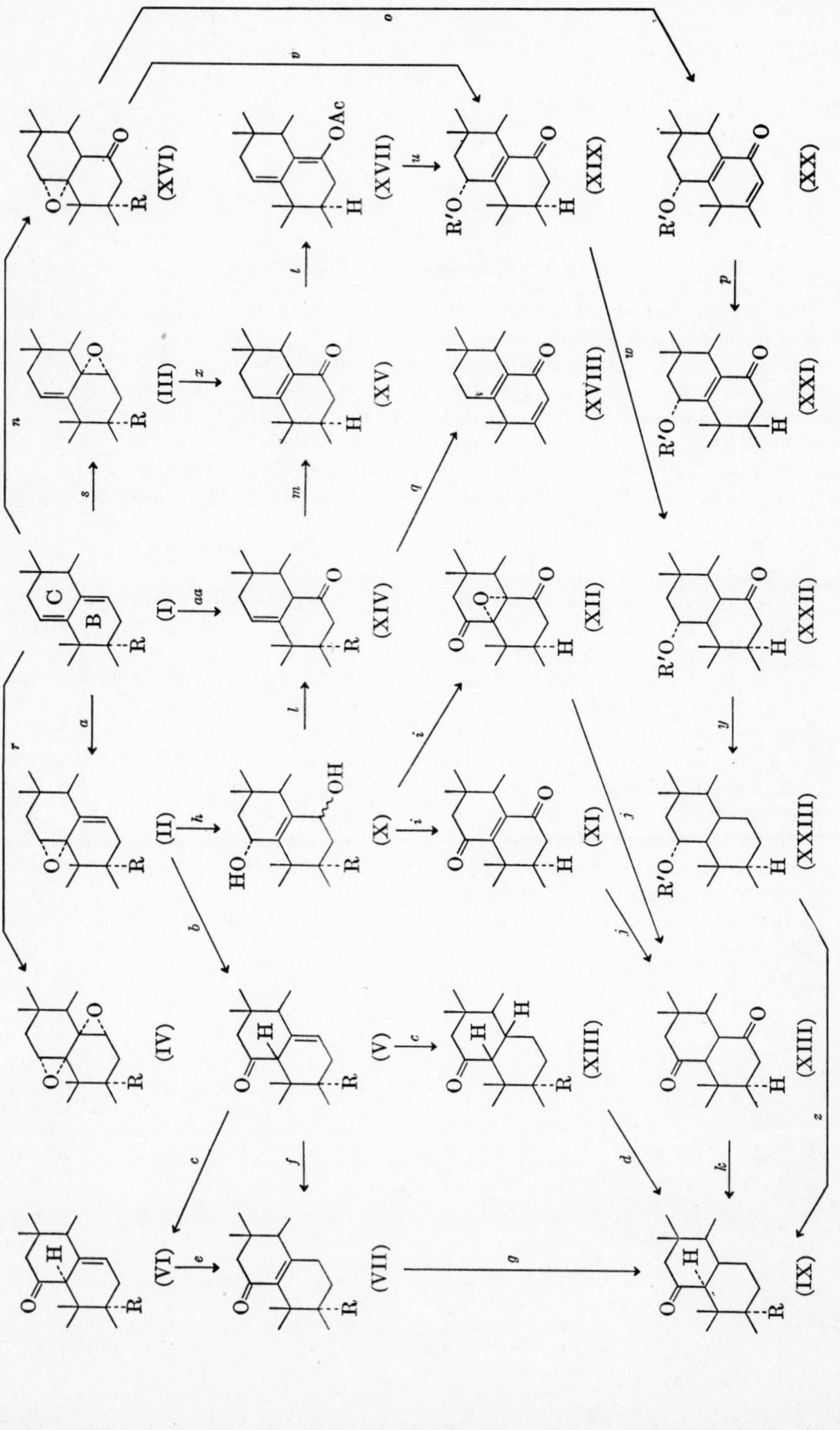

Q. 11-OXYGENATED STEROIDS FROM 7,9(11)-DIENES

R = H, or OH or OAc. R' = H, or Ac, or Bz. Side chain (C-17) = C_8H_{17}, C_9H_{17}, C_9H_{19}, or $COCH_3$, etc. The 3-hydroxy group is usually protected as the acetate or benzoate.

(a) $PhCO_3H$ or monoperphthalic acid (1 mole)-C_6H_6 or Et_2O (Chamberlin et al., 1951, 1953; Heusser et al., 1951, 1952a; Budziarek et al., 1952a, b [R = H], Bladon et al. 1953a; Inhoffen and Mengel, 1954 [R = OH or OAc]).

(b) $BF_3 \cdot Et_2O$ in C_6H_6 (short time) or in Et_2O (long time).

(c) H_2-PtO_2-AcOH or dioxane.

(d) KOH-EtOH rx.

(e) Al_2O_3-C_6H_6.

(f) $BF_3 \cdot Et_2O$-C_6H_6 (long time) (Bladon et al., 1953b). The direct formation of (VII) from (II) by treatment with $BF_3 \cdot Et_2O$ for a long time was previously reported by Heusser et al., (1951), Schoenewaldt et al. (1952), and Sondheimer et al. (1952).

(g) Li-NH_3 (Schoenewaldt et al., 1952; Sondheimer et al., 1952).

(h) Acidic Al_2O_3, (Chamberlin et al., 1953) or 2 N-H_2SO_4 in dioxane (Heusser et al., 1951).

(i) CrO_3-Me_2CO (Chamberlin et al., 1953; Heusser et al., 1951).

(j) Zn-AcOH (Chamberlin et al., 1953; Heusser et al., 1951; Fieser et al., 1951a; Fieser and Herz, 1953).

(k) $N_2H_4 \cdot H_2O$-$O(C_2H_4OH)_2$-KOH at 200° (Chamberlin et al., 1953; Fieser and Herz, 1953; Tsuda and Hayatsu, 1955b) or two steps: (1) $(CH_3\ddot{S}H)_2$-HCl, (2) Raney Ni-dioxane. (Heusser et al., 1951).

(l) H_2O_2-AcOH (Heusser et al., 1952b).

(m) $BF_3 \cdot Et_2O$-C_6H_6 (Heusser et al., 1952a).

(n) Performic acid (various conditions) (Stork et al., 1951; Bladon et al., 1953a; Budziarek et al., 1952a) or H_2O_2-AcOH-NH_4molybdate (Inhoffen and Mengel, 1954).

(o) KOH-MeOH (Inhoffen and Mengel, 1954; Bladon et al., 1953a [R = OH]].

(p) H_2-Raney Ni-dioxane.

(q) KOH-MeOH (Inhoffen and Mengel, 1954 [R = OH]).

(r) $PhCO_3H$ (2 moles) (Chamberlin et al., 1953) or H_2O_2-HCO_2H-$CHCl_3$ (Bladon et al., 1953a).

(s) H_2O_2-HCO_2H (Djerassi et al., 1951) (III) and (XIV) are by-products.

(t) IPA-Ts$\bar{O}$H-C_6H_6.

(u) Monoperphthalic acid (Djerassi et. al., 1951).

(v) Alkaline hydrolysis (Stork et al., 1951).

(w) H_2-Pd/C-EtOH.

(x) Alkaline rearrangement (Djerassi et al., 1951).

(y) Wolff Kishner reduction.

(z) CrO_3 oxidation (Stork et al., 1951).

(aa) H_2O_2-HCO_2H-$CHCl_3$ (Budziarek et al., 1952a).

Additional Notes

The main product of the reaction between the weakly acidic peracids (perbenzoic and monoperphthalic acids) and 7,9(11)-dienes is the $\Delta 7$-$9\alpha,11\alpha$-epoxide, when 1 mole of peracid is used. Excess peracid results in the formation of diepoxides (see reactions a and r).

The main product of the reaction between the more acidic peracids (peracetic acid and performic acid) and 7,9(11)-dienes are compounds of type (XVI). Various other compounds (III and XIV) are formed as by-products (see reactions n and s).

The following types of compounds can be considered as readily available from 7,9(11)-dienes: (II), (V), (X) (XIII), (XVI), (XIX), and (XX) and compounds derived therefrom).

Various other oxidants have been used to prepare 11-oxygen compounds from 7,9(11)-dienes: $K_2Cr_2O_7$-AcOH (Fieser and Herz, 1953), and NBS-tert-BuOH, $AgNO_3$, CrO_3 (Fieser et al., 1951b).

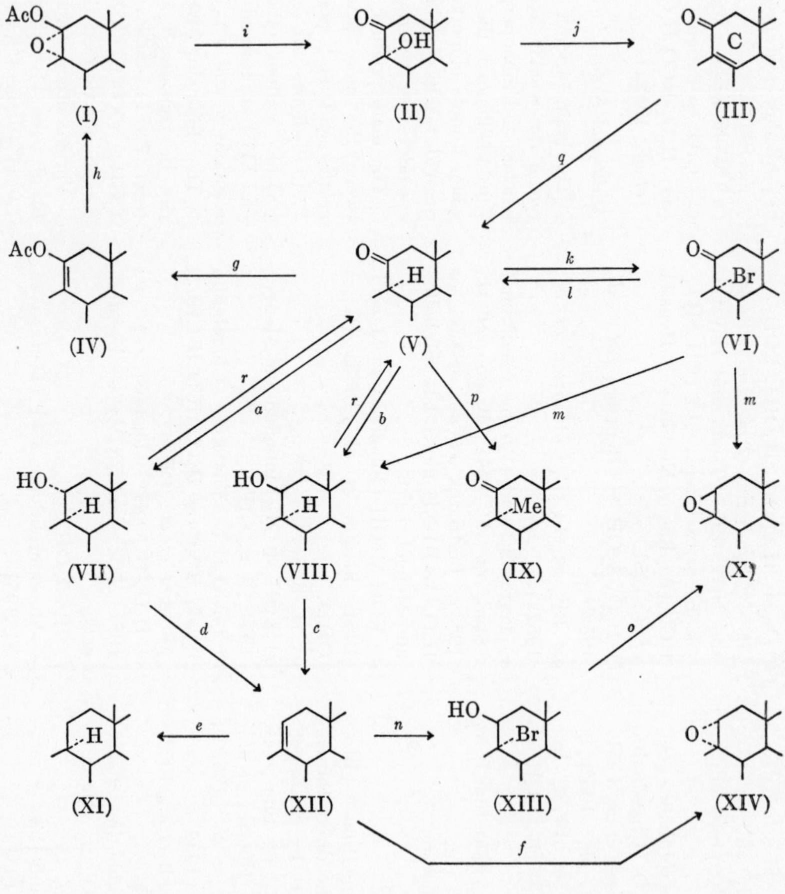
AcO
O
i
O
OH
j
O
C
(I)
(II)
(III)
h
q
AcO
g
O
H
k
l
O
Br
(IV)
(V)
(VI)
r
a
r
b
p
m
m
HO
H
HO
H
O
Me
O
(VII)
(VIII)
(IX)
(X)
d
c
o
H
e
n
HO
Br
O
(XI)
(XII)
(XIII)
(XIV)
f

R. 11-Oxygen Functions

General Notes

Most of the reactions outlined in the chart have been carried out in the ergostane series.

The 11β-hydroxyl group is sterically hindered and is not acetylated under mild conditions (Ac$_2$O-Py hot or cold) but can be acetylated by AcCl-PhNMe$_2$-CHCl$_3$ (Crawshaw *et al.*, 1954). 11α-Hydroxyl groups can be acetylated by Ac$_2$O-Py in the cold (Crawshaw *et al.*, 1954).

11-Ketosteroids do not give the usual ketonic reactions and derivatives. They are only reduced to the corresponding unsubstituted 11-methylene compound, by the drastic Kishner Wolff conditions of Barton *et al.*, 1955; see also Djerassi and Thomas, 1954.

(*a*) Na-*n*-PrOH (Heusser *et al.*, 1952c; Herzog *et al.*, 1953), or Na-EtOH (Crawshaw *et al.*, 1954).

(*b*) LiAlH$_4$-Et$_2$O (Crawshaw *et al.*, 1954).

(*c*) POCl$_3$-Py.

(*d*) POCl$_3$-Py.

(*e*) H$_2$-PtO$_2$-AcOH.

(*f*) Monoperphthalic acid-Et$_2$O.

(*g*) Ac$_2$O-TsOH rx. or IPA-TsOH rx.

(*h*) Monoperphthalic acid-Et$_2$O.

(*i*) KOH-MeOH.

(*j*) SOCl$_2$-Py (Crawshaw *et al.*, 1954).

(*k*) Br$_2$-HBr-AcOH.

(*l*) NaBH$_4$-MeOH.

(*m*) LiAlH$_4$-Et$_2$O yields 50% (X) and 30% (VIII).

(*n*) NBS-aq. HClO$_4$-Me$_2$CO.

(*o*) *tert*-KOBu-*tert*-BuOH (Henbest *et al.*, 1955).

(*p*) Treatment of (V, Δ^8 or Δ^7) with MeI-*tert*-BuOH-*tert*-KOBu gives (IX, Δ^7). (Jones *et al.*, 1958).

(*q*) See Section VI, Q.

(*r*) CrO$_3$-Py (Johns *et al.*, 1954).

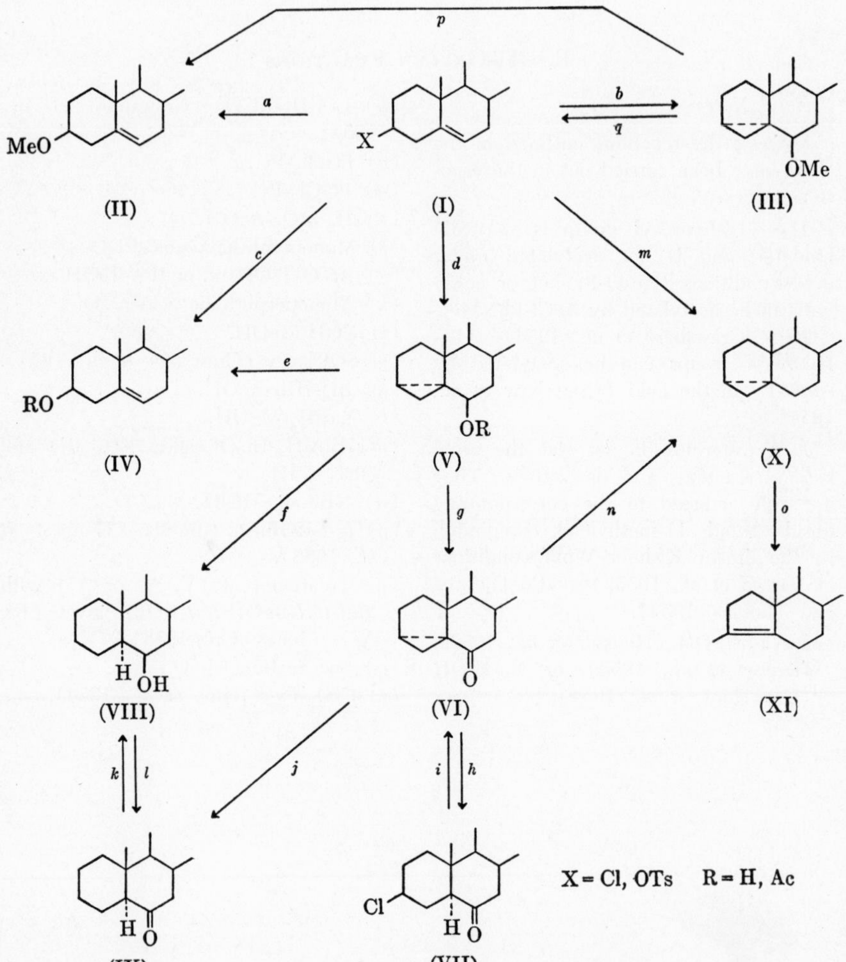

(II) (I) (III)

(IV) (V) (X)

(VIII) (VI) (XI)

(IX) (VII) X = Cl, OTs R = H, Ac

S. 3,5-CYCLO COMPOUNDS (i-STEROIDS)

General references: Schmid and Kägi (1950); Shoppee and Summers (1952b).

(a) MeOH (Diels and Blumberg, 1911).

(b) MeOH-KOAc (Wagner-Jauregg and Werner, 1932).

(c) Ac_2O (Wallis et al., 1937).

(d) Ac_2O-KOAc (Wallis et al., 1937).

(e) AcOH-H_2SO_4 Acidic media, in general, cause rearrangement of 3,5-cyclo steroids to the 3β-hydroxy Δ^5-compounds (Fieser and Fieser, 1949).

(f) H_2-Pd-dioxane (Shoppee and Summers, 1952b).

(g) CrO_3.

(h) HCl-AcOH (Ladenburg et al., 1939; Ford et al., 1938; Heilbron et al., 1938b).

(i) KOH-EtOH rx. (Windaus and Dalmer, 1919; Dodson and Riegel, 1948).

(j) H_2-Pd-AcOH (Windaus and Dalmer, 1919; Windaus and von Staden, 1921).

(k) $LiAlH_4$-Et_2O.

(l) CrO_3-AcOH (Shoppee and Summers, 1952b).

(m) $LiAlH_4$-Et_2O (Schmid and Karrer, 1949) Product is contaminated with cholest-5-ene.

(n) $N_2H_4 \cdot H_2O$-NaOEt at 180° (Schmid and Kägi, 1950).

(o) HCl-AcOH rx. (Schmid and Kägi, 1950). For the synthesis of (XI) see Shoppee and Summers (1952a).

(p) MeOH-TsOH rx. (McKennis, 1948).

(q) HX (X = Cl, Br, I) (Benyon et al., 1936).

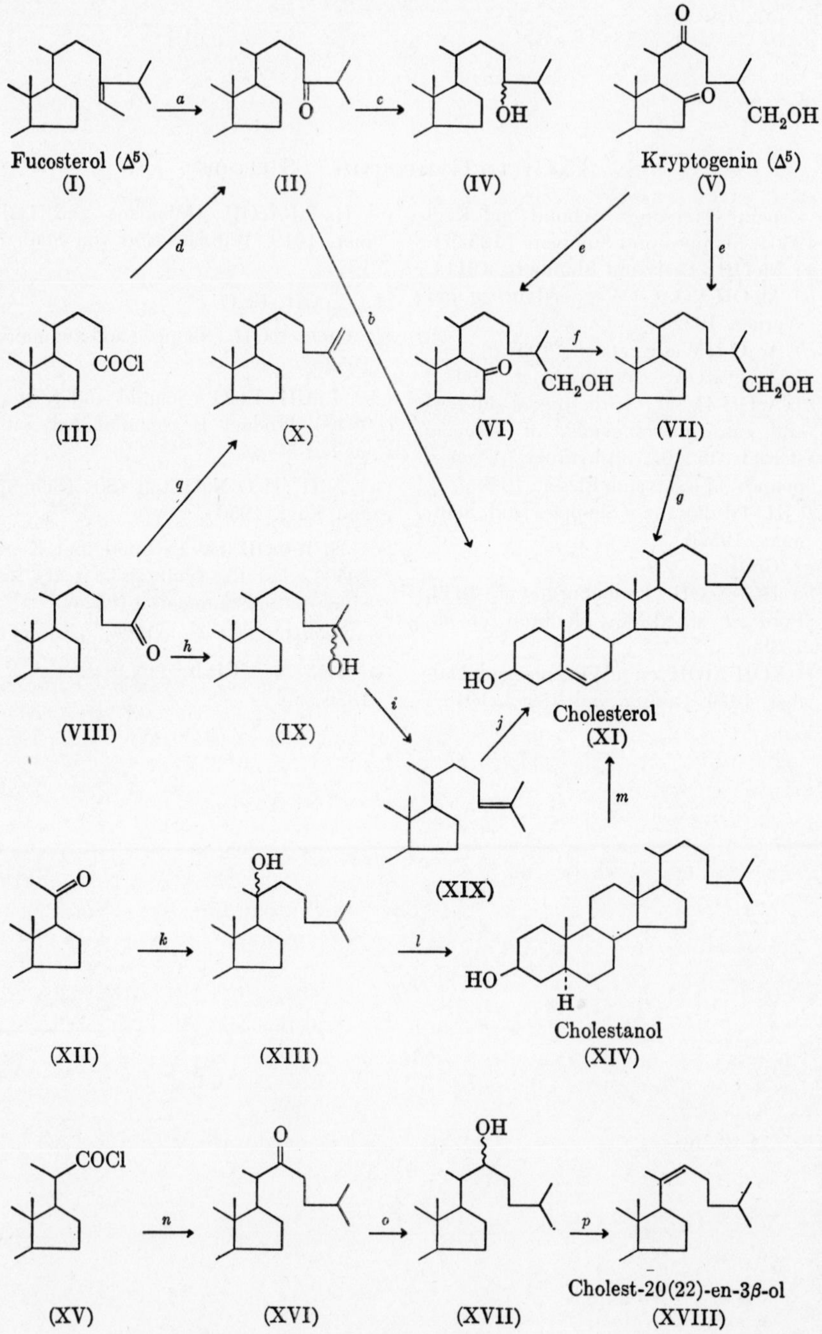

Fucosterol (Δ^5)
(I)

(II)

(IV)

Kryptogenin (Δ^5)
(V)

(III)

(X)

(VI)

(VII)

(VIII)

(IX)

Cholesterol
(XI)

(XIX)

(XII)

(XIII)

Cholestanol
(XIV)

(XV)

(XVI)

(XVII)

Cholest-20(22)-en-3β-ol
(XVIII)

T. Cholesterol Derivatives Substituted in the Side Chain

Many of the processes outlined in Chart 18 are suitable for the preparation of cholesterol labeled with C^{14}, and some have been so used.

(a) O_3-AcOH (Hey et al., 1950) Alternative procedures involving protection of the Δ^5-double bond as a 3,5-cyclo steroid 6-methyl ether were described by Hey et al. (1952) and by Bergmann and Klosty (1951) (See Section VI, S.

(b) Zn/Hg-AcOH-HCl rx. (Hey et al., 1950) or N_2H_4-NaOEt-EtOH heat (Riegel and Kaye, 1944) or two stages: (1) $(CH_2SH)_2$-HCl; (2) Raney Ni-MeOH rx. (de Vries and Backer, 1950).

(c) Al(OPr^{iso})$_3$-i-PrOH (Riegel and Kaye, 1944; Ercoli and de Ruggieri, 1953) One of the two isomers (IV) is identical with cerebrosterol isolated from horse brain (Ercoli et al., 1953).

(d) CdPr$_2$^{iso}-Et$_2$O (Riegel and Kaye, 1944; de Vries and Backer, 1950). The latter authors describe the preparation of several homologs of (II) by using other cadmium alkyls.

(e) Zn/Hg-HCl-EtOH rx.

(f) N_2H_4-(HO(CH$_2$ · CH$_2$O)$_3$H-KOH-195°.

(g) Two steps: (1) MsCl (1 mole)-Py; (2)LiAlH$_4$Et$_2$O (Scheer et al., 1956) The product from process e is a mixture of (VI) and (VII) which is converted to pure (VII) by process f.

(h) MeMgI-C$_6$H$_6$-Et$_2$O.

(i) POCl$_3$-Py rx.

(j) H_2-Pd/C-EtOH (Ryer et al., 1950). A similar series of reactions was described by Dauben and Bradlow (1950) except that in i PBr$_3$-C$_6$H$_6$ rx. was used, and in j the nuclear double bond was protected by the formation of a 3,5-cyclo steroid 6-methyl ether (cf. Section VI, S). For the preparation of some analogous compounds see Ryer et al. (1953). The series of reactions h, i, j has been used to prepare 26-C^{14}-cholesterol (Anfinsen and Horning, 1953). For the structure of (XIX) see Idler and Fagerlund (1957).

(k) $(CH_3)_2$ · CH(CH$_2$)$_3$ · MgBr-Et$_2$O (Petrow and Stuart-Webb, 1956; cf. Woodward et al., 1952). The compound (XIII, Δ^5), a 20ξ-hydroxy-cholesterol, is a possible intermediate in the biological convertion of cholesterol into corticosteroids (Lynn et al., 1955). See Chapter 8.

(l) Two steps: (1) Ac$_2$O-AcOH rx; (2) (2) H_2-PtO$_2$-AcOH.

(m) Three stages, see Sections VI, C, H, and I. Working in the saturated 5α-H series, the processes k, l, and m were used by Woodward et al. (1952). in the total synthesis of cholesterol.

(n) $(CH_3)_2$·CH·CH$_2$·CH$_2$CdCl.

(o) LiBH$_4$-THF.

(p) POCl$_3$-Py (Fieser and Huang, 1953; cf. Cole and Julian, 1945).

(q) Ph$_3$·P $=$ CH$_2$—Et$_2$O (Idler and Fagerlund, 1957).

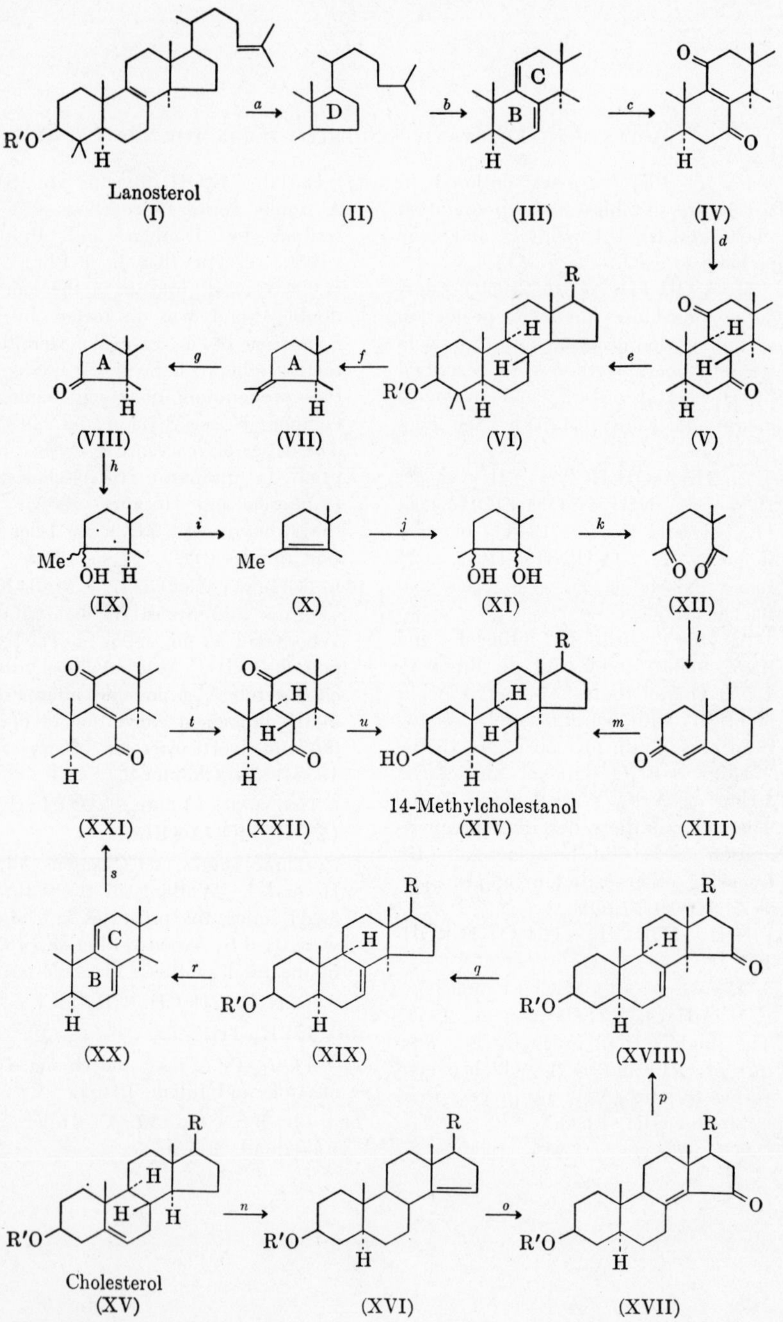

Lanosterol
(I)

(II)

(III)

(IV)

(VIII)   (VII)   (VI)   (V)

(IX)   (X)   (XI)   (XII)

(XXI)   (XXII)   14-Methylcholestanol   (XIII)
                            (XIV)

(XX)   (XIX)   (XVIII)

Cholesterol
(XV)   (XVI)   (XVII)

R = C$_8$H$_{17}$; R′ = H, Ac, or Bz

U. Interrelation of Cholesterol and Lanosterol

(a) Catalytic hydrogenation.

(b) SeO$_2$-AcOH.

(c) CrO$_3$-AcOH.

(d) Zn-AcOH The literature describing these four stages is discussed by Voser et al. (1950). They also describe an alternative but longer route from (V) to (VI).

(e) Wolff Kishner reduction using Na dissolved in O(CH$_2$·CH$_2$OH)$_2$ and anhydrous hydrazine at 210° for 24 hours. These special conditions are necessary to remove the sterically hindered 11-keto group, and also the 15-keto group in 14-methylsteroids (Barton et al., 1955).

(f) PCl$_5$-light petroleum.

(g) O$_3$-CH$_2$Cl$_2$ at —60°.

(h) MeMgBr.

(i) Fullers earth.

(j) OsO$_4$-Et$_2$O, osmate decomposed with LiAlH$_4$.

(k) Pb(OAc)$_4$-AcOH.

(l) NaOMe-MeOH.

(m) Two steps: (1) Li-NH$_3$, (2) LiAlH$_4$ cf. Section VI, C (Barton et al., 1954a).

(n) See Section VI, E.

(o) Permonophthalic acid followed by HCl-MeOH (Barton and Laws, 1954).

(p) Excess MeI-tert-KOBu-tert-BuOH.

(q) Vigorous Wolff Kishner reduction as in e.

The steps r, s, t, and u are similar to b, c, d, and e (Barton et al., 1954b).

Additional reference for all the steps above: Woodward et al. (1957).

For reviews on the tetracyclic triterpenes (e.g. lanosterol) see Gascoigne and Simes (1955); Jones and Halsall (1955), and Simonsen and Ross (1957).

NOTE: In (II) and (VI), a 14α-methyl group should be inserted; in (XVI), there should be a double bond between C-7 and C-8.

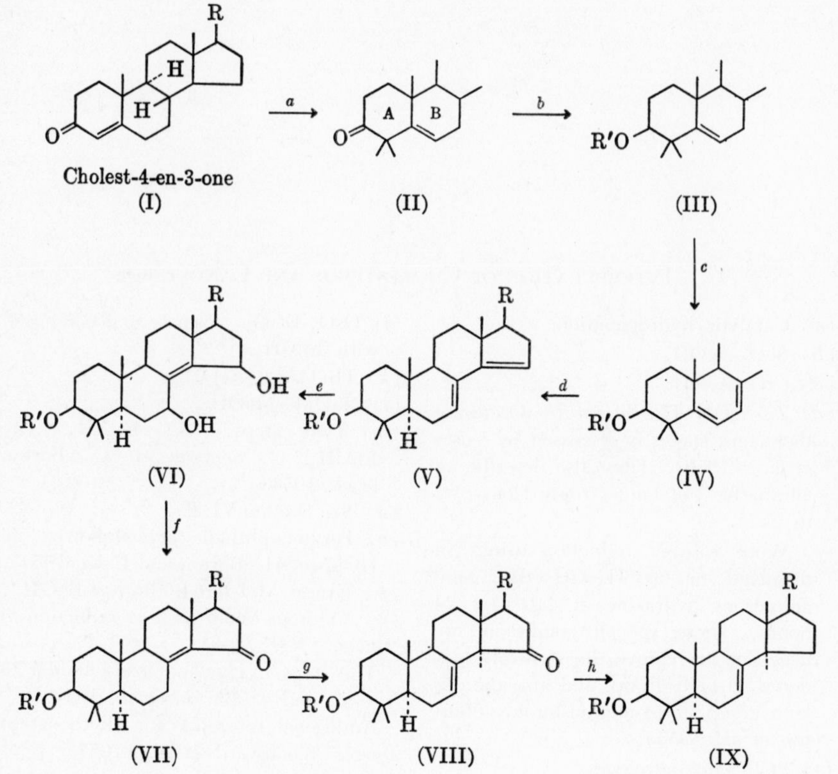

Cholest-4-en-3-one
(I)

(II)

(III)

(VI)

(V)

(IV)

(VII)

(VIII)

(IX)

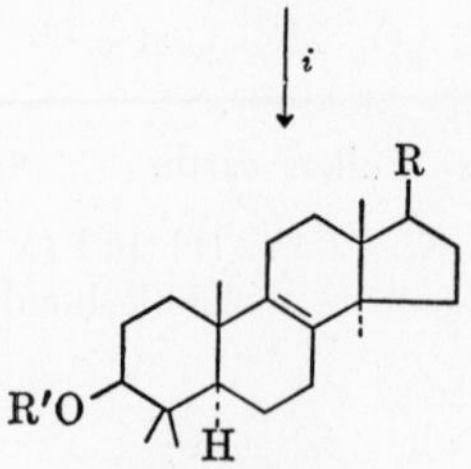

V. Synthesis of Lanostenol

$R = C_8H_{17}$ $R' = H$, or Ac, or Bz.

All the processes are described by Woodward *et al.* (1954, 1957).

(*a*) MeI-*tert*-KOBu-*tert*-BuOH, Cholest-5-en-3-one can be used as starting material.

(*b*) LiAlH$_4$.

(*c*) NBS followed by collidine.

(*d*) HCl-CHCl$_3$ at —40° then NH$_3$-MeOH at —60°.

(*e*) Monoperphthalic acid-Et$_2$O and then hydrolysis.

(*f*) HCl-EtOH.

Lanost-8-enol
(X)

(*g*) Large excess of MeI and *tert*-KOBu.

(*h*) Vigorous Wolff Kishner reduction by the method of Barton *et al.* (1955) (cf. Section VI, U).

(*i*) HCl-CHCl$_3$ (only partial isomerization occurs).

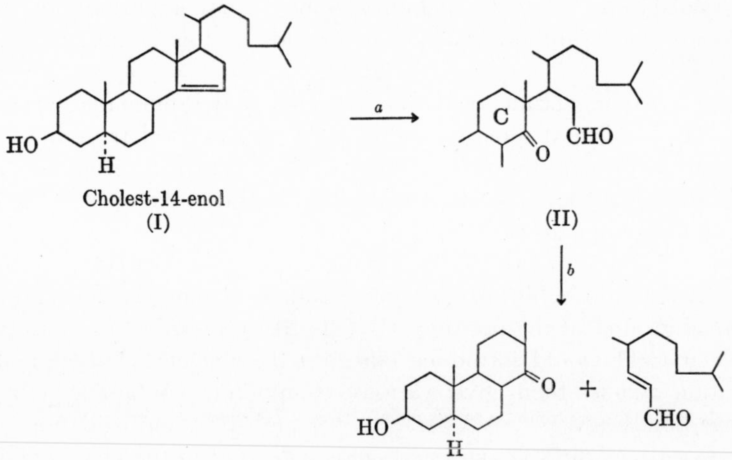

Cholest-14-enol
(I)

(II)

(III)   +   (IV)

W. THE ABSOLUTE CONFIGURATION OF CHOLESTEROL

(a) O_3.

(b) Pyrolysis in cyclohexane at 210-220°.

These reactions were first used by Achtermann (1934) and Laucht (1935) in the ergosterol series. The corresponding reactions in the cholesterol series were carried out by Cornforth et al. (1954, 1957). They showed that the 4,8-dimethyl-non-2-en-al (IV) which contains the asymmetric carbon (C-20) of the side chain of cholesterol, corresponds in configuration to (+)-citro-

nellal, from which it was synthesized. Since (+)-citronellal has itself been correlated with (+)-methylsuccinic acid and hence with D-glyceraldehyde, and since the absolute configuration of D-glyceraldehyde has been shown to correspond to the sense of the usual Fischer projection formulas, (by the X-ray crystallographic method of Bijvoet et al., 1951), the formulas used for steroids represent their absolute configurations (for more detailed discussions see Mills and Klyne, 1954).

X. Oxidation of Cholesteryl Acetate Dibromide with Chromic Acid

The oxidation of cholesteryl acetate dibromide with CrO_3-AcOH at temperatures up to 30° is used industrially for the preparation of androst-5-en-3β-ol-17-one (dehydroepiandrosterone I), an important intermediate in hormone synthesis. Up to 9% yields of this compound can be obtained.

In practice the crude oxidation product is debrominated with zinc and acetic acid, and separated into acidic and neutral fractions. From the neutral fraction, the semicarbazone of (I) is easily prepared, being more insoluble than the derivatives of the other ketones, which are present in smaller quantities.

The initial attack of the chromium trioxide on the saturated sterol side chain results probably in the introduction of one or more tertiary hydroxyl groups, at the positions C-17, C-20, and C-25. In a similar way attack at C-14 would introduce one into the nucleus. Subsequent dehydration would then give various compounds containing ethylenic double bonds ($\Delta^{17(20)}$, Δ^{20}, $\Delta^{20(22)}$, Δ^{24}, and Δ^{25}), and oxidation would then give the various ketones and acids indicated in the chart below. It would seem that the majority of the oxidative splitting occurs between C-17 and C-20 to yield (I) and (II) (Billeter and Miescher, 1947; Georg, 1954, p. 1583S; Fieser and Fieser, 1949, p. 365).

Compounds Isolated

Ketones with Intact Steroid Nucleus

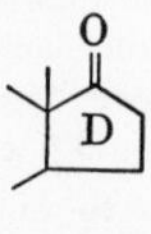

(I) *a,b* 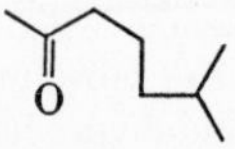   (II) *c* 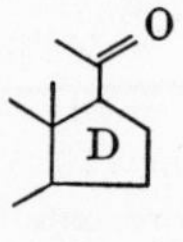   (III) *a,b* 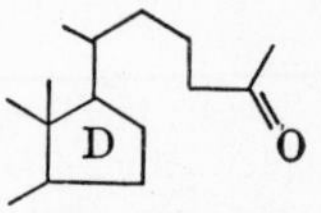   (IV) *a,d,e,i,j*

Acids with Intact Steroid Nucleus

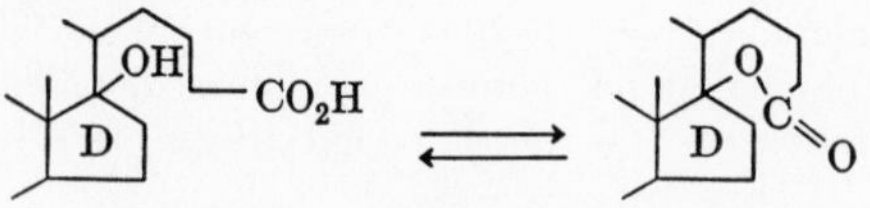

(V) *e,f,g*   (VI) *e,f,g*

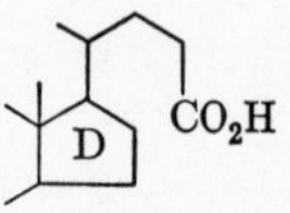

(VII) *h* 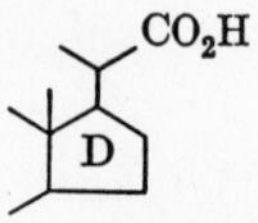   (VIII) *h* 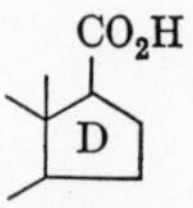   (IX) *h*

Compounds with Ring D Opened

(X) h   (XI) h   (XII) b

(a) Ruzicka and Fischer (1937).
(b) Köster and Logemann (1940).
(c) Windaus and Resau (1913).
(d) Hattori (1938).
(e) Miescher and Fischer (1939).

(f) Billeter and Miescher (1947).
(g) Billeter and Miescher (1949).
(h) Wieland and Miescher (1949).
(i) Ryer et al. (1950).
(j) Dauben and Bradlow (1950).

Y. THE CHEMICAL OXIDATION OF CHOLESTEROL

The oxidation of cholesterol by hexavalent chromium compounds (chromic acid, sodium dichromate) has been studied by Fieser (1953a, c, d). The formulas of the compounds he, and others, have characterized are listed below (cf. Fieser, 1954b, and p. 23).

(I)   (II)   (III)

(IV)   (V)   (VI)

(VII)   (VIII)   (IX)

For recent work on the oxidation of cholesterol by ozone see Lettré and Jahn (1957a, b), and by periodic acid see Graber et al. (1956).

Z. The Superficial Oxidation of Cholesterol

Cholesterol is relatively stable towards aerial oxidation in the macro-crystalline state, but when finely divided and exposed to excess oxygen, oxidation takes place very rapidly.

These conditions are met, in particular, when cholesterol, in colloidal aqueous solution stabilized with sodium stearate, is aerated (Winter-steiner and Bergström, 1941; Bergström and Wintersteiner, 1941, 1942a, b; for a review see Bergström, 1943). The reaction is rapid at 85° C., but slower at 37°, and does not proceed at all at 4°. It is catalyzed by cupric ions, and to a lesser extent by ferrous and zinc ions. Manganese and cyanide ions inhibit the reaction, as do organic reducing agents such as phenol and salicylaldoxime. The chief products are 7-keto-cholesterol and 7α- and 7β-hydroxycholesterol, and their dehydration products.

Oxidation also occurs when cholesterol in thin films is exposed to air, and irradiated with ultraviolet light. In this case besides the products mentioned above, various acids are produced, presumably by oxidative ring opening (Windaus *et al.*, 1941).

Similarly when cholesterol in aqueous solution (as sodium cholesteryl succinate) or acetic acid solution, is exposed to X-rays in the absence of air, oxidation occurs to yield 7-ketocholesterol and cholestane-$3\beta,5\alpha,6\beta$-triol and other compounds derived therefrom (Keller and Weiss, 1950); Weiss and Keller, 1950).

These processes all bear the characteristics of free-radical reactions, and it is generally believed that the initial attack on cholesterol occurs at the 7 position, to yield the 7-hydroperoxide (II). This can lose water to yield 7-ketocholesterol (III), or it can react with more choles-terol to yield a 7-hydroxyl derivative (V); the oxygen atom being re-leased is taken up to form an epoxide (IV). Subsequent dehydration or oxidation processes would account for the formation of the other compounds that are isolated. It is possible that with irradiation by X-rays (where the presence of oxygen is not necessary), attack of hydroxyl radicals (derived from the solvent) on the 5,6-double bond takes place (cf. Clemo et al., 1950). It is noteworthy that little or no oxidation of the 3-hydroxy group occurs.

The proposed 7-hydroperoxide intermediate (II) has not been isolated, although in the similar case of the aerial oxidation of cholest-5-en-3-one, a 6-hydroperoxide has been obtained in crystalline form (see Section VI, I) (Fieser et al., 1955).*

Bearing in mind the ease of oxidation of cholesterol under suitable conditions, it is seen that many of the reports in the literature of the isolation of oxygenated derivatives, are open to question. Thus the substance "oxycholesterol" (Lifschütz, 1907) was originally thought to be a single entity, and an extensive literature grew up. Later, it was shown to be a mixture containing, inter alia, 7α- and 7β-hydroxycholesterols, cholestane-6-one, 7-ketocholesterol, cholest-4-en-3β,6β-diol, cholestane-3β,5α,6β-triol, and cholesta-3,5-diene-7-one. All these substances can be formally derived from products of the aerial oxidation of cholesterol. The view held generally now, is that when large amounts of these substances are isolated from natural sources, they are probably artifacts, but that small amounts are indeed present in tissues, where they are intermediates in cholesterol metabolism (cf. Prelog et al., 1943; Haslewood, 1944).

It is clearly difficult to decide to what extent these oxidation products are artifacts of the working up process, but the conditions usually prevailing are ideal for their formation, unless air is rigorously excluded. Even in the absence of the emulsifying action of biological material, oxidation can occur; e.g. in the recovery of cholesterol from the dibromide (Smith, 1954). Working in a nitrogen atmosphere is a good precaution which can be applied to most sterol work, and samples (particularly noncrystalline ones) should be stored at low temperature, in the dark (or in amber glass bottles), and in a nitrogen atmosphere (or in vacuo).

Cholesterol labeled with C^{14} is particularly labile in the presence of air (Dauben and Payot, 1956), and is converted into the usual mixture of oxidation products.

VII. Physico-Chemical Measurements on Steroids

A. MELTING POINT

The use of a microscope fitted with a Kofler block in the determination of the melting point of steroids has become quite general. Only small

---

* Recently, Gollnick and Neumüller (1957) have obtained a Δ^6-5-hydroperoxide by photochemical oxidation of cholesterol.

quantities of material are needed and when polarized light is used, changes of crystalline form and occurrence of liquid crystals (meso-morphic phases) are easily observed. Fieser (1953a) has observed that melting points of cholesterol taken in open capillaries are often several degrees lower than those taken in evacuated capillaries and the method has much to commend itself particularly with high-melting steroids.

B. SPECIFIC ROTATION

This is a *sine quâ non* of steroid chemistry. It serves as an additional identification of a compound, and as a guide to the degree of purity. The molecular rotation of a compound has also a good deal of signifi-cance; Barton and his co-workers have developed the idea of molecular rotation differences in connection with structural determinations in the steroid series. In its simplest terms the principle may be stated thus: the changes in molecular rotation observed in going from a sterol to the corresponding (a) acetate, (b) benzoate, (c) ketone, etc., are charac-teristic of the nature of the nuclear unsaturation of the sterol, and to a much lesser extent upon the nature of the C-17 side chain.

The specific rotation is defined by

$$[\alpha]_D = \frac{\alpha_D \times 100}{l \times c}$$

where $[\alpha]_D$ is the specific rotation for light of the sodium D line, α_D is the rotation observed in a solution of concentration c grams per 100 ml. solution, contained in a tube decimeters long.

The molecular rotation is defined

$$[M]_D = \frac{[\alpha]_D \times M.W.}{100}$$

where $[M]_D$ is the molecular rotation and M.W. is the molecular weight of the substance.

The solvent used has some influence on the values of $[\alpha]_D$ obtained. Chloroform is most often used but suffers from the disadvantage that traces of hydrochloric acid present cause decomposition of unstable steroids. Barton and Bruun (1951) used carbon tetrachloride as an alternative; methylene chloride being another. Both of these solvents give results comparable with those obtained with chloroform. Results of $[\alpha]_D$ obtained using dioxane as solvent are often 4° to 6° more positive than those in chloroform (Fieser and Fieser, 1949). A compilation of the specific rotations of steroids has been published (Mathieu and Petit, 1956).

Recently Djerassi and his co-workers (1955a, b, c; 1956a, b; Djerassi and Closson, 1956; Djerassi and Ehrlich, 1956; Djerassi and Klyne, 1956) have been studying the optical rotatory dispersion of steroids (i.e. the variations of the optical rotation with changes in wavelength) and the technique promises to become very valuable.

C. ULTRAVIOLET ABSORPTION SPECTRA

The recording of the ultraviolet absorption spectrum of steroids in solution is of great value for characterizing systems of conjugated double bonds and ketone groups. The best review of the characteristic band frequencies and intensities is that of Dorfman (1953).

D. INFRARED ABSORPTION SPECTRA

The infrared spectra of a great number of steroids have now been recorded in the literature and they are of great value in identification and diagnostic purposes. The subject of infrared spectra in general is dealt with by Jones and Sandorfy (1956) and by Bellamy (1954). The infrared spectra of steroids have been examined by R. N. Jones and his co-workers, who have published their results in numerous papers (principally in the *Journal of the American Chemical Society*), and in an Atlas of Steroid Spectra (Dobriner *et al.*, 1953). A detailed discussion would be out of place here, but it is sufficient, perhaps, to mention the particular value of measurements of the frequency of the carbonyl absorption bands. The nature and environment of ketone and ester groupings can thereby be ascertained. The method has been extended by Castells and Meakins (1956) to determine double bond positions, since the nature of the carbonyl groups, which result from the splitting of a double bond, is characteristic of the position of the double bond. The presence or absence of an hydroxyl group in a molecule is also easily verified by the infrared spectrographic method.

E. MISCELLANEOUS PHYSICO-CHEMICAL METHODS

The technique of nuclear magnetic resonance (N.M.R.) spectrometry is (as regards its applications) still in its infancy, and widespread use is dependent upon commercial production of cheaper instruments. The method permits the location and characterization of hydrogen atoms (among others) in a molecule. This information is not readily available from infrared and ultraviolet absorption spectrometry, or even by X-ray crystallographic measurements. N.M.R. spectrometry has recently made its début in the steroid field (Allinger, 1956).

The use of X-ray crystallography in the determination of steroid structures has been mentioned in Section V, A. This is a complex technique that can only be applied to a limited number of compounds, since extensive calculations are involved. However X-ray powder spectroscopy has recently been introduced for identification purposes in the steroid group (Parsons *et al.*, 1956).

The use of the mass spectrometer in determining molecular weights of, and the nature of the side chain in sterols, is also a recent innovation (de Mayo and Reed, 1956).

VIII. Digitonide Formation

Windaus (1909) discovered that mixing an alcoholic solution of cholesterol with an alcoholic solution of the steroid saponin, digitonin, results in the precipitation of a 1:1 molecular complex of cholesterol and digitonin, known as cholesterol digitonide. The reaction is extensively used for the detection and estimation of cholesterol; the low solubility of the complex making the test very sensitive. Immediate precipitation occurs when a solution of 1 mg. cholesterol in 1 ml. 95% ethanol is treated with 1 drop of 1% digitonin in 95% ethanol and a turbidity is discernible with one-tenth this amount of cholesterol (1 part to 10,000). The reaction has been used directly as a gravimetric method for the determination of cholesterol, the theoretical conversion factor (cholesterol:digitonide = 0.239) being very favorable; but more often the precipitation with digitonin is used to affect a preliminary separation; the cholesterol being recovered from the digitonide (see below) and estimated by methods described in Chapter 3 and in the Appendix.

A. STRUCTURAL REQUIREMENTS FOR DIGITONIDE FORMATION

The formation of insoluble complexes is not restricted to digitonin on the one hand or cholesterol on the other. The saponins tigonin and gitonin and the alkaloid tomatine give precipitates with cholesterol. Table IV gives the presently accepted structures of these compounds together with the solubilities of their cholesterol complexes. Gitonin has been recommended as an alternative to digitonin as giving a more insoluble derivative and increasing the sensitivity of the test fivefold (de Graeve, 1942; Delsal, 1943). Commercial digitonin frequently contains gitonin as an impurity (Klass *et al.*, 1955). This fact and also the variable and uncertain amounts of water of crystallization of the digitonide, should be borne in mind in interpreting direct gravimetric results. Moreover, digitonin also forms molecular complexes with many non-steroid substances, e.g. phenols and terpene alcohols (Windaus *et al.*, 1923; Windaus and Weinhold, 1923).

Besides cholesterol most naturally occurring sterols having a 3β-hydroxyl group yield insoluble digitonides. Those having a 3α-hydroxyl or no hydroxyl group are not precipitated. This rule which was suggested by Fernholz (1935) is still true but in the wider field of steroids

TABLE IV

SAPONINS

The Saponins are Glycosides of the Sapogenins (XVII) (see p. 83).

Saponin	Formula	M.W.	Sapogenin component	Sugar components	Solubility of cholesterol complex mg./100 ml. 95% EtOH at 18°
Tigonin	$C_{56}H_{92}O_{27}$	1197	Tigogenin (R = R^1 = H)[f]	2 Glucose, 2 galactose, 1 xylose[f]	150[a]
Gitonin	$C_{50}H_{82}O_{23}$	1051	Gitogenin (R = OH, R^1 = H)[de]	3 Galactose, 1 pentose[f]	10[b]
Digitonin	$C_{56}H_{92}O_{29}$	1229	Digitogenin (R = R^1 = OH)[d]	2 Glucose, 2 galactose,[f] 1 xylose	14[c]
Tomatine	$C_{50}H_{83}O_{21}N$	1034	Tomatidine (R = R^1 = H, NH replacing O in ring F)[g]	2 Glucose, 1 xylose 1 galactose[g]	"sparingly"[h]

REFERENCES

(a) Tschesche (1936).
(b) Windaus and Schneckenburger (1913).
(c) Windaus (1909).
(d) Klass et al. (1955); Djerassi et al. (1956a).

(e) Herran et al. (1954).
(f) Fieser and Fieser (1949).
(g) McKenna (1953).
(h) Schulz and Sander (1957).

as a whole many exceptions in both senses have been noted, consequently caution is needed in using the test to decide the presence or absence of a 3β-hydroxyl group in a steroid. In attempting to correlate digitonin precipitability with the structure of steroids, the situation is complicated by statements in the literature e.g.: "precipitated with digitonin" without indication of the condition employed. Haslam and Klyne (1953) have studied the precipitation with digitonin quantitatively. They found in two typical cases (cholesterol and dehydroepiandrosterone) that the law of mass action is obeyed, and that [minimum steroid concentration for precipitation] $\times$ [concentration of digitonin] $=$ constant, over a range of digitonin concentrations. They estimated the value of the constant, the "solubility product," in a number of cases and found that the value depended on the structure of the steroid. Their findings are summarized briefly below. The constant "S" quoted is $10^8 \times$ the "solubility product" which is in moles^2 per liter^2.

The compounds which yield the most insoluble digitonides have $S = 4$ to 16. (This corresponds to precipitation in 0.2 to 0.8% solution in 98% ethanol containing 0.8% digitonin.) This group probably includes all the naturally occurring sterols of the cholestanol, ergostanol, stigmastanol, campestanol, and poriferastanol types having 3β-hydroxyl groups and either Δ^5 double bonds or 5α-hydrogen atoms (*trans* A/B), and also similar synthetic compounds of the androstane, pregnane, cholanic acid, and etianic acid series. At the other extreme the correponding 3α-hydroxyl derivatives have $S = 2000$ (i.e. they are not precipitated). Inversion of configuration at C-5 (i.e. 5β-hydrogen *cis* A/B) while retaining a 3β-hydroxyl group gives compounds (e.g. coprostanol) which have $S = 70$. These form digitonides but only in more concentrated solution (cf. Fieser and Fieser, 1949, p. 103). Haslam and Klyne were able to utilize this fact to separate 5β-steroids from the corresponding Δ^5 compounds. Introduction of additional double bonds or of keto groups at C-6, C-7, C-11, or C-12 (hecogenin) or C-20 (pregnane series) does not affect the precipitability appreciably. 17-Keto groups raise the value of S to 140. Turner (1953) has shown that on forming the digitonide of a ketosteroid the frequency of the strong ketone band in the infrared spectrum, increases by about 10 cm^{-1}. He discusses this in relation to the structure of these digitonides. Introduction of additional hydroxyl groups at C-4, C-6, and C-7 does not affect the precipitability, but in the pregnane and androstane series additional 20β- and 17-hydroxyl groups raise the value of S to 140 and 1,000 respectively.

Cardiac aglycones (frequently these have 14β-hydrogen or hydroxyl) do not give insoluble digitonides and sapogenins (5α-H, $S = 70$; 5β-H, $S = 280$) yield digitonides with difficulty.

Steroids which have 3β-acetoxyl groups and 3 keto groups do not yield insoluble digitonides ($S \sim 1000$ to 2000). An exception is cholestan-3-one ($S = 140$). Furthermore the introduction into 3β-hydroxyl compounds of bulky acyloxy grouping at for example C-7 makes the digitonides more soluble.

Inversion of the angular methyl group at C-10 as in lumisterol (XVIII)* confers digitonide solubility. Here the 3β-hydroxyl group has the relatively unstable axial conformation while in epilumisterol (XIX) which gives an insoluble digitonide (Barnett *et al.*, 1940) the 3α-hydroxyl

(XVII)   (XVIII)   (XIX)

group is equatorial as in normal steroids. In fact one can consider epilumisterol as being the enantiomorph of ergosterol as far as rings A and B are concerned. The completely enantiomorphic forms of the natural steroids, however, are not precipitated by digitonin, this fact was utilized by Woodward *et al.* (1952) to resolve the racemate of the first totally synthetic steroid.

While it is difficult to formulate a hard and fast rule, it appears that extreme digitonide insolubility is characteristic of 3β-hydroxy-5α-H or Δ⁵-steroids with simple hydrocarbon chains. Epimerization of the hydroxyl group or its removal or protection leads to complete digitonide solubility. Other modifications of the essentially planer structure (e.g. 5β-H or 14β-H, introduction of large numbers of polar groups or of bulky groups, or of the noncoplanar side chains of sapogenins) leads to compounds whose digitonides have solubilities between the two extremes.

Even stated in these broad terms the rule has many exceptions. One example is 5α-pregn-2-en-20-one (Liebermann *et al.*, 1948) which even with no 3-hydroxyl gives an insoluble digitonide. Cholesterylamine (Windaus and Adamla, 1911), 3β-aminocholestane (Dodgson and Haworth, 1952), and conessine (Bertho, 1950; Haworth *et al.*, 1953) all give insoluble digitonides, but here it is clear the 3β-amino (or dimethyl-

---

* The formula of lumisterol used here is the recently revised one due to Castells *et al.* (1958).

amino) group is able to fulfill the function of the hydroxyl group. In contrast the thiol group is not so able, for thiocholesterol is not precipitated (Strating and Backer, 1950).

While the digitonin test is of value, it is appropriate to repeat the warning first given by Noller (1939). He pointed out that to decide the configuration of 3-hydroxyl group in a new steroid, a reliable decision can be expected only if both epimers are available and tested. It is seen then that configurations of hydroxyl groups based solely on the digitonin test and otherwise unsupported should be accepted with reserve, particularly since there are now many other criteria available.

B. Use of Digitonin in Separations

Digitonin is most frequently used for the separation of 3β-(precipitable) and 3α-hydroxy (not precipitable) steroids, but it has also been successfully applied to the separation of 5β-H and Δ^5 steroids (Haslam and Klyne, 1953) (see p. 82).

After precipitation is complete, it is necessary to split the digitonide into its components and to recover unprecipitated steroid and digitonin from the supernatant solution. This is best done by the method of Schoenheimer and Dam (1933). The digitonide is dissolved in cold pyridine and ether added. This precipitates the digitonin, at which time the steroid can be recovered from the solution. This method has been improved by Bergmann (1940). On a small scale the method of (Christiani and Pailer, 1937) can be applied. Here the digitonide is heated in vacuum; the steroid sublimes leaving a (slightly decomposed) residue of digitonin. This method is satisfactory for simple sterols but is clearly inapplicable to thermally labile steroids. Other methods depend on acetylation of the digitonide (Windaus, 1910), the acetylated steroid and (acetylated) digitonin do not form a complex, and the steroid acetate can be extracted with ether.

In analytical work and when large quantities are used, it is important to recover the very expensive digitonin in a reusable form and here the method of Schoenheimer and Dam is best used.

IX.   Color Reactions of Steroids

Table V shows the more important color reactions.

A. Tests Depending on Halochromic Salt Formation

(Table V, 1–9)

Many steroids when treated with acid reagents (Lewis acids) give intense colors. The actual color produced with a steroid depends on the acid used and on other variable conditions (e.g. concentration). It

TABLE V
COLOR REACTIONS

No.	Test	Conditions	Color	Inference	Notes and references
1.	Liebermann Burchard	Steroid in Ac_2O or Ac_2O-$CHCl_3$ treated with H_2SO_4	Violet, red, or green	Given by most unsaturated steroids	Liebermann (1885); Burchard (1890) cf. Chapter 1
2.	Salkowski	Steroids in $CHCl_3$ treated with H_2SO_4	Red	Given by most unsaturated steroids	Salkowski (1872, 1908)
3.	Rosenheim	Steroids in $CHCl_3$ treated with CCl_3CO_2H	Red turning blue	Steroid dienes or those sterol monoenes which dehydrate readily	Rosenheim (1929), Schoenheimer and Evans (1936)
4.	Tschugaeff	Steroids in AcOH treated with AcCl-ZnCl and heated	Cherry red	———	Tschugaeff (1900)
5.		Steroid heated with HCO_2H at 95° C.	Various, also fluorescence in UV light	Many 17-hydroxysteroid hormones	Boscott (1949)
6.	Lifschutz (A)	Steroid and $(Ph . CO \cdot O)_2$ heated in AcOH treated with H_2SO_4.	Blue-green, violet	Given by most unsaturated steroids	Lifschütz (1908)
7.	Lifschutz (B)	Steroid in AcOH (+a little $FeCl_3$) treated with H_2SO_4	Red, violet, blue, green	Typical of "oxycholesterol" (see p. 77).	Lifschütz (1907), Bergstrom and Wintersteiner (1942a)
8.	Tortelli-Jaffe	Steroid in AcOH treated with Br_2 in $CHCl_3$	Green	Steroid has double bond easily rearranged to $\Delta^{8(14)}$	Tortelli and Jaffe (1915), Haussler and Brauchli (1929)

Table V (continued)

No.	Test	Conditions	Color	Inference	Notes and references
9.	Kägi-Miescher	Steroid in AcOH treated with anisaldehyde, conc. H_2SO_4, and warmed	Violet	Given mainly by 17-OH steroids	Miescher (1946)
10.	Tetranitro-methane	Steroid in $CHCl_3$ or Et_2O treated with $C(NO_3)_4$ in Et_2O	Yellow or orange	Given by most unsaturated compounds	See text
11.	Zimmermann	Steroid in EtOH treated with m-$C_6H_4(NO_2)_2$+KOH	Violet	Ketosteroids, keto groups at 3,17,20	See text
12.	Carr-Price	Steroid in $CHCl_3$ treated with $SbCl_3$ in $CHCl_3$	—	—	See Mueller (1949)
13.		Steroid in AcOH-C_6H_6 treated with SeO_2 at room temperature	Yellow, red	Δ^7 double bond	Nakanishi et al. (1953), see page 22.

appears that steroids having, or capable of forming by dehydration, two double bonds give the very intense colors when treated with acids alone.

The Liebermann-Burchard reaction is often used for quantitative work (see Chapter 3) and both it and the related Salkowski reaction have been investigated more fully than the others. According to Brieskorn and Capuano (1953), the essential mechanism is the same in both tests, the acetic anhydride in the Liebermann-Burchard test serving only as a diluent for the sulfuric acid. Thus, when the ratio $H_2SO_4:Ac_2O$ is high, the red-purple color characteristic of the Salkowski reaction is obtained, when it is low (the usual quantitative Liebermann-Burchard conditions; Schoenheimer and Sperry, 1934) a green color is formed. The acetic anhydride can be replaced by acetic acid, ethyl acetate, or butanol.

In the Liebermann-Burchard and Salkowski reactions, the steroid is ultimately converted to polymeric unsaturated hydrocarbons. Thus treatment of cholesterol in chloroform with sulfuric acid gave on adding water a substance formulated as bischolestadienyl (Brieskorn and Capuano, 1953) (see Section VI, K). This had been shown by Dulou et al. (1951) to be a mixture of 3,3'-bischolesta-3,5-dienyl and probably 3,3'-bischolesta-2,4-dienyl. The necessary oxidizing agent is the sulfuric acid itself, which is reduced to sulfur dioxide.

Lange and co-workers (1949) have shown that the first stage in the treatment of sterols with acid is the formation of colorless sterolium salts. Indeed with equimolar amounts and perchloric or hexafluorophosphoric ($HPCl_6$) acids in chloroform simple sterols gave rise to colorless crystalline salts ($ROH_2^+ + ClO_4^-$ and $ROH_2^+ + PF_6^-$) which give back the sterol on treating with water. Only with excess acid does a color develop. These workers suggest that the subsequent steps are successively: dehydration to form a conjugated diene, combination of the diene (e.g. cholesta-3,5-diene) with excess acid to give a purple-colored halochromic salt, and finally formation of a polymerized dieneoid hydrocarbon which gives a brown halochromic salt with excess acid. It is well known that the colors produced in most of these reactions changes with time, and the scheme outlined above offers some explanation of this. The fading of the colors being due to the polymerization process.

The different speeds with which color develops with different types of steroids has permitted the separate estimation of "fast acting" (Δ^7 and $\Delta^{5,7}$) and "slow acting" (Δ^5) steroids (Moore and Baumann, 1952; Cook et al., 1954; see Chapter 3).

The diene formed is not necessarily of the 3,5-cholestadiene type which is in some cases impossible to form, e.g. 4,4-dimethylcholesterol which gives a positive Liebermann-Burchard test (personal communication from Dr. R. Stevenson, 1957). Here the diene formed is possibly 3-iso-propylidene norcholesta-5-ene. It is not necessary for the two double bonds or potential double bonds in the steroid to be near together, for recent work in the related triterpenoid series has shown the great mobility of double bonds (and angular methyl groups) under acidic conditions (Allan *et al.*, 1956).

The other color reactions mentioned in Table V probably have a similar basis, but they either employ weaker acids and are hence more selective (nos. 3–5) or they include an oxidizing reagent which can increase the length of the conjugated diene chain (nos. 6–8).

By treating steroids with sulfuric acid in the absence of a solvent colors are produced which are sufficiently characteristic and reproducible to be used for identification and estimation. This spectrometric method was introduced by Zaffaroni (1950) for cortical hormones and extended to steroids sapogenins (Diaz *et al.*, 1952) and steroids in general (Bernstein and Lenhard, 1953). These last authors (1954) have attempted to correlate the structure of steroids with their spectra in sulfuric acid particularly in the 220–300 mμ region.

The colors produced are yellowish and different from those formed in the Liebermann-Burchard reaction.

B. OTHER TESTS

Compounds containing one double bond give yellow colors with tetranitromethane (no. 9). Conjugated dienes and trienes give progressively more reddish colors. α,β-Unsaturated aldehydes, ketones, and acids give no color and the test is not restricted to steroids (Ruzicka *et al.*, 1929; Roth, 1953). The test is conveniently carried out on a porcelain tile. The colors formed with singly unsaturated compounds are not deep, concentrated solutions and a blank test are essential. Nitrogen and sulfur (thiol) compounds give yellow colors also and hence interfere. Heilbronner (1953) has studied the reaction using a spectrophotometer.

The Zimmermann reaction (Zimmermann, 1935, 1936) occurs between *m*-dinitrobenzene, alkali, and a ketone containing an activated methylene group. A violet color is produced with ketosteroids having a carbonyl group in the molecule in any position other than positions 6, 7, 11, or 12 (Kaziro and Shimada, 1937; Broadbent and Klyne, 1954). The test is commonly used for the spectrophotometric determination of 17-keto-steroids which give a maximum at 520 mμ. The reaction may be used for the determination and estimation of ketosteroids related to cholesterol (see Chapter 3, p. 133, and Appendix).

X. Tables of Physical Constants of Cholesterol Derivatives

Constants of the more important cholesterol derivatives are given in Tables VI–XIII. Many compounds, particularly benzoate esters, show the phenomenon of liquid crystal formation (see Georg, 1954, p. 1627S). In these cases the melting point first quoted is the temperature of liquefaction, the second figure (in parentheses) is that at which the melt becomes clear. Specific rotations are for dilute (approximately 1%) solutions in chloroform at room temperature, unless otherwise stated. The principal peaks only of the ultraviolet absorption spectra are given, and these have usually been determined in alcoholic solution.

The letters and roman numerals after the names of the compounds, are cross-references to the formulas in Section VI of this chapter.

TABLE VI

CHOLESTERYL ESTERS AND ETHERS

Compound	m.p. (° C.)	$[\alpha]_D$ (degrees)
Formate	97	—52
Acetate	116	—43
Propionate	97 (113)	—41
n-Butyrate	102 (111)	—35
n-Valerate	88 (90)	—35
Isovalerate	110 (111)	—35
Caproate	94 (95)	—33
Caprylate	105 (106)	—32
Caprate	83 (91)	—29
Laurate	92	—28
Myristate	73 (80)	—27
Palmitate	75 (81)	—25
Stearate	71 (80)	—25
Oleate	35 (49)	—20
Linoleate	43	—24
Linolenate	49 (74)	—24
Benzoate	147 (181)	—14
p-Nitrobenzoate	193 (261)	— 6
3,5-Dinitrobenzoate	193	—15
Ethyl carbonate (cathylate)	83 (104)	—32 (C_6H_6)
Methanesulfonate	123	—36
p-Toluenesulfonate	140	—40
Methyl ether	84	—46
Dicholesteryl ether	198	—38

TABLE VII
HYDROCARBONS AND HALOGENATED HYDROCARBONS

Compound	m.p. (°C)	$[\alpha]_D$ (degrees)	λ_{max} (mμ)	ε_{max}
Cholestane G(XVIII)	80	+ 24		
Coprostane G(XXII)	72	+ 25		
3,5-Cyclocholestane S(X)	78	+ 80		
Cholest-1-ene F(XI)	70	+ 13		
Cholest-2-ene F(1) G(XIII)	76	+ 67		
Coprost-2-ene G(XVII)	48	+ 23		
Cholest-3-ene G(XIX)	73	+ 65		
Cholest-4-ene G(XV)	84	+ 76		
Cholest-5-ene G(XIV)	92	— 56		
Cholest-8(9)-ene	94	+ 56		
Cholest-8(14)-ene	54	+ 21		
Cholest-14-ene	74	+ 27		
Cholesta-2,4-diene K(VIII)	69	+159	267	6300
			275	6300
Cholesta-2,6-diene	71	— 1		
Cholesta-3,5-diene K(VI)	80	—130	235	19,700
Cholesta-4,6-diene K(V)	92	+ 4	238	24,000
Cholesta-5,7-diene K(IV)	89	—127	280	11,000
Cholesta-8,14-diene	84	— 23		
Cholesta-2,4,6-triene E(VI)	72	+ 3	296	14,300
			305	13,600
Cholesta-3,5,7-triene	69	—122	303	12,500
			315	16,000
			330	11,000
3-Methyl-A-norcholest-3-ene S(XI)	98	+ 45		
B-Norcholestane	45	+ 11		
B-Norcholesta-3,5-diene	76	—119		
3,3′-Bischolesta-3,5-dienyl K(XIX)	247	—260	298	47,900
			312	63,100
			323	47,000
3α-Chlorocholestane G(VII)	105	+ 31		
3β-Chlorocholestane G(VIII)	115	+ 27		
3α-Chlorocoprostane G(XII)	75	+ 31		
3β-Chlorocoprostane G(XI)	123	+ 23		
3β-Bromocoprostane	113	+ 18		
3β-Chlorocholest-1-ene F(XVII)	101	+100		
3β-Chlorocholest-5-ene G(IX)	97	— 26		
5α-Chlorocholestane G(X)	97	+ 5		
7α-Chlorocholestane	78	— 21		
7β-Chlorocholestane	68	+ 77		
7α-Bromocholestane	109	— 20		

TABLE VIII
HYDROXYL COMPOUNDS

Compound	m.p. (°C)	$[\alpha]_D$ (degrees)	λ_{max} (mμ)	ε_{max}
Cholestan-1α-ol F(XIII)	95(105)	+ 35		
acetate	75	+ 43		
Cholestan-1β-ol F(XIV)	82	+ 23		
acetate	Amorphous	+ 28		
Cholestan-2α-ol F(XV)	181	+ 27		
acetate	90	— 1		
Cholestan-2β-ol F(V)	154	+ 34		
acetate	78	+ 27		
Cholestan-3α-ol C(IV)	182	+ 26		
acetate	95	+ 30		
benzoate	100			
Cholestan-3β-ol C(II)	142	+ 23		
acetate	110	+ 14		
benzoate	140(157)	+ 20		
Coprostan-3α-ol C(VIII)	117	+ 30		
acetate	88	+ 44 (C_6H_6)		
benzoate	86			
Coprostan-3β-ol C(VII)	101	+ 28		
acetate	89			
benzoate	125	+ 31		
Cholest-1-en-3β-ol F(XVI)	132	+ 55		
acetate	86	+ 58		
benzoate	142	+ 95		
Cholest-4-en-3α-ol C(X)	84	+121		
acetate	83			
Cholest-4-en-3β-ol C(IX)	132	+ 44		
acetate	85			
Cholest-5-en-3α-ol M(XVIII)	141	— 45		
acetate	85	— 13		
benzoate	100	— 29		
Cholest-5-en-3β-ol C(I)	149	— 39		
acetate	115	— 44		
benzoate	147(181)	— 15		
Cholest-6-en-3β-ol	126	— 88		
acetate	108	— 93		
benzoate	133	— 85		
Cholest-7-en-3β-ol D(VI)	122	+ 7		
acetate	119	+ 4		
benzoate	157(176)	+ 7		

TABLE VIII (*continued*)

Compound	m.p. (° C)	$[\alpha]_D$ (degrees)	λ_{max} (mμ)	ε_{max}
Cholest-8(9)-en-3α-ol	183	+ 56		
acetate	87	+ 40		
Cholest-8(9)-en-3β-ol D(VIII)	129	+ 50		
acetate	129	+ 32		
benzoate	140(165)	+ 41		
Cholest-8(14)-en-3β-ol D(V)	121	+ 23		
acetate	78	+ 8		
benzoate	115(140)	+ 6		
Cholest-9(11)-en-3β-ol	123	+ 27		
acetate	105	+ 23		
Cholest-14-en-3β-ol D(IX)	132	+ 32		
acetate	92	+ 23		
benzoate	170	+ 33		
Cholest-20(22)-en-3β-ol T(XVIII)	117	+ 7		
acetate	97	+ 1		
Cholesta-4,6-dien-3β-ol E(V)	127	− 38 ⎫	232	17,800
acetate	79	− 72 ⎬	239	20,100
benzoate	129	− 81 ⎭	248	12,700
Cholesta-5,7-dien-3β-ol D(II)	143	−114 ⎫	272	11,250
acetate	130	− 85 ⎬	282	11,900
benzoate	143(187)	− 53 ⎭	293	6,650
Cholesta-5,8(9)-dien-3β-ol E(III)	148	− 55		
acetate	122	− 48		
benzoate	150			
Cholesta-5,25-dien-3β-ol T(X)	132	− 41		
acetate	112	− 44		
Cholesta-6,8(9)-dien-3β-ol D(VII)	122	− 18	275	5,300
acetate	112	− 11		
benzoate	146(180)	− 3		
Cholesta-7,9(11)-dien-3β-ol E(XII) Q(I)			243	10,000
benzoate	134	+ 32 (dioxane)		
Cholest-7,14-dien-3β-ol E(IX)	118		244	11,500
acetate	87	−126		
benzoate	150			
Cholesta-8(9),14-dien-3β-ol	120(126)	− 13	250	20,000
acetate	102	− 23		

TABLE VIII (*continued*)

Compound	m.p. (°C)	[α]$_D$ (degrees)	λ$_{max}$ (mμ)	ε$_{max}$
Cholesta-8(9),24-dien-3β-ol D(X)	109	+ 50		
acetate	108	+ 35		
benzoate	127(136)	+43		
Cholesta-14,24-dien-3β-ol D(XI)	137	+ 37		
benzoate	122	+ 30		
Cholesta-5,7,9(11)-trien-3β-ol E(VII), P(II)	121	+168	324	11,200
acetate	90	+220		
benzoate	142	+194		
Cholestan-4α-ol G (XXIII)	189	+ 5		
acetate	113	+ 16		
benzoate	116	— 20		
Cholestan-4β-ol G(XX)	132	+ 29		
benzoate	115	+ 57		
Cholest-5-en-4α-ol	145	— 50		
acetate	123	— 27		
Cholest-5-en-4β-ol	132	— 59		
acetate	108	— 70		
Cholestan-5α-ol K(XIII)	110	+ 10		
Cholestan-6α-ol	130	+ 35		
acetate	96	+ 69		
benzoate	105	+ 63		
Cholestan-6β-ol S(VIII)	82	+ 8		
acetate	75	— 8		
benzoate	80			
Coprostan-6β-ol	Oil	+ 21		
acetate	111	+ 22		
Cholest-4-en-6α-ol	140	+ 64		
acetate	98	+ 79		
Cholest-4-en-6β-ol	87	+ 62		
acetate	77	+ 74		
3,5-Cyclocholestan-6α-ol	86	+ 83		
3,5-Cyclocholestan-6β-ol S(V)	75	+ 24		
acetate	73	+ 48		
Cholestan-7α-ol	98	+ 11		
acetate	117	— 12		
benzoate	165	— 22		

TABLE VIII (*continued*)

Compound	m.p. (°C)	$[\alpha]_D$ (degrees)	λ_{max} (mμ)	ε_{max}
Cholestan-7β-ol	119	+ 51		
acetate	66	— 61		
benzoate	108	+ 87		
Cholest-4-en-7β-ol	124	+ 90		
acetate	97	+ 78		
benzoate	160	+ 94		
Cholest-5-en-7β-ol K(III)	106			
benzoate	109	+114		
B-Norcholestan-3β-ol	78	— 31		
B-Norcholest-5-en-3β-ol				
N(XXIII)	117	— 90		
acetate	79	— 87		
benzoate	136	— 54		
3β-Chlorocholestan-1α-ol	123	+ 34		
7β-Chlorocholestan-3β-ol O(IX)				
acetate	119	— 22		
7α-Bromocholest-5-en-3β-ol O(VII)				
acetate	110	—245		
benzoate	140	—172		
7β-Chlorocholest-5-en-3β-ol O(VIII)				
benzoate	151	+ 61		
5α,6α-Dichlorocholestan-3β-ol J(VIII)	172	+ 2		
benzoate	249	+ 12		
5α,6β-Dichlorocholestan-3β-ol J(V)	144	— 27		
acetate	90	— 29		
benzoate	131	— 20		
5α,6β-Dibromocholestan-3β-ol J(V)	114	— 44		
acetate	114	— 46		
benzoate	136	— 33		
5β,6α-Dibromocoprostan-3β-ol J(IX)	143	+ 47		
benzoate	164	+ 82		

TABLE IX

DIHYDROXYL COMPOUNDS AND TRIHYDROXYL COMPOUNDS

Compound	m.p. (°C.)	$[\alpha]_D$ (degrees)		
Cholestane-1α,3α-diol	210	+ 25		
diacetate	106	+ 54		
Cholestane-1α,3β-diol	156	+ 40		
1-acetate	63	+ 34		
3-acetate	197	+ 20		
diacetate	118	+ 27		
Cholestane-2α,3α-diol	214	+ 32		
diacetate	135	+ 29		
Cholestane-2α,3β-diol	214	+ 28		
diacetate	107	— 27		
Cholestane-2β,3α-diol F(III)	202	+ 42		
3-acetate	113	+ 33		
diacetate	135	+ 57		
2-acetate-3-methanesulfonate F(IV)	130	+ 19		
Cholestane-2β,3β-diol	177	+ 43		
diacetate	112(119)	+ 38		
Cholestane-2α,5α-diol K(IX)	155	+ 20		
2-acetate	142	+ 9		
Cholestane-3α,4β-diol	236	+ 16		
diacetate	133	— 10		
Cholestane-3β,4β-diol	199	+ 20		
diacetate	135	— 8		
Cholest-5-ene-3β,4β-diol L(III)	177	— 60		
diacetate	170	— 96		
dibenzoate	151	— 54		
Cholestane-3α,5α-diol	199	+ 18		
3-acetate	133	— 1		
Cholestane-3β,5α-diol M(XIII)	225	+ 21		
3-acetate	186	+ 12		
5-acetate	159	+ 30		
diacetate	141	+ 32		
Coprostane-3α,5β-diol	193	+ 47		
3-acetate	148	+ 51		
Coprostane-3β,5β-diol	149			
3-acetate	81			
Cholest-6-ene-3β,5α-diol O(XI)	181	— 16		
3-acetate	143	— 22		
3-benzoate	175	— 26		
Cholesta-7,9(11)-diene-3β,5α-diol P(X)				
3-acetate	173	+ 74	λ_{max}	242 mμ
			ε_{max}	13,100

TABLE IX (*continued*)

Compound	m.p. (° C.)	$[\alpha]_D$ (degrees)
Cholestane-3β,6α-diol	217	+ 38
diacetate	108	+ 39
dibenzoate	215	
Cholestane-3β,6β-diol	191	+ 13
3-acetate	144	— 6
6-acetate	125	+ 1
diacetate	139	— 23
Coprostane-3β,6β-diol	200	+ 24
diacetate	139	+ 13
6-acetate	144	+ 11
Cholest-4-ene-3β,6α-diol	178	+ 29
diacetate	167	— 25
dibenzoate	199	+ 84
Cholest-4-ene-3β,6β-diol L(V)	258	+ 6
diacetate	136	— 13
dibenzoate	182	— 74
Cholestane-3β,7α-diol O(VI)	152	+ 8
3-acetate	117	± 0
diacetate	139	— 17
dibenzoate	154	+ 23
Cholestane-3β,7β-diol O(V)	168	+ 53
3-acetate	75	+ 35
diacetate	87	+ 55
dibenzoate	152	+ 68
Cholest-5-ene-3β,7α-diol O(III)	188	— 95
diacetate	124	—175
dibenzoate	152	—110
Cholest-5-ene-3β,7β-diol O(IV)	178	+ 7
diacetate	110	+ 54
dibenzoate	172	+ 98
Cholestane-3β,15α-diol		
diacetate	147	+ 50
dibenzoate	192	+ 75
Cholest-5-ene-3β,16β-diol	178	— 33
diacetate	176	
Cholest-5-ene-3β,20ξ-diol T(XIII)	125	— 52
3-acetate	156	— 58
Cholest-5-ene-3β,24ξ-diol T(IV)		
isomer 1 (cerebrosterol)	176	— 48
diacetate	97	— 28
dibenzoate	181	— 16

TABLE IX (*continued*)

Compound	m.p. (° C.)	$[\alpha]_D$ (degrees)
isomer 2	183	— 26
diacetate	100	— 37
dibenzoate	142	— 12
Cholest-5-ene-3β,25-diol T(IX)	182	— 39
3-acetate	143	— 40
diacetate	126	— 36
Cholestane-3β,26-diol	181	+ 28
diacetate	120	+ 11
Cholest-5-ene-3β,26-diol T(VII)	178	— 30
diacetate	129	— 35
Cholestane-4α,5α-diol	135	+ 14
4-acetate	149	+ 35
Cholestane-4β,5α-diol	172	+ 27
4-acetate	176	+ 38
diacetate	148	+ 60
Cholestane-5α,6α-diol	181	+ 15
6-acetate	118	+ 24
Cholestane-5α,6β-diol	60(125)	— 3
6-acetate	114	
diacetate	76	— 33
Coprostane-5β,6α-diol	142	+ 31
6-acetate	Oil	+ 33
3α,3′α-Bischolest-4-enyl-3β,3′β-diol K(VIII)	205	+110
7,7′-Bis-3β-hydroxy-cholesta-5,8(9)-dienyl P(XV)	197	
diacetate	202	
6β-Chlorocholestane-3β,5α-diol J(II)	174	— 8
3-acetate	185	— 35
3-benzoate	203	— 20
6β-Bromocholestane-3β,5α-diol J(II)	135	
Cholestane-3β,5α,6α-triol	239	
3,6-diacetate	187	
Cholestane-3β,5α,6β-triol M(XI)	245	+ 3
3-acetate	210	— 18
3,6-diacetate	166	— 45
3-acetate-6-methanesulfonate M(XV)	142	— 31
Cholest-9(11)-ene-3β,5α,8α-triol P(XI)		
3-acetate	170	+ 65

TABLE X

KETONES

Compound	m.p. (°C)	$[\alpha]_D$ (degrees)	λ_{max} (mμ)	ε_{max}
Cholestan-1-one F(VIII)	89	+114		
Cholest-2-en-1-one	57	+121	224	8,100
Cholestan-2-one F(XI)	•130	+ 51		
Cholesta-3,5-dien-2-one K(XVI)	124	— 77	291	16,100
Cholestan-3-one C(III)	129	+ 44		
Coprostan-3-one C(VI)	63	+ 38		
Cholest-1-en-3-one H(XIII)	95	+ 65	231	9,800
Cholest-4-en-3-one H(V)	82	+ 89	240	18,000
Cholest-5-en-3-one H(IV)	127	— 4		
Cholest-7-en-3-one	147	+ 26		
Cholesta-1,4-dien-3-one H(XVII)	112	+ 28	245	14,000
Cholesta-4,6-dien-3-one H(VIII)	82	+ 33	285	25,000
Cholesta-4,7-dien-3-one H(VII)	88			
Cholesta-1,4,6-trien-3-one H(XIX)	83	± 0	224	12,000
			256	11,000
			300	12,000
Cholestan-4-one G(XXI) L(X)	100	+ 31		
Coprostan-4-one L(IX)	110	+ 41		
Cholest-5-en-4-one H(XXX)	111	— 32 (EtOH)	241	7,200
Cholestan-6-one S(IX)	98			
Coprostan-6-one	133	— 44		
3,5-Cyclocholestan-6-one S(VI)	98	+ 46		
Cholestan-7-one	118			
Coprostan-7-one	109			
Cholest-5-en-7-one K(II)	125			
Cholesta-3,5-dien-7-one N(V)	114	—300	277	24,400
Cholesta-1,3,5-trien-7-one	121	—784	230	
Cholesta-3,5,8(9)-trien-7one N(IV)	120	—261	281	25,300
B-Norcholest-4-en-3-one	62	+ 30	235	14,900
Cholestane-3,6-dione	172	+ 2		
Cholest-4-ene-3,6-dione Y(IX)	130	— 14	252	10,300
Cholest-4-ene-3,7-dione (enol form)	186	— 53	322	13,500
2α-Bromocholestan-3-one H(XII)	170	+ 38		
2α-Iodocholest-4-en-3-one H(XVI)	127	+ 40	258	8,100
6α-Chlorocholest-4-en-3-one J(XII)	126	+ 61	239	19,000

TABLE X (*continued*)

Compound	m.p. (° C)	$[\alpha]_D$ (degrees)	λ_{max} (mμ)	ε_{max}
6β-Chlorocholest-4-en-3-one J(VII)	130	+ 17	241	15,000
6α-Bromocholest-4-en-3-one J(XII)	113	+ 53	238	15,800
6β-Bromocholest-4-en-3-one J(VII)	130	+ 6	244	13,700
6α-Bromocholesta-1,4-dien-3-one H(XVIII)	144	+ 31	250	17,000
2α,2β-Dibromocholestan-3-one H(XIV)	147	+104		
2α,4α-Dibromocholestan-3-one H(XV)	195	+ 3		
5α,6β-Dichlorocholestan-3-one J(VI)	117	− 27		
5α,6β-Dibromocholestan-3-one J(VI)	74	− 53		

TABLE XI

HYDROXYKETONES

Compound	m.p. (° C.)	$[\alpha]_D$ (degrees)	λ_{max} (mμ)	ε_{max}
Cholestan-3β-ol-6-one N(XIV)	140	— 6		
acetate	129	— 16		
benzoate	174	+ 4		
Cholest-4-en-3β-ol-6-one	143			
acetate	128			
Cholestan-3β-ol-7-one N(XI)	169	— 36		
acetate	149	— 36		
benzoate	170	— 18		
Cholest-5-en-3β-ol-7-one N(X) O(I)	170	—103	235	14,000
acetate	159	—103		
benzoate	159	— 54		
Cholest-8(9)-en-3β-ol-7-one Q(XV) benzoate	150	— 13	252	6,300
Cholesta-5,8(9)-dien-3β-ol-7-one[a] N(VII) (Tsuda)	155		239	26,900
acetate	152	— 67		
benzoate	164	— 31		
Cholesta-5,8(9)-dien-3β-ol-7-one[a] Q(XVIII) (Inhoffen) acetate	171	— 9	248	12,800
Cholestan-3β-ol-11-one Q(IX)	151	+ 49 (dioxane)		
Cholestan-3β-ol-15-one	175	+ 47		
acetate	143	+ 38		
benzoate	149	+ 40		
Cholest-8(14)-en-3β-ol-15-one U(XVII) acetate	135	+116	260	14,500
benzoate	156	+103		
Cholestan-3β-ol-16-one benzoate	123			
Cholest-14-en-3β-ol-16-one benzoate	143	+103	230	16,200
Cholestan-3β-ol-22-one T(XVI)	127	— 2		
acetate	115	— 10		
Cholest-5-en-3β-ol-22-one	143	— 55		
acetate	152	— 63		

[a] See comment on p. 57.

TABLE XI (*continued*)

Compound	m.p. (°C.)	$[\alpha]_D$ (degrees)	λ_{max} (mμ)	ε_{max}
Cholest-5-en-3β-ol-24-one T(II)	138	— 39		
acetate	128	— 43		
Cholestan-5α-ol-2-one K(XII)	183	+ 29		
Cholest-3-en-5α-ol-2-one K(XV)	173	+ 36	223	7,900
4ξ-Methoxycholestan-5α-ol-2-one K(XIV)	154	+ 35		
Cholestan-5α-ol-3-one M(XIX)	208	+ 40		
Coprostan-5β-ol-3-one	152	+ 63		
Cholestan-5α-ol-4-one	159	+ 55		
Coprostan-5β-ol-6-one	103	— 18		
Coprostan-6β-ol-3-one acetate	115	+ 20		
Cholest-4-en-6α-ol-3-one	159	+ 82	240	16,000
acetate	106	+ 82		
Cholest-4-en-6β-ol-3-one Y(II) I(XII)	194	+ 38 (dioxane)		
acetate	104	+ 40 (dioxane)	236	13,500
Cholest-4-en-7β-ol-3-one	184	+ 63	243	15,500
acetate	102	+ 77		
benzoate	167	+ 81		
25-Norcholest-5-en-3β-ol-25-one T(VIII) X(IV)	127			
acetate	142			
benzoate	145			
7α-Bromocholestan-3β-ol-6-one N(XV) acetate	145	+ 39		
6β-Bromocholestan-5α-ol-3-one J(III)	182			
6β-Chlorocholestan-5α-ol-3-one J(III)	216			
8ξ-Bromocholest-5-en-3β-ol-7-one N(VI)			233	14,800
acetate	152	—130		
benzoate	200	— 84		
6ξ,8ξ-Dibromocholestan-3β-ol-7-one N(VIII) acetate	80			

TABLE XII
DIHYDROXYKETONES, HYDROXYDIKETONES, AND DIHYDROXYDIKETONES

Compound	m.p. (° C.)	$[\alpha]_D$ (degrees)	λ_{max} (mμ)	ε_{max}
Cholestane-4α,5α-diol-3-one				
L(II)	208	+ 44		
4-acetate	227			
Cholestane-3β,5α-diol-6-one				
N(XVIII)				
3-acetate	234	— 43		
3-benzoate	231	— 26		
Cholest-9(11)-ene-3β,5α-diol-7-one				
Q(XIV)				
3-acetate	186	— 26		
Coprost-8(9)-ene-3β,11α-diol-7-				
one Q(XXI)	145	— 51 (dioxane)	253	8,400
3,11-dibenzoate	140	+ 53		
Cholesta-5,8(9)-diene-3β-11α-				
diol-7-one Q(XX)			251	13,000
diacetate	167	+ 90		
dibenzoate	221	+164		
Cholesta-5-ene-3β,26-diol-16-one				
T(VI)	171	—156		
diacetate	116	—118		
Cholestan-5α-ol-3,6-dione Y(III)	231	— 19		
Cholestan-3β-ol-6,7-dione N(XVI)				
acetate	157	—108	275	10,700
Cholestan-3β-ol-7,11-dione				
Q(XIII)				
benzoate	200	+ 3 (dioxane)		
Cholest-5-en-3β-ol-7,11-dione				
N(III)				
benzoate	235	— 33	234	8,900
Cholest-8(9)-en-3β-ol-7,11-dione				
Q(XI)			268	6,300
benzoate	158	+ 46 (dioxane)		
Cholesta-5,8(9)-dien-3β-ol-7,11-				
dione N(II)				
benzoate	146	+ 92	270	10,700
Cholestane-3β,26-diol-16,22-dione	172	—139		
diacetate	123	—133		
dibenzoate	173	—103		
Cholest-5-ene-3β,26-diol-16,22-				
dione T(V) (kryptogenin)	186			
diacetate	153	—167		
dibenzoate	186			
Cholestane-4α,5α-diol-3,6-dione	245	—16		
4-acetate	226			

TABLE XIII
EPOXIDES AND EPIDIOXIDES

Compound	m.p. (°C)	$[\alpha]_D$ (degrees)	λ_{max} (mμ)	ε_{max}
1α,2α-Epoxycholestane F(XII)	88	+ 10		
2α,3α-Epoxycholestane F(II)	105	+ 37		
2β,3β-Epoxycholestane F(IX)	88	+ 51		
3α,5α-Epoxycholestane M(V)	86	+ 59		
4α,5α-Epoxycholestan-2-one K(X)	172	+141		
4β,5β-Epoxycholestan-3-one M(IV)	117	+135		
5α,6α-Epoxycholestan-3β-ol M(XIV)	143	— 45		
acetate	103	— 45		
benzoate	166	— 28		
5β,6β-Epoxycoprostan-3β-ol M(VI)	132	+ 11		
acetate	111	± 0		
benzoate	173	+ 16		
Cholesterol-α,β-epoxide[1:1 Compound of M(VI) and M(XIV)]	108	— 15		
acetate	112	— 21		
benzoate	151	+ 4		
6α,7α-Epoxycholestan-3β-ol acetate	180	— 23		
9α,11α-Epoxycholestane-3β,5α-diol-7-one Q(XVI) 3-acetate	183	— 42		
14α,15α-Epoxycholestan-3β-ol-16-one benzoate	154(185)			
1α,4α-Epidioxycholesta-2,5-dien-7-one	196	— 79	232	11,600
2α,5α-Epidioxycholest-3-ene K(X)	114	+ 48		
5α,8α-Epidioxycholesta-6,9(11)-dien-3β-ol P(VII) acetate	138	+108		
3β-Chloro-1α,2α-epoxycholestane	131	+ 28		

REFERENCES

Achtermann, T. (1934). *Z. Physiol. Chem.* **225**, 141.

Adam, N. K. (1941). "The Physics and Chemistry of Surfaces," 3rd ed., p. 79. Oxford Univ. Press, London and New York.

Adam, N. K., and Rosenheim, O. (1929). *Proc. Roy. Soc.* **A126**, 25.

Allan, G. G., Fayez, M. B. E., Spring, F. S., and Stevenson, R. (1956). *J. Chem. Soc.* p. 456.

Allinger, N. L. (1956). *J. Org. Chem.* **21**, 1180.

Alt, G., and Barton, D. H. R. (1952). *Chem. & Ind. (London)* p. 1103.

Anderson, R. C., Stevenson, R., and Spring, F. S. (1952). *J. Chem. Soc.* p. 2901.

Anfinsen, C. B., Jr., and Horning, M. G. (1953). *J. Am. Chem. Soc.* **75**, 1511.

Antonucci, R., Bernstein, S., Giancola, D., and Sax, K. J. (1951). *J. Org. Chem.* **16**, 1159.

Antonucci, R., Bernstein, S., Littell, R., Sax, K. J., and Williams, J. H. (1952). *J. Org. Chem.* **17**, 1341.

Barnett, J., Heilbron, I. M., Jones, E. R. H., and Verrill, K. J. (1940). *J. Chem. Soc.* p. 1390.

Barr, T., Heilbron, I. M., Jones, E. R. H., and Spring, F. S. (1938). *J. Chem. Soc.* p. 334.

Barton, D. H. R. (1946). *J. Chem. Soc.* p. 1116.

Barton, D. H. R. (1949). *J. Chem. Soc.* p. 2174.

Barton, D. H. R. (1950). *Experientia* **6**, 316.

Barton, D. H. R. (1953). *J. Chem. Soc.* p. 1027.

Barton, D. H. R., and Brooks, C. J. W. (1951). *J. Chem. Soc.* p. 277.

Barton, D. H. R., and Bruun, T. (1951). *J. Chem. Soc.* p. 2728.

Barton, D. H. R., and Cookson, R. C. (1956). *Quart. Revs. (London)* **10**, 44.

Barton, D. H. R., and Cox, J. D. (1948a). *J. Chem. Soc.* p. 783.

Barton, D. H. R., and Cox, J. D. (1948b). *J. Chem. Soc.* p. 1354.

Barton, D. H. R., and Cox, J. D. (1949) *J. Chem. Soc.* p. 214.

Barton, D. H. R., and Laws, G. F. (1954). *J. Chem. Soc.* p. 52.

Barton, D. H. R., and Miller, E. (1950a). *J. Am. Chem. Soc.* **72**, 372.

Barton, D. H. R., and Miller, E. (1950b). *J. Am. Chem. Soc.* **72**, 1066.

Barton, D. H. R., and Rosenfelder, W. J. (1949). *J. Chem. Soc.* p. 2459.

Barton, D. H. R., and Rosenfelder, W. J. (1951). *J. Chem. Soc.* p. 1048.

Barton, D. H. R., Cox, J. D., and Holness, N. J. (1949). *J. Chem. Soc.* p. 1771.

Barton, D. H. R., Ives, D. A. J., and Thomas, B. R. (1953a). *Chem. & Ind. (London)* p. 1180.

Barton, D. H. R., Hassel, O., Pitzer, K. S., and Prelog, V. (1953b). *Nature* **172**, 1096; cf. *Science* **119**, 49 (1954).

Barton, D. H. R., Ives, D. A. J., and Thomas, B. R. (1954a). *J. Chem. Soc.* p. 903.

Barton, D. H. R., Ives, D. A. J., Kelly, R. B., Woodward, R. B., and Patchett, A. A. (1954b). *Chem. & Ind. (London)* p. 605.

Barton, D. H. R., Ives, D. A. J., and Thomas, B. R. (1955). *J. Chem. Soc.* p. 2056.

Baxter, R. A., and Spring, F. S. (1943). *J. Chem. Soc.* p. 613.

Beckett, C. W., Pitzer, K. S., and Spitzer, R. (1947). *J. Am. Chem. Soc.* **69**, 2488.

Bellamy, L. J. (1954). "The Infra-Red Spectra of Complex Molecules." Methuen, London.

Benyon, J. H., Heilbron, I. M., and Spring, F. S. (1936). *J. Chem. Soc.* p. 907.

Berg, C. J., and Wallis, E. S. (1946). *J. Biol. Chem.* **162**, 683.

Bergmann, W. (1934a). *J. Biol. Chem.* **104**, 317.

Bergmann, W. (1934b). *J. Biol. Chem.* **104**, 553.

Bergmann, W. (1940). *J. Biol. Chem.* **132**, 471.

Bergmann, W. (1952). *In* "Progress in the Chemistry of Fats and Other Lipids," (R. T. Holman, W. O. Lundberg, and T. Malkin, eds.), Vol. 1, pp. 18-69. Pergamon Press, London.

Bergmann, W., and Dusza, J. P. (1957). *Ann.* **603**, 36-43.

Bergmann, W., and Klosty, M. (1951). *J. Am. Chem. Soc.* **73**, 2935.

Bergmann, W., and Low, E. M. (1947). *J. Org. Chem.* **12**, 67.

Bergmann, W., and McTigue, F. H. (1948). *J. Org. Chem.* **13**, 738.

Bergmann, W., and Ottke, R. C. (1949). *J. Org. Chem.* **14**, 1085.

Bergmann, W., and Stansbury, H. A. (1944). *J. Org. Chem.* **9**, 281.

Bergmann, W., and Stevens, P. G. (1948). *J. Org. Chem.* **13**, 10.

Bergmann, W., Hirschmann, F. B., and Skau, E. L. (1939). *J. Org. Chem.* **4**, 29.

Bergmann, W., Schedl, H. P., and Low, E. M. (1945). *J. Org. Chem.* **10**, 580.

Bergström, S. (1943). *Arkiv. Kemi Mineral. Geol.* **16A** (10), 1.

Bergström, S., and Wintersteiner, O. (1941). *J. Biol. Chem.* **141**, 597.

Bergström, S., and Wintersteiner, O. (1942a). *J. Biol. Chem.* **145**, 309.

Bergström, S., and Wintersteiner, O. (1942b). *J. Biol. Chem.* **145**, 327.

Bernal, J. D., (1932). *Nature* **129**, 277; *Chem. & Ind. (London)* p. 464.

Bernstein, S., and Lenhard, R. H. (1953). *J. Org. Chem.* **18**, 1146.

Bernstein, S., and Lenhard, R. H. (1954). *J. Org. Chem.* **19**, 1269.

Bernstein, S., Binovi, L. J., Dorfman, L., Sax, K. J., and SubbaRow, Y. (1949). *J. Org. Chem.* **14**, 433.

Bertho, A. (1950). *Ann.* **569**, 1.

Bide, A. E., Henbest, H. B., Jones, E. R. H., Peevers, R. W., and Wilkinson, P. A. (1948a). *J. Chem. Soc.* p. 1783.

Bide, A. E., Henbest, J. B., Jones, E. R. H., and Wilkinson, P. A. (1948b). *J. Chem. Soc.* p. 1788.

Bijvoet, J. M., Peeddeman, A. F., and van Bommel, A. J. (1951). *Nature* **168**, 271.

Bills, C. E., and Honeywell, E. M. (1928). *J. Biol. Chem.* **80**, 15.

Billeter, J. R., and Miescher, K. (1947). *Helv. Chim. Acta* **30**, 1409.

Billeter, J. R., and Miescher, K. (1949). *Helv. Chim. Acta* **32**, 564.

Birch, A. J. (1950). *J. Chem. Soc.* p. 2325.

Bladon, P., Fabian, J., Henbest, H. B., Koch, H. P., and Wood, G. W. (1951). *J. Chem. Soc.* p. 2402.

Bladon, P., Clayton, R. B., Greenhalgh, C. W., Henbest, H. B., Jones, E. R. H., Lovell, B. J., Silverstone, G., Wood, G. W., and Woods, G. F. (1952a). *J. Chem. Soc.* p. 4483.

Bladon, P., Henbest, H. B., Wood, G. W. (1952b). *J. Chem. Soc.* p. 2737.

Bladon, P., Henbest, H. B., Jones, E. R. H., Wood, G. W., Eaton, D. C., and Wagland, A. A. (1953a). *J. Chem. Soc.* p. 2916.

Bladon, P., Henbest, H. B., Jones, E. R. H., Lovell, B. J., Wood, G. W., Woods, G. F., Elks, J., Evans, R. M., Hathway, D. E., Oughton, J. F., and Thomas, G. H. (1953b). *J. Chem. Soc.* p. 2921.

Bladon, P., Henbest, H. B., Jones, E. R. H., Lovell, B. J., and Woods, G. F. (1954). *J. Chem. Soc.* p. 125.

Bondzynski, S. (1896). *Ber.* **29**, 476.

Boscott, R. J. (1949). *Nature* **164**, 140.

Bretschneider, H., and Ajtai, M. (1943). *Monatsh. Chem.* **74**, 57.

Bridgewater, R. J., and Shoppee, C. W. (1953). *J. Chem. Soc.* p. 1709.

Brieskorn, C. H., and Capuano, L. (1953). *Chem. Ber.* **86**, 866.

Broadbent, I. E., and Klyne, W. (1954). *Biochem. J.* **56**, xxx.

Budziarek, R., Newbold, G. T., Stevenson, R., and Spring, F. S. (1952a). *J. Chem. Soc.* p. 2892.

Budziarek, R., Johnson, F., and Spring, F. S. (1952b). *J. Chem. Soc.* p. 3410.

Burchard, H. (1890). *Chem. Zentr.* [I]**61**, 25.

Buser, W. (1947). *Helv. Chim. Acta* **30**, 1379.

Butenandt, A., and Hausmann, E. (1937). *Ber.* **70**, 1154.

Butenandt, A., and Wolff, A. (1935). *Ber.* **68**, 2091.

Butenandt, A., and Wolz, H. (1938). *Ber.* **71**, 1483.

Butenandt, A., Schramm, G., Wolff, A., and Kudszus, H. (1936). *Ber.* **69**, 2779.

Butenandt, A., Mamoli, L., Dannenberg, H., Masch, L. W., and Paland, J. (1939). *Ber.* **72**, 1617.

Callow, R. K. (1931). *Biochem. J.* **25**, 87.

Carter, P. W., Phipers, R. F., and Heilbron, I. M. (1939). *Proc. Roy. Soc. (London)* **B128**, 82.

Castells, J., and Meakins, G. D. (1956). *Chem. & Ind. (London)* p. 248.

Chakravorty, P. N., and Levin, R. H. (1942). *J. Am. Chem. Soc.* **64**, 2317.

Chamberlin, E. M., Ruyle, W. V., Erickson, A. E., Chemerda, J. M., Aliminosa, L. M., Erickson, R. L., Sita, G. E., and Tishler, M. (1951). *J. Am. Chem. Soc.* **73**, 2396.

Chamberlin, E. M., Ruyle, W. V., Erickson, A. E., Chemerda, J. M., Aliminosa, L. M., Erickson, R. L., Sita, G. E., and Tishler, M. (1953). *J. Am. Chem. Soc.* **75**, 3477.

Christiani, A. V., and Pailer, M. (1937). *Mikrochim. Acta* **1**, 26.

Ciba Conference. (1951). *Chem. & Ind. (London)* S.N. 1 (June 23rd); *Helv. Chim. Acta* **34**, 1680; *J. Chem. Soc.* p. 3526.

Clayton, R. B., Crawshaw, A., Henbest, H. B., Jones, E. R. H., Lovell, B. J., and Wood, G. W. (1953a). *J. Chem. Soc.* p. 2009.

Clayton, R. B., Henbest, H. B., and Jones, E. R. H. (1953b). *J. Chem. Soc.* p. 2015.

Clayton, R. B., Henbest, H. B., and Smith, M. (1957). *J. Chem. Soc.* p. 1982.

Clemo, G. R., Keller, M., and Weiss, J. (1950). *J. Chem. Soc.* p. 3470.

Cole, W., and Julian, P. L. (1945). *J. Am. Chem. Soc.* **67**, 1369.

Conca, R. J., and Bergmann, W. (1953). *J. Org. Chem.* **18**, 1104.

Cook, R. P., Kliman, A., and Fieser, L. F. (1954). *Arch. Biochem. Biophys.* **52**, 439.

Corey, E. J. (1954). *J. Am. Chem. Soc.* **76**, 175.

Cornforth, J. W., Youhotsky, I., and Popják, G. (1954). *Nature* **173**, 536.

Cornforth, J. W., Gore, I. Y., and Popják, G. (1957). *Biochem. J.* **65**, 94.

Cram, D. J., and Allinger, N. L. (1956). *J. Am. Chem. Soc.* **78**, 5275.

Crawshaw, A., Henbest, H. B., and Jones, E. R. H. (1954). *J. Chem. Soc.* p. 731.

Crowfoot, D. (1944). *Vitamins and Hormones* **2**, 409.

Daglish, A. F., Green, J., and Poole, V. D. (1953). *Chem. & Ind. (London)*, p. 1207.

Dane, E., Wang, Y., and Schulte, W. (1936). *Z. physiol. Chem.* **245**, 80.

Dauben, W. G., and Bradlow, H. L. (1950). *J. Am. Chem. Soc.* **72**, 4248.

Dauben, W. G., and Bradlow, H. L. (1952). *J. Am. Chem. Soc.* **74**, 559.

Dauben, W. G., and Eastham, J. F. (1951a). *J. Am. Chem. Soc.* **73**, 3260.

Dauben, W. G., and Eastham, J. F. (1951b). *J. Am. Chem. Soc.* **73**, 4463.

Dauben, W. G., and Fonken, G. J. (1956). *J. Am. Chem. Soc.* **78**, 4736.

Dauben, W. G., and Payot, P. H. (1956). *J. Am. Chem. Soc.* **78**, 5657.

Dauben, W. G., Eastham, J. F., and Michaeli, R. A. (1951). *J. Am. Chem. Soc.* **73**, 4496.

Dauben, W. G., Blanz, E. J., Jiu, J., and Michaeli, R. A. (1956). *J. Am. Chem. Soc.* **78**, 3752.

Daughenbaugh, P. J., and Allison, J. B. (1929). *J. Am. Chem. Soc.* **51**, 3665.

de Graeve, P. (1942). *Bull. soc. chim. France* [V]**9**, 938.

Delsal, J. L. (1943). *Bull. soc. chim. biol.* **25**, 361.

de Mayo, P., and Reed, R. I. (1956). *Chem. & Ind.* (*London*) p. 1481.

de Vries, H., and Backer, H. J. (1950). *Rec. trav. chim.* **69**, 759.

Diaz, G., Zaffaroni, A., Rosenkranz, G., and Djerassi, C. (1952). *J. Org. Chem.* **17**, 747.

Diels, O., and Abderhalden, E. (1906). *Ber.* **39**, 884.

Diels, O., and Blumberg, P. (1911). *Ber.* **44**, 2847.

Diels, O., Gädke, W., and Körding, P. (1927). *Ber.* **60**, 140; *Ann.* **459**, 1.

Dimroth, K., and Trautmann, G. (1936). *Ber.* **69**, 669.

Djerassi, C. (1951). *Org. Reactions* **6**, 229.

Djerassi, C., and Closson, W. (1956). *J. Am. Chem. Soc.* **78**, 3761.

Djerassi, C., and Ehrlich, R. (1956). *J. Am. Chem. Soc.* **78**, 440.

Djerassi, C., and Klyne, W. (1956). *Chem. & Ind.* (*London*) p. 988.

Djerassi, C., and Scholz, C. R. (1947a). *J. Am. Chem. Soc.* **69**, 2404.

Djerassi, C., and Scholz, C. R. (1947b). *Experientia* **3**, 107.

Djerassi, C., and Scholz, C. R. (1949). *J. Am. Chem. Soc.* **71**, 3962.

Djerassi, C., and Thomas, G. H. (1954). *Chem. & Ind.* (*London*) p. 1228.

Djerassi, C., Rosenkranz, G., Romo, J., Kaufmann, S., and Pataki, J. (1950). *J. Am. Chem. Soc.* **72**, 4534.

Djerassi, C., Mancera, O., Stork, G., and Rosenkranz, G. (1951). *J. Am. Chem. Soc.* **73**, 4496.

Djerassi, C., Foltz, E. W., and Lippman, A. E. (1955a). *J. Am. Chem. Soc.* **77**, 4354.

Djerassi, C., with Foltz, E. W., and Lippman, A. E. (1955b). *J. Am. Chem. Soc.* **77**, 4359.

Djerassi, C., with Lippman, A. E., and Foltz, E. W. (1955c). *J. Am. Chem. Soc.* **77**, 4364.

Djerassi, C., Closson, W., and Lippman, A. E. (1956a). *J. Am. Chem. Soc.* **78**, 3163.

Djerassi, C., Grossnickle, T. T., and High, L. B. (1956b). *J. Am. Chem. Soc.* **78**, 3166.

Dobriner, K., Katzenellenbogen, E. R., and Jones, R. N. (1953). "Infrared Absorption Spectra of Steroids." Interscience, New York.

Dodgson, D. P., and Haworth, R. D. (1952). *J. Chem. Soc.* p. 67.

Dodson, R. M., and Riegel, B. (1948). *J. Org. Chem.* **13**, 424.

Doering, W. v. E., and Aschner, T. C. (1949). *J. Am. Chem. Soc.* **71**, 838.

Dorée, C. (1909). *J. Chem. Soc.* p. 648.

Dorée, C., and Gardner, J. A. (1908). *Proc. Roy. Soc.* **B80**, 227.

Dorfman, L. (1953). *Chem. Revs.* **53**, 47.

Dulou, R., Chopin, J., and Raoul, Y. (1951). *Bull. soc. chim. France* [V]**18**, 616.

Eastham, J. F., and Teranishi, R. (1955). *Org. Syntheses* **35**, 39.

Eck, J. C., and Hollingsworth, E. W. (1941). *J. Am. Chem. Soc.* **63**, 107.

Eck, J. C., van Peursem, R. L., and Hollingsworth, E. W. (1939). *J. Am. Chem. Soc.* **61**, 171.

Ercoli, A., and de Ruggiere, P. (1953). *J. Am. Chem. Soc.* **75**, 3284.

Ercoli, A., Frisco, S. D., and de Ruggiere, P. (1953). *Gazz. Chim. Ital.* **83**, 78.

Fagerlund, U. H. M., and Idler, D. R. (1956). *J. Org. Chem.* **21**, 372.

Fernholz, E. (1935). *Z. physiol. Chem.* **232**, 97.

Fernholz, E., and MacPhillamy, H. B. (1941). *J. Am. Chem. Soc.* **63**, 1155.

Fernholz, E., and Stavely, H. E. (1939). *J. Am. Chem. Soc.* **61**, 142.

Fernholz, E., and Stavely, H. E. (1940). *J. Am. Chem. Soc.* **62**, 428, 1875.

Fernholz, E., and Ruigh, W. L. (1941). *J. Am. Chem. Soc.* **63**, 1157.

FIAT. (1947). "The Development and Manufacture of Synthetic Hormones in Germany." British Intelligence Objectives Sub-Committee Fiat Final Report No. 996. H.M. Stationery Office, London.

Fieser, L. F. (1950). *Experientia* **6**, 312.

Fieser, L. F. (1951). *J. Am. Chem. Soc.* **73**, 5007.

Fieser, L. F. (1953a). *J. Am. Chem. Soc.* **75**, 4395.

Fieser, L. F. (1953b). *J. Am. Chem. Soc.* **75**, 5421.

Fieser, L. F. (1953c). *J. Am. Chem. Soc.* **75**, 4386.

Fieser, L. F. (1953d). *J. Am. Chem. Soc.* **75**, 4377.

Fieser, L. F. (1954a). *J. Am. Chem. Soc.* **76**, 1945.

Fieser, L. F. (1954b). *Science* **119**, 710.

Fieser, L. F. (1955a). *Org. Syntheses* **35**, 36.

Fieser, L. F. (1955b). *Org. Syntheses* **35**, 43.

Fieser, L. F., and Bhattacharyya, B. K. (1953). *J. Am. Chem. Soc.* **75**, 4418.

Fieser, L. F., and Fieser, M. (1949). "Natural Products Related to Phenanthrene," 3rd ed. Reinhold, New York.

Fieser, L. F., and Herz, J. E. (1953). *J. Am. Chem. Soc.* **75**, 121.

Fieser, L. F., and Huang, W.-Y. (1953). *J. Am. Chem. Soc.* **75**, 5356.

Fieser, L. F., and Romero, M. A. (1953). *J. Am. Chem. Soc.* **75**, 4716.

Fieser, L. F., and Stevenson, R. (1954). *J. Am. Chem. Soc.* **76**, 1728.

Fieser, L. F., Fieser, M., and Chakravarti, R. N. (1949). *J. Am. Chem. Soc.* **71**, 2226.

Fieser, L. F., Herz, J. E., and Huang, W.-Y. (1951a). *J. Am. Chem. Soc.* **73**, 2397.

Fieser, L. F., Babcock, J. C., Herz, J. E., Huang, W.-Y., and Schneider, W. P. (1951b). *J. Am. Chem. Soc.* **73**, 4053.

Fieser, L. F., Herz, J. E., Klohs, M. W., Romero, M. A., and Utne, T. (1952). *J. Am. Chem. Soc.* **74**, 3309.

Fieser, L. F., Greene, T. W., Bischoff, F., Lopez, G., and Rupp, J. J. (1955). *J. Am. Chem. Soc.* **77**, 3228.

Ford, E. G., Chakravorty, P. N., and Wallis, E. S. (1938). *J. Am. Chem. Soc.* **60**, 413.

Fujimoto, G. I. (1951). *J. Am. Chem. Soc.* **73**, 1856.

Fürst, A., and Koller, F. (1947). *Helv. Chim. Acta* **30**, 1454.

Fürst, A., and Plattner, P. A. (1949). *Helv. Chim. Acta* **32**, 275.

Gascoigne, R. M., and Simes, J. J. H. (1955). *Quart. Revs. (London)* **9**, 328.

Georg, A. (1954). *In* "Elsevier's Encyclopaedia of Organic Chemistry" (F. Radt, ed.), Vol. 14, Suppl. pp. 1347S–1868S. Elsevier, Amsterdam.

Georg, A. (1956). *In* "Elsevier's Encyclopaedia of Organic Chemistry" (F. Radt, ed.), Vol. 14, Suppl., pp. 1869S–2214S. Elsevier, Amsterdam.

Grasshof, H. (1934a). *Z. physiol. Chem.* **223**, 249.

Grasshof, H. (1934b). Z. physiol. Chem. **225**, 197.

Gray, G. W. (1956). J. Chem. Soc. p. 3733.

Hackmann, J. T. (1950). Rec. trav. chim. **69**, 433.

Haslam, R. M., and Klyne, W. (1953). Biochem. J. **55**, 340.

Haslewood, G. A. D. (1944). Nature **154**, 29.

Hassel, O. (1943). Tidsskr. Kjemi, Bergvesen Met. **3**, 32.

Hassel, O., and Ottar, B. (1947). Acta Chem. Scand. **1**, 929.

Hattori, J. (1938). J. Pharm. Soc. Japan **58**, 548; Chem. Abstr. **32**, 7473 (1938).

Hattori, J. (1940). J. Pharm. Soc. Japan **60**, 334.

Hauptmann, H. (1947). J. Am. Chem. Soc. **69**, 562.

Haussler, E. P., and Brauchli, E. (1929). Helv. Chim. Acta **12**, 187.

Haworth, R. D., McKenna, J., and Whitfield, G. H. (1953). J. Chem. Soc. p. 1102.

Heath-Brown, B., Heilbron, I. M., and Jones, E. R. H. (1940). J. Chem. Soc. p. 1482.

Heilbron, I. M. (1942). J. Chem. Soc. p. 79.

Heilbron, I. M., and Wilkinson, D. G. (1932). J. Chem. Soc. p. 1708.

Heilbron, I. M., Jones, E. R. H., and Spring, F. S. (1937). J. Chem. Soc. p. 801.

Heilbron, I. M., Jackson, H., Jones, E. R. H., and Spring, F. S. (1938a). J. Chem. Soc. p. 102.

Heilbron, I. M., Hodges, J., and Spring, F. S. (1938b). J. Chem. Soc. p. 759.

Heilbron, I. M., Kennedy, T., Spring, F. S., and Swain, G. (1938c). J. Chem. Soc. p. 869.

Heilbronner, E. (1953). Helv. Chim. Acta. **36**, 1121.

Henbest, H. B., and Jones, E. R. H. (1948). J .Chem. Soc. p. 1792.

Henbest, H. B., and Lovell, B. J. (1957). J. Chem. Soc. p. 1965.

Henbest, H. B., and Wilson, R. A. L. (1956). J. Chem. Soc. p. 3289.

Henbest, H. B., Jones, E. R. H., Wagland, A. A., and Wrigley, T. I. (1955). J. Chem. Soc. p. 2477.

Herran, J., Rosenkranz, G., and Sondheimer, F. (1954). J. Am. Chem. Soc. **76**, 5531.

Hershberg, E. B., Oliveto, E., Rubin, M., Staendle, H., and Kuhlen, L. (1951). J. Am. Chem. Soc. **73**, 1144.

Herzog, H. L., Jevnik, M. A., and Hershberg, E. B. (1953). J. Am. Chem. Soc. **75**, 269.

Heusser, H., Eichenberger, K., Kurath, P., Dallenbach, H. R., and Jeger, O. (1951). Helv. Chim. Acta **34**, 2106.

Heusser, H., Heusler, K., Eichenberger, K., Honegger, C. G., and Jeger, O. (1952a). Helv. Chim. Acta **35**, 295.

Heusser, H., Anliker, R., Eichenberger, K., and Jeger, O. (1952b). Helv. Chim. Acta **35**, 936.

Heusser, H., Anliker, R., and Jeger, O. (1952c). Helv. Chim. Acta **35**, 1537.

Hey, D. H., Honeyman, J., and Peal, W. J. (1950). J. Chem. Soc. p. 2881.

Hey, D. H., Honeyman, J., and Peal, W. J. (1952). J. Chem. Soc. p. 4836.

Heymann, H., and Fieser, L. F. (1952). Helv. Chim. Acta **35**, 631.

Hodinář, Z., and Pelc, B. (1956). Collection Czechoslov. Chem. Communs. **21**, 264.

Hoppe-Seyler, F. (1863). Jahresberichte p. 545.

Humnicki, V. (1897). Z. physiol. Chem. **22**, 396.

Hunziker, F., Müllner, F. X., Reuteler, K. G., and Schaltegger, H. (1955). Helv. Chim. Acta **38**, 1316.

Idler, D. R., and Baumann, C. A. (1952). J. Biol. Chem. **195**, 623.

Idler, D. R., and Fagerlund, U. H. M. (1955). *J. Am. Chem. Soc.* **77**, 4142.

Idler, D. R., and Fagerlund, U. H. M. (1957). *J. Am. Chem. Soc.* **79**, 1988.

Inhoffen, H. H. (1936). *Ber.* **69**, 1134

Inhoffen, H. H. (1947). *Angew. Chem.* **59**, 207.

Inhoffen, H. H., and Huang, M. (1938). *Ber.* **71**, 1720.

Inhoffen, H. H., and Mengel, W. (1954). *Chem. Ber.* **87**, 146.

Inhoffen, H. H., and Stoeck, G. (1949). *Ann.* **563**, 131.

Inhoffen, H. H., and Zühlsdorff, G. (1941). *Ber.* **74**, 604.

Inhoffen, H. H., and Zühlsdorff, G. (1943). *Ber.* **76**, 233.

Inhoffen, H. H., and Zühlsdorff, G., and Huang, M. (1940). *Ber.* **73**, 451.

James, D. R., and Shoppee, C. W. (1956). *J. Chem. Soc.* p. 1064.

Johns, W. F., Lukes, R. M., and Sarett, L. H. (1954). *J. Am. Chem. Soc.* **76**, 5026.

Johnson, F., Newbold, G. T., and Spring, F. S. (1954). *J. Chem. Soc.* p. 1302.

Johnston, J. D., Gautschi, F., and Bloch, K. (1957). *J. Biol. Chem.* **224**, 185.

Jones, E. R. H., and Halsall, T. G. (1955). *Fortschr. Chem. org. Naturstoffe* **12**, 44.

Jones, E. R. H., Wilkinson, P. A., and Kerloque, R. H. (1942). *J. Chem. Soc.* p. 391.

Jones, R. N., and Sandorfy, C. (1956). *In* "Technique of Organic Chemistry" (A. Weissberger, ed.), Vol. 9, p. 247. Interscience, New York.

Josephy, E., and Radt, F., ed. (1940) *In* "Elsevier's Encyclopaedia of Organic Chemistry," Vol. 14. Elsevier, Amsterdam.

Julian, P. L., Cole, W., Magnani, H., and Meyer, E. W. (1945). *J. Am. Chem. Soc.* **67**, 1728.

Kaziro, K., and Shimada, T. (1937). *Z. physiol. Chem.* **249**, 220.

Keller, M., and Weiss, J. (1950). *J. Chem. Soc.* p. 2709.

Kind, C. A., and Bergmann, W. (1942). *J. Org. Chem.* **7**, 341.

Klass, D. L., Fieser, L. F., and Fieser, M. (1955). *J. Am. Chem. Soc.* **77**, 3829.

Klyne, W. (1954). *Progr. in Stereochem.* **1**, 36-89.

Köster, H., and Logemann, W. (1940). *Ber.* **73**, 298.

Ladenburg, K., Chakravorty, P. N., and Wallis, E. S. (1939). *J. Am. Chem. Soc.* **61**, 3283.

Lange, W., Folzenlogen, R. G., and Kolp, D. G. (1949). *J. Am. Chem. Soc.* **71**, 1733.

Lardelli, G., and Jeger, O. (1949). *Helv. Chim. Acta* **32**, 1817.

Laubach, G. D., Schreiber, E. C., Agnello, E. J., Lightfoot, E. N., and Brunings, K. J. (1953). *J. Am. Chem. Soc.* **75**, 1514.

Laubach, G. D., Schreiber, E. C., Agnello, E. J., and Brunings, K. J. (1956). *J. Am. Chem. Soc.* **78**, 4783.

Laucht, F. (1935). *Z. physiol. Chem.* **237**, 236.

Laws, G. F. (1953). *J. Chem. Soc.* p. 4185.

Lettré, H. (1933). *Z. physiol. Chem.* **321**, 73.

Lettré, H., and Tschesche, R. (1954). In "Über Sterine, Gallensäuren und verwandte Naturstoffe" (H. Lettré, Inhoffen, and R. Tschesche, eds.), Erster Band, Enke, Stuttgart.

Lewis, D. A., and McGhie, J. F. (1956). *Chem. & Ind.* **1956**, 550.

Liebermann, C. (1885). *Ber.* **18**, 1803.

Lieberman, S., Dobriner, K., Hill, B. R., Fieser, L. F., and Rhoades, C. P. (1948). *J. Biol. Chem.* **172**, 263.

Lifschütz, J. (1907). *Z. physiol. Chem.* **50**, 436.

Lifschütz, J. (1908). *Ber.* **41**, 252.

Loebisch, W. (1872). *Ber.* **5**, 510.

Lynn, W. S., Jr., Staple, E., and Gurin, S. (1955). *Federation Proc.* **14**, 783.

Lyon, A. M., and Bergmann, W. (1942). *J. Org. Chem.* **7**, 428.

McKennis, H. (1948). *J. Am. Chem. Soc.* **70**, 675.

MacPhillamy, H. B. (1942). *J. Am. Chem. Soc.* **64**, 1732.

Mancera, O., Barton, D. H. R., Rosenkranz, G., and Djerassi, C. (1952). *J. Chem. Soc.* p. 1021.

Marker, R. E., Whitmore, F. C., and Kamm, O. (1935). *J. Am. Chem. Soc.* **57**, 2358.

Mauthner, J. (1894). *Monatsh. Chem.* **15**, 87.

Mauthner, J. (1906). *Monatsh. Chem.* **27**, 421.

Mauthner, J. (1907). *Monatsh. Chem.* **28**, 1113.

Mauthner, J. (1909). *Monatsh. Chem.* **30**, 635.

Mauthner, J., and Suida, W. (1894). *Monatsh. Chem.* **15**, 85.

Mauthner, J., and Suida, W. (1896). *Monatsh. Chem.* **17**, 579.

Mauthner, J., and Suida, W. (1903). *Monatsh. Chem.* **24**, 648.

Mazur, A. (1941). *J. Am. Chem. Soc.* **63**, 883, 2442.

Meystre, C., and Wettstein, A. (1946). *Experientia* **2**, 408.

Meystre, C., Frey, H., Voser, W., and Wettstein, A. (1956). *Helv. Chim. Acta* **39**, 734.

Miescher, K. (1946). *Helv. Chim. Acta* **29**, 743.

Miescher, K., and Fischer, W. H. (1939). *Helv. Chim. Acta* **22**, 155.

Miescher, K., and Kägi, H. (1941). *Helv. Chim. Acta* **24**, 986.

Mills, J. A., and Klyne, W. (1954). *Progr. in Stereochem.* **1**, 177-222.

Moore, P. R., and Baumann, C. A. (1952). *J. Biol. Chem.* **195**, 615.

Mosettig, E., and Scheer, I. (1952). *J. Org. Chem.* **17**, 764.

Mueller, A. (1949). *J. Am. Chem. Soc.* **71**, 924.

Nace, H. R. (1951). *J. Am. Chem. Soc.* **73**, 2379.

Nakanishi, K., Bhattacharyya, B. K., and Fieser, L. F. (1953). *J. Am. Chem. Soc.* **75**, 4415.

Nes, W. R., and Mosettig, E. (1953). *J. Org. Chem.* **18**, 276.

Nes, W. R., Kostic, R. B., and Mosettig, E. (1956). *J. Am. Chem. Soc.* **78**, 436.

Noller, C. R. (1939). *J. Am. Chem. Soc.* **61**, 2717.

Oppenauer, R. V. (1941). *Org. Syntheses* **21**, 18. (Also Coll. Vol. III, p. 207).

Ott, A. C., Murray, M. F., and Pederson, R. L. (1952). *J. Am. Chem. Soc.* **74**, 1239.

Page, I. H., and Rudy, H. (1930). *Biochem. Z.* **220**, 304.

Parsons, J., Beher, W. T., and Baker, G. D. (1956). *Anal. Chem.* **28**, 1514.

Petrow, V. (1937). *J. Chem. Soc.* p. 1077.

Petrow, V., and Stuart-Webb, I. A. (1956). *J. Chem. Soc.* p. 4675.

Pickard, C. W., and Seymour, D. E. (1945). *J. Soc. Chem. Ind.* (*London*) **64**, 304.

Plattner, P. A., and Lang, W. (1944). *Helv. Chim. Acta* **27**, 1872.

Plattner, P. A., Petrzilka, T., and Lang, W. (1944). *Helv. Chim. Acta* **27**, 513.

Plattner, P. A., Heusser, H., and Kulkarni, A. B. (1948). *Helv. Chim. Acta* **31**, 1822.

Plattner, P. A., Fürst, A., and Els, H. (1954). *Helv. Chim. Acta* **37**, 1399.

Porsche, J. D. (1945). U.S. Patent 2371467 to Armour and Co.; *Chem. Abstr.* **39**, 3885 (1945).

Porsche, J. D., and Solms, F. J. (1940). U.S. Patent 2191260 to Armour and Co.; *Chem. Abstr.* **34**, 4527 (1940).

Prelog, V., Ruzicka, L., and Stein, P. (1943). *Helv. Chim. Acta* **26**, 222.

Riegel, B., and Kaye, I. A. (1944). *J. Am. Chem. Soc.* **66**, 724.

Ringold, H. J., Rosenkranz, G., and Sondheimer, F. (1956). *J. Org. Chem.* **21**, 239.

Rivett, D. E. A., and Wallis, E. S. (1950). *J. Org. Chem.* **15**, 35.

Romo, J., Djerassi, C., and Rosenkranz, G. (1950a). *J. Org. Chem.* **15**, 896.

Romo, J., Rosenkranz, G., and Djerassi, C. (1950b). *J. Org. Chem.* **15**, 1289.

Romo, J., Rosenkranz, G., Djerassi, C., and Sondheimer, F. (1954). *J. Org. Chem.* **19**, 1509.

Rosenheim, O. (1929). *Biochem. J.* **23**, 47.

Rosenheim, O., and King, H. (1932). *Chem. & Ind. (London)* **466**, 954; *Nature* **130**, 135.

Rosenheim, O., and Starling, W. W. (1937). *J. Chem. Soc.* p. 377.

Rosenkranz, G., Kaufmann, S., Pataki, J., and Djerassi, C. (1950a). *J. Am. Chem. Soc.* **72**, 1046.

Rosenkranz, G., Mancera, O., Gatica, J., and Djerassi, C. (1950b). *J. Am. Chem. Soc.* **72**, 4077.

Roth, H. (1953). *In* "Methoden der Organischen Chemie" (Houben Weyl); (E. Müller, ed.), Vol. II, p. 281, 4th completely revised edition. Georg Thieme, Stuttgart.

Ruyle, W. V., Jacob, T. A., Chemerda, J. M., Chamberlin, E. M., Rosenburg, D. W., Sita, G. E., Erickson, R. L., Aliminosa, L. M., and Tishler, M. (1953). *J. Am. Chem. Soc.* **76**, 2604.

Ruzicka, L., and Bosshard, L. (1937). *Helv. Chim. Acta* **20**, 244.

Ruzicka, L., and Fischer, W. H. (1937). *Helv. Chim. Acta* **20**, 1291.

Ruzicka, L., Huyser, H. W., Pfeiffer, M., and Seidel, C. F. (1929). *Ann.* **471**, 25.

Ruzicka, L., Goldberg, M. W., and Brüngger, H. (1934a). *Helv. Chim. Acta* **17**, 1389.

Ruzicka, L., Brüngger, H., Eichenberger, E., and Meyer, J. (1934b). *Helv. Chim. Acta* **17**, 1407.

Ruzicka, L., Bosshard, W., Fischer, W. H., and Wirz, H. (1936). *Helv. Chim. Acta* **19**, 1147.

Ryer, A. I., Gerbert, W. H., and Murrill, N. M. (1950). *J. Am. Chem. Soc.* **72**, 4247.

Ryer, A. I., Gerbert, W. H., and Murrill, N. M. (1953). *J. Am. Chem. Soc.* **75**, 491.

Salkowski, E. (1872). *Pflüger's Arch. ges. Physiol.* **6**, 207.

Salkowski, E. (1908). *Z. physiol. Chem.* **57**, 523.

Sandqvist, H., and Bengtsson, B. E. (1931). *Ber.* **64**, 2167.

Scheer, I., Thompson, M. J., and Mosettig, E. (1956). *J. Am. Chem. Soc.* **78**, 4733.

Schenck, F., Buchholz, K., and Wiese, O. (1936). *Ber.* **69**, 2696.

Schmid, H., and Kägi, K. (1950). *Helv. Chim. Acta* **33**, 1582.

Schmid, H., and Karrer, P. (1949). *Helv. Chim. Acta* **32**, 1371.

Schoenewaldt, E., Turnbull, L., Chamberlin, E. M., Reinhold, D., Erickson, A. E., Ruyle, W. V., Chemerda, J. M., and Tishler, M. (1952). *J. Am. Chem. Soc.* **74**, 2696.

Schoenheimer, R. (1930). *Z. physiol. Chem.* **192**, 86.

Schoenheimer, R. (1935). *J. Biol. Chem.* **110**, 461.

Schoenheimer, R., and Dam, H. (1933). *Z. physiol. Chem.* **215**, 59.

Schoenheimer, R., and Evans, E. A. (1936). *J. Biol. Chem.* **114**, 567.

Schoenheimer, R., and Sperry, W. M. (1934). *J. Biol. Chem.* **106**, 745.

Schreiber, J., and Eschenmoser, A. (1955). *Helv. Chim. Acta* **38**, 1529.

Schwenk, E., and Whitman, B. (1937). *J. Am. Chem. Soc.* **59**, 949.

Seeback, E., and Reichstein, T. (1944). *Helv. Chim. Acta* **27**, 948.

Shepherd, D. A., Donia, R. A., Campbell, J. A., Johnson, B. A., Holysz, R. P., Slomp, G., Jr., Stafford, J. E., and Pederson, R. L., and Ott, A. C. (1955). *J. Am. Chem. Soc.* **77**, 1212.

Shoppee, C. W. (1946a). *J. Chem. Soc.* p. 1138.

Shoppee, C. W. (1946b). *J. Chem. Soc.* p. 1147.

Shoppee, C. W. (1956). *In* "Perspectives in Organic Chemistry" (Sir Alexander Todd, ed.), pp. 315-346. Interscience. New York.

Shoppee, C. W., and Shoppee, E. (1953). *In* "Chemistry of Carbon Compounds" (E. H. Rodd, ed.), Vol. 2, Part B, pp. 765-875. Elsevier, Amsterdam.

Shoppee, C. W., and Summers, G. H. R. (1950). *J. Chem. Soc.* p. 687.

Shoppee, C. W., and Summers, G. H. R. (1952a). *J. Chem. Soc.* p. 2528.

Shoppee, C. W., and Summers, G. H. R. (1952b). *J. Chem. Soc.* p. 3361.

Skau, E. L., and Bergmann, W. (1938). *J. Org. Chem.* **3**, 166.

Slomp, G., Jr., Shealy, Y. F., Johnson, J. L., Donia, R. A., Johnson, B. A., Holysz, R. P., Pederson, R. L., Jensen, A. O., and Ott, A. C. (1955). *J. Am. Chem. Soc.* **77**, 1216.

Smedley-Maclean, I. (1928). *Biochem. J.* **22**, 22.

Smith, L. L. (1954). *J. Am. Chem. Soc.* **76**, 3232.

Sobel, A. E., and Rosen, M. J. (1941). *J. Am. Chem. Soc.* **63**, 3536.

Sobel, A. E., and Spoerri, P. E. (1941). *J. Am. Chem. Soc.* **63**, 1259.

Sondheimer, F., Yashin, R., Rosenkranz, G., and Djerassi, C. (1952). *J. Am. Chem. Soc.* **74**, 2696.

Šorm, F. (1947). *Collection Czechoslov. Chem. Communs.* **12**, 437.

Šorm, F., and Dyková, H. (1948). *Collection Czechoslov. Chem. Communs.* **13**, 407.

Squire, E. N. (1951). *J. Am. Chem. Soc.* **73**, 2586.

Stavely, H. E., and Bergmann, W. (1937a). *J. Org. Chem.* **1**, 567.

Stavely, H. E., and Bergmann, W. (1937b). *J. Org. Chem.* **1**, 575.

Stavely, H. E., and Bollenback, G. N. (1943). *J. Am. Chem. Soc.* **65**, 1500.

Steiger, M., and Reichstein, T. (1937). *Helv. Chim. Acta* **20**, 1040.

Stevenson, R., and Fieser, L. F. (1956). *J. Am. Chem. Soc.* **78**, 1409.

Stokes, W. M., Fish, W. A., and Hickey, F. C. (1956). *J. Biol. Chem.* **220**, 415.

Stork, G., Romo, J., Rosenkranz, G., and Djerassi, C. (1951). *J. Am. Chem. Soc.* **73**, 3546.

Strating, J., and Backer, H. J. (1950). *Rec. trav. chim.* **69**, 909.

Striebel, P., and Tamm, C. (1954). *Helv. Chim. Acta* **37**, 1095.

Swell, L., and Treadwell, C. R. (1955). *J. Biol. Chem.* **212**, 141.

Szpilfogel, S. A., Posthumus, T. A. P., de Winter, M. S., and Van Dorp, D. A. (1956). *Rec. trav. chim.* **75**, 475.

Tanret, C. (1908). *Compt. rend.* **147**, 75.

Tortelli, M., and Jaffe, E. (1915). *Chem. Z.* **39**, 14.

Tschesche, R. (1936). *Ber.* **69**, 1665.

Tschesche, R., and Hagedorn, A. (1935). *Ber.* **68**, 2247.

Tschugaeff, L. (1900). *Z. angew. Chem.* **14**, 618.

Tsuda, K., and Hayatsu, R. (1955a). *J. Am. Chem. Soc.* **77**, 665.

Tsuda, K., and Hayatsu, R. (1955b). *J. Am. Chem. Soc.* **77**, 6582.

Tsuda, K., Arima, K., and Hayatsu, R. (1954). *J. Am. Chem. Soc.* **76**, 2933.

Tsujimoto, M., and Koyanagi, H. (1934). *J. Soc. Chem. Ind. Japan Suppl.* **37**, 81B, 436B.

Tsujimoto, M., and Koyanagi, H. (1935). *J. Soc. Chem. Ind. Japan Suppl.* **38**, 118B.

Turner, R. B. (1950). *J. Am. Chem. Soc.* **72**, 582.

Turner, R. B. (1953). *J. Am. Chem. Soc.* **75**, 4362.

Ushakov, M. I., and Kosheleva, N. F. (1944). *J. Gen. Chem. (U.S.S.R.)* **14**, 1138; *Chem. Abstr.* **40**, 4071 (1946).

Valentine, F. R., and Bergmann, W. (1941). *J. Org. Chem.* **6**, 452.

Vavon, M. G., and Jakubowicz, B. (1933). *Bull. soc. chim. France* **53**, 581.

Voser, W., Montavon, M., Günthard, H. H., Jeger, O., and Ruzicka, L. (1950). *Helv. Chim. Acta* **33**, 1893.

Wagner-Jauregg, T., and Werner, L. (1932). *Z. physiol. Chem.* **213**, 119.

Wallis, E. S., and Chakravorty, P. N. (1937). *J. Org. Chem.* **2**, 335.

Wallis, E. S., Fernholz, E., and Gephart, F. T. (1937). *J. Am. Chem. Soc.* **59**, 137.

Weiss, J., and Keller, M. (1950). *Experientia* **6**, 379.

Westphalen, T. (1915). *Ber.* **48**, 1064.

Wettstein, A. (1940). *Helv. Chim. Acta.* **23**, 388.

Wieland, H., and Asano, M. (1929). *Ann.* **473**, 300.

Wieland, H., and Benend, W. (1942). *Ber.* **75**, 1708.

Wieland, H., and Benend, W. (1943). *Ann.* **554**, 1.

Wieland, H., and Coutelle, G. (1941). *Ann.* **548**, 270.

Wieland, H., and Görnhardt, L. (1947). *Ann.* **557**, 248.

Wieland, H., and Gough, G. A. C. (1930). *Ann.* **482**, 36.

Wieland, P., and Miescher, K. (1949). *Helv. Chim. Acta* **32**, 1922.

Wieland, H., and Vocke, F. (1930). *Z. physiol. Chem.* **191**, 69.

Wieland, H., Rath, F., and Benend, W. (1941). *Ann.* **548**, 19.

Wilds, A. L., and Djerassi, C. (1946a). *J. Am. Chem. Soc.* **68**, 2125.

Wilds, A. L., and Djerassi, C. (1946b). *J. Am. Chem. Soc.* **68**, 1712.

Windaus, A. (1906). *Ber.* **39**, 518.

Windaus, A. (1909). *Ber.* **42**, 238.

Windaus, A. (1910). *Z. physiol. Chem.* **65**, 110.

Windaus, A. (1916). *Ber.* **49**, 1724.

Windaus, A. (1919). *Ber.* **52**, 170.

Windaus, A. (1920). *Ber.* **53**, 488.

Windaus, A., and Adamla, J. (1911). *Ber.* **44**, 3055.

Windaus, A., and Brunken, J. (1928). *Ann.* **460**, 225.

Windaus, A., and Dalmer, O. (1919). *Ber.* **52**, 162.

Windaus, A., and Linsert, O. (1928). *Ann.* **465**, 148.

Windaus, A., and Resau, C. (1913). *Ber.* **46**, 1246.

Windaus, A., and Schneckenburger, A. (1913). *Ber.* **46**, 2628.

Windaus, A., and von Staden, A. (1921). *Ber.* **54**, 1059.

Windaus, A., and Stange, O. (1936). *Z. physiol. Chem.* **244**, 218.

Windaus, A., and Uibrig, C. (1914). *Ber.* **47**, 2384.

Windaus, A., and Uibrig, C. (1915). *Ber.* **48**, 857.

Windaus, A., and Weinhold, R. (1923). *Z. physiol. Chem.* **126**, 299.

Windaus, A., and Welsch, A. (1909). *Ber.* **42**, 612.

Windaus, A., Klänhardt, F., and Weinhold, R. (1923). *Z. physiol. Chem.* **126**, 308.

Windaus, A., Auhagen, E., Bergmann, W., and Butte, H. (1930). *Ann.* **477**, 268.

Windaus, A., Linsert, O., and Eckhardt, H. J. (1938). *Ann.* **534**, 22.

Windaus, A., Bursian, K., and Riemann, U. (1941). *Z. physiol. Chem.* **271**, 177.
Wintersteiner, O., and Bergström, S. (1941). *J. Biol. Chem.* **137**, 785.
Wintersteiner, O., and Moore, M. (1943). *J. Am. Chem. Soc.* **65**, 1503.
Wintersteiner, O., and Ruigh, W. L. (1942). *J. Am. Chem. Soc.* **64**, 2453.
Woodward, R. B., Sondheimer, F., Taub, D., Heusler, K., and McLamore, W. M. (1952). *J. Am. Chem. Soc.* **74**, 4223.
Woodward, R. B., Inhoffen, H. H., Larson, H. O., and Menzel, K. H. (1953). *Ber.* **86**, 594.
Woodward, R. B., Patchett, A. A., Barton, D. H. R., Ives, D. A. J., and Kelly, R. B. (1954). *J. Am. Chem. Soc.* **76**, 2852.
Woodward, R. B., Patchett, A. A., Barton, D. H. R., Ives, D. A. J., and Kelly, R. B. (1957). *J. Chem. Soc.* p. 1131.
Yoder, L., Sweeney, O. R., and Arnold, L. K. (1945). *Ind. Eng. Chem.* **37**, 374.
Zaffaroni, A. (1950). *J. Am. Chem. Soc.* **72**, 3828.
Zimmermann, W. (1935). *Z. physiol. Chem.* **233**, 257.
Zimmermann, W. (1936). *Z. physiol. Chem.* **245**, 47.

Supplementary References

Bladon, P., Cornforth, J. W., and Jaeger, R. H. (1958). *J. Chem. Soc.* p. 863.
Burgstahler, A. W. (1957). *J. Am. Chem. Soc.* **79**, 6047.
Castells, J., Jones, E. R. H., Williams, R. J. W., and Meakins, G. D. (1958). *Proc. Chem. Soc.* p. 7.
Coleman, D. L., and Baumann, C. A. (1957). *Arch. Biochem. Biophys.* **71**, 287.
Fieser, L. F. (1957). *In* "Festschrift Arthur Stoll," p. 489. Verlag Birkhäuser, Basel.
Fieser, L. F., Huang, W. Y., and Bhattacharyya, B. K. (1957). *J. Org. Chem.* **22**, 1380.
Gollnick, K., and Neumüller, A. O. (1957). *Ann.* **603**, 46.
Graber, R. P., Snoddy, C. S., Jr., Arnold, H. B., and Wendler, N. L. (1956). *J. Org. Chem.* **21**, 1517.
Jones, E. R. H., Meakins, G. D., and Stevenson, J. S. (1958). In press.
Klyne, W. (1957). "The Chemistry of the Steroids." Methuen, London.
Lettré, H., and Jahn, A. (1957a). *Angew. Chem.* **69**, 266.
Lettré, H., and Jahn, A. (1957b). *Ann.* **608**, 43.
McKenna, J. (1953). *Quart. Revs.* (*London*) **7**, 231.
Mathieu, J. P., and Petit, A. (1956). "Tables de Constantes et Donées Numériques. 6. Constantés Selectionnés, Pouvoir Rotatoire Naturel. I. Stéroides." Masson, Paris.
Nazarov, I. N., and Bergel'son, L. D. (1955). "Khimiya Steroidnykh Gormonov" (Chemistry of Steroid Hormones). Izdatel'stvo Akad. Nauk S.S.S.R., Moscow.
Schulz, G., and Sander, H. (1957). *Z. physiol. Chem.* **308**, 122.
Shoppee, C. W. (1958). "Chemistry of the Steroids." Butterworths, London.
Simonsen, Sir John, and Ross, W. C. J. (1957). "The Terpenes," Vol. 4, pp. 37-115; Vol. 5, pp. 1-57. Cambridge Univ. Press, London and New York.
Sondheimer, F., Amendolla, C., and Rosenkranz, G. (1953). *J. Am. Chem. Soc.* **75**, 5932.

Chapter 3

METHODS OF ISOLATION AND ESTIMATION OF STEROLS

Robert P. Cook and James B. M. Rattray

"Say not the struggle naught availeth."

CLOUGH.

I. Introduction

In broad principle there are three main methods for estimating chemical compounds: (1) enrichment methods by which the compound is isolated in a pure form; (2) methods in which some chemical reaction of a more or less specific nature is used; and (3) physical methods in which some physical property of the compound is measured. These basic principles are discussed in more detail in their respective sections, but most methods involve a combination of principles.

Cholesterol is related to other compounds which have similar physical properties and which give similar chemical reactions so that highly specific methods for the determination of cholest-5-en-3β-ol are not to be expected. The available methods do give a good and general picture of the sterols and related compounds but the ideal method still eludes us.

The sterols are usually classed as part of the lipid component of the tissues but an exact definition of lipid is difficult to make (see Bloor, 1943; Deuel, 1951). The component of tissues soluble in fat solvents such as ethyl ether and insoluble in water is considered as lipid, a good critique of the subject being given by Lovern (1957).

Extraction methods are suitable for determining the relation of the sterols to the lipid component, but as the sterols themselves may be combined with protein or with carbohydrate, special methods must be employed if such complexes are to be studied. Excellent practical accounts of techniques for the extraction of lipid from tissues, the determination of fatty acids and of phospholipids are given in "Methods in Enzymology" (Colowick and Kaplan, 1957); for the estimation of glycerol a good general method is described by Voris *et al.* (1940).

A complete bibliography on the subject of sterol estimation is beyond the scope of this chapter and we have been forced to be selective, but recent general reviews are given by Chevallier (1953), Zak and Ressler (1955), and Lovern (1956a).

II. Isolation Procedures

A. Extraction of Lipid

In the extraction process the requirements are that the solvent will disrupt the complexes with protein or with carbohydrate and that no chemical change in the lipid will be produced by oxidation or enzyme action. The extraction process should be one of immediate fixation of the constituents in the state they might be expected to be in the tissues, the conditions of extraction being therefore of some importance. "Wet" or "dry" extraction of the tissues may be used.

In wet extraction the fresh tissue is extracted with a solvent, usually a lower aliphatic alcohol (methanol or ethanol), which is commonly combined with another solvent. Bloor (1928) used a mixture of ethanol-ethyl ether (3:1 v/v) but the proportions are not critical (cf. Boyd, 1936). Other solvent mixtures are used, e.g. chloroform-methanol (2:1 v/v), the lipid extract being washed with water (Folch et al., 1951). Good accounts of such a method are given for brain tissue by Sperry (1954) and for blood plasma by Sperry and Brand (1955). The method is eminently suitable for small amounts of tissue but for large-scale work considerable amounts of solvent are required (at least ten times the weight of tissue). For complete extraction it is advisable to homogenize the tissue in the solvent prior to extraction. Tough tissues such as skin should be ground with sand. Folch et al. (1957) report a simple method for the isolation and purification of total lipids from animal tissues.

In dry extraction the tissue is dried under the most favorable conditions and it is generally considered that freeze-drying is the best method, but drying in vacuo in a steam-jacketed vessel can be speedy and effective with large amounts of material. The dried material is then extracted conveniently in a continuous extractor. We ourselves extract first with ethanol, then grind the material and re-extract with ether. The use of purified solvent (particularly peroxide-free ethyl ether) and the carrying out of drying operations in vacuo or in a stream of inert gas needs no stressing. The evaporator devised by Craig et al. (1950) is useful for removing final traces of solvent.

An account of the methods used by us is given in the Appendix.

It is advisable to fractionate the lipid extract as soon as possible for chemical change may occur on storage (e.g. Boyd, 1937). It has been found, however, by Halliday (1939) that preservation of tissues in formalin does not affect the total cholesterol content but the phospholipids undergo a change. For blood plasma heparin is preferred to oxalate which has a diluting effect (Sperry and Schoenheimer, 1935).

If storage is necessary, refrigeration at a low temperature in an inert gas atmosphere is advocated. The use of amber glassware to avoid photochemical change is excellent procedure; alternatively specimens should not be exposed to strong light.

B. SAPONIFICATION AND PREPARATION OF UNSAPONIFIABLE MATTER

One method of investigating lipid extracts is to hydrolyze (saponify) the material with an alkali in alcoholic solution whereby the esterified fatty acids of the lipid including the steryl esters form alkali salts (soaps), the liberated alcohols constituting the neutral fraction. After dilution with water, the higher alcohols and sterols are separated from the hydrolyzed material by extraction with an organic solvent which is immiscible in water, ethyl ether being commonly used. The material recovered from the solvent forms the unsaponifiable (nonsaponifiable) matter. In addition to alcohols previously esterified it contains also saturated and unsaturated hydrocarbons (e.g. squalene) and is in general of complex composition.

The method is useful for concentrating the total sterol component of a tissue but is limited by the extracting power of the solvent used, the choice of which depends on the further investigation needed. If the less polar sterols such as cholesterol are to be studied, petroleum ether is a suitable solvent, but if the more polar dihydroxysterols are to be investigated a more exhaustive extraction should be made; good solvents for this purpose are chloroform or ethyl acetate.

If an analysis is needed only of total unsaponifiable matter (or of sterols), the organism or tissue is hydrolyzed in concentrated alkali and the unsaponifiable matter removed by extraction and analyzed (e.g. Dorée, 1909; Abell et al., 1952).

Steryl esters vary in their ease of saponification, the esters of higher saturated fatty acids (e.g. palmitic and stearic) being more resistant to hydrolysis than the esters of unsaturated fatty acids. Ideal conditions of saponification are difficult to state, but a popular reagent is ethanolic potassium hydroxide used in the ratio (by weight) of lipid 100:KOH 30:ethanol 500 at the ebullition temperature, under reflux in an atmosphere of nitrogen for 3 hours (cf. Hilditch, 1956). Claisen's alkali (KOH 10:methanol 100 w/v) and sodium ethylate are also favored while milder alkalies (such as baryta), acid, and cold saponification have been advocated. In plant tissues where sterol is often bound to carbohydrate, hydrolysis with mineral acid is usually necessary to liberate bound sterol.

The unsaponifiable matter is extracted from the hydrolyzate (this may be alkaline but some favor neutralization before extraction) with the chosen solvent. The solvent extract is washed with water to remove soaps but resaponification may be necessary to ensure complete hydrolysis. Treatment with urea is useful in that adducts are formed with straight chain compounds which can thus be separated from sterols (e.g. Schlenk, 1954). In drying the unsaponifiable matter it has been observed that part is volatile at 50° C. (Lemeland, 1922), a finding which we can confirm.

The drastic nature of the saponification process is often criticized (cf. Sperry, 1955) but modifications such as cold saponification are not entirely satisfactory. Unless a fractionation technique is used to separate the various fatty acid esters prior to saponification (see p. 124) no information is obtained on the form of combination. The enzymatic hydrolysis by esterase (Kelsey and Longenecker, 1941) is a milder procedure but is incomplete with the glycerides (Clément et al., 1954). The saponification process, as such, is established and convenient but a simple, rapid, and specific method of hydrolysis is much needed.

C. Acids

This chapter is concerned primarily with sterols but the acid components are given some attention because of their association with sterol metabolism.

The acids present in the saponified material are a complex mixture, the greatest part consisting of saturated and unsaturated higher fatty acids which can be extracted with ethyl ether after acidification of the soap solution. A small part consists of lower fatty acids (C_2–C_{10}) which are recovered by steam distillation. The fatty acids are best converted into methyl esters and analyzed by (for example) gas-liquid chromatography (James and Martin, 1956). Bile acids when present, e.g., in fecal extracts, are extracted with ethyl ether; their separation and estimation is described on p. 134.

D. Fractionation of Lipid, Unsaponifiable Matter, and of Sterols

In the newer methods of analysis, refinements in procedures have been introduced so that the individual components of a complex may be separated by relatively mild methods. These enrichment methods are employed to study the components of tissues whether they are in the form of extracted lipid or parts thereof.

In principle there are two basic methods for separating compounds present in the same phase (see Martin, 1950, for a theoretical study of the problem). The first is by distributing the material between two phases, examples being solvent partition (a method already described in separating the neutral fraction), crystallization, and distillation. The second method depends on separation by diffusional processes, the components moving differentially under pressure, concentration, or temperature gradients. Gravitational or electric fields may also be used to effect separation and are described in Chapter 5. The basic methods may be used separately, but combinations of the methods are commonly employed. Equilibration between phases can be repeated many times in a *countercurrent* manner so that without performing separate operations a small enrichment factor will give rise to a separation of components. Examples of this are countercurrent liquid-liquid fractionation and chromatography of adsorption and of partition types. All the variants of these methods are not described but relevant references are given.

1. Distribution between Phases

a. Solvent partition and crystallization. The differential solubilities of the component lipids in solvents may be used to make a semi-quantitative separation.

The relative insolubility of phospholipids in acetone is often used to separate them from other lipid components but at the same time this solvent removes water-soluble compounds such as urea, amino acids, and alkali salts (see Bloor, 1929; Folch and Van Slyke, 1939). Although the separation of sterols from glycerides by differential solubilities is not satisfactory (Clément *et al.*, 1954), Brown and his colleagues have firmly established the low-temperature separation of glycerides as a method of fractionation (e.g. Brown and Kolb, 1955).

A cholesterol-poor unsaponifiable matter may be prepared by crystallization of the major part of the cholesterol from methanol, a process used by Hardegger *et al.* (1943) in the study of human atheromatous aortas. The component parts so separated are purified by other methods.

Solvent separation methods as such are limited by the fact that mutual solubilities affect the precipitations and that for satisfactory results a minimum of 1 gm. is needed. We have found the method of value when combined with adsorption chromatography.

The use of crystallization per se is in general limited to the penultimate fractions of a separation. A good example is the use of glacial acetic acid for separating cholestanol from samples of cholesterol (Fieser, 1953a). The method can be made quantitative on samples of not less than 100 mg.

b. Distillation. An unusual quantitative molecular microdistillation of cholesterol from its esters is described by Koehler and Hill (1949).

2. Diffusional Methods

a. Countercurrent Fractionation. The application of this method to the separation of lipid components is reviewed by Ahrens (1956). The apparatus initially devised by Craig has, in various modifications (see Craig *et al.* 1951), found widespread acceptance and has been used with success by Ahrens and Craig (1952) to separate the components of bile; by Polonovski and Jarrier (1955) to determine serum cholesterol, and by Abell *et al.* (1952) in an examination of serum cholesterol who report that 99% of the cholesterol is in fact Δ^5-cholestenol. The method is of value on account of the mildness of the fractionating procedure and it gives an all inclusive analysis. Disadvantages are the finding of suitable solvent "pairs" and the size of the apparatus.

b. Chromatography. Various types of chromatography are distinguished but for simplicity two main types are considered. In *adsorption* chromatography the material to be fractionated is placed on a column of adsorbent which is considered to be "active." The fractionation is carried out by eluting with solvents of increasing polarity, e.g. from the nonpolar hydrocarbon solvents in petroleum ether, or preferably using hydrocarbons such as pentane or heptane to the very polar solvent methanol.* In *partition* chromatography the supporting medium, e.g. cellulose fiber paper is considered as inert and the separation is made by partition between two immiscible phases, the stationary bound to the supporting medium and the mobile. Good general reviews are given by Block *et al.* (1955); Lederer and Lederer (1957); and a good summary of the separation of steroids and sterols is given by Bush (1954a).

(i) *Adsorption chromatography.* Following the pioneer experiments of Trappe (1940, 1941) this method is now of wide application in the study of lipid components. There are a wealth of adsorbents; useful general adsorbents are silicic acid with or without diatomaceous earth ("celite") for the separation of lipid extracts, and alumina for separating the components of the unsaponifiable matter. Adsorbents are standardized by the method of Brockmann and Schodder (1941). A simple method for the determination and adjustment of adsorbents, and of the eluting power of solvents is described by Keuning *et al.* (1957).

The method is applicable to large or small amounts of material. With large quantities the fractions may be estimated by standard chemical procedures while with small quantities of material determinations are made on the fractions by colorimetric or other methods.

---

* To avoid ambiguity the following terms are defined: eluent is the solvent placed on the column for developing purpose and the issuing solvent with dissolved material we call the effluent, the term eluate is synonymous.

Examples of the method used on lipid extracts are: the fractionation of the main components of a lipid extract of blood plasma by Fillerup and Mead (1953); the separation of neutral fat from cholesteryl esters in a lipid extract from haddock flesh by Lovern (1956b); and the separation of free and combined cholesterol in plasma by Kerr and Bauld (1953). For the separation of lipids including sterols, in small amounts of material the use of glass fiber paper impregnated with silicic acid promises to be of importance (Dieckert and Reiser, 1956).

In the separation of unsaponifiable matter from human feces, stanols appeared in the benzene effluent, stenols in the ether effluent, and the polar di- and tri-hydroxylated sterols with the ethanol (Cook et al., 1956). Fecal sterols were also fractionated by Coleman et al. (1956) and plant leaf sterols by Wall and Kelley (1947). The use of the colored azoyl esters for separating the various sterols present in skin and in fecal extracts of various animals is described by Idler and Baumann (1952) and by Wells et al. (1955). The constituents of "isocholesterol" have been separated by the chromatography of their benzoates or labeled p-iodobenzoates (Stokes, 1957).

Adsorption chromatography is a valuable method since it needs the minimum of apparatus and reagents but the essentially simple method with all its possible variants must be learned by experience. Disadvantages are the time factor and that for fine resolutions the process must be repeated and preferably interposed with a chemical procedure (cf. Riddell and Cook, 1955). The possibility also of artifact formation including oxidation should always be remembered. An account of the method as used by us is given in the Appendix.

(ii) *Partition chromatography.* The considerable literature on the separation of the steroids and sterols is reviewed by Heftmann (1955). Partition chromatography may be carried out either on a column of adsorbent such as "celite" (e.g. Mosbach et al., 1953; Danielsson, 1956) or on cellulose paper. As paper chromatography is of more general application it will be discussed here with more emphasis on the term "paper" than "partition."

The main systems used for the separation of sterols and steroids are shown in Table I. A useful adaptation of the Zaffaroni system for the separation of the weakly polar sterols is that of Neher and Wettstein (1952); this technique is used in this laboratory (e.g. Riddell and Cook, 1955) and is described in the Appendix. The Bush system has been used mainly for studying steroid hormones (Bush, 1954a). Reverse phase chromatography has been used for the separation of cholesterol and its derivatives by Kritchevsky and Calvin (1950), by Martin and Bush (1955), and by Martin (1957).

An interesting application is the separation of zymosterol from other sterols (Alexander and Schwenk, 1957). Descending or ascending movement of the mobile phase may be used; the ascending technique is used by Michaleč (1956) to separate cholesterol and its esters in blood serum and by Lata and Vestling (1952) to separate the cholesterol in adrenal tissue.

After development the component spots may be located by spraying the chromatogram with a suitable color reagent (see Kritchevsky and Kirk, 1952) which may possibly characterize the particular compound. A semi-quantitative measure of the amount present may be made by

TABLE I
SOME TYPES OF PARTITION CHROMATOGRAPHY[a]

Solvent phase		References
Stationary	Mobile	
Nonvolatile and polar	Volatile and nonpolar	Zaffaroni *et al.* (1950)
Volatile and polar	Volatile and nonpolar	Bush (1952)
Less polar	More polar	Reversed phase (Howard and Martin 1950)

[a] A list of solvent systems used in steroid and sterol analysis is given by Bush (1954a).

measuring the amount of color. Other methods such as absorption in the ultraviolet or the measurement of radioactivity can be used in special cases (see Comar, 1955, for a general account of radioisotopes including autoradiography and paper chromatography). Values for the movement of the component spots are given either as R_f values—the ratio of the band movement to the movement of the advancing front or better as R_T values—the ratio between the distance run in a given time with respect to an accompanying sterol (e.g. Riddell and Cook, 1955).

Paper chromatography is now firmly established but the results should always be viewed critically (see Bush, 1954b). There is, for example, in mixtures a "displacement effect" of one compound on another (Savard, 1954). A precaution with compounds is to elute with a suitable solvent and examine by some other method, e.g. infrared analysis (cf. Smith and States, 1954).

With the sterols the method has limitations, e.g. it is difficult to separate a mixture of C_{27}, C_{28}, and C_{29} stenols with a double bond in position 5. Such a mixture is, however, of relatively rare occurrence and the method is suitable for separating monohydroxy- from dihydroxy-sterols.

E. Separation of Cholesterol from Associated Compounds

1. Dibromide Formation

As described in Chapter 2 the Δ^5-stenols form dibromides which are relatively insoluble in the usual solvents particularly at 0° C. The stanols are not precipitated and a differential analysis of stenols and stanols may be made (Schoenheimer, 1930). On a preparative scale Fieser (1953b) obtained a yield of 84% and using a quantitative method Haenni (1941) reports yields of 94%. Haenni bases a method for estimating cholesterol on an iodometric titration of the dibromide; a modification is to brominate the digitonide (Orlowski and Simon, 1954). The Δ^5-stenols may be recovered from the dibromide and if cholesterol is so treated it is of a high degree of purity (cf. Schwenk and Werthessen, 1952). It is worth stressing, however, that autoxidation of the cholesterol and some associated compounds may occur during the process (e.g. Smith, 1954).

2. Measurement of Unsaturation

The degree of unsaturation of cholesterol is measured commonly by the pyridine sulfate dibromide method of Rosenmund and Kuhnhenn (1923) or on a microscale (3–5 mg.) by the procedure of Yasuda (1931, 1937), and using these methods the theoretical iodine value (number) of 65.8 is obtained with pure samples.

Stenols with double bonds in other positions, e.g. Δ^7 or the dienes give values which differ from theory, as does oxidation with perbenzoic acid. Unsaturation values obtained on unknown sterols by these methods should therefore be treated with caution. Hydrogenation of stenols is also used and the process can be made selective for particular unsaturated linkages (see Bergmann, 1952, for examples).

The position of an unsaturated linkage in the side chain is determined conveniently by ozonolysis whereby a volatile aldehyde is produced which is commonly determined as its 2,4-dinitrophenylhydrazone. Bergmann (1952) reports examples of the use of this method and Toyama et al. (1952) give working details of the technique.

3. Oxalic Acid Adduct Formation

This method may be used to separate sterols from other constituents of the unsaponifiable matter (cf. Alexander and Schwenk, 1957). A recovery value of 80% is obtained by this method for cholesterol (Schwenk, personal communication).

4. Removal of Ketones

We have found that even after purification certain samples of cholesterol, usually slightly yellow in color, contain ketonic impurities. These may be removed either as the Girard complex using the reagent T (trimethylammoniumacetohydrazide chloride) or as the 2,4-dinitrophenylhydrazone (cf. Fieser and Bhattacharyya, 1953; Stadtman, 1957).

III. Quantitative Determination of Sterols

In Section II details were given for the isolation of cholesterol; this procedure although desirable is lengthy and not always practicable. In the methods described below use is made of some of the chemical properties of the sterol molecule in order to estimate it in a mixture of other compounds.

A. DIGITONIN PRECIPITATION

The reaction, and its specificity, of sterols with an ethanolic solution of digitonin to form an insoluble molecular complex is described in Chapter 2, pp. 80-84. Free sterol is determined by direct precipitation and total sterol determined after saponification of the extract, ester sterol being obtained by difference. The method is commonly used to estimate 3β-sterols in tissues. The sterol may be recovered from the digitonide by methods described on p. 84.

1. Gravimetric Determination

The weight of the sterol digitonide is more than four times (4.18 for cholesterol) greater than that of the sterol so that relatively small amounts of sterol may be estimated. Apart from questions of specificity the best conditions for precipitation and washing the complex are of importance (e.g. Gardner et al., 1938; Sobel and Mayer, 1945; Sperry and Webb, 1950). An interesting observation which we can confirm, is that in the presence of aluminum ions precipitation is complete within five minutes (Obermer and Milton, 1937; Brown et al., 1954). The digitonides vary in their solubilities, use being made of this to separate sterols, e.g. the separation of coprostanol from cholestanol by methanol (Schoenheimer and Dam, 1933), and of the sterols in serum by ethanol (Sobel et al., 1953).

2. Microdetermination

With small amounts of digitonide estimations may be made by *oxidative* methods using chromic acid. The remaining chromic acid may be determined by titration with thiosulfate (e.g. Okey, 1930; Boyd, 1938); or the CO_2 liberated from the digitonide on oxidation estimated gasometrically in the Van Slyke apparatus (Kirk et al., 1934; Folch et al., 1940). These oxidative methods may be used for a complete lipid analysis. A *nephelometric* or *turbidimetric* method is also used (Pollak and Wadler, 1952; Stenger, 1955). We have found this method convenient for following the formation of free sterol liberated from ester combination during enzymatic hydrolysis. The digitonides of stenols give *color reactions* and use is made of this to determine them (Section III, C). A variant is the estimation of the carbohydrate moiety of the digitonin by the anthrone reagent (Feichtmeir and Bergerman, 1953). An interesting method due to Schmidt-Thomé and Augustin (1942) is based on the original discovery of the use of digitonin, namely, the inhibition by cholesterol of the erythrocyte hemolysis produced by digitonin; a sensitivity of 1 μg. is claimed.

Criticisms of digitonin as a reagent are that samples vary in purity and that it is expensive. It is generally agreed that, since its introduction by Windaus (Chapter 1), its use has stood the test of time. Used with care the method is valuable for determining the total 3β-sterol content of tissues in both large or small amount.

Glycosides other than digitonin (Chapter 2, p. 80) have been proposed, e.g. gitonin was used by Delsal (1947) to determine the cholesterol content of cerebrospinal fluid.

B.   Estimation of Hydroxysteroids

Nonspecific methods which depend on the reaction of the hydroxyl group of sterols, are the formation of pyridinium cholesteryl sulfate with its subsequent colorimetric determination (Sobel *et al.*, 1951), and a method in which the steroid acetates are converted into acetohydroxamic acids which are then determined by their color reaction with iron salts (Baggett *et al.*, 1955).

C.   Colorimetric Determination

The chemical basis of the tests by which steroids and sterols give colors when treated with acid reagents is described in Chapter 2. The amount of color produced obeys Beer's Law so that the sterol may be estimated and in some methods the amount is as small as 10 μg. The more commonly used methods only are described.

1. Liebermann-Burchard Method

The history of this reaction is given in Chapter 1. In its simplest form the method consists in adding acetic anhydride and a small amount of concentrated sulfuric acid to a solution of the sterol in a suitable organic solvent when a sequence of colors is produced which for cholesterol ranges from a transient permanganate color, particularly in strong solution, through shades of green-blue and fading to shades of green-brown (see later).

The method has a wide application and the types of compound giving the reaction, the colors produced, and the rapidity of development, is shown in Table II. It is worthy of emphasis that although cholestan-3β-ol does not react, a color is given with coprostanol (Reiss, 1955).

There is a prolific literature on this popular test which seems to invite modifications. Used intelligently it is a simple and informative method suitable for a tentative identification and well suited for *comparative* analyses. Various factors must be considered in making the method of value.

Temperature. This affects the reaction and use may be made of this for differentiating sterols. The "fast acting" sterols such as Δ^7- and $\Delta^{5,7}$-stenols react at 0° C. and may be differentiated from the "slow acting" Δ^5-stenols (Cook *et al.*, 1954). For the estimation of the latter the reaction is carried out at a definite temperature on the range 20–25° C.

Light. The color developed in the dark is more blue-green than green, while in light it is green. Light affects the component(s) absorbing at 340–550 mμ but not that at 620 mμ, at which measurements are usually made (Kenny, 1952; Kabara, 1954). Although the use of completely shielded baths for color development is recommended, we consider it sufficient to develop in the absence of direct light.

Solvent. A number of solvents have been proposed, glacial acetic acid is now the most commonly used solvent because it dissolves the digitonide, but it has a dilution effect; for the most intense color the solvent should be used in the ratio of 1 to 2 of the color developer. The presence of water affects the rate of color development and anhydrous reagents must be used. Chloroform is also used and a direct extraction of cholesterol from plasma by chloroform is the basis of the popular method of Kingsley and Schaffert (1949). Acetic anhydride is the solvent favored by Love (1957).

Color reagent. The most usual consists of 1 volume of concentrated sulfuric acid added to 19 volumes of cooled acetic anhydride and it is essential that the reagent is prepared freshly for each set of determinations. A variant for the direct estimation of cholesterol in plasma is the use of *p*-toluenesulfonic acid instead of the sulfuric acid (Pearson *et al.*, 1953), a method which is well suited for routine analysis (Leppänen, 1956).

Absorption maximum. Measurement of color intensity is made when it is considered to have reached its maximum blue-green color. The use of a recording spectrophotometer would be of value for this, but in most methods the measurement is made after 30 minutes for a temperature of 25° C. We consider, however, that the individual worker should standardize his temperature and time factors, and moreover use for each

TABLE II
THE LIEBERMANN-BURCHARD REACTION

Compound	Maximum intensity[a]		Color after 20 hours	Remarks and references
	Color	Time for development (min.)		
Δ^5-Stenols (and $\Delta^{5,22}$-stenols) of C_{27}, C_{28}, and C_{29} series	Blue-green	35	Green-brown	For quantitative determination conditions must be standardized; see text (Ref. 2, 9)
Cholesterol esters	Blue-green	35	Green-brown	Color intensities of palmitic and oleic esters about 25% greater than free sterol (Ref. 4); Linoleate ester about 10% greater (Ref. 9)
Cholesterol digitonide	Blue-green	35	More green than brown	Intensity may be greater than cholesterol equivalent (see text)
25-Hydroxycholesterol	Blue-green	35	Brown	Intensity 55% that of cholesterol after 35 min. (Ref. 9)
Coprostanol (3β-ol)	Blue	90	Green	Intensity 40% that of cholesterol after 35 min. (Ref. 1, 7, 9)
Cholestan-3α-ol	Green-blue	90	Green-brown	Intensity 15% that of cholesterol after 35 min. (Ref. 7, 9)
Cholestan-3β-ol		None		Some samples (? impurity) give 10% reaction (Ref. 7, 9)
Δ^7-Cholestenol (lathosterol)	Blue-green	1–2	Brown	
$\Delta^{5,7}$-Cholestadienol (7-dehydrocholesterol)	Blue-green	1–2	Brown	
$\Delta^{8,24}$-Cholestadienol (zymosterol)	Blue-green	1–2	Brown	Fast-acting sterols (Ref. 2, 6, 9)
Δ^5-Cholest-$3\beta,7\beta$-diol (7-hydroxycholesterol)	Green	1–2	Green	

TABLE II (continued)

| Compound | Color | Maximum intensity[a] | | Remarks and references |
		Time for development (min.)	Color after 20 hours	
Lanosterol	Fluorescent yellow-green	60	Green-yellow	The reaction may be used quantitatively (Ref. 5, 9)
Squalene (at 38°)	Light brown	120	Deep brown	For quantitative determination see Ref. 8 Ref. 9
Farnesol	No apparent reaction			

Steroid (C_{27}) *ketones.* Negative results were obtained with cholestanone, coprostanone, Δ^4- and Δ^5-cholest-3-one, 7-ketocholesterol acetate, and ketone 104 (Ref. 9).

Bile acids. Chenodeoxycholic acid gives a blue-green color which may be used quantitatively (Ref. 3); the other bile acids give yellow colors (Ref. 11).

Nonsteroids. Blue-green colors are given by carotene and linoleic acid (Ref. 11). Mono- and dihydroxy-benzene derivatives and isoprenoid compounds give a variety of colors (Ref. 10, 11; see also Table II, Chapter 9).

Artifacts. The following give a "fast-acting" reaction: the residue left after the distillation of some commercial samples of petroleum ether and an acetic acid extract of rubber stoppers (Ref. 9).

NOTE: The results shown are as for 0.5 mg. compound using a ratio of 1 acetic acid solvent to 2 of color reagent (acetic anhydride 19:concentrated sulfuric acid 1). Total volume 3–5 ml.; temperature 20° C. The times for a maximum color intensity have a variation of ± 10% of the given times.

[a] The color intensity is measured at 620 mμ for "fast" and "slow" acting sterols, at 550 mμ for lanosterol, and at 400 mμ for squalene.

References: 1. Coleman *et al.* (1956); 2. Idler and Baumann (1953); 3. Isaksson (1954); 4. Kenny (1952); 5. Luddy *et al.* (1953); 6. Moore and Baumann (1952); 7. Reiss (1955); 8. Wheatley (1953); 9. Observations from this laboratory. We are indebted to Drs. D. H. R. Barton, L. F. Fieser, A. Ryer, and V. R. Wheatley for gifts of pure compounds; 10. Coelho and Alves (1946); 11. Kent (1952).

series of determination a high and a low cholesterol standard rather than relying on a predetermined calibration curve.

The intensity of the color is commonly read at 620 mμ but other wavelengths, in particular 460 mμ may be used (cf. Kenny, 1952). Attempts to determine cholesterol by estimating the color after 20 hours were not satisfactory (Sperry and Brand, 1943).

The addition of 1,4-dioxane reduces the rate of color development and combined with acetic anhydride is used as an extracting agent for the determination of the total cholesterol of plasma (Saifer and Kammerer, 1946).

Lanosterol may be differentiated from cholesterol in a mixture by its absorption at 550 mμ (Luddy et al., 1953). Squalene is determined, after chromatographic separation, by the absorption at 400 mμ produced after development for 2 hours at 38° C. (Wheatley, 1953).

The method may be combined with digitonin precipitation as in the popular Schoenheimer-Sperry method (see Sperry and Webb, 1950). The digitonides sometime give a color greater than equivalent amount of cholesterol and samples of digitonin do give a slight but positive Liebermann-Burchard reaction (Yasuda, 1936). We suggest that all samples be tested before use or alternatively that the standard cholesterol be subjected to the digitonin precipitation.

In the Appendix our modification of the Schoenheimer-Sperry procedure is described.

2. Tschugaeff Method (For history see Chapter 1)

In this method a solution of the sterol in chloroform or in glacial acetic acid is treated with zinc chloride and acetyl chloride and heated at 60° C. for 15 minutes or the reaction is allowed to develop at 20° C. for 4 hours. Cholesterol, its esters and digitonide give a cherry red color (maximum 528 mμ), Δ^7-cholestenol gives a yellow color (maximum 395 mμ). We find that cholestanol gives a slight reaction. The method is useful for 10–50 μg. of cholesterol (Rose et al., 1941; Hanel and Dam, 1955). The comparative merits of this method compared with the Liebermann-Burchard reaction are discussed admirably by Schön and Gey (1956).

3. Sulfuric Acid-Iron Method

The color reagent consists of a dilute solution of ferric chloride in glacial acetic acid and concentrated sulfuric acid which is added to the material under test dissolved in acetic acid. Cholesterol, its esters and digitonide give purple colors of equal intensity (maximum 560 mμ), cholestanol giving a yellow color. The color develops rapidly at room temperature and amounts of 10–50 µg. may be determined (Zlatkis *et al.,* 1953; Zak *et al.,* 1954a, 1954b). The method can be used directly on 0.1 ml. samples of serum (e.g. MacIntyre and Ralston, 1954) and is suitable for certain clinical determinations. A critical review is given by Swinnen (1955) and Herrmann (1957) proposes that the method is best accompanied by a saponification-extraction procedure.

D. DETERMINATION OF COMPOUNDS RELATED TO CHOLESTEROL

Although this chapter is concerned primarily with cholesterol and other sterols, some other compounds are so closely connected with sterol metabolism that a general account of their separation and determination is given. These compounds are the steroid ketones particularly of the C_{27} series, the bile acids, and squalene. For the estimation of the steroid hormones the reader is referred to the specialized texts.

1. *Steroid Ketones by Zimmermann Method* (see Chapter 2, p. 88)

This reaction which is reviewed by Zimmermann (1955) may be carried out at 25° or at 0° C. (Wilson, 1954). The violet color produced has a specific maximum absorption dependent on the position of the oxo group (e.g. Broadbent and Klyne, 1954). We find Wilson's procedure of carrying out the reaction at 0° C. useful in distinguishing "fast acting" stanones from "slow acting" stenones (see Table III). The technique may be used to estimate 5–50 µg. of ketosteroid, and in the Appendix practical details are given.

TABLE III

ZIMMERMANN REACTION OF SOME KETOSTEROIDS RELATED TO CHOLESTEROL[a]

Compound	Absorption maximum (mµ) for development time at 0° C of		Color intensity at 0° C. with respect to cholestanone after	
	one-quarter hr.	3 hr.	one-quarter hr.	3 hr.
Cholestanone (cholestan-3-one)	560	560	100	100
Coprostan-3-one	580	540	70	25
Cholest-4-en-3-one	600	600	25	50
Cholest-5-en-3-one	600	600	10	30
Ketone 104	500	No absorption	10	0
25-Ketonorcholesterol	540	Broad absorption 400–600	5	10
7-Ketocholesteryl acetate		No absorption	0	0

[a] The results shown for color intensity are semi-quantitative (± 10%). The reactions were carried out with 100 µg. ketosteroid dissolved in ethanol (0.4 ml.) to which was added *m*-dinitrobenzene solution (0.4 ml.) and potassium hydroxide solution (0.4 ml.); see text.

2. Bile Acids and Salts

The acids present in the *bile* are conjugated with glycine or taurine and if the combined form is to be determined special methods are used. The procedure of Doubilet (1936) is useful for general purposes but where the facilities allow the method of countercurrent extraction gives a complete analysis (Ahrens and Craig, 1952). A useful rapid method for determining the total conjugated bile acids is described by Harold and Chaikoff (1954).

The individual conjugates and/or bile acids present are separated by one of the various types of chromatography (see p. 123). To mention individual examples would be tedious and invidious; the reader is referred to the review by Bergström and Borgström (1956), where an account of recent methods of estimation is also described.

The bile salts in the *blood* are sometimes determined (e.g. Wysocki *et al.*, 1955). The *feces* contain a complex mixture of metabolized bile acids for which special methods must be used (e.g. Bergström and Norman, 1953; Edwards and Cook, 1955).

3. Biosynthetic Compounds

These are so varied (see Chapter 6) that a short summary of all compounds is not practicable. Squalene may be estimated (after chromatographic separation) as the hexachloride (Fitelson, 1943) or by a variant of Liebermann-Burchard procedure (e.g. Wheatley, 1953).

A reflection on colorimetric methods. Most of the color tests described in Chapter 2, Table V have been or may be used for the estimation of sterols or their metabolic products and our selection of methods has been a relatively meager one. Colorimetric methods have been, are, and always will be favored by the biochemist, especially those working in clinical laboratories on account of their convenience and relative simplicity. They are indeed useful for rapid and *comparative* estimations, but unless it is known what specific compound is giving the reaction the results should be viewed with caution.

IV. Physical Methods

The physical properties of a compound are used to identify the chemical species and physical methods may be used to estimate a compound. A quick method of determination is available in cases where some striking physical property is present, e.g. a marked absorption in some specific range of the electromagnetic spectrum. There are numerous texts on the use of physical methods but a short, clear account of general principles and their application is given by Harley and Wiberley (1954).

Comprehensive surveys of recent advances in the use of physical methods are given in Analytical Reviews (1956) and in the treatises on "Physical Techniques in Biological Research" (Oster and Pollister, 1955, 1956).

A. Optical Activity

The extent and degree of optical rotation is stressed by Bergmann (1952) as a means of differentiating sterols. We have found this method of value in chromatography in following the separation of the dextro-rotatory stanols from the levo-rotatory stenols. Using 10 mg. of sterol in a volume of 1 ml. an estimation may be made with some degree of accuracy; moreover the compound is recoverable after determination. The scope of the method could be increased by the use of microcells and photomultiplier tubes.

B. Absorption Spectrophotometry

Absorption of radiation in the ultraviolet, visible, and infrared ranges of the electromagnetic spectrum is used in estimations of the sterols and their metabolic products. Thus in the visible range the color intensities in colorimetric methods are estimated routinely. In the ultraviolet region absorption spectrophotometry is the common method for estimating 7-dehydrocholesterol and ergosterol (e.g. Glover et al., 1952). Steroids with a conjugate double bond system including α,β-unsaturated ketones absorb strongly in the ultraviolet (see the extensive review by Dorfman, 1953). Information on the extinction coefficients of various C_{27} steroids is given in Chapter 2.

The infrared (2.5 to 25 μ) while used at present mainly for identification (Chapter 2, p. 79) has been used for the estimation of cholesterol (Guy et al., 1955). An application of both ultraviolet and infrared spectrophotometry to the determination of the semicarbazones of the 3-ketosteroids of the C_{27} series is described by Dannenberg et al. (1956).

Freeman et al. (1957) describe a method of serum lipid analysis based on chromatography and infrared spectrophotometric assay of the separated fractions. Beher et al. (1957) question the value of infrared spectrophotometry for identifying sterols in mixtures, with which criticism we agree. They find that sterols may be easily differentiated by X-ray diffraction powder methods.

The method of *spectrophotofluorimetry* in its various forms (e.g. Bowman et al., 1955) has been applied by Albers and Lowry (1955) to the estimation of cholesterol. A sensitivity of 0.1 μg. is possible with the method.

C. Polarography

The principle of this technique developed by Heyrovsky consists in measuring the decomposition voltage of a compound with the dropping mercury electrode. A detailed treatment is given by Kolthoff and Lingane (1952). The method is used to estimate reducible compounds particularly steroid ketones. An account of the method used for the ketones related to cholesterol is given by Robertson (1955). The determination of cholesterol after oxidation to cholestenone by the Oppenauer (1937) reaction is described by Wolfe *et al.* (1940).

We should like to conclude this section with the observation that to list all the proposed physical methods for the estimation of cholesterol would increase greatly our allotted space and moreover lead us into fields in which we have had no practical experience. As with the chemical methods the procedures are varied and ingenious, to mention but two: microscopic fusion analysis (Gilpin, 1951) and surface film measurements (Keyl and Jones, 1954).

V. Sterols in Parts of the Cell and in Plants

A. Separation of Cellular Components

In the preceding sections the methods used to determine the sterol content of whole tissues have been discussed. Newer methods have been developed which separate the component parts of a tissue including the cell into the so-called cell organelles. In principle the method consists of homogenizing the tissue in a sucrose (or other suitable) solution which is then separated by differential centrifugation into a floating layer ("fat"), a supernatant layer derived mainly from the cytoplasm, microsomes, mitochondria, and a lowermost layer of cell nuclei. The technique is described by Hogeboom (1955) and a good review of the result obtained is given by Claude (1954). The separate cell fractions are removed and analyzed for their lipid composition. Examples of the separations for various tissues are described in Chapter 4.

B. Plant Carbohydrate-Sterol Complexes

In plants a portion of the sterol is associated with carbohydrates to form glycosides known as phytosterolins or sterolins (see review by Bergmann, 1953). The combined sterol is liberated by hydrolysis with acid. Most of the studies on the sterol glycosides consist of isolation procedures there being little quantitative information. Briefly, the methods for isolation consist in removal of lipid (including free and ester sterol) by extraction or by chromatography. The sterolins are then extracted from the aqueous medium by a suitable solvent.

VI. Summary and Conclusions

The writers have been, and the reader will be, impressed by the variety of methods available for the determination of what appears at first sight to be a single chemical entity. What (or who) is cholesterol? The single species cholest-5-en-3β-ol is difficult to isolate. Its relatives have similar properties and reactions. One is reminded in the field of inorganic chemistry of the group of rare earth metals, the separation

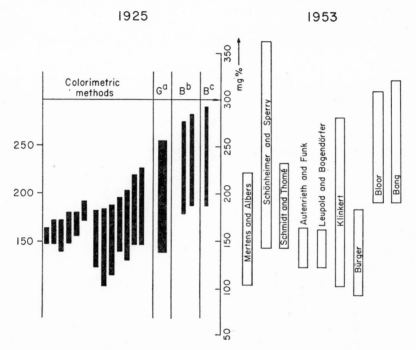

Fig. 1. A comparison of the results obtained using different methods of analysis on normal human blood serum. Hueck (1925); Mertens and Albers (1953). Gᵃ, gravimetric methods; Bᵇ, Bloor's method; Bᶜ, Bang's method (1918). References to older European methods are given by Hueck.

(and estimation) of which calls for considerable skill and patience. The concept of a chemical species is discussed thoughtfully by Timmermans (1941).

In estimating "cholesterol" the analyst must ask what information is required. If absolute values for *cholesterol* are needed the most elaborate methods of analysis *must* be employed. If, however, the group reaction of, in particular, Δ⁵-stenols is measured then simpler and more rapid methods may be used. These *comparative* values are suitable for

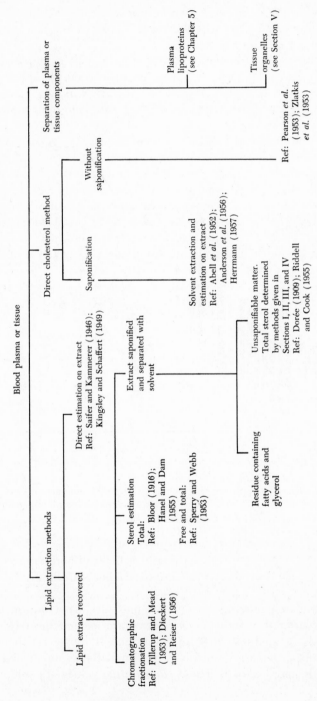

Fig. 2. A summary of the main principles of the methods commonly used for determining sterols (and associated lipids) in whole tissues or the parts thereof. Ref: signifies the reference for a particular method.

the clinical biochemist. "Direct" methods are most favored at the time of writing (June, 1957) but a preliminary saponification and extraction give apparently more consistent results.

The comparison of different methods is an invidious topic and in Fig. 1 we show the range of values obtained with blood plasma or serum using the current techniques in Germany in the years 1925 and 1953.

A summary of the methods commonly used to isolate and/or estimate cholesterol is given in Fig. 2.

Factors determining estimations are time, expense, and personal preference. In scientific research the last is generally the main consideration but the others are of importance in clinical practice. We should like to make the plea that if a determination is made it should be carried out by the best available (not necessarily the most rapid) procedure. We doubt if anybody has yet died because the value of his blood cholesterol was not known within the hour. In passing we observe that from their printed figures some analysts obtain, using the methods described, an apparent accuracy of 1 in 10^3 or even 1 in 10^4. We consider an accuracy of 1 in 10^2 (1 in 100) with an error of $\pm 1\%$ is suitable for most purposes.

REFERENCES

Abell, L. L., Levy, B. B., Brodie, B. B., and Kendall, F. E. (1952). *J. Biol. Chem.* **195**, 357-366.

Ahrens, E. H., Jr. (1956). *In* "Biochemical Problems of Lipids" (G. Popják and E. Le Breton, eds.), pp. 30-41. Butterworths, London.

Ahrens, E. H., Jr., and Craig, L. C. (1952). *J. Biol. Chem.* **195**, 763-778.

Albers, R. W., and Lowry, O. H. (1955). *Anal. Chem.* **27**, 1829-1831.

Alexander, G. J., and Schwenk, E. (1957). *Arch. Biochem. Biophys.* **66**, 381-387.

Analytical Reviews (1956). *Anal. Chem.* **28**, 559-782.

Anderson, J. T., Keys, A., Fidanza, F., Keys, M. H., Bronte-Stewart, B., Kupcs, P., and Werner, L. (1956). *Clin. Chem.* **2**, 145-159.

Baggett, B., Engel, L. L., and Fielding, L. L. (1955). *J. Biol. Chem.* **213**, 87-97.

Bang, I. (1918). *Biochem. Z.* **91**, 86-103.

Beher, W. T., Parsons, J., and Baker, G. D. (1957). *Anal. Chem.* **29**, 1147-1151.

Bergmann, W. (1952). *In* "Progress in the Chemistry of Fats and Other Lipids" (R. T. Holman, W. O. Lundberg, and T. Malkin, eds.), Vol. 1, pp. 18-69. Pergamon Press, New York.

Bergmann, W. (1953). *Ann. Rev. Plant Physiol.* **4**, 383-426.

Bergström, S., and Borgström, B. (1956). *Ann. Rev. Biochem.* **25**, 177-200, especially pp. 187-188.

Bergström, S., and Norman, A. (1953). *Proc. Soc. Exptl. Biol. Med.* **83**, 71-74.

Block, R. J., Durrum, E. L., and Zweig, G. (1955). "A Manual of Paper Chromatography and Paper Electrophoresis." Academic Press, New York.

Bloor, W. R. (1916). *J. Biol. Chem.* **24**, 227-231.

Bloor, W. R. (1928). *J. Biol. Chem.* **77**, 53-73.

Bloor, W. R. (1929). *J. Biol. Chem.* **82**, 273-286.

Bloor, W. R. (1943). "Biochemistry of the Fatty Acids." Reinhold, New York.

Bowman, R. L., Caulfield, P. A., and Udenfriend, S. (1955). *Science* **122**, 32-33.

Boyd, E. M. (1936). *J. Biol. Chem.* **114**, 223-234.
Boyd, E. M. (1937). *J. Biol. Chem.* **121**, 485-496.
Boyd, E. M. (1938). *Am. J. Clin. Pathol.* **8**, 77-90.
Broadbent, I. E., and Klyne, W. (1954). *Biochem. J.* **56**, proc. xxx-xxxi.
Brockmann, H., and Schodder, H. (1941). *Ber.* **74**, 73-78.
Brown, H. H., Zlatkis, A., Zak, B., and Boyle, A. J. (1954). *Anal. Chem.* **26**, 397-399.
Brown, J. B., and Kolb, D. K. (1955). *In* "Progress in the Chemistry of Fats and Other Lipids" (R. T. Holman, W. O. Lundberg, and T. Malkin, eds.), Vol. 3, pp. 57-94. Pergamon Press, New York.
Bush, I. E. (1952). *Biochem. J.* **50**, 370-378.
Bush, I. E. (1954a). *Brit. Med. Bull.* **10**, 229-236.
Bush, I. E. (1954b). *Recent Progr. in Hormone Research* **9**, 321-335.
Chevallier, F. (1953). *Ann. nutrition et aliment.* **7**, 225-243.
Claude, A. (1954). *Proc. Roy. Soc.* **B142**, 177-186.
Clément, G., Clément, J., and Louedec, A. (1954). *Arch. sci. physiol.* **8**, 233-250.
Coelho, F. P., and Alves, F. A. (1946). *Nature* **157**, 803.
Coleman, D. L., Wells, W. W., and Baumann, C. A. (1956). *Arch. Biochem. Biophys.* **60**, 412-418.
Colowick, S. P., and Kaplan, N. O., eds. (1957). "Methods in Enzymology," Vol. 3, see the following articles: pp. 299-317; 317-328; 328-345; 358-367; 367-372; 372-382. Academic Press, New York.
Comar, C. L. (1955). "Radioisotopes in Biology and Agriculture." McGraw-Hill, New York.
Cook, R. P., Kliman, A., and Fieser, L. F. (1954). *Arch. Biochem. Biophys.* **52**, 439-450.
Cook, R. P., Edwards, D. C., and Riddell, C. (1956). *Biochem. J.* **62**, 225-234.
Craig, L. C., Gregory, J. D., and Hausmann, W. (1950). *Anal. Chem.* **22**, 1462.
Craig, L. C., Hausmann, W., Ahrens, E. H., Jr., and Harfenist, E. J. (1951). *Anal. Chem.* **23**, 1236-1244.
Danielsson, H. (1956). *Acta Chem. Scand.* **10**, 1045.
Dannenberg, H., Scheurlen, H., and Simmer-Rühle, I. (1956). *Ann.* **600**, 68-80.
Delsal, J. L. (1947). *Compt. rend. soc. biol.* **141**, 268-269.
Deuel, H. J., Jr. (1951). "The Lipids," Vol. 1. Interscience, New York.
Dieckert, J. W., and Reiser, R. (1956). *J. Am. Oil Chemists' Soc.* **33**, 123-126.
Dorée, C. (1909). *Biochem. J.* **4**, 72-106.
Dorfman, L. (1953). *Chem. Revs.* **53**, 47-144.
Doubilet, H. (1936). *J. Biol. Chem.* **114**, 289-308.
Edwards, D. C., and Cook, R. P. (1955). *Biochem. J.* **61**, 671-676.
Feichtmeir, T. V., and Bergerman, J. (1953). *Am. J. Clin. Pathol.* **23**, 599-602.
Fieser, L. F. (1953a). *J. Am. Chem. Soc.* **75**, 4395-4403.
Fieser, L. F. (1953b). *J. Am. Chem. Soc.* **75**, 5421-5422.
Fieser, L. F., and Bhattacharyya, B. K. (1953). *J. Am. Chem. Soc.* **75**, 4418-4423.
Fillerup, D. L., and Mead, J. F. (1953). *Proc. Soc. Exptl. Biol. Med.* **83**, 574-577.
Fitelson, J. (1943). *J. Assoc. Offic. Agr. Chemists* **26**, 506-511.
Folch, J., and Van Slyke, D. D. (1939). *J. Biol. Chem.* **129**, 539-546.
Folch, J., Schneider, H. A., and Van Slyke, D. D. (1940). *J. Biol. Chem.* **133**, proc. xxxiii-xxxiv.
Folch, J., Ascoli, I., Lees, M., Meath, J. A., and Le Baron, F. N. (1951). *J. Biol. Chem.* **191**, 833-841.
Folch, J., Lees, M., and Sloane Stanley, G. H. (1957). *J. Biol. Chem.* **226**, 497-509.

Freeman, N. K., Lindgren, F. T., Ng, Y. C., and Nichols, A. V. (1957). *J. Biol. Chem.* **227**, 449-464.

Gardner, J. A., Gainsborough, H., and Murray, R. (1938). *Biochem. J.* **32**, 15-18.

Gilpin, V. (1951). *Anal. Chem.* **23**, 365-374.

Glover, M., Glover, J., and Morton, R. A. (1952). *Biochem. J.* **51**, 1-9.

Guy, J., Detour, G. H., and Weinmann, S. H. (1955). *Ann. biol. clin.* (*Paris*) **13**, 43-48.

Haenni, E. O. (1941). *J. Assoc. Offic. Agr. Chemists* **24**, 119-147.

Halliday, N. (1939). *J. Biol. Chem.* **129**, 65-69.

Hanel, H. K., and Dam, H. (1955). *Acta Chem. Scand.* **9**, 677-682.

Hardegger, E., Ruzicka, L., and Tagmann, E. (1943). *Helv. Chim. Acta* **26**, 2205-2221.

Harley, J. H., and Wiberley, S. E. (1954). "Instrumental Analysis." Wiley, New York.

Harold, F. M., and Chaikoff, I. L. (1954). *Proc. Soc. Exptl. Biol. Med.* **86**, 302-303.

Heftmann, E. (1955). *Chem. Revs.* **55**, 679-711.

Herrmann, R. G. (1957). *Proc. Soc. Exptl. Biol. Med.* **94**, 503-505.

Hilditch, T. P. (1956). "The Chemical Constitution of Fats," 3rd ed. Chapman and Hall, London.

Hogeboom, G. H. (1955). *In* "Methods in Enzymology" (S. P. Colowick and N. O. Kaplan, eds.), Vol. 1, pp. 16-19. Academic Press, New York.

Howard, G. A., and Martin, A. J. P. (1950). *Biochem. J.* **46**, 532-538.

Hueck, W. (1925). *Verhandl. deut. pathol. Ges.* **20**, 18-66.

Idler, D. R., and Baumann, C. A. (1952). *J. Biol. Chem.* **195**, 623-628.

Idler, D. R., and Baumann, C. A. (1953). *J. Biol. Chem.* **203**, 389-396.

Isaksson, B. (1954). *Acta Chem. Scand.* **8**, 889-897.

James, A. T., and Martin, A. J. P. (1956). *Biochem. J.* **63**, 144-152.

Kabara, J. J. (1954). *J. Lab. Clin. Med.* **44**, 246-249.

Kelsey, F. E., and Longenecker, H. E. (1941). *J. Biol. Chem.* **139**, 727-740.

Kenny, A. P. (1952). *Biochem. J.* **52**, 611-619.

Kent, S. P. (1952). *A.M.A. Arch. Pathol.* **54**, 439-442.

Kerr, L. M. H., and Bauld, W. S. (1953). *Biochem. J.* **55**, 872-875.

Keuning, K. J., van Dijk, G. J., and Wiggers de Vries, M. J. (1957). *Rec. trav. chim.* **76**, 747-756.

Keyl, A. C., and Jones, K. K. (1954). *J. Invest. Dermatol.* **23**, 17-21.

Kingsley, G. R., and Schaffert, R. R. (1949). *J. Biol. Chem.* **180**, 315-328.

Kirk, E., Page, I. H., and Van Slyke, D. D. (1934). *J. Biol. Chem.* **106**, 203-234.

Koehler, A. E., and Hill, E. (1949). *J. Biol. Chem.* **179**, 1-10.

Kolthoff, I. M., and Lingane, J. J. (1952). "Polarography," 2nd ed., Vols. 1 and 2. Interscience, New York.

Kritchevsky, D., and Calvin, M. (1950). *J. Am. Chem. Soc.* **72**, 4330.

Kritchevsky, D., and Kirk, M. R. (1952). *Arch. Biochem. Biophys.* **35**, 346-351.

Lata, G. F., and Vestling, C. S. (1952). *Anal. Chem.* **24**, 208-209.

Lederer, E., and Lederer, M. (1957). "Chromatography." 2nd ed. Elsevier, Amsterdam.

Lemeland, P. (1922). *Bull. soc. chim. biol.* **4**, 300-321.

Leppänen, V. (1956). *Scand. J. Clin. & Lab. Invest.* **8**, 201-206.

Love, E. B. (1957). *Brit. Med. J.* (i), 701.

Lovern, J. A. (1956a). *Proc. Nutrition Soc.* (*Engl. and Scot.*) **15**, 46-51.

Lovern, J. A. (1956b). *Biochem. J.* **63**, 373-380.

Lovern, J. A. (1957). "The Chemistry of Lipids of Biochemical Significance," 2nd ed. Wiley, New York.

Luddy, F. E., Turner, A., Jr., and Scanlan, J. T. (1953). *Anal Chem.* **25**, 1497-1499; see *Anal. Chem.* **26**, 491, for correction.

MacIntyre, I., and Ralston, M. (1954). *Biochem. J.* **56**, proc. xliii.

Martin, A. J. P. (1950). *Biochem. Soc. Symposia (Cambridge, Engl.) No.* **3**, 4-20.

Martin, R. P., and Bush, I. E. (1955). *Federation Proc.* **14**, 252.

Martin, R. P. (1957). *Biochim. et Biophys. Acta* **25**, 408-416.

Mertens, E., and Albers, C. (1953). *Z. physiol. Chem.* **293**, 244-253.

Michaleč, C. (1956). *Biochim. et Biophys. Acta* **19**, 187-188.

Moore, P. R., and Baumann, C. A. (1952). *J. Biol. Chem.* **195**, 615-621.

Mosbach, E. H., Nierenberg, M., and Kendall, F. E. (1953). *J. Am. Chem. Soc.* **75**, 2358-2360.

Neher, R., and Wettstein, A. (1952). *Helv. Chim. Acta* **35**, 276-283.

Obermer, E., and Milton, R. (1937). *J. Lab. Clin. Med.* **22**, 943-948.

Okey, R. (1930). *J. Biol. Chem.* **88**, 367-379.

Oppenauer, R. V. (1937). *Rec. trav. chim.* **56**, 137-144. Reviewed by Djerassi, C. (1951). *In* "Organic Reactions" (R. Adams, ed.), Vol. 6, pp. 207-272. Wiley, New York.

Orlowski, M., and Simon, J. (1954). *Acta Biochim. Polon.* **1**, 231-238.

Oster, G., and Pollister, A. W., eds. (1955, 1956). "Physical Techniques in Biological Research," Vols. 1, 2, 3. Academic Press, New York.

Pearson, S., Stern, S., and McGavack, T. H. (1953). *Anal. Chem.* **25**, 813-814.

Pollak, O. J., and Wadler, B. (1952). *J. Lab. Clin. Med.* **39**, 791-794.

Polonovski, J., and Jarrier, M. (1955). *Ann. biol. clin. (Paris)* **13**, 564-569.

Reiss, O. K. (1955). *Federation Proc.* **14**, 268.

Riddell, C., and Cook, R. P. (1955). *Biochem. J.* **61**, 657-671.

Robertson, D. M. (1955). *Biochem. J.* **61**, 681-688.

Rose, A. R., Schattner, F., and Exton, W. G. (1941). *Am. J. Clin. Pathol. Tech. Suppl.* **5**, 19-23.

Rosenmund, K. W., and Kuhnhenn, W., with von Rosenberg-Gruszynsky, D., and Rosetti, H. (1923). *Z. Untersuch. Nahr. u. Genussm.* **46**, 154-59; *Chem. Abstr.* **18**, 477-478 (1924).

Saifer, A., and Kammerer, O. F. (1946). *J. Biol. Chem.* **164**, 657-677.

Savard, K. (1954). *Recent Progr. in Hormone Research* **9**, 185-211.

Schlenk, H. (1954). *In* "Progress in the Chemistry of Fats and Other Lipids" (R. T. Holman, W. O. Lundberg, and T. Malkin, eds.), Vol. 2, pp. 243-267. Pergamon Press, New York.

Schmidt-Thomé, J., and Augustin, H. (1942). *Z. physiol. Chem.* **275**, 190-207.

Schoenheimer, R. (1930). *Z. physiol. Chem.* **192**, 77-86.

Schoenheimer, R., and Dam, H. (1933). *Z. physiol. Chem.* **215**, 59-63.

Schön, H., and Gey, F. (1956). *Z. physiol. Chem.* **303**, 81-90.

Schwenk, E., and Werthessen, N. T. (1952). *Arch. Biochem. Biophys.* **40**, 334-341.

Smith, L. L. (1954). *J. Am. Chem. Soc.* **76**, 3232-3234.

Smith, L. L., and States, S. J. (1954). *Texas Repts. Biol. and Med.* **12**, 543-550.

Sobel, A. E., and Mayer, A. M. (1945). *J. Biol. Chem.* **157**, 255-264.

Sobel, A. E., Goodman, J., and Blau, M. (1951). *Anal. Chem.* **23**, 516-519.

Sobel, A. E., Goldberg, M., and Slater, S. R. (1953). *Anal. Chem.* **25**, 629-635.

Sperry, W. M. (1954). *J. Biol. Chem.* **209**, 377-386.

Sperry, W. M. (1955). *Federation Proc.* **14**, 284.

Sperry, W. M., and Brand, F. C. (1943). *J. Biol. Chem.* **150**, 315-324.

Sperry, W. M., and Brand, F. C. (1955). *J. Biol. Chem.* **213**, 69-76.
Sperry, W. M., and Schoenheimer, R. (1935). *J. Biol. Chem.* **110**, 655-658.
Sperry, W. M., and Webb, M. (1950). *J. Biol. Chem.* **187**, 97-110.
Stadtman, T. C. (1957). *In* "Methods in Enzymology" (S. P. Colowick and N. O. Kaplan, eds.), Vol. 3, pp. 392-394. Academic Press, New York.
Stenger, E. G. (1955). *Klin. Wochschr.* **33**, 534-536.
Stokes, W. M. (1957). *Arch. Biochem. Biophys.* **67**, 272-279.
Swinnen, J. A. A. (1955). *Pharm. Tijdschr. Belgie* **32**, 25-33.
Timmermans, J. (1941). "Chemical Species." Macmillan, New York.
Toyama, Y., Kita, M., and Tanaka, T. (1952). *Bull. Chem. Soc. Japan* **25**, 355-357.
Trappe, W. (1940). *Biochem. Z.* **305**, 150-161; **306**, 316-336; **307**, 97-106.
Voris, L., Ellis, G., and Maynard, L. A. (1940). *J. Biol. Chem.* **133**, 491-498.
Wall, M. E., and Kelley, E. G. (1947). *Anal. Chem.* **19**, 677-683.
Wells, W. W., Coleman, D. L., and Baumann, C. A. (1955). *Arch. Biochem. Biophys.* **57**, 437-444.
Wheatley, V. R. (1953). *Biochem. J.* **55**, 637-640.
Wilson, H. (1954). *Arch. Biochem. Biophys.* **52**, 217-235.
Wolfe, J. K., Hershberg, E. B., and Fieser, L. F. (1940). *J. Biol. Chem.* **136**, 653-687.
Wysocki, A. P., Portman, O. W., and Mann, G. V. (1955). *Arch. Biochem. Biophys.* **59**, 213-223.
Yasuda, M. (1931). *J. Biol. Chem.* **94**, 401-409.
Yasuda, M. (1936). *J. Biochem. (Tokyo)* **24**, 429-442.
Yasuda, M. (1937). *J. Biochem. (Tokyo)* **25**, 417-433.
Zaffaroni, A., Burton, R. B., and Keutmann, E. H. (1950). *Science* **111**, 6-8.
Zak, B., and Ressler, N. (1955). *Am. J. Clin. Pathol.* **25**, 433-446.
Zak, B., Dickenham, R. C., White, E. G., Burnett, H., and Cherney, P. J. (1954a). *Am. J. Clin. Pathol.* **24**, 1307-1315.
Zak, B., Moss, N., Boyle, A. J., and Zlatkis, A. (1954b). *Anal. Chem.* **26**, 776-777.
Zimmermann, W. (1955). *Z. physiol. Chem.* **300**, 141-146.
Zlatkis, A., Zak, B., and Boyle, A. J. (1953). *J. Lab. Clin. Med.* **41**, 486-492.

CHAPTER 4

DISTRIBUTION OF STEROLS IN ORGANISMS AND IN TISSUES

Robert P. Cook

> *"To the small part of ignorance that we arrange and
> classify we give the name knowledge."*
>
> AMBROSE BIERCE

I. Introduction

In any consideration of the sterols their content in normal tissues must be known before embarking on hypotheses as to their functions and metabolism. This section deals with all tissues other than blood which on account of the detailed studies merits a separate chapter (Chapter 5).

The mass of information on the amounts of sterols and related compounds in the whole and component parts of organisms is difficult to summarize briefly. The analyses are of varying degrees of merit showing variations which are in part real but which are also due to the methods of extraction and estimation used (see Chapter 3). The values given in the literature for "cholesterol" are here reported as sterol. Over thirty years ago Anderson (1926) showed clearly that the properties of cholesterol from different sources were divergent and more recently Fieser (1954) has shown the presence of the "companions" of cholesterol, i.e. sterols other than Δ^5-cholestenol, which accompany the isolated compound. Moreover Schwenk and Werthessen (1952) demonstrated that the digitonin-precipitated cholesterol from various animal organs showed considerable losses (45–81%) on purification through the dibromide compound. The major sterol present in the tissues of mammals is undoubtedly cholesterol but the amount present varies from tissue to tissue and from species to species; e.g. the main sterol in the skin epidermis of the rat is Δ^7-cholestenol (Wells and Baumann, 1954b). Most estimation procedures are not specific for any one sterol (see Chapter 3).

Wherever possible values obtained by gravimetric methods, even of early publication date, have been taken and are expressed in terms of fresh tissue. The method of quoting results on water- and neutral fat-free basis enhances the amounts of "essential lipids" but such results are biased and where this method has been employed recalculated values are given. In the tables extreme ranges are generally shown but a *typical* value has been assessed, this being subject to a variation of ± 25%,* i.e. a typical value of 10 represents a range of 7.5 to 12.5.

II. Whole Organisms

A. MICROORGANISMS

1. Bacteria

It is stated by Asselineau and Lederer (1953) that, with the exception of *Azotobacter chroococcum* (see Sifferd and Anderson, 1936), the lipids of bacteria including pathogens do not contain sterols. Their reported presence in bacterial lipid extracts is attributed to artifacts from stoppers and the hands of the investigator! Nevertheless a careful study by Dauchy *et al.* (1956) showed that *Escherichia coli* does contain a small but definite amount of sterol.

2. Protozoa

A small amount has been reported in the species investigated (Chapter 12). Sterols are necessary as growth factors (Chapter 13).

---

* The percentage sign (%) is used to express gram (gm.) of sterol per (/) 100 gm. of tissue.

B. Fungi

The predominant sterol is ergosterol (C_{28}) but C_{27} sterols are found. The chemistry and distribution has been reviewed by Fieser and Fieser (1949) and by Bergmann (1953). In *yeasts* the lipid content varies considerably, for example the food yeast *Rhodotorula* contains a third of its dry weight as lipid (Usdin and Burrell, 1952). The amount of unsaponifiable matter is variable, the sterols forming about half and squalene being present in appreciable amount. The commoner *molds* contain, depending on species and on cultural conditions, 0.1 to 1.5% of their dry weight as sterol and the *Basidiomycetes* (mushrooms) contain about 0.3% of their dry weight, mainly as ergosterol (Pruess *et al.*, 1931).

C. Invertebrates

Marine sponges, shell fish, and crustacea have been studied extensively by Bergmann and his associates and by Toyama and his colleagues and found to contain a complex mixture of C_{27}, C_{28}, and C_{29} stenols and stanols (Chapter 12). Representative values for edible molluscs and crustacea are given in Table I. The sterols form about a third to a half of the unsaponifiable matter and many contain a high percentage of provitamin D. The results are of interest in comparative biochemistry but the contribution to normal human diets is slight.

D. Vertebrates

The values for the total sterol of whole mammals have a range 0.12 to 0.31 gm. per 100 gm. fresh tissue, a typical value being 0.2% or about 0.7% of the dry weight. During growth in the rat there is an initial rise but later the value falls (Channon, 1925; Williams *et al.*, 1945a). On starvation the percentage of sterol (and of phospholipids) is unchanged.

III. Distribution in Animal Tissues

A. Introduction

In the words of Le Gros Clark (1952) a tissue is defined as "an assemblage of cellular and fibrous elements, in which one particular type of cell or fibre usually predominates, organized to form the material basis of one of the functional systems of the body". Thus tissues have elements in common but the differences in composition are sufficiently great to warrant individual attention. The treatment given here is to group together the tissues into systems which have a common group of functions. The amount of blood left in organs after death varies considerably (Hansard, 1956) but the quoted analyses are for tissues drained as free as possible from blood. Other factors determining composition are age, sex and state of nutrition, and attention is drawn in the text to these when known. The values given in the Tables are generally for adult, well fed animals of either sex and the information is concerned

TABLE I

LIPID, UNSAPONIFIABLE MATTER, AND TOTAL STEROL COMPOSITION
OF WHOLE ORGANISMS[a]

Organism		Lipid[b]	Unsaponifiable matter	Total sterol[c]	References
			gm./100 gm. fresh tissue		
Yeast *Saccharomyces* sp.		2–5	—	0.1–0.3	Heiduschka and Lindner (1929); Kleinzeller (1948)
Molluscs					
Oyster	Meat	3.6	—	0.33	Okey (1945)
Clam	Meat	1.3	0.23	0.15	Toyama *et al.* (1953)
Crustacea					
Crab	Whole	—	0.19	0.05	Dorée (1909)
	Meat	1.0	—	0.15	Okey (1945)
Fish					
Mackerel		—	0.09	0.02	Dorée (1909)
Snake					
Grass snake		—	0.18	0.08	Dorée (1909)
Bird					
Chicken					
Newly hatched		—	—	0.65	Dam (1931)
Two weeks old		—	—	0.2	
Mammals					
Mouse	Normal	3–9	—	0.30	Schoenheimer and Breusch (1933)
	Starved	2.3	—	0.31	Terroine and Weill (1913)
Rat		18–20	0.3	0.22	Channon (1925); Cook (1956)
Rabbit		—	0.21	0.12	Dorée (1909)
Dog		—	—	0.18	Beumer and Lehmann (1923)
Cat		—	—	0.15	Menschick and Page (1933)

[a] The sign — in this and subsequent tables means not determined.

[b] The values given in the literature show great variations, those cited may be regarded as typical.

[c] Total sterol in yeast and in invertebrates is a mixture of C_{27} and C_{28} series sterols (see Bergmann, 1949).

mainly with human tissues, but references to values for typical laboratory animals or domestic species are given by Mayer and Schaeffer (1913), and for dog's tissues by Wiese and Hansen (1951; see also references marked *). For obvious reasons data on fresh, mature human subjects are rare and disease and post mortem change may influence the results.

B. The Alimentary Tract and Its Secretions and Excretions

Analyses of some of the parts and secretions in the adult human are given in Table II. The low sterol content of the gut is typical of in-

TABLE II
Tissues of the Alimentary Tract, Saliva, and Thoracic Lymph

Tissues	Lipid	Sterol	Remarks and References
	gm./100 gm. fresh tissue		
Gums (human)	2	0.2	Phospholipid 1; Hodge (1933)
Whole intestine (human)	5	0.1	Phospholipid 0.6; Jowett (1931)
Esophagus (human)	—	0.07	The mean dry weight values of Bür-
Duodenum (human)	—	0.09	ger and Oeter (1929) have been recalculated on an 80% water
Ileum (human)	—	0.08	basis. The original values show a considerable range. Schoenheimer
Sigmoid colon (human)	—	0.1	et al. (1930) found that sterol formed (as % unsaponifiable mat-
Intestinal mucosa (human)	—	0.2	ter of mucosa) small intestine 79, large intestine 75
Whole intestinal mucosa (dog)	1.5	—	Unsaponifiable matter 0.3; Sperry (1932) gave analyses for various portions of dogs' intestinal mucosa
Small intestine mucosa (guinea pig)	—	0.2	Unsaponifiable matter 0.4; Glover et al. (1952) (see text)
	mg./100 ml. fresh tissue		
Saliva	—	2.5–9	Phospholipid 1-5; Hawk et al. (1956)
Thoracic lymph (fasting)	420	25	Phospholipid 75; Reiser (1937)

voluntary muscle (see Section III, E). The intestinal mucosa contains somewhat more sterol present mainly as stenol (Bürger and Oeter, 1929; Schoenheimer et al., 1930). The guinea pig intestine mucosal sterol is remarkable in consisting of approximately 25% of 7-dehydrocholesterol (Glover et al., 1952). The intestines of the rat, pig, ox, sheep have unsaponifiable matter 0.4–0.8% and sterol about 0.2% but only 0.01 to

0.04% of this is present as 7-dehydrocholesterol (Glover *et al.*, 1952). The stomachs of the ox (tripe) contain lipid 4.1% and sterol 0.15% (Okey, 1945).

1. Glands

The scanty information shows that the human pancreas contains about 12% lipid (Mitchell *et al.*, 1945) and the ox pancreas has a lipid content of 7% of which unsaponifiable matter forms 18% (Bloor, 1928).

2. Intestinal contents

Analyses of the contents of the jejunum (Blankenhorn and Ahrens, 1955) and of the ileum (Gardner *et al.*, 1935) show that they contain cholesterol and its esters.

3. Lymph

Typical values for fasting human lymph are given in Table II and the hepatic and intestinal lymph have been studied in the rat (Bollman and Flock, 1951). The transport of lipids in human chyle is described in Chapter 7.

4. Fecal Excretion

The excretion of sterols (and other lipids) is dependent on diet and the subject of the fecal excretion of sterols and the cholesterol to coprostanol transformation is described in Chapter 7.

C. Liver and Bile

1. Liver

This much analyzed organ still lacks an exact chemical knowledge although it forms the center piece of the body's intermediary metabolism.

a. Mammalian Livers. A typical composition in adult mammals is (as %) water 75, protein and including extractives 16, glycogen 3, ash 1, and ether-extractable material 5. Values for the lipids of the adult human, rat, and ox livers are given in Table III. These show a similar pattern of distribution and analyses of the livers of other species are similar (cf. Tsujimoto and Koyanagi, 1939). Phospholipids constitute about 40%, glycerides about 40%, the remainder being made up of neutral matter including sterols and their esters, fat-soluble vitamins, etc., and free fatty acids.

(*i*) *Unsaponifiable matter.* This contains hydrocarbons, saturated and unsaturated. Squalene has been isolated from pig liver (Schwenk *et al.*, 1954) but the unsaturated hydrocarbon from human liver is undefined (Dimter, 1941). About a half to two-thirds is present as digitonin precipitable sterols. The sterols of normal ox liver were isolated by Freytag and Smith (1933) who concluded that cholesterol formed two-thirds of the unsaponifiable matter. Examination of their data shows that only a quarter can be regarded as reasonably pure Δ^5-cholestenol, the true content of which is unknown. Cholestanol forms about 2% of the total sterol and the presence of companions and degradation compounds has been shown (e.g. Schoenheimer et al., 1930; Cain and Morton, 1955; Rattray et al., 1956).

TABLE III

WATER CONTENT, TOTAL LIPID, PHOSPHOLIPID, UNSAPONIFIABLE MATTER, TOTAL STEROL, AND PERCENTAGE OF COMBINED STEROL IN THE FRESH LIVERS OF ADULT HUMANS, RATS, AND OXEN[a]

		Human liver	Rat liver	Ox liver
		gm./100 gm. fresh tissue		
Water	T[b]	75	70	70
Total lipid	R[c]	2.4–8.5	3.2–8.2	4.0–7.0
	T	6	6	6
Phospholipid	R	1.5–3.0	1.0–4.2	2.5–3.7
	T	2.5	2.5	3.0
Unsaponifiable matter	R	0.1–0.8	0.25–0.7	—
	T	0.6	0.6	0.3
Total sterol	R	0.2–0.4	0.2–0.5	0.2–0.3
	T	0.3	0.3	0.25
Combined sterol (% of	R	12–38	12–35	—
total sterol)	T	20	20	20

[a] From values cited in the literature. Human: Dimter (1941); Fex (1920); Man et al. (1945); Theis (1929); Ralli et al. (1941). Rat: Cook (1956); Okey (1945); Sperry and Stoyanoff (1935a); see also text. Ox: Bloor (1928); Dimter (1941); Isaksson (1954a); Kaucher et al. (1943); Okey (1945).

[b] T = typical value.

[c] R = range of value.

(ii) *Cholesteryl ester.* Analyses show a typical value of about 20% combined sterol. On account of this small amount there is little information on the fatty acid composition of the esters present in normal livers but the esters have been analyzed in the cholesterol fatty liver (Chapter 15).

(iii) *Age.* In the livers of the fetal and newly born infant (Dimter, 1941) and rat (Williams et al., 1945b) the amounts of lipid are somewhat greater than in the adult and the sterol content and amount combined slightly higher. The liver of the newly born guinea pig is remarkable for a fat content of about 17% (Imrie and Graham, 1920).

(*iv*) *Sex.* The liver of the female rat contains less total sterol and the amount combined is significantly lowered (Okey *et al.*, 1934).

(*v*) *Diet.* Starvation in experimental animals, e.g. mice, causes an initial increase in total lipid followed by a decrease to about normal values (Hodge *et al.*, 1941). The weight of the liver in a fully starved animal is decreased considerably but there is no decrease in the absolute amount of sterol present (Terroine, 1914-1915). On diets low in fat particularly in essential fatty acids there is an increase in the amount of sterol particularly in the combined fraction and this occurs even though the plasma level falls (Alfin-Slater *et al.*, 1954).

b. Bird Livers. The liver of the newly hatched chick contains about 14% lipid and of this 7 to 8% is esterified sterol and 1% is in the free form, thereafter the lipid and sterol levels fall reaching after 22 days a value of 0.3 to 0.4% sterol and in the adult 0.3% (Entenman *et al.*, 1940; Sperry and Stoyanoff, 1935b). The subject of sterol changes in the developing chick embryo is described in Chapter 6. The goose fatty liver, the basis of pâté de foie gras, is the subject of study by Flock *et al.* (1937).

c. Fish Livers. Because of their economic importance, e.g. as a source of fat-soluble vitamins, there is a large literature on the liver lipid composition of a variety of fish (see Hilditch, 1956, for review). The Elasmobranch (cartilage fish) liver oils divide broadly into three classes based on the content and composition of unsaponifiable matter (1) in the Rajidae (e.g. skate) the content is 1–2% consisting mainly of sterols, (2) the gray dogfish (*Squalus acanthias*) and ratfish (*Chimaera monstrosa*) livers contain 10–35% consisting mainly of glyceryl ethers (such as batyl alcohol) combined as fatty acid esters, (3) certain species of shark with large and fatty livers contain 50–80% consisting of large amounts of squalene with some glyceryl ethers and sterols. An account of the distribution is given by Heller *et al.* (1957).

In the Teleosts (bony fish) the livers of the Gadidae (cod family) contain 40–65% of lipid, mainly glycerides, and act as the main fat store. The unsaponifiable matter forms about 1% of the lipid and in cod liver oil the sterol content is 0.5–0.6% (Pihl, 1952). In the Clupeidae (herring family), the small livers have a low lipid content of which unsaponifiable matter forms about 10% and in these fish the flesh is fatty (see Table VIII).

The main sterol present is apparently cholesterol but the livers of cod are rich in 7-dehydrocholesterol and vitamin D_3. The distribution of squalene is erratic and although found in largest amount in certain sharks it is also found in the liver of teleosts.

d. Distribution of Lipid in the Liver Cell. By the use of the differential centrifugation technique (Chapter 3) good studies have been made on the cellular distribution of lipids and of sterol in the liver cell of the mouse (Kretchmer and Barnum, 1951) and rat. The results obtained are in general agreement and values for the rat are shown in synopsis in Table IV.

TABLE IV

DISTRIBUTION OF LIPID COMPONENTS IN THE SEPARATED PARTS OF RAT LIVER CELLS[a]

	Floating layer and supernatant	Micro- somes	Mito- chondria	Nuclei
Part as per cent of cell	20–30	25–35	30–40	15–20
Lipid (as % of fraction dry wt.)	10	30	20	15
Distribution of lipid (as % total lipid)				
Neutral fat	68	0	1	3
Phospholipids	28	94	93	93
Total sterol	4	6	6	5
Combined sterol (as % total sterol)	25–70	6	3	4
Values as % of cellular total of:				
Lipid	9	50	35	6
Sterol	25	55	14	6

[a] From the results of Rice et al. (1953); Schotz et al. (1953); and Spiro and McKibbin (1956). A well-detailed account of the distribution and nature of the lipids is given by Clément et al. (1956).

In normal cells the microsomes ("submicroscopic layer") contain both absolutely and relatively the greatest amount of lipid which consists mainly of phospholipid, the small amount of sterol being nearly all in the free condition. The supernatant layer and floating layer of fat when present consists mainly of neutral fat (68%), the sterol (about 4%) being present in the esterified form. On feeding cholesterol to animals the large increase of esterified sterol is concentrated mainly in the floating layer, there being only small increases in the other cellular components (see Chapter 15).

2. Bile

The values given in Table V show the variability of composition. In animals possessing a gall bladder the solids are concentrated about 5 times. In hepatic bile the concentration of sterol is low, bile salts and phospholipids of the oleo-palmitic lecithin type constituting the greater part of the solid matter; the amounts of neutral fat, free fatty acids and soaps are small (Polonovski and Bourrillon, 1952b). The bile of the herbivorous ox contains a small but definite amount of sterol. The amount of combined sterol in bile is small and the form of conjugation is unknown. In both fistula and gall bile 2–3% of stanols are present, sterols constituting 70% of the unsaponifiable matter in hepatic bile

TABLE V

THE SOLIDS, STEROL, PHOSPHOLIPIDS, AND BILE SALTS PRESENT IN HUMAN, RAT, AND OX BILES[a]

		Human		Rat	Ox
		Hepatic (gm./100 ml.)	Bladder (gm./100 ml.)	hepatic (gm./100 ml.)	bladder (gm./100 ml.)
Solids	R[b]	1–4	5–16	—	6–11
	T[c]	2	11	—	8
Sterol	R	0.004–0.21	0.01–1.3	1 mg./24 hr.	0.04–0.09
	T	0.1	0.4	0.01	0.06
Phospholipids	R	0.1–0.6	1.0–5.8	—	0.5–1.4
	T	0.3	1.5	—	1
Bile salts	R	0.7–1.4	1.0–9.2	0.1–0.5	1–7
	T	1	5	0.3	3
Main bile acids present		Mixed glycine and taurine conjugates of mainly chenodeoxycholic acid		Taurocholic and tauro-chenodeoxy-cholic acids	Mixed glycine and taurine conjugates of mainly cholic acid
Amount secreted per day (ml.)	R	200–1100	—	9.2–16.5	—
	T	700	—	12	—

[a] Fox (1927-1928), human; Friedman et al. (1951), rat; Isaksson (1954a), ox; (1954b), human; Polonovski and Bourrillon (1952a), human and ox; Portman et al. (1955), rat; Siperstein et al. (1954), rat.

[b] R = range of value.

[c] T = typical value.

and 91% in bladder bile (Schoenheimer et al., 1930). The presence of other steroidal compounds including ketones and sex hormones has been demonstrated (e.g. Pearlman, 1944).

The subject of the conversion of cholesterol to bile acids and the enterohepatic circulation are described in Chapter 7. The composition and etiology of gallstones is discussed in Chapter 10.

D. CIRCULATORY, EXCHANGE AND/OR EXCRETORY TISSUES

This section deals with the sterol content of organs and tissues, other than the liver, which are concerned in the circulation and maintenance of equilibrium, by exchange or excretion, of the blood. These tissues are the heart and blood vessels, lungs, kidneys, and for convenience the spleen is included. Analyses are given in Table VI.

The heart is encased in connective tissue, the subepicardial layer of which contains varying amounts of adipose tissue in different individuals. Analyses of the whole organ are thus of limited significance and values for the ventricular muscle only are given. The lipid distribution of the conducting tissue of ox heart has been studied by Mallov *et al.* (1953). The values given for lung, kidney, and spleen are similar in other animals (e.g. ox, see Bloor, 1928; rat, see Okey, 1945; and for a thorough investigation of unsaponifiable constituents of the kidney in many animal species see Lowe *et al.*, 1957).

1. Blood Vessels. Because of the pathological changes occurring in the aorta and some other arteries (see Chapter 10) some account of the "normal" vessels is given although it is generally agreed that the natural process of aging is difficult to disentangle from the pathological process which moreover may occur also in young subjects.

The blood vessels are composed typically from the lumen outwards, of an inner layer (tunica intima) lined by endothelium, a middle layer containing elastic and muscular components (tunica media), and an outer layer of connective tissue which contains adipose tissue (tunica adventitia). It is usual to strip the outermost layer before analysis. In Table VI the analyses of the combined intimal and medial coats in subjects presumed free of atheroma show the low sterol content of the pulmonary artery and of the vena cava; these vessels are seldom affected by atherosclerosis.

In Table VII are given values for whole aortas (intimal and medial layers) in subjects free of arterial disease. A mathematical correlation (e.g. Buck and Rossiter, 1951) has been made between the lipid and the sterol content of the aorta with the age of the subject but the variations in an age group make the results of doubtful value. It is of interest to remark that studies of the aorta of the horse show that there is no increase in the sterol content with increasing age (Gerritzen, 1932). The sterol content of the aortas of normal and of cholesterol-fed rabbits were determined by McMillan *et al.* (1955), and of dogs by Norcia *et al* (1956).

E. Muscular Tissue

Three types of muscle are found in the animal body, namely, skeletal or voluntary, visceral or involuntary, and cardiac. Basically all types consist of the contractile element or myofibril, sarcoplasm, granules containing the respiratory enzymes, and connective tissue proteins enclosing the fibers. Blood vessels and nervous elements are also present.

TABLE VI

THE STEROL CONTENT OF HUMAN VENTRICULAR MUSCLE, BLOOD VESSELS, LUNG, KIDNEY, AND SPLEEN

Tissue	Range	Typical	Remarks and Reference
	gm./100 gm. fresh tissue		
Heart (ventricular muscle)	0.09–0.18	0.15	Phospholipid 1.8%, combined sterol about 25% (Refs. 2, 8)
Blood vessels			
Aorta	—	0.4	Lipid and sterol content vary with age and presence of atherosclerosis (see text and Table VII)
Aorta (5)	0.29–1.13	—	These analyses (number in brackets) were made on the vessels of 5 subjects (4 female) aged 33–52 years whose death was due to causes other than vascular disease. The amount of combined sterol was about 40% of the total (Ref. 4)
Coronary artery (3)	—	0.32, 0.43, 0.74	
Iliac (2)	—	0.44, 0.63	
Pulmonary artery (2)	—	0.20, 0.49	
Abdominal vena cava (2)	—	0.11, 0.17	
Lung	0.13–0.33	0.2	These values are mainly from fetal subjects (Ref. 1, 4). An adult lung analyzed in this laboratory gave a value of 0.19%, all in the free form. Lung has a lipid content of 1–2%
Kidney	0.25–0.33	0.3	The first tissue analyzed by Windaus (9). Sterol forms 88% of the unsaponifiable matter and contains 4% of stanols (7). There is slight difference between cortex and medulla (6). The tissue contains about 3% lipid and 1.6% phospholipid (Refs. 5, 8)
Spleen	0.16–0.37	0.3	The values for sterol are mainly from fetal or infant subjects (1, 4). The lipid content is about 2%, consisting mainly of phospholipid (8).

References: 1. Beumer (1920-1921); 2. Bloor (1936); 3. Fex (1920); 4. Jones *et al.* (1956); 5. Jowett (1931); 6. Popják (1943); 7. Schoenheimer *et al.* (1930); 8. Thannhauser *et al.* (1939); 9. Windaus (1910).

TABLE VII

TYPICAL WEIGHTS, LIPID, AND CHOLESTEROL CONTENT[a,b] OF PRESUMED NORMAL
HUMAN AORTAS[c] IN VARIOUS AGE GROUPS

Age group (years)	Fresh weight (gm.)	Lipid (gm.)	Sterol (gm.)
10–30	11	0.1	0.03
31–40	15	0.2	0.06
41–50	19	0.4	0.08
51–60	24	0.7	0.1
61–80+	34	1.2	0.2 +

[a] Calculated on 70% water basis.

[b] The values are composite and have been taken from the results of Faber (1946);
Faber and Lund (1949); and Landé and Sperry (1936). Values for the lipid components of normal (and of atheromatous) arteries are given by Hirsch and Weinhouse (1940) and by Buck and Rossiter (1951).

[c] The values are for whole aortas (medial and intimal layers) from aortic valves to the bifurcation of the iliac vessels.

1. Skeletal Muscle

This forms the major tissue of the animal body. In the typical 70 kg. man the skeletal muscles weigh approximately 30 kg. (about 40% of body wt.). Another aspect is that, in the form of flesh or "meat" of mammalian, avian, fish (and even of amphibian or reptilian origin), muscle is an important article in the diet of man.

The muscles are encased in connective tissue which according to the location varies in amount and in its content of neutral fat. This may vary from 6% in veal to 60% in pork and in some cuts of butcher meat the amount of fat is greater than the protein content (e.g. Callow, 1946).

Values for the composition of skeletal muscle of various animals are given in Table VIII. These and determinations on other animals show a low content of sterol which is present mainly in the free form, values for combined sterol being about 30% of the total.

Values for the domestic fowl are given in Table VIII but in some wild species of bird somewhat higher values are found (Tati, 1941). The two varieties of fish tabulated illustrate the difference between those in which the liver is the main fat depot (e.g. cod) and those having fat deposited in the muscle such as herrings and mackerel.

a. Growth. In growing rats the total lipid of skeletal muscles decreases with age but the content of phospholipids and glycolipids (cerebrosides) increase (Williams et al., 1945b); the sterol content is greater in young animals than in old.

2. Visceral Muscle

Involuntary or striped muscle controls the activity of the gastro-intestinal tract where it is found in greatest amount. Analyses are given in Table II. It is also found in the walls of blood vessels and in the uterus (Table X). In the urinary bladder sterols are more concentrated in the mucosa than in the involuntary muscle. The sterols are unesteri-

TABLE VIII

THE WATER, LIPID, PHOSPHOLIPID, AND STEROL CONTENT OF THE SKELETAL MUSCLE OF VARIOUS ANIMALS[a]

Animal		Water	Lipid	Phospho-lipid	Sterol	References
		gm./100 gm. fresh tissue[b]				
Frog		75	2	1.5	0.06	3
Fish						
Cod		72	1–3	1.2	0.06	3, 6, 7
Herring		60–70	6–18	—	0.08	
Birds (*Gallus domesticus*)						
Light meat	Young	75		—	0.07	1, 3
			3			
	Adult	71		0.7	0.03	
Dark meat	Young	77		—	0.10	1, 3
			2			
	Adult	72		1.1	0.06	
Mammals						
Rat	15 day	75	7	1.5	0.2	8
	75 day	72	4	2.1	0.08	5, 8
Pig	Young	76	3	—	0.08	1
	Adult	71	5	0.8	0.05	1
Ox	Young	75	6	1.2	0.09	1, 3, 5
	Adult	73	2	0.8	0.06	1, 3, 5
Human	Range	72–84	3.4–22.0	0.5–0.9	0.06–0.22	1, 2, 4
	Typical	75		0.7	0.12	

[a] The values given in the literature for water and lipid content show considerable variation. Those given must be regarded as typical with a range of at least ± 10% about the stated value. Complete lipid analysis are given in reference 3.

[b] Separated as free as possible from adipose tissue and gross interstitial fat (see text).

References:

1. Del Vecchio *et al.* (1955)
2. Jowett (1931)
3. Kaucher *et al.* (1943)
4. Mitchell *et al.* (1945)
5. Okey (1945)
6. Pihl (1952)
7. Reay *et al.* (1946)
8. Williams *et al.* (1945b)

fied and contain, especially in the rodents, relatively large amounts of "fast acting" sterols (Finlayson *et al.*, 1957).

3. Cardiac Muscle

Similar values to those for human ventricle muscle are found in other species (Bloor, 1936). The physiological role of the sterol and other lipids in muscle is discussed in Chapter 9.

F. Nervous System

1. Brain and Nerves

Analyses of the whole brains of a variety of adult vertebrates show that they contain (as approximate %) water 78, protein 8, and lipid 12. The complex lipid consists of (as approximate % lipid) phospholipids 50, cerebrosides 25, and free sterol 17, there being only a small amount in the combined form. Sterol constitutes about 2% of the fresh weight or 10% of the dry weight. Next to the adrenal gland it is the tissue richest in sterol.

a. Development. The size of the brain (as % body wt.) decreases from 10–12 in the fetus to 2 in the adult and the percentage of water decreases from 90 to 80. The sterol content shows a progressive increase during growth and the myelination process.

Values for whole human brain, some of its parts and for other parts of the nervous system are shown in Table IX. A review on the lipids (and other constituents) of the nervous system of vertebrates is given by Rossiter (1955); the lipids of the nervous system of invertebrates, which resemble those of vertebrates except in the low amount of cerebroside, are reviewed by McColl and Rossiter (1950).

b. Sterols Present. The brain and spinal cord of animals are a good source of Δ^5-cholestenol and in fact one of the main sources of industrial cholesterol is from the spinal cord of cattle. Recent investigations have shown the presence of a number of companions and/or isomers of cholesterol. Cerebrosterol was isolated from brain by Ercoli *et al.* (1953); cholestanol or other stanols forms 1% of the sterol (Schoenheimer *et al.*, 1930) and the presence of "oxycholesterol" has been known for some time (Rosenheim, 1914; Nedzvetskii *et al.*, 1953). Fast-acting sterols are present and the Δ^7-cholestenol content is about 1% of the total sterol (Nakanishi *et al.*, 1953). *Ergosterol* (but more probably 7-dehydrocholesterol) was demonstrated spectrophotometrically and found to constitute (as % total sterol) in the fetus 0.05, infant 0.02, and the adult 0.006 (Page and Menschick, 1931). Cholesteryl ether has been found in the spinal cord of cattle (Silberman and Silberman-Martyncewa, 1945).

It is generally agreed that the greatest part of the sterol is in the free condition. The small amount of combined sterol may be derived from the cells present in the gray matter.

c. Localization of Constituents. Very complete studies on this subject were made by Brante (1949) and it is generally considered that the greatest concentration of sterol (and of cerebroside) is present in the medullary sheath.

TABLE IX

TYPICAL VALUES FOR THE COMPOSITION OF THE BRAIN, GRAY AND WHITE MATTER, SPINAL CORD, AND PERIPHERAL NERVES IN HUMANS

	Water	Total lipid[a]	Phospho-lipids	Sterol	Cere-broside	References
	gm./100 gm. fresh tissue					
Whole brain						
Fetus	90	1–3	—	0.4	—	Rosenheim (1914); Rossiter (1955)
Infant						
5 days	90	7	—	0.5	—	
3 months	79		—	0.7	—	
Adult	77	12–15	6	1.9	2.0	
Gray matter						
Infant	91	2.9	1.9	0.5	0.5	Johnson *et al.* (1949)
Adult	85	5.2	3.4	1.0	0.9	
White matter						
Infant	91	3.3	2.1	0.7	0.6	Johnson *et al.* (1949)
Adult	71	16.0	7.0	4.2	4.8	
Spinal cord, adult	74	18	—	3.9	—	Dimitz (1910)
Femoral, sciatic, and post-tibial nerves	67	8–9	4.6	1.5	1.8	Randall (1938)

[a] Approximations.

The phospholipids and cerebrosides of brain particularly the white matter are in the form of complexes known as proteolipids (Folch and Lees, 1951). These complexes of protein and lipid behave as lipids as regards solubilities in distinction to the lipoproteins which behave more like proteins. The exact form of combination of the cholesterol in brain is not known but some suggestions on the subject are given in Chapter 9.

2. The Eye

The lipid and sterol content of parts of the eye have some importance. In the *lens* the sterol content increases with age, values being (as % dry wt.) birth 0.2, 20–40 years 0.5, 40–60 years 1.0, and old age 1.2; these values (as mg./100 gm. fresh tissue) correspond to about 50, 125, 250, and 300, and about a sixth of the sterol is esterified. In cases of incipient or developed cataract the sterol content was no higher (Salit and O'Brien, 1935; Bunge, 1938).

The *retina* contains 0.2% sterol (Krause, 1934) and histochemical studies suggest that it is found in greatest amount in the inner synaptic layer (Chapter 9). The lipid and sterol content of various other parts of the eye were determined by Krause (1934-1935).

G. REPRODUCTIVE SYSTEMS

1. Male Reproductive System

a. Testes. The glands stripped of covering tissues and of weight 10 to 24 gm. in a group of men aged 19 to 80 years contained 45 to 125 mg. of sterol in the total tissue, which is equivalent to about 0.5 gm./100 gm. fresh tissue (Leupold, 1921). The lipids of rats' testes consist mainly of phospholipids. The total sterol content is about 0.3% of the fresh weight, more sterol being combined in young than in older rats (Williams *et al.*, 1945b). The conversion process of sterol to testosterone is discussed in Chapter 8.

b. Spermatozoa. Sperm cells have an external lipid layer or capsule which is apparently lipoprotein (Mann, 1954). The lipid of ram spermatozoa contains about 8% of free cholesterol (Lovern *et al.*, 1957).

Prostatic fluid contains about 80 mg. of sterol per 100 ml., this comprising about a quarter of the lipid and *seminal plasma* contains 100 mg. of sterol per 100 ml., constituting over half of the lipid (Scott, 1945).

2. Female Reproduction and Lactation

a. Ovary. Values for woman and for the cow are given in Table X. Cholesteryl palmitate was isolated from cows' ovaries and volatile acids were present (Cartland and Hart, 1925). The rabbit corpora lutea have a high lipid and sterol content which increase markedly during pregnancy (Boyd, 1935a) but in the guinea pig (Boyd, 1936a) and sow (Bloor *et al.*, 1930; Boyd and Elden, 1935) the amounts are less and do not increase greatly. The ovaries of the frog have a high content of lipid including sterols (Boyd, 1938), the sterol containing 0.8% of 7-dehydrocholesterol (Morton and Rosen, 1949).

b. Uterus and Genital Tract (Table X). The composition of the muscular wall of the uterus is that of involuntary muscle. Studies of the uterus, muscle, and mucosa, and of vaginal mucosa in various stages of the menstrual cycle have been made in the monkey *Macaca* (Van Dyke

TABLE X

FEMALE REPRODUCTIVE ORGANS AND MILK OF WOMAN, COW, AND RAT

		Water	Lipid	Phospholipid	Sterol	References
Ovary				gm./100 gm. fresh tissue		
Human whole ovary		81	2.1	1.6	0.2	Jowett (1931)
Corpus luteum (cow)		83	2.2	1.2	0.2	Cartland and Hart (1925)
Ovary residue (cow)		—	4.3	0.3	0.5	Tourtelotte and Hart (1926-1927)
Uterus (human)		80	1.5	0.7	0.2	Jowett (1931)
Placenta (human at term)		87	1.6	0.9	0.2	Pratt *et al.* (1946); Čmelik (1951)
Milk				gm./100 ml. fresh tissue		
Human	Range	—	1-9	—	0.01-0.04	Bürger (1928)
	Typical	—	4	—	0.02	
Cow	Range	—	2-6	0.03-0.1	0.01-0.02	Nakamishi (1931)
	Typical	—	3.5	—	0.01	Nataf *et al.* (1948)
Rat		69	9	—	0.06	Okey *et al.* (1938)

and Chen, 1940) and in the sow (Okey *et al.*, 1930). There is a general increase in the mucosal lipids and in the sterol content in the luteal and menstrual phases.

c. Placenta (Table X). The human placenta at term ("an aged organ") has a low content of lipid and of sterol (Pratt *et al.*, 1946). The developing placenta has been investigated for its lipid composition in the rabbit (Boyd, 1935b) and pig (Boyd, 1936b). The jelly of Wharton (Boyd, 1935c) has a low lipid content.

d. Mammary Gland. In mice the glands contain a high percentage of lipid present mainly as neutral fat; of the lipid, phospholipids form about 1% and sterol 0.2%. In lactating glands the amount of fat is decreased (Johnson and Dutch, 1952).

e. Milk. Values for the milk of woman, cow, and rat are given in Table X. Milk fat consists mainly of triglycerides, sterols forming only 0.2–1% of it. Opinion is divided as to whether the sterol is in the free or combined form. The considerable literature on the subject of milk fat has been reviewed (e.g. Deuel, 1955, pp. 791-798).

3. Avian Eggs

In addition to the dietary interest of the eggs of domestic birds, the subject of the changes occurring in the developing egg has attracted attention (Chapter 6). Sterols form about 2% of the yolk's dry weight or 6% of its lipid.

a. Composition of the Average Hen's Egg. The weight is about 55 gm. being composed of (as %) shell and membranes 10, white 60, and yolk 30. The yolk consists of (as %) water 50, ash 1.5, "protein" 17, and ether-extractable material 31.5. The lipid consists of (as %) neutral fat 59, phospholipids 35, unsaponifiable matter 6; sterols form 60% of the unsaponifiable matter and about 10% is esterified (Haenni, 1941; Terroine and Belin, 1927).

A typical whole hen's egg contains 6 gm. protein, 6 gm. "fat," and 0.25–0.3 gm. of sterol. The main sterol is apparently Δ^5-cholestenol, Δ^7-cholestenol constituting about 1% of the total sterol (Nakanishi *et al.*, 1953; Miller and Baumann, 1954). A sterol (about 0.2%) with a conjugate double bond system (ergosterol or 7-dehydrocholesterol) is also present (e.g. Windaus and Stange, 1936). The $\Delta^{5,24}$-cholestadienol and an isomer were found by Stokes *et al.* (1956) in the developing chick embryo. The duck's egg is said to contain 0.5 gm. of sterol, (Gaujoux and Krijanowsky, 1932).

A review of the composition of the eggs of various animals is given by Needham (1931; 1950).

4. Fetal Animals

Analyses of the individual organs of human fetuses were made by Beumer (1920-1921). The sterol content of most tissues was of the same order as in the adult with the exceptions of the brain and the adrenal gland (see below), these tissues containing much less sterol than in adult. Beumer computed that the whole fetus contained 0.30% at 3 months and 0.34% at 8 months. More recent analyses by Jones *et al.* (unpublished work) give similar values to those obtained previously. Popják (1946) found that the whole fetus of the rabbit had a sterol content of 0.8% of the dry weight, which is equivalent to about 0.2% of the fresh weight.

H. ENDOCRINE GLANDS

1. Adrenals

Analyses of the adrenals of adult humans and of ox are shown in Table XI. In man the gland consists mainly of cortex (about 10:1) which is difficult to separate from medulla. In the human fetus and infant the gland is larger but the amounts of lipid and of sterol are less (Beumer, 1920-1921).

There are apparently two types of adrenal gland, a "nonfatty" type

TABLE XI

THE ADRENAL GLANDS OF ADULT MAN AND OF THE OX

		Man	Ox Cortex	Medulla
		gm./100 gm. fresh tissue		
Water	R[a]	50–76	—	—
	T[b]	65	67	80
Lipid	R	5–30	—	—
	T	20	6.3	5.6
Phospholipid	T	3.7	3.1	2.5
Total sterol	R	2.6–15.0	—	—
	T	10	0.26	0.35
Ester (as % total sterol)	R	80–90	10	15–31
References		Fex (1920); Adams Baxter (1949); unpublished observations from this laboratory	Brown *et al.* (1937); Leulier and Revol (1930)	

[a] R = range of value.
[b] T = typical value.

present in the ox and sheep, but not horse, and a "fatty" type of lower water content found in most animal species. The values quoted for total sterol in the adrenal of the *rat* vary from 2–10% of the fresh weight, the greater part being in the combined form (e.g. Sperry and Stoyanoff, 1935a). A careful study of the adrenals of female rats in various stages of the reproductive cycle showed values of 1.3–2.8%; the amount of total and combined sterol was significantly lowered in spayed, pregnant and parturient animals (Andersen and Sperry, 1937). In the *rabbit* typical values are (as approximately % fresh wt.) lipid 13, phospholipid 2, sterol 6, and 80–90% of the sterol is combined (MacLachlan *et al.*, 1941). The rabbit adrenal is susceptible to increase after feeding cholesterol. The marked variations in sterol composition have been attributed to factors such as "stress" and in Chapter 9 further information is given on the subject.

There is little accurate information on the sterol pattern; sterols form 46% of the unsaponifiable matter and 4% of the sterols are saturated (Schoenheimer *et al.*, 1930). The striking feature is the large amount of esterified sterols present but there is little information on the acids combined (cf. Rosenheim and Tebb, 1909). Conversions occurring in this gland are discussed in Chapter 8.

2. Other Glands

a. Pituitary. The values (as % fresh wt.) in the ox are anterior lobe, lipid 3.2, total sterol 0.38; posterior lobe, lipid 4.0, total sterol 0.43 (McArthur, 1919).

b. Thymus, Thyroid, and Pineal Glands. The few references to the composition of these glands in young animals show a lipid content of about 2% and sterol 0.2% (Jones *et al.*, unpublished work).

I. SUPPORTIVE TISSUES

This term is used for various types of connective tissue including the skeletal structures. Miscellaneous body fluids are included also for convenience.

1. Adipose Tissues

The term includes such widely scattered tissues as that present in the orbits of the eyes, subcutaneous tissue (panniculus adiposus), omental, mesenteric, and perirenal fat. The tissue (or parts of it) is regarded as a potential nuisance in interpreting analytical data ("nonessential fat") and as a real nuisance by the overweight since it is difficult to remove. An interesting review of this important tissue is given by Wells (1940). The amounts and patterns of distribution show big individual, age, and sex variations. Typical analyses are given in Table XII and values for the tissue in other animals are of the same order, showing a moderate sterol content.

TABLE XII

THE COMPOSITION OF HUMAN ADIPOSE TISSUE (SUBCUTANEOUS, OMENTAL, OR MESENTERIC) AND OF WHITE BONE MARROW

		Adipose tissue	Marrow (femoral or tibial)
		gm./100 gm. fresh tissue	
Water	R[a]	2–50	—
	T[b]	13	20
Lipid	R	56–97	—
	T	80	65
Phospholipids		—	2
Unsaponifiable matter	T	0.3	—
Sterol	R	0.09–0.32	—
	T	0.2	0.2
References		Jaeckle (1902); Wacker (1912); Eckstein (1925); Del Vecchio et al. (1955)	Beumer and Bür-ger (1913); Hazen (1949)

[a] R = range of value.
[b] T = typical value.

2. Bone Marrow

White bone marrow found in long bones such as the femur and tibia acts in the mature animal as a fat store, typical analyses being shown in Table XII. Red bone marrow found in cancellous bone such as the sternum is a hemopoietic tissue and contains 0.28 gm. % of sterol (Hazen, 1949).

3. Bone

The lipid content of bone is very low but recently attention has been drawn to the presence in oseocollagen of 2.8–4 mg. % fresh weight of sterol in the form of a protein complex (Pikulev, 1955). The enamel of teeth contains 8 mg. % of sterol (Hess et al., 1956).

4. Cartilage

The costal cartilages in children to 9 years contained sterol (as % fresh weight) 0.02, increasing to 0.13 at the fifth decade of life, thereafter there was little increase (Bürger and Schlomka, 1927).

5. Connective Tissues (Areolar Tissue, etc.)

The lipids present in the connective tissue of rats and rabbits have been analyzed and shown to contain cholesterol and its esters. There was no significant correlation between lipid values in the serum and in the connective tissue (Noble and Boucek, 1955).

6. Body Fluids

There are scattered references to the lipid and sterol content of such body fluids and secretions as cerebrospinal fluid, nasal secretion, etc., under normal conditions, i.e. when free of cells, the sterol content of these fluids is low. Normal human cerebrospinal fluid contains not more than 0.2 mg. of sterol/100 ml. (Plaut and Rudy, 1933; see also Bloor, 1943, p. 363).

J. THE SKIN, ITS APPENDAGES AND SECRETIONS

In adult man the skin and its appendages form about 6% of the body weight and in furred or feathered animals this percentage is approximately doubled. This complex tissue consists of, from within outwards, the dermis or corium, a connective tissue containing vascular and nervous elements, and the epidermis and its appendages such as hair, fur, or feathers; nails, etc., are classed as appendages. The epidermis is layered, the active metabolic basement cell layer being covered with layers of keratinizing cells. The sebaceous and sweat glands (when present) are epidermal structures in origin, their secretion covering the outer layer including the appendages. The relative amounts of dermis and epidermis and of the number and activity of the glands vary in different parts of the body so adding to the complexity. The major constituent of the tissue is connective tissue protein (approximately 17%), mainly collagen and keratin.

The tissue is refractory to extraction which accounts for the varying analyses obtained but typical values for human and for rat skin are given in Table XIII. Model studies of the lipid distribution in the individual layers of the entire skins of the ox, sheep, and goat were made by Koppenhoefer (1936–1938). With regard to *age* it has been found that the percentage of sterol in human skin decreases with increasing age (Bürger and Schlomka, 1928; Meyer, 1930–1931).

1. Sterols Present.

Cholesterol is present in the skin of all animals but the presence of other sterols ("oxycholesterol") has been known for some time. Recently "fast acting" sterols (mainly Δ^7-cholestenol) have been found in large amount in the epidermis of rats and other rodents (Moore and Baumann, 1952; Idler and Baumann, 1952; Miller and Baumann, 1954). This sterol (lathosterol) has been found also in the whole skin of the dog and in wool fat (Nakanishi *et al.*, 1953) but in human

TABLE XIII

TYPICAL VALUES FOR THE SKIN, APPENDAGES, AND SECRETIONS IN THE HUMAN AND IN THE RAT

	Water	Lipid	Unsaponifiable matter	Total sterol	References
Human					
Whole skin	63	—	—	0.3	Bürger and Schlomka (1928), Meyer (1930-1931)
Epidermis	—	5	1.8	0.9	Unna and Golodetz (1909); Eckstein and Wile (1926)
Dermis	—	—	—	0.2	
Hair					
Adult	—	3.6	—	0.4	Eckstein (1927); Nicolaides and Foster (1956)
Child	—	6.1	—	0.15	
Nails	—	0.9	0.4	0.2	Unna and Golodetz (1909)
Sebum[a]	—	100%	32%	5%	Wheatley (1952)
Cerumen	—	21	7	—	Akobjanoff et al. (1954); Wheatley (1954)
Vernix caseosa	87	8.6	2.6	0.4	Unna and Golodetz (1909); Čmelik et al. (1952); Wheatley (1954)
Rat					
Whole skin					
Male	60	12.5	—	0.35	Taylor et al. (1948); Okey (1945)
Female	54	22.0	—	0.25	
Epidermis	—	—	—	6.9[b]	Wells and Baumann (1954a)
Dermis	—	—	—	0.4[c]	
Sebum[a]	—	100%	41%	10.3%	Wheatley and James (1957)

[a] Values given for sebum as per cent of total lipid.
[b] The total sterol contains 4.0 gm./100 gm. of Δ^7-cholestenol, 92% of which is esterified.
[c] The sterol is mainly cholesterol (0.3 gm./100 gm.), 18% of which is esterified.

epidermis the amount is only about 2% of the total sterol (Miller and Baumann, 1954; unpublished observations from this laboratory). Small amounts of 7-dehydrocholesterol are present in the skin of animals (Windaus and Bock, 1937; Glover et al., 1952), and in the human values are (as % total sterol) infant 0.15, adult 0.42 (Hentschel and Schindel, 1930). The presence of C_{29} sterol in toad's skin is reported by Hüttel and Behringer (1936). A curious older observation is the presence of silicic acid esters of sterols in birds' feathers (Drechsel, 1897). Frantz et al. (1957) report sterol analyses of rats' skin, including an unknown sterol present solely as ester.

2. *Sebum.* The "skin fat" of animals is complex in composition but cholesterol is always present and Δ^7-cholestenol is found in quantity in the sebum of rats and mice. In the sheep the C_{30} triterpenes ("isocholesterol") which consist mainly of lanosterol and of agnosterol, are present in amounts of 4 to 10% (Lederer and Pau-Kiun, 1945; Truter, 1951). Squalene is present in about 5% concentration in human sebum but is absent from that of the rat. An interesting study of the composition of sebum of various mammals is given by Wheatley and James (1957).

Analyses of human smegma (i.e. preputial fat) which may be regarded as altered sebum shows that it contains 1.0% squalene (Sobel, 1949) and that the sterol present is mainly esterified cholestanol (Kamat et al., 1956).

The skin is an active tissue as regards lipid and in particular sterol metabolism. The extensive literature is reviewed in a recent monograph (Rothman, 1954). It is to be hoped that the present interest in skin and its appendages will help to elucidate some of the pathways and functions of sterols.

K. EXCRETION

The knowledge that cholesterol is being continually formed and metabolized has altered the older views as to the importance of excretory paths for the sterol as such (see Chapters 5, 6, and 7). Sterols, however, leave the animal organism by three routes.

(a) *Fecal Excretion.* This pathway for the sterols and their metabolic products is described in Chapter 7.

(b) *Skin Secretion.* The amount of sebum secreted in the average adult has been calculated to be 1 to 2 gm. per day and with a sterol content of about 5% this corresponds to a loss of 50 to 100 mg. per day (see Section III, J and Cook, 1952).

(c) *Urinary Excretion.* Although the urine is an important excretory pathway for steroid hormone metabolites, normal human urine contains only about 1 mg. of cholesterol per liter (i.e. about 1–2 mg. per day). A well-documented discussion on the subject is given by Kayser and Balat (1952).

IV. Sterols in Plants

Plant sterols are of importance as starting materials for the preparation of other steroids and because they are constituents of food. The sterols may be stanols or stenols generally containing twenty-eight or twenty-nine carbon units with double bonds present in positions 5, 7, and/or 22 (Chapter 2). An excellent review of their chemistry and distribution is given by Bergmann (1953).

The sterols occur in plants as the free alcohols, combined with fatty acids to form esters or as ethers united with carbohydrates usually glucose, forming phytosterolins.

The determination of lipid in plants is often difficult because of its

TABLE XIV

TYPICAL VALUES FOR LIPID AND STEROL CONTENT OF SOME VEGETABLE TISSUES

	Lipid	Unsaponifiable matter	Sterol	References
	gm./100 gm. tissue			
Cereals				
Wheat grain (parts as % total)				
Endosperm (85)	1	0.06	0.05	Anderson and Nabenhauer (1924)
Bran (13)	4	0.1	0.1	
Embryo (2)	11	0.6	0.2	
Wheaten flour	2	0.1	0.02	Haenni (1941)
Leafy plants				
Pasturage (dry)	4–6	1–2	0.5–1.0	See Hilditch (1956)
Cabbage	—	—	— 0.01	
Legumes				
Peas	1–2	0.3	0.1	Terroine et al. (1927)
Soya bean	16	0.5	0.1	
	Values as % lipid			
Plant oils				
Wheat germ oil	100	3–6	2	Anderson and Moore (1923); Williams (1950)
Corn oil	100	1.6	0.8	
Cotton seed oil	100	0.9	0.2	
Olive oil	100	0.8	0.2	
Peanut (Arachis) oil	100	0.7	0.2	
Soya bean oil	100	1.2	0.2	

close association with carbohydrate. In many cases it is necessary to hydrolyze with acid before solvent extraction. Some of the values given in Table XIV must be regarded as reasonable approximations.

In the seeds of cereal plants the embryo is richest in lipid which contains 5–6% of unsaponifiable matter. This is composite in nature containing aliphatic alcohols, tocopherols, carotenoids, etc., and about 25% of sterols which consist mainly of sitosterols. Bran contains less fat but the unsaponifiable matter has a similar composition. The endosperm which forms the basis for refined flours has a low fat content and the small amount of unsaponifiable matter consists mainly of sterols. Values for the sterol content of flour are given in Table XIV; similar values being obtained for other cereals. Leafy plants are relatively low in sterol but the large amount eaten makes their intake considerable with herbivorous animals. The seeds of leguminous plants contain sterols and a study of the changes occurring in developing soyabeans was made by Mac-Lachlan (1936). The oils from the seed coats of fatty plants or from nuts have similar compositions (see Table XIV). Of interest is the squalene content which varies (as mg. per 100 gm. of oil) from 4–700, being found in highest concentration in olive oil (Fitelson, 1943). In fruit, lipid as generally understood is low in amount, the sterol content varying from 7 to 14 mg. per 100 gm. fresh weight (Achard et al., 1934). A large part is probably present as glucoside (e.g. Ma and Schaffer, 1953). The sterol content of root vegetables such as potatoes is low (Schwartz and Wall, 1955).

V. The Sterol Content of Foodstuffs

In discussing the tissues of animals and of plants we have described also certain foodstuffs. It would be possible to make an elaborate table showing the sterol content of all foodstuffs. Such tables have been presented by Okey (1945) for foods consumed in the United States and by Pihl (1952) for Norwegian diets. In Table XV a generalized picture of the main foodstuffs is given, including "derived" products such as butter and cheese. The information given in the other sections should allow a more exact computation if necessary. Additional references to the sterol content of foodstuffs are given by Achard et al. (1934) and Lange (1950).

A. Human Intake

Estimates of the human intake are: (as grams per day) *infant*, on breast feeding 0.05–0.1, on mixed feeding 0.06; *adult*, on fat free diet 0.04–0.1, on mixed diet 0.2–0.4, on fat-rich diet 1.4 (Bürger, 1928). Values found by us in Scottish students on a normal mixed diet are for animal sterols 0.4–0.8, average 0.6; plant sterols 0.05–0.15, average 0.1. An average intake of 0.5 has been assessed by Pihl for Norwegian diets. The major factor in increasing dietary sterol is the consumption of hens eggs. One pound of lean beef steak is needed to supply about the same amount of sterol (0.3 gm.). The effect of dietary sterol on the level in the blood plasma is discussed in Chapter 5.

TABLE XV
THE STEROL CONTENT OF THE MAJOR FOODSTUFFS

Sterol content	Foods (gm./100 gm.)[a]
Rich (> 0.2 gm.)	Butter 0.2–0.3, one whole egg 0.3, brains 1.5–2.0
Medium (0.2 gm.)	Cheeses 0.05–0.2, liver 0.2–0.3 Kidneys 0.3–0.4, animal fat 0.2
Low (< 0.2 gm.)	Muscle from animals ("meat") or fish 0.05–0.1, full-cream cows milk (0.01)
Poor	Cereals, bread, vegetables, and fruit

[a] 100 g. is equivalent to about 4 ounces.

VI. Conclusions

In reviewing the literature and in the light of our own personal experience, a feeling of dissatisfaction has been felt with the values reported for "cholesterol." As indications of the total sterol or rather substances precipitated by digitonin and/or reacting with the Liebermann-Burchard reagent the values are reasonably correct but obviously more exact work is needed. The following generalizations may be made.

Apart from certain bacteria, sterols are found in all living organisms being present in every tissue and, it would seem, in all parts of cells. Cell nuclei are rich in lipid composed mainly of phospholipids and the sterol content is (as % dry weight) 3 to 5% (Stoneburg, 1939; Tyrrell and Richter, 1951). Lipids, mainly phospholipids and neutral fat, form 33% of the dry weight of *cytochrome oxidase*, free cholesterol constituting 1% (Marinetti *et al.*, 1957).

The tissues of the animal body have an apparent hierarchy as regards sterol content. High (i.e. greater than 1%) are the adrenal glands and nervous tissue. In most animals, the adrenals, particularly the cortex, are the richest source of sterol which is found largely in the combined form as fatty acid esters. The nervous system, particularly the white matter, contains a large amount of free sterol.

Medium in content are tissues closely concerned with blood such as the livers, kidneys, and lungs, these containing 0.2 to 0.4 gm. per 100 gm.

of tissue. The content of combined sterol is about a quarter of the total. Glandular and adipose tissues are similar in nature.

Low in content is muscular tissue and the supportive tissues such as bone and cartilage are very low. Milk must be considered as a secretion low in sterol.

Two parts of the skin may be differentiated, the outer layer and its secretion is high in content but the dermis must be classified with the medium content tissues.

The estimated distribution for a total sterol content of 140 gm. in a 70 kg. man (i.e. 0.2%) is shown in Table XVI. Variations of from 105 to 175 gm. (i.e. 0.15 to 0.25%) might be expected but the values given are reasonable approximations. It is of interest that the total sterol content

TABLE XVI
ESTIMATED DISTRIBUTION OF STEROL IN A 70 KG. MAN[a]

System	Wt. (gm.)	Sterol (gm./100 gm.)	Sterol in tissues (gm.)	Tissue sterol as approximate % of total body sterol
Alimentary tract and appendages	2500	0.15	3.8	3
Heart (350 gm.), lungs (950 gm.), kidneys (300 gm.), spleen (200 gm.), blood vessels (200 gm.)	2000	0.25	5.0	4
Liver	1700	0.3	5.1	4
Blood	5400	0.2	10.8	8
Muscle	30,000	0.1	30.0	21
Brain and nervous system	1600	2.0	32.0	23
Adrenal glands	12	10.0	1.2	1
Other glands	100	0.2	0.2	—
Bone marrow (red and white)	3000	0.25	7.5	5
Connective tissue (including adipose) and body fluids	12,100	0.25	31.3	22
Skin	4200	0.3	12.6	9
Skeleton	7000	0.01	0.7	—
			140	

[a] The values for weights of the various tissues are taken from those given by Parker (1948), the values for skin are those of Wilmer (1940). Tissue weights of the normal rat are given by Caster et al. (1956).

of the fetus is similar to that of the adult but the relative amounts in the brain and suprarenals are low. In the fetus the sterol appears to be more evenly distributed throughout the tissues.

This "static" information allows us to do no more than guess at the roles of sterol but an exact definition and quantitation of the chemical entities concerned is a necessary prelude to this. The dynamic aspect of sterols in the tissues is discussed in Chapters 5, 6, and 7.

REFERENCES

Any worker on the lipids including sterols is under a debt to W. R. Bloor and to Harry Deuel both of whose books are veritable "gold mines" of information. But even they do not exhaust the large and scattered information on the sterol content of living organisms. The references given in the text and tables of this chapter have been selected but additional references with extensive analyses and/or bibliographies (marked with an asterisk) are given here, a note being added of the organisms investigated.

*Achard, C., Levy, J., and Georgiakakis, N. (1934). *Arch. maladies app. digest. of maladies nutrition* **24**, 785-793. Continental European foodstuffs.

Adams, E., and Baxter, M. (1949). *A.M.A. Arch. Pathol.* **48**, 13-26.

Akobjanoff, L., Carruthers, C., and Senturia, B. H. (1954). *J. Invest. Dermatol.* **23**, 43-50.

Alfin Slater, R. B., Aftergood, L., Wells, G. F., and Deuel, H. J., Jr. (1954). *Arch. Biochem. Biophys.* **52**, 180-185.

Andersen, D. H., and Sperry, W. M. (1937). *J. Physiol. (London)* **90**, 296-302.

Anderson, R. J. (1926-27). *J. Biol. Chem.* **71**, 407-418.

Anderson, R. J., and Moore, M. G. (1923). *J. Am. Chem. Soc.* **45**, 1944-1953.

Anderson, R. J., and Nabenhauer, F. P. (1924). *J. Am. Chem. Soc.* **46**, 1717-1721.

Asselineau, J., and Lederer, E. (1953). *In* "Fortschritte der Chemie organischer Naturstoffe" (L. Zechmeister, ed.), Vol. 10, pp. 170-273. Springer, Vienna.

*Bergmann, W. (1949). *J. Marine Research (Sears Foundation)* **8**, 137-176. A large number of marine invertebrates.

*Bergmann, W. (1953). *Ann. Rev. Plant Physiol.* **4**, 383-426. Various plant species.

Beumer, H. (1920-1921). *Monatsschr. Kinderheilk.* **19**, 409-421.

Beumer, H., and Bürger, M. (1913). *Z. exptl. Pathol. Therap.* **13**, 367-370.

Beumer, H., and Lehmann, F. (1923). *Z. ges. exptl. Med.* **37**, 274-280.

Blankenhorn, D. H., and Ahrens, E. H., Jr. (1955). *J. Biol. Chem.* **212**, 69-81.

Bloor, W. R. (1928). *J. Biol. Chem.* **80**, 443-459.

Bloor, W. R. (1936). *J. Biol. Chem.* **114**, 639-648.

*Bloor, W. R. (1943). "Biochemistry of the Fatty Acids." Reinhold, New York.

Bloor, W. R., Okey, R., and Corner, G. W. (1930). *J. Biol. Chem.* **86**, 291-306.

Bollman, J. L., and Flock, E. V. (1951). *Am. J. Physiol.* **164**, 480-485.

Boyd, E. M. (1935a). *J. Biol. Chem.* **108**, 607-617

Boyd, E. M. (1935b). *Biochem. J.* **29**, 985-993.

Boyd, E. M. (1935c). *J. Biol. Chem.* **111**, 667-669.

Boyd, E. M. (1936a). *J. Biol. Chem.* **112**, 591-595.

Boyd, E. M. (1936b). *Can. J. Research* **B14**, 155-159.

Boyd, E. M. (1938). *J. Physiol. (London)* **91**, 394-397.

Boyd, E. M., and Elden, C. A. (1935). *Endocrinology* **19**, 599-602.

Brante, G. (1949). *Acta Physiol. Scand.* **18 Supplement 63**, 189 pp.

Brown, J. B., Knouff, R. A., Conlin, M. M., and Schneider, B. M. (1937). *Proc. Soc. Exptl. Biol. Med.* **37**, 203-205.

Buck, R. C., and Rossiter, R. J. (1951). *A.M.A. Arch. Pathol.* **51**, 224-237.

*Bürger, M. (1928). *Ergeb. inn. Med. u. Kinderheilk.* **34**, 583-701. Human tissues.

Bürger, M., and Oeter, H. D. (1929). *Z. physiol. Chem.* **182**, 141-147.

Bürger, M., and Schlomka, G. (1927). *Z. ges. exptl. Med.* **55**, 287-302.

Bürger, M., and Schlomka, G. (1928). *Klin. Wochnschr.* **7**, 1944.

Bunge, E. (1938). *Archiv. Ophthalmol. Graefe's* **139**, 50-61.

Cain, J. C., and Morton, R. A. (1955). *Biochem. J.* **60**, 274-283.

Callow, E. H. (1946). *In* "The Nation's Food" (A. L. Bacharach and T. Rendle, eds.), pp. 236-239. Soc. Chem. Ind., London.

Cartland, G. F., and Hart, M. C. (1925). *J. Biol. Chem.* **66**, 619-637.

Caster, W. O., Poncelet, J., Simon, A. B., and Armstrong, W. D. (1956). *Proc. Soc. Exptl. Biol. Med.* **91**, 122-126.

Channon, H. J. (1925). *Biochem. J.* **19**, 424-432.

Clément, G., Clément, J., and Le Breton, E. (1956). *In* "Biochemical Problems of Lipids" (G. Popják and E. Le Breton, eds.), pp. 385-394. Butterworth, London.

Čmelik, S. (1951). *Biochem. Z.* **322**, 150-151.

Čmelik, S., Petrak-Longhino, N., and Mihelic, F. M. (1952). *Biochem. Z.* **322**, 355-359.

Cook, R. P. (1952). *Biochem. Soc. Symposia.* **No. 9**, 14-29.

Cook, R. P. (1956). Unpublished work.

Dam, H. (1931). *Biochem. Z.* **232**, 269-273.

Dauchy, S., Kayser, F., and Villoutreix, J. (1956). *Compt. rend. soc. biol.* **150**, 1974-1977.

Del Vecchio, A., Keys, A., and Anderson, J. T. (1955). *Proc. Soc. Exptl. Biol. Med.* **90**, 449-451.

Deuel, H. J., Jr. (1955). "The Lipids," Vol. 2. Interscience, New York.

Dimitz, L. (1910). *Biochem. Z.* **28**, 295-319.

Dimter, A. (1941). *Z. physiol. Chem.* **271**, 293-315.

Dorée, C. (1909). *Biochem. J.* **4**, 72-106.

Drechsel, E. (1897). *Zentr. Physiol.* **11**, 361-2.

Eckstein, H. C. (1925). *J. Biol. Chem.* **64**, 797-806.

Eckstein, H. C. (1927). *J. Biol. Chem.* **73**, 363-369.

Eckstein, H. C., and Wile, U. J. (1926). *J. Biol. Chem.* **69**, 181-186.

Entenman, C., Lorenz, F. W., and Chaikoff, I. L. (1940). *J. Biol. Chem.* **133**, 231-241.

Ercoli, A., Di Frisco, S., and de Ruggieri, P. (1953). *Gazz. chim. ital.* **83**, 78-86.

Faber, M. (1946). *Acta Med. Scand.* **125**, 418-427.

Faber, M., and Lund, F. (1949). *A.M.A. Arch. Pathol.* **48**, 351-361.

Fex, J. (1920). *Biochem. Z.* **104**, 82-174.

Fieser, L. F. (1954). *Science* **119**, 710-716.

Fieser, L. F., and Fieser, M. (1949). "Natural Products related to Phenanthrene," 3rd ed. Reinhold, New York.

Finlayson, J. S., Gaylor, J. L., and Baumann, C. A. (1957). *Proc. Soc. Exptl. Biol. Med.* **95**, 742-744.

Fitelson, J. (1943). *J. Assoc. Offic. Agr. Chemists* **26**, 506-511.

Flock, E. V., Bollman, J. L., Hester, H. R., and Mann, F. C. (1937). *J. Biol. Chem.* **121**, 117-129.

Folch, J., and Lees, M. (1951). *J. Biol. Chem.* **191**, 807-817.

Fox, F. W. (1927-1928). *Quart. J. Med.* **21**, 107-121.

Frantz, I. D., Jr., Dulit, E., and Davidson, A. G. (1957). *J. Biol. Chem.* **226**, 139-144.

Freytag, F. C., and Smith, H. G. (1933). *J. Biol. Chem.* **100**, 309-317.

Friedman, M., Byers, S. O., and Michaelis, F. (1951). *Am. J. Physiol.* **164**, 786.

Gardner, J. A., Gainsborough, H., and Murray, R. M. (1935). *Biochem. J.* **29**, 1139-1144.

Gaujoux, E., and Krijanowsky, A. (1932). *Compt. rend. soc. biol.* **110**, 1083-4.

Gerritzen, P. (1932). *Z. ges. exptl. Med.* **85**, 700.

Glover, M., Glover, J., and Morton, R. A. (1952). *Biochem. J.* **51**, 1-9.

Haenni, E. O. (1941). *J. Assoc. Offic. Agr. Chemists* **24**, 119-147.

Hansard, S. L. (1956). *Proc. Soc. Exptl. Biol. Med.* **91**, 31-34.

Hawk, P. B., Oser, B. L., and Summerson, W. H. (1956). "Practical Physiological Chemistry," 13th ed. Churchill, London.

Hazen, E. C. (1949). *Farm. neuva (Madrid)* **14**, 562-568.

Heiduschka, A., and Lindner, H. (1929). *Z. physiol. Chem.* **181**, 15-23.

Heller, J. H., Heller, M. S., Springer, S., and Clark, E. (1957). *Nature* **179**, 919-920.

Hentschel, H., and Schindel, L. (1930). *Klin. Wochschr.* **9**, 262 (1 p.).

Hess, W. C., Lee, C. Y., and Peckham, S. C. (1956). *J. Dental Research* **35**, 273-275.

Hilditch, T. P. (1956). "The Chemical Constitution of Fats," 3rd ed. Chapman and Hall, London.

Hirsch, E. F., and Weinhouse, S. (1940). *A.M.A. Arch. Pathol.* **29**, 31-41.

Hodge, H. C. (1933). *J. Biol. Chem.* **101**, 55-61.

Hodge, H. C., MacLachlan, P. L., Bloor, W. R., Stoneburg, C. A., Oleson, M. C., and Whitehead, R. (1941). *J. Biol. Chem.* **139**, 897-916.

Hüttel, R., and Behringer, H. (1936). *Z. physiol. Chem.* **245**, 175-180.

Idler, D. R., and Baumann, C. A. (1952). *J. Biol. Chem.* **195**, 623-628.

Imrie, C. G., and Graham, S. G. (1920). *J. Biol. Chem.* **41**, xlviii.

Isaksson, B. (1954a). *Acta Physiol. Scand.* **32**, 281-290.

Isaksson, B. (1954b). *Acta Soc. Med. Upsaliensis* **59**, 277-295; **59**, 307-361.

Jaeckle, H. (1902). *Z. physiol. Chem.* **36**, 53-84.

Johnson, A. C., McNabb, A. R., and Rossiter, R. J. (1949). *Biochem. J.* **44**, 494-498.

Johnson, R. M., and Dutch, P. H. (1952). *Arch. Biochem. Biophys.* **40**, 239-244.

Jones, R. J., Wissler, R. W., Le Roy, G. V., and Gould, R. G. (1956). Unpublished work.

Jowett, M. (1931). *Biochem. J.* **25**, 1991-1998.

Kamat, V. B., Panse, T. B., and Khanolkar, V. R. (1956). *Current Sci. (India)* **25**, 261-262.

*Kaucher, M., Galbraith, H., Button, V., and Williams, H. H. (1943). *Arch. Biochem.* **3**, 203-215. Muscle of various species.

Kayser, F., and Balat, R. (1952). *Bull. soc. chim. biol.* **34**, 806-812.

Kleinzeller, A. (1948). *Advances in Enzymol.* **8**, 299-341.

Koppenhoefer, R. M. (1936). *J. Biol. Chem.* **116**, 321-341.

Koppenhoefer, R. M. (1937). *J. Am. Leather Chemists' Assoc.* **32**, 627.

Koppenhoefer, R. M. (1938). *J. Am. Leather Chemists' Assoc.* **33**, 203-215.

Krause, A. C. (1934). *Acta Ophthalmol.* **12**, 372-374.

Krause, A. C. (1934-1935). *Am. J. Physiol.* **110**, 182-186.

Kretchmer, N., and Barnum, C. P. (1951). *Arch. Biochem. Biophys.* **31**, 141-147.

Landé, K. E., and Sperry, W. M. (1936). *A.M.A. Arch. Pathol.* **22**, 301-312.

*Lange, W. J. (1950). *J. Am. Oil Chemists' Soc.* **27**, 414-422: A compilation of the sterol content of animal and plant tissues.

Lederer, E., and Pau-Kiun, T. (1945). *Bull. soc. chim. biol.* **27**, 419-424.

Le Gros Clark, W. E. (1952). "The Tissues of the Body," 3rd ed. Oxford Univ. Press, London and New York.

Leulier, A., and Revol, L. (1930). *Bull. histol. appl. physiol. et pathol. et tech. microscop.* **7**, 241-250.

Leupold, E. (1921). *Beitr. pathol. Anat. u allgem. Pathol.* **69**, 305-341.

Lovern, J. A., Olley, J., Hartree, E. F., and Mann, T. (1957). *Biochem. J.* **67**, 630-643.

Lowe, J. S., Morton, R. A., and Vernon, J. (1957). *Biochem. J.* **67**, 228-234.

Ma, R. M., and Schaffer, P. S. (1953). *Arch. Biochem. Biophys.* **47**, 419-423.

McArthur, C. G. (1919). *J. Am. Chem. Soc.* **41**, 1225-1240.

McColl, J. D., and Rossiter, R. J. (1950). *J. Cellular Comp. Physiol.* **36**, 241-250.

MacLachlan, P. L. (1936). *J. Biol. Chem.* **114**, 185-191.

MacLachlan, P. L., Hodge, H. C., and Whitehead, R. (1941). *J. Biol. Chem.* **139**, 185-191.

McMillan, G. C., Horlick, L., and Duff, G. L. (1955). *A.M.A. Arch. Pathol.* **59**, 285-290.

Mallov, S., McKibbin, J. M., and Robb, J. S. (1953). *J. Biol. Chem.* **201**, 825-838.

Man, E. B., Kartin, B. L., Durlacher, S. H., and Peters, J. P. (1945). *J. Clin. Invest.* **24**, 623-643.

Mann, T. (1954). "The Biochemistry of Semen." Wiley, New York.

Marinetti, G. V., Scaramuzzino, D. J., and Stotz, E. (1957). *J. Biol. Chem.* **224**, 819-826.

*Mayer, A., and Schaeffer, G. (1913). *J. physiol. et pathol. gen.* **15**, 534-548: Organs of fish, snake, amphibia, guinea pigs, rabbits and dogs.

Menschick, W., and Page, I. H. (1933). *Z. physiol. Chem.* **218**, 95-103.

Meyer, A. (1930-1931). *Z. Kinderheilk.* **50**, 597-607.

Miller, W. L., Jr., and Baumann, C. A. (1954). *Proc. Soc. Exptl. Biol. Med.* **85**, 561-564.

Mitchell, H. H., Hamilton, T. S., Steggerda, F. R., and Bean, H. W. (1945). *J. Biol. Chem.* **158**, 625-637.

Moore, P. R., and Baumann, C. A. (1952). *J. Biol. Chem.* **195**, 615-621.

Morton, R. A., and Rosen, D. G. (1949). *Biochem. J.* **45**, 612-627.

Nakanishi, H. (1931). *Nagoya J. Med. Sci.* **5**, 190-191.

Nakanishi, K., Bhattacharyya, B. K., and Fieser, L. F. (1953). *J. Am. Chem. Soc.* **75**, 4415-4417.

Nataf, B., Mickelsen, O., Keys, A., and Petersen, W. E. (1948). *J. Nutrition* **36**, 495-506.

Nedzvetskii, S. V., Panyukov, A. N., and Shpats, T. A. (1953). *Biokhimiya* **18**, 315-318 [*Chem. Abstr.* **48**, 1511 (1954)].

Needham, J. (1931). "Chemical Embryology," Vols. 1–3. Cambridge Univ. Press, London and New York. Eggs of various species.

Needham, J. (1950). "Biochemistry and Morphogenesis." Cambridge Univ. Press, London and New York.

Nicolaides, N., and Foster, R. C., Jr. (1956). *J. Am. Oil Chemists' Soc.* **33**, 404-409.

Noble, N. L., and Boucek, R. J. (1955). *Circulation Research* **3**, 344-350. See also: Boucek, R. J., Noble, N. L., and Kao, K-Y. T. (1955). *Ibid.* **3**, 519-524.

Norcia, L. N., Gonzalez, I. E., Shetlar, M. R., Peter, J., and Furman, R. H. (1956). *Circulation* **14**, 501.

*Okey, R. (1945). *J. Am. Dietet. Assoc.* **21**, 341-344: American foodstuffs.

Okey, R., Bloor, W. R., and Corner, G. W. (1930). *J. Biol. Chem.* **86**, 307-314.

Okey, R., Gillum, H. L., and Yokela, E. (1934). *J. Biol. Chem.* **107**, 207-212.

*Okey, R., Godfrey, L. S., and Gillum, F. (1938). *J. Biol. Chem.* **124**, 489-499. Pregnant and lactating rat.

Page, I. H., and Menschick, W. (1931). *Biochem. Z.* **231**, 446-459.

Parker, H. M. (1948). *Advances in Biol. and Med. Physics* **1**, 223-285.

Pearlman, W. H. (1944). *J. Am. Chem. Soc.* **66**, 806-809.

*Pihl, A. (1952). *Scand. J. Clin. & Lab. Invest.* **4**, 115-121: Scandinavian foodstuffs.

Pikulev, A. T. (1955). Ukrain. *Biokhem. Zhur.* **27**, 517-521.

Plaut, F., and Rudy, H. (1933). *Z. ges. Neurol. Psychiat.* **146**, 229-261.

Polonovski, M., and Bourrillon, R. (1952a). *Bull. soc. chim. biol.* **34**, 703-711.

Polonovski, M., and Bourrillon, R. (1952b). *Bull. soc. chim. biol.* **34**, 712-719.

Popják, G. (1943). *Biochem. J.* **37**, 468-470.

Popják, G. (1946). *J. Physiol. (London)* **105**, 236-254.

Portman, O. W., Mann, G. V., and Wysocki, A. P. (1955). *Arch. Biochem. Biophys.* **59**, 224-232.

Pratt, J. P., Kaucher, M., Richards, A. J., Williams, H. H., and Macy, I. G. (1946). *Am. J. Obstet. Gynecol.* **52**, 665-668.

Pruess, L. M., Peterson, W. H., Steenbock, H., and Fred, E. B. (1931). *J. Biol. Chem.* **90**, 369-384.

Ralli, E. P., Rubin, S. H., and Rinzler, S. (1941). *J. Clin. Invest.* **20**, 93-97 (see also 413-417).

Randall, L. O. (1938). *J. Biol. Chem.* **125**, 723-728.

Rattray, J. B. M., Cook, R. P., and James, A. T. (1956). *Biochem. J.* **64**, Proc. 10 P.

Reay, G. A., Cutting, C. L., and Shewan, J. M. (1946). *In* "The Nation's Food" (A. L. Bacharach and T. Rendle, eds.) pp. 269-299. Soc. Chem. Ind., London.

Reiser, R. (1937). *J. Biol. Chem.* **120**, 625-633.

Rice, L. I., Schotz, M. C., Alfin-Slater, R. B., and Deuel, H. J., Jr. (1953). *J. Biol. Chem.* **201**, 867-871; see also *J. Biol. Chem.* **204**, 19-26.

Rosenheim, M. C. (1914). *Biochem. J.* **8**, 82-83.

Rosenheim, O., and Tebb, M. C. (1909). *J. Physiol. (London)* **38**, Proc. liv.

Rossiter, R. J. (1955). *In* "Neurochemistry" (K. A. C. Elliott, I. H. Page, and J. H. Quastel, eds.), pp. 11-52. C. C Thomas, Springfield, Illinois.

Rothman, S. (1954). "Physiology and Biochemistry of the Skin." Univ. of Chicago Comm. on Publications in Biol. and Med. Univ. Chicago Press, Chicago, Illinois.

Salit, P. W., and O'Brien, C. S. (1935). *A.M.A. Arch. Ophthalmol. (Chicago)* **13**, 227-237.

Schoenheimer, R., and Breusch, F. (1933). *J. Biol. Chem.* **103**, 439-448.

Schoenheimer, R., von Behring, H., and Hummell, R. (1930). *Z. physiol. Chem.* **192**, 93-96.

Schotz, M. C., Rice, L. I., and Alfin-Slater, R. B. (1953). *J. Biol. Chem.* **204**, 19-26.

Schwartz, J. J., and Wall, M. E. (1955). *J. Am. Chem. Soc.* **77**, 5442-5443.

Schwenk, E., and Werthessen, N. T. (1952). *Arch. Biochem. Biophys.* **40**, 334-341.

Schwenk, E., Todd, D., and Fish, C. A. (1954). *Arch. Biochem. Biophys.* **49**, 187-206.

Scott, W. W. (1945). *J. Urol.* **53**, 712-718.

Sifferd, R. H., and Anderson, R. J. (1936). *Z. physiol. Chem.* **239**, 270-272.

Silberman, H., and Silberman-Martyncewa, S. (1945). *J. Biol. Chem.* **159**, 603-604.

Siperstein, M. D., Harold, F. M., Chaikoff, I. L., and Dauben, W. G. (1954). *J. Biol. Chem.* **210**, 181-191.

Sobel, H. (1949). *J. Invest. Dermatol.* **13**, 333-338.

Sperry, W. M. (1932). *J. Biol. Chem.* **96**, 759-768.

Sperry, W. M., and Stoyanoff, V. A. (1935a). *J. Nutrition* **9**, 131-155.

Sperry, W. M., and Stoyanoff, V. A. (1935b). *J. Nutrition* **9**, 157-161.

Spiro, M. J., and McKibbin, J. M. (1956). *J. Biol. Chem.* **219**, 643-651.

Stokes, W. M., Fish, W. A., and Hickey, F. C. (1956). *J. Biol. Chem.* **220**, 415-430.

Stoneburg, C. A. (1939). *J. Biol. Chem.* **129**, 189-196.

Tati, Y. (1941). *Japan. J. Med. Sci. II* **4**, 233-249.

Taylor, J. D., Paul, H. E., and Paul, M. F. (1948). *Arch. Biochem. Biophys.* **17**, 421-428.

*Terroine, E. F. (1914-1915). *J. physiol. et path. gén.* **16**, 408-418. Starvation and overfeeding in rabbit, dog and birds.

Terroine, E. F., and Belin, P. (1927). *Bull. soc. chim. biol.* **9**, 1074-1084.

*Terroine, E. F., and Weill, J. (1913). *J. physiol. et path. gén.* **15**, 549-563. Starvation in mouse, rabbit and dog.

*Terroine, E. F., Bonnet, R., Kopp, G., and Vechot, J. (1927). *Bull. soc. chim. biol.* **9**, 678-691. Whole animals and vegetable seeds.

Thannhauser, S. J., Benotti, J., Walcott, A., and Reinstein, H. (1939). *J. Biol. Chem.* **129**, 717-719.

Theis, E. R. (1929). *J. Biol. Chem.* **82**, 327-334.

Tourtellotte, D., and Hart, M. C. (1926-1927). *J. Biol. Chem.* **71**, 1-13.

Toyama, Y., Takagi, T., and Tanaka, T. (1953). *Bull. Chem. Soc. Japan* **26**, 154-156.

Truter, E. V. (1951). *Quart. Revs. (London)* **5**, 390-404.

Tsujimoto, M., and Koyanagi, H. (1939). *J. Soc. Chem. Ind. Japan* **42**, 421B-422B.

Tyrrell, L. W., and Richter, D. (1951). *Biochem. J.* **49**, li.

Unna, P. G., and Golodetz, L. (1909). *Biochem. Z.* **20**, 469-502.

Usdin, V. R., and Burrell, R. C. (1952). *Arch. Biochem. Biophys.* **36**, 172-177.

Van Dyke, H. B., and Chen, G. (1940). *Am. J. Anat.* **66**, 411-423.

Wacker, L. (1912). *Z. physiol. Chem.* **80**, 383-408.

Wells, H. G. (1940). *J. Am. Med. Assoc.* **114**, 2177-2182 and 2284-2289.

Wells, W. W., and Baumann, C. A. (1954a). *Arch. Biochem. Biophys.* **53**, 471-478.

Wells, W. W., and Baumann, C. A. (1954b). *Proc. Soc. Exptl. Biol. Med.* **87**, 519-521.

Wheatley, V. R. (1952). Livre Jubilaire 1901-1951 de la soc. belge. Dermatol. et Syphil., pp. 91-103. Imprim. Med. et Sci. (S.A.), Brussels.

Wheatley, V. R. (1954). *Biochem. J.* **58**, 167-172.

Wheatley, V. R., and James, A. T. (1957). *Biochem. J.* **65**, 36-42.

*Wiese, H. F., and Hansen, A. E. (1951). *Texas Repts. Biol. and Med.* **9**, 516-544. Tissues of the dog.

Williams, H. H., Galbraith, H., Kaucher, M., and Macy, I. G. (1945a). *J. Biol. Chem.* **161**, 463-474. This and the succeeding paper give detailed analyses of rats' tissues at various growth periods.

*Williams, H. H., Galbraith, H., Kaucher, M., Moyer, E. Z., Richards, A. J., and Macy, I. G. (1945b). *J. Biol. Chem.* **161**, 475-484.

Williams, K. A. (1950). "Oils, Fats and Fatty Foods," 3rd ed. Churchill, London.

Wilmer, H. A. (1940). *Proc. Soc. Exptl. Biol. and Med.* **43**, 386-388.

Windaus, A. (1910). *Z. physiol. Chem.* **65**, 110-117.

Windaus, A., and Bock, F. (1937). *Z. physiol. Chem.* **245**, 168-170.

Windaus, A., and Stange, O. (1936). *Z. physiol. Chem.* **244**, 218-220.

CHAPTER 5

THE PHYSIOLOGY OF THE CIRCULATING CHOLESTEROL AND LIPOPROTEINS

George S. Boyd and Michael F. Oliver

181

This chapter is concerned with the blood cholesterol and cholesterol-bearing liproproteins in normal man, and in certain common and domestic species. An extensive review on this subject was made by Byers *et al.* (1952) and the current interest in the field has since added considerably to our knowledge. For reasons of space we have been forced to be selective but wherever possible the original investigators of any particular aspect have been duly acknowledged, and thereafter selected reports are cited, with notes on species differences or disharmony in results.

I. The Distribution of Cholesterol between the Formed Elements of the Blood and the Blood Plasma

The earliest work on the circulating cholesterol was obtained from analysis of extracts of whole blood, but later the distribution of this sterol between cells and plasma was studied (Boyd, 1937). It was found that the cholesterol concentration of plasma was altered by certain factors whereas the cholesterol content of the erythrocytes was unaffected, and thus the medium of choice for quantitative studies appeared to be plasma. As a consequence of the introduction of the digitonin procedure for the estimation of sterols (see Chapter 3) it is possible to estimate the unesterified or "free cholesterol" in a lipid extract; in another portion of this extract, hydrolysis of the esterified cholesterol followed by an estimation of the cholesterol content yields the "total cholesterol," the difference between the "total cholesterol" and the "free cholesterol" giving the "esterified cholesterol." In this presentation it is taken that Δ^5-cholestenol is the main sterol present but there is evidence that other sterols are present in plasma, e.g. Δ^7-cholestenol (Nakanishi *et al.*, 1953), and 7-dehydrocholesterol (Koehler and Hill, 1953). Boyd (1933a, b) determined the free and esterified cholesterol partition between the cells and the plasma in a group of normal young women. The collective data are shown in Table I. In the human, the *free cholesterol:ester cholesterol* ratio in red blood cells is about 4:1, in white blood cells it is about 3:1, while in plasma it is about 1:3.*

TABLE I
THE DISTRIBUTION OF CHOLESTEROL IN HUMAN BLOOD[a]

	Free (mg./100 ml.)	Ester (mg./100 ml.)	Total (mg./100 ml.)
Whole blood	80	110	190
Red blood cells	120	30	150
White blood cells	240	80	320
Plasma	50	170	220

[a] Modified from E. M. Boyd (1937; 1942).

The analysis of the formed elements of the blood is quite different from that of the fluid carrying them, suggesting that different cholesterol molecular groups are present outside and inside the cells. This distribution of free and esterified cholesterol prevailing at the cell membrane has been shown to be dynamic in nature, since plasma cholesterol labeled with carbon-14 rapidly exchanges with unlabeled cholesterol in the red cells. Conversely, C^{14}-labeled cholesterol in red cells rapidly exchanges with unlabeled cholesterol present in plasma (see Chapter 7). In this equilibration reaction, the "free cholesterol" of both cells and plasma seems to be more labile than the esterified cholesterol.

II. The Physical State of the Plasma Cholesterol

A. THE LIPOPROTEINS

The circulating cholesterol is present in two chemically distinct thermostable compounds, namely free or unesterified cholesterol and esterified cholesterol, in which the cholesterol is usually combined with long-chain unsaturated fatty acids. All lipids including the sterols are hydrophobic; hence the transparent appearance of a fasting plasma sample must be due to the presence in plasma of some constituent solubilizing the water-insoluble lipids—this is most likely to be a phospholipid-protein complex.

This solubilization process cannot be a random adsorption of lipid on to protein, because all attempts to "reconstitute" a lipid-protein mixture quantitatively similar to plasma have failed so far. Nevertheless, by

* Boyd's values for ester sterol in the red blood cells are not in agreement with more recent determinations. It is generally considered that the cholesterol present is mainly, if not entirely, free cholesterol (see Chapter 7, Ed.).

the relatively mild procedure of shaking plasma with a lipid solvent in the cold, it is possible to extract most of the lipid components from this fluid, showing that, whatever the nature of the soluble complexes, the lipid hydrophilic bonds are fairly easily broken. In the case of cholesterol ester, it is difficult to imagine what type of linkage binds the lipid to a polypeptide structure.

Macheboeuf (1929) was the first to isolate from serum a conjugated protein which appeared upon repeated precipitation to retain a constant ratio of lipid to protein. Blix *et al.* (1941) showed by electrophoretic separation of the plasma proteins, that practically all the protein components in plasma had lipid in association with them, but most of the plasma lipids were found in combination with the α- and β-globulin fractions. Equilibration experiments of the kind described above (Gould, 1951) suggest that, in structure and function, the lipoproteins of plasma are of variable composition and behave like carrier molecules of the clathrate type; in these complexes the lipids are possibly held to the peptide by secondary valence bonds of the Van der Waals form. While extensive studies have been conducted on the cholesterol containing macromolecules (lipoproteins) of the blood plasma, little information is available on the cholesterol complexes prevailing within the cells (see Chapter 4).

B. Methods of Investigation

1. General

The elegant low temperature ethanol controlled fractionation procedures developed by Cohn *et al.* (1946) allowed the separation of the two main lipid-protein or lipoprotein classes, namely, the α- and β-lipoproteins. These lipoproteins were shown to have quite different molecular weights, net charges, molecular sizes, shapes, and chemical compositions. The subject of lipoproteins is reviewed by Chargaff (1944), Edsall (1947), Russ *et al.* (1951), Nikkilä (1953); Swahn (1953), and Gofman *et al.* (1954). From quantitative studies employing the Cohn procedure, Oncley *et al.* (1950) have shown that in the human about 75% of the plasma cholesterol is associated with the β-lipoprotein, the remaining 25% being associated with the α-lipoprotein. A modification of the Cohn method has been applied to the routine estimation of α and β-lipoproteins by Russ *et al.* (1951). Oncley *et al.* (1957) have described a method using dextran sulfate as a specific complexing agent for β-lipoproteins. This simple and rapid method may prove valuable in the future.

2. Ultracentrifugal Methods

Another independent and precise method by which determinations of the plasma lipoprotein concentrations can be measured is the ultracentrifugal procedure developed by Gofman and his school (Gofman *et al.*, 1949). In this method the lipoproteins are first separated into certain major classes by performing a preparative centrifugal separation, and then each lipoprotein class is examined by means of an analytical ultracentrifugal determination.

Since it has been shown by this method that the β-lipoprotein is not homogeneous these workers have rigorously standardized their procedure and assigned arbitrary "flotation rates" to the various components of the lipoprotein. Hence it is possible to measure variations in certain discrete categories of the β-lipoprotein in health and in disease (Gofman *et al.*, 1954). Since it is difficult to isolate in quantity these subdivisions of the β-lipoprotein, few quantitative data on the chemical compositions of these lipoproteins have emerged to date but, in general, the lower density fractions of the β-lipoproteins (low S_f values) contain more sterol than the higher density fractions of this lipoprotein.*

3. Electrophoretic Methods

The lipoproteins of plasma can be separated by the technique of electrophoresis, based on the fundamental observations of Tiselius (1930, 1939). In this method the plasma proteins are separated in a buffered medium, due to their different net charges and hence different rates of migration. Electrophoresis can be carried out in an inert supporting medium such as filter paper (Durrum *et al.*, 1952; Fasoli, 1952, 1953; Nikkilä, 1953; Swahn, 1953; Boyd, 1954) or starch (Kunkel and Slater, 1952).

This method allows the separation of the protein constituents of plasma and is followed by the chemical examination of the zones of separated proteins. The distribution of cholesterol between the various protein fractions of plasma after zone electrophoresis on paper has been utilized by Nikkilä (1953) and Boyd (1954) for the determination of the α- and β-lipoprotein concentrations present in plasma. A comparison of the several techniques is made by Hillyard *et al.* (1955; 1956).

C. Physical Characteristics

Physical data indicate that the β-lipoproteins are spherical complexes of about 18.5 mμ diameter, molecular weight 1.3×10^6. Chemical data indicate that this group of lipoproteins contains about 39% cholesterol ester, 8% free cholesterol, 29% phospholipids (with trace amounts of

---

* S_f = Svedberg flotation values. The customary unit of migration rate in the ultracentrifuge is the Svedberg. One Svedberg unit is 1×10^{-13} cm./sec./dyne/gm. Flotation indicates that the density of the molecules is lighter than the medium and that the molecules are undergoing flotation.

other lipids), and 23% protein. Oncley (1956) has discussed some of the recent work on the lipoproteins and suggests that, in these complexes, the proteins and phospholipids are arranged peripherally while the uncharged lipids are concentrated at the center of the molecular spheres.

The α- and β-lipoproteins are almost certainly synthesized in the liver and may also be degraded there or in the reticulo-endothelial system elsewhere in the body. Whether these two different conjugated proteins exist independently, or how, where, and when they interact *in vivo* has yet to be fully investigated. From isotopic labeling experiments (Gitlin and Cornwell, 1956) it seems that the half-life of the α-lipoprotein is about 4 days and the half-life of the β-lipoprotein may be a little shorter. The precise structure, metabolism, and function of the cholesterol-bearing α- and β-lipoproteins of plasma remain a problem, indeed a challenge for the future.

III. Species Differences

The plasma (or serum) cholesterol levels have been reported in a vast number of different animal species. Typical results of some of these observations using several methods are recorded. The values obtained from one species to another differ so markedly that the phylogenetic significance is still obscure (Table II).

IV. Race

The influence of race on the plasma cholesterol concentration in humans has received a great deal of attention within recent years, mainly because this measurement has been correlated with the various national mortalities from coronary artery disease. From these studies designed to throw light on the etiology of a disease state, we obtain most of our information on the so-called physiological normals of the particular population under observation. It is difficult to dissociate primary genetic characteristics from environmental habits. The latter include economic status, social and religious habits, and these in turn dictate the quantity and quality of the diet and the energy expenditure of the group (Fig. 1). It is possible that environmental factors are largely responsible for the average plasma cholesterol level of all nations. The emigration of apparently healthy individuals, who presumably have average plasma cholesterol levels, from a comparatively uncivilized community to one more economically independent has emphasized the importance of environmental factors, because these individuals rapidly acquire the average plasma cholesterol level of their country of adoption. A good example of this is shown by the Yemenite immigrants into Israel (Toor *et al.,* 1957). However, environmental factors may not always account for

TABLE II

PLASMA OR SERUM CHOLESTEROL OF VARIOUS SPECIES
(Typical values as mg./100 ml.)[a]

Species	Cholesterol	References
Herbivores		
Guinea pig	40	1, 7, 8
Hamster	57	6
Rabbit	40	1, 6, 7, 8
Ox	90	1, 2, 3, 7, 8
Sheep	70	7, 8
Omnivores		
Mouse	97	8
Rat	50	1, 6, 8
Hog	110	2, 7
Carnivores		
Cat	95	1, 8
Dog	About 140, low-fat diet; 280, high-fat diet	1, 2, 7, 8, 9
Primates		
Cebus monkeys	93	5
Avian		
Chicken		
Cockerel	100	1
Hen		
Nonlaying	116–152	4
Laying	208–285	

[a] Typical values are given, the range and standard deviations are to be found in the cited references.

References

1. Boyd (1944); values given for general lipid composition.
2. Darraspen *et al.* (1949); values given for free and total sterol.
3. Isaksson (1954); effect of age in cattle studied.
4. Leveille *et al.* (1957); plasma level and period of laying studied; for values for whole blood in poultry see Lorenz *et al.* (1938a).
5. Mann *et al.* (1952).
6. Marx *et al.* (1951); effect of cholesterol feeding on blood and on liver levels also studied.
7. Mayer and Schaeffer (1913); these observations on the serum and the red blood cells of animals are still of interest.
8. Morris and Courtice (1955); values given for other lipids and a comparative study of the lipoprotein patterns was made.
9. Wiese and Hansen (1951); a thorough study of dogs' blood on high and on low fat-containing diets.

the observed racial differences since the cholesterol level of the Navajo Indian living in the United States is low (Page *et al.*, 1956) but their diet is said to be not appreciably different from other Americans (Gilbert, 1955).

The average plasma or serum cholesterol levels of "normal" subjects have been determined in many countries by a wide variety of analytical methods. The mean serum cholesterol of adults in the fourth decade in several countries is listed in Table III.

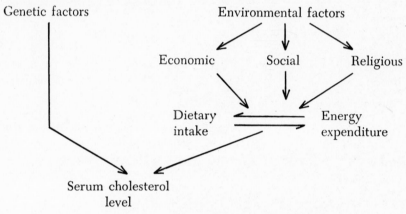

FIG. 1.　Some factors which may influence the circulating cholesterol.

V.　The Effect of Diet

The presence or absence of a post-absorptive effect on the serum cholesterol, and the possible influence of the habitual intake of one type of dietary regimen must be taken into account in any consideration of the influence of the diet on plasma cholesterol levels. Diets may also vary in caloric content or be isocaloric with different distributions of calories between protein, fat, and carbohydrate. Furthermore, it is axiomatic that all lipid metabolism, including the plasma cholesterol levels, must be profoundly affected by the caloric balance between energy intake and energy expenditure.

A.　ANIMALS

In many animals the addition of cholesterol to the diet results in a plasma hypercholesterolemia. The rabbit and the chicken have been much used in experimental studies and an account of these is given in Chapter 10. In the dog, cholesterol feeding will only result in plasma hypercholesterolemia if the animals are rendered hypothyroid (Steiner and Kendall, 1946). In the dog total fasting is followed by hyperlipemia and a progressive decrease in circulating cholesterol (Mayer and Schaeffer, 1913; Terroine, 1914; Mann and White, 1953). The feeding of cholesterol and cholic acid to hypothyroid rats produces marked hypercholesterolemia (Page and Brown, 1952) and other dietary studies in rats are described in Chapter 7. In the monkey, it has been found that cholesterol feeding accompanied by a diet deficient in sulfur-containing amino

TABLE III

RACIAL DIFFERENCES IN HUMAN PLASMA (OR SERUM) CHOLESTEROL[a]

Range (as mg./100 ml.)	Country and reference
180–230	Canada (Little et al., 1954)
	Denmark (Kornerup, 1950)
	Eskimos (Alaskan—Wilber and Levine, 1950; Canadian—Corcoran and Rabinowitch, 1937)
	Germany (Schettler, 1950)
	Great Britain (Oliver and Boyd, 1953b)
	Holland (Groen et al., 1950)
	Italy (Keys et al., 1954a)
	South Africa (White—Bronte-Stewart et al., 1955)
	Spain (Keys et al., 1954b)
	Sweden (Biorck et al., 1957)
	United States (Keys et al., 1950a, b)
	Yugoslavia (Brozek et al., 1957)
140–180	South Africa (Bantu—Bronte-Stewart et al., 1955)
100–140	Japan (farmers—Keys at al., 1957b; miners—Keys et al., 1957c)
	Nigeria (Mann et al., 1955a)

[a] Values for males in the fourth decade of life.

acids causes a plasma hypercholesterolemia to develop (Mann et al., 1953), while other reports seem to suggest that a diet rich in eggs will not only produce a plasma hypercholesterolemia in the monkey, but the condition can progress to yield in time (30 months) a xanthomatous lesion (Mann and Andrus, 1956).

B. MAN

1. Calories

The habitual consumption of food in excess of caloric requirements always results in a net weight gain and it has been shown, in the human, that overfeeding with resultant weight gain is accompanied by elevation of the serum cholesterol (Anderson et al., 1952) while underfeeding with a resultant loss of weight causes depression of the serum cholesterol concentration (Walker et al., 1953). In addition,

Mann *et al.* (1955b) have shown that feeding healthy young men twice their normal caloric intake fails to influence their serum cholesterol levels so long as they are allowed to increase their energy expenditure accordingly, but when their energy output is restricted while on this regimen their serum cholesterol levels rise markedly. It will be interesting to find out whether the serum cholesterol level would be altered indefinitely if one of these dietary alterations were continued over a long period; the duration of the usual type of experiment is too short to answer this question.

2. *Cholesterol*

In man the plasma cholesterol is largely independent of dietary cholesterol. Ingestion of excess cholesterol produces only slight and transient changes in plasma cholesterol (Collen *et al.*, 1949; Keys, 1949; Keys *et al.*, 1950a). However, very large amounts of cholesterol, such as 150 g. of egg yolk powder (containing 2.5% cholesterol and 15.2% lecithin) in 400 ml. of milk twice daily for 48 days produce a significant but transient increase in plasma cholesterol in man (Messinger *et al.*, 1950) while Cook *et al.* (1956) have shown a similar effect on a high cholesterol (egg) diet over a shorter period. Reduction of dietary cholesterol does not produce a significant decrease in plasma cholesterol (Keys *et al.*, 1950a; Wilkinson *et al.*, 1950).

3. *Fat*

Diets rich in fat, but not necessarily in cholesterol, are associated in man with high levels of plasma cholesterol (Widal *et al.*, 1913; Keys *et al.*, 1955). It is probable that the high levels of plasma cholesterol found in westernized communities, when compared with more primitive racial groups, are closely related to the fact that fat contributes one-third or more of the total daily calories in most civilized countries. A rice–fruit diet devoid of both cholesterol and fat produces a prompt and substantial (35%) fall in the plasma cholesterol of men with normal cholesterol levels (Kempner, 1948) and also of patients with idiopathic hypercholesterolemia (Keys *et al.*, 1950a). This reduction is largely due to restriction of total fat rather than to restriction of cholesterol (Keys, 1952).

Until recently, animal (saturated) and vegetable (unsaturated) fats were regarded as interchangeable in so far as their effect on the serum cholesterol was concerned (Hildreth *et al.*, 1951). Nutritional studies on vegetarians compared with nonvegetarians indicate that high plasma cholesterol levels are closely associated with the intake of animal or saturated fatty acids and the lack of unsaturated fatty acids. The plasma cholesterol of the complete vegetarian, who has a free intake of vegetable fats, is lower than that of the lacto-ovo-vegetarian, who is allowed milk and eggs in his diet, while both vegetarian groups have lower cholesterol levels than the nonvegetarian (Hardinge and Stare, 1954) (see Table IV).

There is strong evidence to indicate that the level of the circulating lipids may be dependent in part on the relative, if not on the absolute, intake of polyethenoid fatty acids. The addition of large quantities of vegetable fat or unsaturated oils to the diet reduces the plasma choles-

TABLE IV
DIETARY REGIMES AND ITS INFLUENCE ON HUMAN PLASMA CHOLESTEROL[a]

	Vegetarian	Lacto-ovo vegetarian	Nonvegetarian
Number of subjects	25	35	30
Daily caloric intake (mean value)	2800	2700	3200
Calories from fat (as % total calories)	35	33	43
Plasma cholesterol (as mg./100 ml.)	206	256	291
(as per cent of vegetarian)	100	124	141

[a] Modified from the results of Hardinge and Stare (1954).

terol significantly, and this fall can be overcome or reversed by the simultaneous feeding of similar amounts of animal fats or hydrogenated vegetable oils (Kinsell et al., 1952, 1953; Ahrens et al., 1954; Beveridge et al., 1955; Bronte-Stewart et al., 1955; Malmros and Wigand, 1955; Ahrens et al., 1957).

Lack of unsaturated fatty acids may result in elevation of the serum cholesterol (Kinsell et al., 1956) and the decrease in the serum cholesterol, which results when fats of vegetable origin are fed, seems to be directly related to the amount of unsaturated fatty acids administered (Friskey et al. 1955; Ahrens et al., 1957). For example, the administration of sunflower seed oil caused depression of the plasma cholesterol in man, and when this oil was separated into saturated and unsaturated fatty acid fractions the latter fraction depressed the serum cholesterol more (Bronte-Stewart et al., 1956). The difference in the effect on plasma cholesterol between animal and hydrogenated fat on the one hand, and natural vegetable oils and marine oils on the other, may depend on the ratio of saturated to unsaturated fatty acids in the respective triglycerides. However, some unsaturated oils have a greater depressant action on the circulating cholesterol than others—for instance, corn oil is more effective than sardine oil and sunflower seed oil—and the suggestion that the serum cholesterol level in man is a simple inverse function of the degree of unsaturation of the dietary fatty acids has recently been refuted (Keys *et al.*, 1957a). Beveridge *et al.* (1956) and Jones *et al.* (1956) suggest that some factor other than unsaturated fatty acids may be concerned.

VI.   Plasma Cholesterol in Man
A.   AGE AND SEX

Possible alterations in the plasma cholesterol level with advancing age has interested many investigators. Studies have been conducted in various countries, and racial and environmental influences (see section on race) may operate to modify the response of the plasma cholesterol of the subjects of certain nations towards the inevitable constraint of old age.

1. Infants

The plasma cholesterol of newborn infants is low and averages 35 mg.%* (Boyd, 1936a; Sperry, 1936) but rises rapidly within the first 10 days to about 130 mg.% (Sperry, 1936). These observations have been extended and amplified by the studies of Rafstedt and Swahn (1954) and Rafstedt (1955).

From the age of 1 year there seems to be no significant increase in plasma cholesterol until puberty (Kornerup, 1950; Adlersberg *et al.*, 1956), and after puberty subsequent changes depend on sex.

2. Males

In men there is a gradual increase in plasma cholesterol with increasing age up to 30 or 35 years (Keys *et al.*, 1950a, b); Tanner, 1951). Thereafter the pattern is less clear. A further increase in plasma cholesterol with advancing age up to the age of 60 has been reported (Melka, 1927; Keys, 1949; Gertler *et al.*, 1950; Keys *et al.*, 1950b; Kornerup, 1950, and Russ *et al.*, 1951), but other investigators have not shown any significant rise in the plasma cholesterol of men with increasing age (Page *et al.*, 1935; Foldes and Murphy, 1946; Oliver and Boyd, 1953b; Little *et al.*, 1954; Adlersberg *et al.*, 1956). In contrast to citizens of Minnesota (Keys *et al.*, 1950b) Italians living in Naples do not show any rise in plasma cholesterol with increasing age (Keys *et al.*, 1952) and it has been suggested that the poorer economic status and lower intake of fat in Italy may contribute towards this difference (see sections on race and diet). It may be concluded that an increase in plasma cholesterol does not occur in all communities with advancing age and that it

---

* Mg.% = mg./100 ml.

is not an obligatory concomitant of aging (Sperry and Webb, 1950). The subject is discussed further in Chapter 10.

3. Females

Whereas the plasma cholesterol levels of both sexes rise in parallel from birth to puberty, cholesterol levels in the female are influenced thereafter by the menstrual cycle, pregnancy and the menopause.

a. Menstrual Cycle. There have been several reports of a rise in plasma cholesterol before menstruation followed by a fall during or after menstruation (Gonalons, 1916; Moynihan, 1925; Okey and Boyden, 1927; Offenkrantz, 1938). This premenstrual rise has been confirmed and, in addition, definite cyclical changes have been observed in plasma cholesterol and lipoprotein cholesterol (Oliver and Boyd, 1953a, 1955b). At ovulation, as determined by a midcycle rise in basal temperature, there occurs a regular fall in plasma ester and total cholesterol and a rather less marked fall in plasma phospholipids; the concentration of cholesterol attached to the β-lipoprotein fraction decreases and the α-lipoprotein cholesterol is increased. In the follicular and luteal phases of the menstrual cycle the plasma ester and total cholesterol and the β-lipoprotein cholesterol increase. It has been suggested that the regular midcycle decrease in plasma cholesterol and β-lipoprotein cholesterol is associated with the endogenous secretion of estrogenic hormone. Maximal estrogen secretion occurs immediately before ovulation (Smith and Smith, 1936; Brown, 1955) and coincides with the lowest plasma cholesterol and β-lipoprotein cholesterol levels. Thus, the plasma cholesterol in women undergoes regular variation during the reproductive years but no such cyclical change occurs in men.

b. Pregnancy. The presence of hypercholesterolemia in pregnancy was first observed by Chauffard *et al.* (1911) and by Neumann and Hermann (1911). Several early studies which were all made at, or just before, term resulted in discordant views concerning the cholesterol levels of advanced pregnancy. Boyd (1937) reviewed these early studies and concluded from his investigations that there is no statistically significant elevation of total cholesterol but that there is a twofold increase in neutral fat. However, other studies have indicated that there is hypercholesterolemia (Dieckmann and Wegner, 1934; Schwarz *et al.*, 1940). Most investigations have been made on pooled blood of different groups of women at each month of pregnancy and a serial study (Oliver and Boyd, 1955a) of the plasma lipids and lipoproteins in the same women during pregnancy and the puerperium has established the presence of hypercholesterolemia which is maximal between the 31st and 33rd weeks of pregnancy; there is a similar elevation of β-lipoprotein cholesterol at this time. This hypercholesterolemia, which is an increase of approximately 50% over the nonpregnant levels, has been variously ascribed to the increased metabolic requirements of lactation (Slemons and Stander, 1923), to decreased elimination of cholesterol in the bile (Pribram, 1923), to the influence of the fetus (Gardner and Gainsborough, 1929) and particularly to endocrine influences (Schiller, 1919; Boyd, 1934; Oliver and Boyd, 1955a).

c. Menopause. A postmenopausal rise in plasma cholesterol was first suggested by Muhlbock and Kaufmann (1938) and confirmed by Oliver and Boyd (1953b) who studied a group of healthy women, ranging in age from 40 to over 70. The plasma cholesterol was found to be significantly higher during the 50–59 decade than during the adjacent 40–49 and 60–69 decades; the numbers in this study were small but further confirmation of a postmenopausal rise in plasma cholesterol was obtained from the investigations of Adlersberg *et al.* (1956).

This rise in the first postmenopausal decade with a subsequent fall in later decades has not yet been explained, and is probably related to the withdrawal of estrogens at this time. However, it is possible that any hormonal imbalance which may affect the plasma cholesterol is temporary and that, subsequently, the lipids regain their former equilibrium in some way.

B. Seasonal Variation

There is a slight and inconstant variation in the plasma cholesterol levels during the 24 hours of the day (Boyd, 1935; Turner and Steiner, 1939). Over a period of several months the plasma cholesterol fluctuates along different individual patterns, and the minimum and maximum cholesterol levels may vary as much as 30% (Man and Gildea, 1937; Schube, 1937). In most, if not all healthy persons the cholesterol in the serum appears to be maintained at a constitutional level from which large deviations do not ordinarily occur (Sperry, 1937).

C. Endocrine Influences

1. Hormones of the Anterior Pituitary

Most of the trophic hormones of the anterior pituitary, such as adrenocorticotropin (ACTH), thyrotropin (TSH), the gonadotropins (follicle-stimulating hormone, FSH and luteinizing hormone, LH), and prolactin, appear to have only one target organ each, while somatotropin (STH) seems to be a hormone of more general action.

Thus in the absence of the adrenal glands no positive metabolic effect of ACTH has been demonstrated, and similarly, in the absence of the thyroid or gonads, TSH or FSH and LH, respectively, appear metabolically inert. Consequently the influences of these substances on lipid metabolism are assumed to be comparable to the metabolic effects of the hormones secreted by the respective target organs.

a. Adrenocorticotropin (ACTH). The results obtained upon the administration of ACTH to humans are conflicting. Conn *et al.* (1950) showed that ACTH produced a fall in the plasma total cholesterol, most of this decrease being due to depression of the plasma ester cholesterol fraction. Upon cessation of ACTH administration the plasma lipid levels returned to normal in a few days. On the other hand Adlersberg *et al.* (1950) found that ACTH given to patients, many of whom were severely ill (and presumably acutely stressed), resulted in elevation of initially low serum cholesterol levels. Mann and White (1953) have extended these studies to dogs and have shown that during the considerable stress of a prolonged episode of fasting, ACTH elevated their serum cholesterol levels. Oliver and Boyd (1955b, 1956b) administered ACTH to healthy humans who were mildly hypercholesterolemic, and in agreement with Conn *et al.* (1950) showed depression of the plasma total cholesterol. Furthermore, Oliver and Boyd (1956b) showed that the cholesterol associated with the β-lipoprotein was depressed, while the cholesterol associated with the α-lipoprotein was elevated. Thus the administration of ACTH to the human produced a plasma lipid response apparently identical with that elicited by a comparable dose of cortisone acetate (which will be discussed in the section devoted to the effects of adrenal steroids).

b. Thyrotropin (TSH). Oliver and Boyd (1955b) administered TSH to human male subjects who had primary myxedema. Under these circumstances it was possible to show that TSH had no influence on the plasma lipids. TSH administered to euthyroid subjects had a metabolic effect apparently identical to that of thyroxine or triiodothyronine and resulted in depression of the plasma cholesterol. The influence of the thyroid hormones on plasma cholesterol is considered later.

c. Gonadotropins. Howard and Furman (1956) showed that chorionic gonadotropin depressed the α-lipoprotein producing a typical androgenic response.

d. Prolactin. Galansino *et al.* (1955) have reported that single or repeated injections of prolactin failed to influence the serum cholesterol or the lipoprotein patterns of normal or depancreatized dogs.

e. Somatotropin (STH). It is now well established that the diabetogenic principle present in the anterior pituitary is somatotropin (growth hormone). Gaebler (1933) showed that growth hormone lowered the respiratory quotient of animals, and Weil and Ross (1949) found that it produced an almost immediate increase in the liver fat of mice. Levin and Farber (1952) have implicated growth hormone in the control of the distribution of lipid between the fat depots and the liver.

In view of this circumstantial evidence, it might be expected that somatotropin would influence the levels of the circulating lipids. Nevertheless, this hormone exerted only a transient influence on the plasma cholesterol in rats (Greenbaum and McLean, 1953) and the administration of beef or porcine STH preparations to rats for prolonged periods failed to affect the plasma cholesterol levels (G. S. Boyd, unpublished observations); similarly these same preparations had no significant effect on the plasma cholesterol of human subjects (Oliver and Boyd, 1956b). However, since beef somatotropin differs from monkey or human somatotropin, both physiologically (Knobil and Greep, 1956) and chemically (Li and Papkoff, 1956), further comment on the effect of growth hormone on the plasma lipids of the human must await the crucial test of the administration of human growth hormone to human subjects.

2. Adrenal Steroids (for formulas see page 317)

The steroids elaborated by the adrenal cortex depend on the species. For this reason it is important to note that, in some experiments, the adrenal steroid preparation administered to certain species is not the same as the endogenous adrenal secretory products. While this approach can produce evidence about the influence of a steroid on the serum cholesterol in a certain species, it may not throw much light on the possible role of the adrenal cortex in the maintenance of the normal cholesterol level in that species. In most mammals the two main steroids secreted by the adrenals are corticosterone (compound B) and 17-hydroxycorticosterone (compound F) and the ratio of compounds B: F in adrenal vein blood is dependent on the species (Bush, 1953). From the experimental standpoint the adrenal steroid which first became available was 11-dehydro-17-hydroxycorticosterone (cortisone, compound E) and the material widely used in clinical investigations was the acetate of this substance. Since 17-hydroxycorticosterone has only become available very recently, while corticosterone is still scarce, most of the observations to be recorded have been made with cortisone acetate and may, therefore, have limited physiological significance.

In hyperadrenocorticism in man (Cushing's Syndrome) no consistent abnormality in plasma cholesterol levels has been found and, although these levels are sometimes elevated, this elevation is possibly related to the diabetes and renal disease which frequently accompany hyperadrenocorticism (Peters and Van Slyke, 1946). In a series of observations on humans who were acutely ill with collagen diseases, Adlersberg *et al.* (1950, 1951) showed that cortisone acetate elevated the serum cholesterol. In these cases, the symptomatic improvement, reduction of fever and return of appetite may have contributed to the rise in cholesterol; Mann and White (1953) interpreted this rise as being due to the removal of stress during the acute phase of the illness permitting low cholesterol levels to return to normal. On the other hand, Oliver and Boyd (1955b; 1956b) studied males who were hypercholesterolemic but otherwise apparently metabolically normal; cortisone acetate lowered the serum cholesterol, and the same results were obtained by the administration of ACTH to these subjects. This suggested that the substances released upon the *in vivo* stimulation of the adrenal cortex acted in a similar manner to cortisone acetate. It seems, therefore, that the administration of ACTH or cortisone acetate to normal humans, or the production of stress by illness, can lead to a decrease in the plasma cholesterol, with a return to the normal level upon recovery from the stress.

The influence of the physiological corticoid affecting electrolyte metabolism (aldosterone) on the serum cholesterol has not been reported yet, but deoxycorticosterone has little effect on the plasma lipids (Oliver and Boyd, 1956b).

In chicks and rabbits the administration of compound E and compound F produced hyperlipemic hypercholesterolemia (Adlersberg *et al.*, 1954; Stamler *et al.*, 1954). However, Mann *et al.* (1955b) observed depression of the serum cholesterol after the administration of cortisone acetate. It has been found that large doses of cortisone acetate administered to rats produce hypercholesterolemia (unpublished observations, Boyd and Oliver).

3. Thyroid Hormones

In most species the experimental reduction of thyroid function results in decreased basal oxygen requirements and elevation of the circulating cholesterol, while an increase in thyroid function is accompanied by increased metabolism and decrease of the circulating cholesterol; this is also true of any spontaneous change in thyroid function in man (Mason *et al.*, 1930; Gildea *et al.*, 1939; Peters and Man, 1943). The increase in cholesterol in hypothyroid states is not solely the result of lowered metabolism, as hypometabolic states in euthryroid subjects are not invariably accompanied by hypercholesterolemia (Mason *et al.*, 1930) and dinitro-*o*-cresol will restore metabolism to normal without reducing the hypercholesterolemia associated with hypothyroidism (Dodds and Robertson, 1933). The principal hormones contained in and secreted by the thyroid appear to be thyroxine and triiodothyronine (see review by Gross and

Pitt-Rivers, 1953). It is well established that thyroid extracts depress the level of circulating cholesterol in hypothyroid and euthyroid humans (Lévy and Lévy, 1931; Gildea et al., 1939; Turner and Steiner, 1939). Thyroxine and triiodothyronine are amino acids and can therefore give rise to the corresponding keto acids. These latter acids yield on oxidative decarboxylation tetraiodothyroacetic acid and triiodothyroacetic acid respectively. Both tetraiodothyroacetic acid and triiodothyroacetic acid lower the circulating cholesterol in hypothyroid and euthyroid humans (Lerman and Pitt-Rivers, 1955; Goolden, 1956; Trotter, 1956; Oliver and Boyd, 1957a). In euthyroid rats Boyd and Oliver (1957) have found that the administration of certain thyroxine analogs elevates the serum cholesterol in this species.

There is no very consistent relationship between serum protein-bound iodine (as a measure of thyroid function) and cholesterol levels, except in middle-aged men (Tucker and Keys, 1951). Large doses of iodides and iodine abolish the hypercholesterolemia which follows the forced feeding of cholesterol to rabbits, but both are ineffective if the thyroid has previously been removed (Turner, 1933).

4. Sex Hormones

a. Estrogens. Estrogens increase the circulating cholesterol and phospholipids, and very greatly increase the level of neutral fat in cockerels and immature hens (Lorenz et al., 1938b; Entenman et al., 1940; Chaikoff et al., 1948; Horlick and Katz, 1949). These changes closely resemble the physiological increase in the circulating lipids which occurs in the pullet at puberty (Lorenz et al. 1938a). The dietary level of fat has no influence on this action of estrogens (Entenman et al., 1938). The total cholesterol in the blood of the hen rose from the region of 120 mg.% to between 200 and 220 mg.% within 48 hours of injections of diethylstilbestrol. One factor in the production of hypercholesterolemia by estrogens may be the depression of thyroid activity which is known to follow estrogen administration at about this dose level (Farbmann, 1944; Koenig et al., 1945). In the rat, diethylstilbestrol reduces the circulating cholesterol (Levin, 1945; Pekkarinen et al., 1952). Hexestrol decreased the circulating cholesterol in rats from 73 to 23 mg.% and depressed hepatic cholesterol biosynthesis to 23% of the control value; moreover, this inhibition of synthesis was independent of the presence of the adrenal gland (Boyd and McGuire, 1956). In guinea pigs and rabbits, diethylstilbestrol reduces the plasma cholesterol (Pekkarinen et al., 1952) and in rabbits, ovariectomy is followed by elevation of the plasma cholesterol (Mininni et al., 1955).

In women there is a lower level of circulating cholesterol at ovulation than during the follicular and luteal phases of the menstrual cycle, and it has been suggested that this may be related to the high secretion of endogenous estrogens at that time (see p. 193). Similarly, the postmenopausal rise in circulating cholesterol may result in part from a reduction of estrogen secretion (see p. 193). The administration of estrogens to postmenopausal women resulted in a decrease in the circulating cholesterol and elevation of the phospholipids (Eilert, 1949, 1953).

In men the administration of estrogens also resulted in depression of the circulating cholesterol and the β-lipoprotein cholesterol, and elevation of the phospholipids (Barr et al., 1952; Oliver and Boyd, 1954; Steiner et al., 1955). This action is true also for estradiol, estrone, and estriol as well as for certain synthetic estrogens (Oliver and Boyd, 1956a, b). Ovariectomy causes elevation of the plasma cholesterol (Robinson et al., 1957).

b. *Androgens.* In men the effect of androgens on the circulating cholesterol appears to be exactly the reverse of that of estrogens (Barr, 1953; Oliver and Boyd, 1955b, 1956a), and methyltestosterone counteracts the depression of cholesterol caused by estrogens (Oliver and Boyd, 1955b; Russ et al., 1955; Oliver and Boyd, 1956a). Orchidectomy in normal men caused elevation of the plasma cholesterol (Teilum, 1937) but the cholesterol level is low in eunuchs (Furman and Howard, 1957).

In the cockerel, androgens have no effect on the hypercholesterolemia produced by estrogens (Stamler et al., 1953). Androgens and estrogens both protect intact female rabbits from cholesterol-induced hypercholesterolemia, but have no such effect in male rabbits (Ludden et al., 1942). Gonadectomy has been reported to cause slight elevation of cholesterol levels in the goat (Luden, 1916).

c. *Progesterone.* The intramuscular administration of progesterone to men has not resulted in any significant change in the circulating cholesterol levels (Oliver and Boyd, 1955b, 1956a).

5. Pancreatic Hormones

a. *Insulin.* In looking for a relationship between the endocrine secretion of the pancreas and the serum cholesterol level, the obvious disturbance to study is diabetes mellitus, in which a deficiency of insulin is often associated with an elevated serum cholesterol (Joslin et al., 1946). As the diabetes is brought under control by parenteral insulin therapy, the serum cholesterol levels tend to decrease. The exogenous administration of small amounts of insulin to individuals who were metabolically normal had little effect on the serum cholesterol levels (Oliver and Boyd, 1955b).

b. Glucagon. The intravenous infusion of glucagon to healthy men resulted in immediate elevation of the blood sugar and slight elevation of the circulating cholesterol a few days later (Oliver and Boyd, 1956b).

6. Epinephrine

As one of the secretions of the adrenal medulla, this amine has a well known effect on carbohydrate metabolism, causing a marked but transient hyperglycemia. Dury and Treadwell (1955) did not observe any significant change in the plasma cholesterol levels following the parenteral administration of epinephrine to humans. It is unlikely that prolonged administration of anything approaching a "physiological dose" of epinephrine will influence the plasma cholesterol.

D. MISCELLANEOUS INFLUENCES

1. Lipid-Mobilizing Factor

Steiger *et al.* (1956) have reported that horse plasma contains a heatstable, dialyzable component—lipid-mobilizing factor (LMF)—which when injected into human subjects produces an almost instantaneous and very marked rise in the plasma cholesterol. This hypercholesterolemia is maintained as long as the injections of LMF are continued. The substance is reported to be a polypeptide of low molecular weight containing eight amino acids (Seifter *et al.*, 1956).

2. Lipotropic Factors

Lipotropic substances prevent the accumulation of excess fat in the liver, or reduce the lipid content of a fatty liver. They include the following dietary constituents, lecithin (Hershey, 1930), choline (Best *et al.*, 1933), methionine (Tucker and Eckstein, 1937), and inositol (Gavin and McHenry, 1940). The spontaneous appearance of a fatty liver in depancreatized dogs led to the identification of a lipotropic substance in the pancreas; this substance was named "lipocaic" and the subject was reviewed by Chaikoff and Entenman (1948). It was argued that all these different agents which could reduce the hepatic lipids might also deplete the arterial lipids, and the correlation between plasma lipid levels and the experimental deposition of lipids in the arterial intima prompted studies concerning the effect of lipotropic agents on the plasma lipids.

Despite individual reports to the contrary, for example Steiner and Domanski (1944), the available data indicates that choline, methionine and inositol do not have any specific effect on the serum cholesterol level in man or in experimental animals. The position has been reviewed by Davidson (1951) and by Katz (1952), but this subject is still under investigation with newer synthetic drugs related to the lipotropic substances (Schettler, 1955).

3. Sulfated Mucopolysaccharides

Large injections of heparin lower the serum cholesterol within 24 hours (Basu and Stewart, 1950) but smaller doses do not have any significant effect (Chandler et al., 1953; Oliver and Boyd, 1953c). Heparin in high dosage lowers the concentration of cholesterol-containing, low-density lipoproteins (Graham et al., 1951) and lowers the concentration of the β-lipoproteins (Nikkilä, 1953). Apart from its anticoagulant action, another effect of heparin in vivo is its clearing of alimentary lipemia (Hahn, 1943; Weld, 1944).

Treburon (sodium salt of polygalacturonic acid methyl ester : methyl glycoside) and dextran sulfate lower the serum cholesterol levels in man (Chandler et al., 1953; Cohen and Tudhope, 1956) and both heparin and dextran sulfate accelerate the electrophoretic mobility of the serum lipoproteins (Dangerfield and Smith, 1955; Jeavons and Ricketts, 1956).

4. Other Factors Tending to Depress the Plasma Cholesterol Level

The following substances have been claimed to lower elevated plasma cholesterol levels in the human and may possibly influence the physiological levels of cholesterol: sitosterols (see Chapter 7), nicotinic acid (Altschul et al., 1955; Parsons et al., 1956), aspirin (Alexander and Johnson, 1956), oxygen inhalation (Altschul and Herman, 1954), irradiation by ultraviolet light (Altschul, 1953, 1955), ethylenediamine tetraacetate "EDTA" (Perry and Schroeder, 1955), and a combination of a surface active agent and a lipotropic substance—a polysorbate-80-choline inositol complex (Sherber and Levites, 1953). Phenyl ethyl acetic acid (α-phenyl butyrate) has been said to lower plasma cholesterol (Mathivat and Cottet, 1953) but this action is not consistent or marked (Oliver and Boyd, 1957b).

5. Factors Tending to Elevate the Plasma Cholesterol Level

The simplest method of elevating the plasma cholesterol level in most species is the introduction of cholesterol into the diet in the presence of a suitable quantity of triglyceride. In certain species, for example the rat, the hypercholesterolemia is intensified by the inclusion of bile salts in the regimen, while in other species depression of thyroid function also tends to increase the plasma cholesterol levels.

The irradiation of skeletal muscle by X-rays, in an animal otherwise shielded from the source, resulted in a rise in the plasma cholesterol

(Weiner *et al.*, 1956) and this rise may be related to the elevated rate of hepatic synthesis of cholesterol observed by Gould *et al.* (1956) to occur in animals some time after irradiation. It is reported that after exposure to cold (1–3° C) for 12 months the plasma cholesterol of rats is elevated (Sellers and You, 1956).

VII. Conclusions

The plasma cholesterol is synthesized almost exclusively in the liver. This sterol is bound to proteins and discharged into the extracellular fluid. The resultant cholesterol-protein complexes permeate the arterial and capillary endothelium and circulate by way of lymphatics and veins back into the blood. This cycle occurs repeatedly for several days until the circulating sterol is withdrawn from the extracellular fluid for utilization or degradation. Thus, any change in the concentration of plasma cholesterol could be attributed to many factors such as an alteration in plasma volume or in capillary permeability, redistribution of existing extracellular cholesterol between interstitial fluid and plasma, an alteration in the rate of hepatic cholesterol synthesis or a change in the rate of tissue utilization or degradation. One isolated measurement of the plasma cholesterol therefore represents the algebraic sum of a large number of variables.

The level of the plasma cholesterol in the normal human is low in infancy and reaches a value of 180–230 mg. per 100 ml. in normal adult males in Western communities at the fourth decade of life. This value is higher than that found in other mammals. The plasma cholesterol in adult women is influenced by the menstrual cycle, pregnancy and the menopause.

Some of the factors which influence the physiological level of the plasma cholesterol have been outlined. Dietetic and endocrine influences affect the plasma cholesterol, but the mechanism of action of most of the factors remains obscure.

REFERENCES

(Asterisk indicates review article)

Adlersberg, D., Schaefer, L. E., and Drachman, S. R. (1950). *J. Am. Med. Assoc.* **144**, 909-914.

Adlersberg, D., Schaefer, L. E., and Drachman, S. R. (1951). *J. Clin. Endocrinol.* **11**, 67-83.

Adlersberg, D., Schaefer, L. E., and Wang, C.-I. (1954). *Science* **120**, 319-320.

Adlersberg, D., Schaefer, L. E., Steinberg, A. G., and Wang, C.-I. (1956). *J. Am. Med. Assoc.* **162**, 619-622.

Ahrens, E. H., Jr., Blankenhorn, D. H., and Tsaltas, T. T. (1954). *Proc. Soc. Exptl. Biol. Med.* **86**, 872-878.

Ahrens, E. H., Jr., Hirsch, J., Insull, W., Jr., Tsaltas, T. T., Blomstrand, R., and Peterson, M. L. (1957). *Lancet* i, 943-953.

Alexander, W. D., and Johnson, K. W. M. (1956). *Clin. Sci.* **15**, 593-601.

Altschul, R. (1953). *Circulation Research* **1**, 185.

Altschul, R. (1955). *Strahlentherapie* **97**, 461-464.

Altschul, R., and Herman, I. H. (1954). *Arch. Biochem. Biophys.* **51**, 308-309.

Altschul, R., Hoffer, A., and Stephen, J. D. (1955). *Arch. Biochem. Biophys.* **54**, 558-559.

Anderson, J. T., Lawler, A., Lowen, M., and Keys, A. (1952). *Federation Proc.* **11**, 181.

Barr, D. P. (1953). *Circulation* **8**, 641-654.

Barr, D. P., Russ, E. M., and Eder, H. A. (1952). *Trans. Assoc. Am. Physicians* **65**, 102-113.

Basu, D. P., and Stewart, C. P. (1950). *Edinburgh Med. J.* **57**, 596-599.

Best, C. H., Ferguson, G. C., and Hershey, J. M. (1933). *J. Physiol. (London)* **79**, 94-102.

Beveridge, J. M. R., Connell, W. F., Mayer, G. A., Firstbrook, J. B., and Dewolfe, M. S. (1955). *J. Nutrition* **56**, 311-320.

Beveridge, J. M. R., Connell, W. F., and Mayer, G. A. (1956). *Can. J. Biochem. and Physiol.* **34**, 441-455.

Biorck, G., Blomquist, G., and Sievers, J. (1957). *Acta Med. Scand.* **156**, 493.

Blix, G., Tiselius, A., and Svensson, H. (1941). *J. Biol. Chem.* **137**, 485-501.

Boyd, E. M. (1933a). *J. Biol. Chem.* **101**, 323-336.

Boyd, E. M. (1933b). *J. Biol. Chem.* **101**, 623-633.

Boyd, E. M. (1934). *J. Clin. Invest.* **13**, 347-363.

Boyd, E. M. (1935). *J. Biol. Chem.* **110**, 61-70.

Boyd, E. M. (1936a). *Am. J. Diseases Children* **52**, 1319-1324.

Boyd, E. M. (1937). *Can. J. Research* **D15**, 1-23.

Boyd, E. M. (1942). *J. Biol. Chem.* **143**, 131-132.

*Boyd, E. M. (1944). *Can. J. Research* **E22**, 39-43. Species variations.

Boyd, G. S. (1954). *Biochem. J.* **58**, 680-685.

Boyd, G. S., and McGuire, W. B. (1956). *Biochem. J.* **62**, 19P.

Boyd, G. S., and Oliver, M. F. (1957). *Bull. schweiz. Akad. med. wiss.* **13**, 384-395.

Bronte-Stewart, B., Keys, A., Brock, J. F., Moodie, A. D., Keys, M. H., and Antonis, A. (1955). *Lancet* ii, 1103-1108.

Bronte-Stewart, B., Antonis, A., Eales, L., and Brock, J. F. (1956). *Lancet* i, 521-526.

Brown, J. B. (1955). *Lancet* i, 320-323.

Brozek, J., Buzina, R., and Mikic, F. (1957). *Am. J. Clin. Nutrition* **5**, 279-285.

Bush, I. E. (1953). *J. Endocrinol.* **9**, 95-100.

*Byers, S. O., Friedman, M., and Rosenman, R. H. (1952). *Metabolism* **1**, 479-503. Plasma cholesterol.

*Chaikoff, I. L., and Entenman, C. (1948). *Advances in Enzymol.* **8**, 171-202. Pancreatic factors.

Chaikoff, I. L., Lindsay, S., Lorenz, F. W., and Entenman, C. (1948). *J. Exptl. Med.* **88**, 373-388.

Chandler, H. L., Lawry, E. Y., Pottie, K. G., and Mann, G. V. (1953). *Circulation* **8**, 723-731.

*Chargaff, E. (1944). *Advances in Protein Chem.* **1**, 1-24. Lipoprotein review.

Chauffard, A., Laroche, G., and Grigaut, A. (1911). *Obstétrique* **4**, 481-484.

Cohen, H., and Tudhope, G. R. (1956). *Brit. Med. J.* ii, 1023-1027.

Cohn, E. J., Strong, L. E., Hughes, W. L., Jr., Mulford, D. J., Ashworth, J. N., Melin, M., and Taylor, H. L. (1946). *J. Am. Chem. Soc.* **68**, 459-475.

Collen, M. F., de Kruif, D., and Geier, F. M. (1949). *Permanente Foundation (Oakland, Calif.) Med. Bull.* **7**, 60-66.

Conn, J. W., Vogel, W. C., Louis, L. H., and Fajans, S. S. (1950). *J. Lab. Clin. Med.* **35**, 504-517.

Cook, R. P., Edwards, D. C., and Riddell, C. (1956). *Biochem. J.* **62**, 225-234.

Corcoran, A. C., and Rabinowitch, I. M. (1937). *Biochem. J.* **31**, 343-348.

Dangerfield, W. G., and Smith, E. B. (1955). *J. Clin. Pathol.* **8**, 132-139.

Darraspen, E., Florio, R., and Emangeard, P. (1949). *Compt. rend. soc. biol.* **143**, 1419-1420.

*Davidson, J. D. (1951). *Am. J. Med.* **11**, 736-748. Lipotropic factors.

Dieckmann, W. J., and Wegner, C. R. (1934). *A.M.A. Arch. Internal Med.* **53**, 540-550.

Dodds, E. C., and Robertson, J. D. (1933). *Lancet* ii, 1137-1139.

Durrum, E. L., Paul, M. H., and Smith, E. R. B. (1952). *Science* **116**, 428-430.

Dury, A., and Treadwell, C. R. (1955). *J. Clin. Endocrinol. and Metabolism* **15**, 818-825.

*Edsall, J. T. (1947). *Advances in Protein Chem.* **3**, 383-479. Plasma lipoprotein review.

Eilert, M. L. (1949). *Am. Heart J.* **38**, 472-473.

Eilert, M. L. (1953). *Metabolism* **2**, 137-145.

Entenman, C., Lorenz, F. W., and Chaikoff, I. L. (1938). *J. Biol. Chem.* **126**, 133-139.

Entenman, C., Lorenz, F. W., and Chaikoff, I. L. (1940). *J. Biol. Chem.* **134**, 495-504.

Farbmann, A. A. (1944). *J. Clin. Endocrinol. and Metabolism* **4**, 17-22.

Fasoli, A. (1952). *Lancet* i, 106.

Fasoli, A. (1953). *Acta Med. Scand.* **145**, 233-235.

Foldes, F. F., and Murphy, A. J. (1946). *Proc. Soc. Exptl. Biol. Med.* **62**, 215-218.

Friskey, R. W., Michaels, G. D., and Kinsell, L. W. (1955). *Circulation* **12**, 492.

Furman, R. H., and Howard, R. P. (1957). *Ann. Internal. Med.* **47**, 969-977.

Gaebler, O. H. (1933). *J. Exptl. Med.* **57**, 349-363.

Galansino, G., Fasoli, A., Magill, A. M., and Foa, P. P. (1955). *Proc. Soc. Exptl. Biol. Med.* **88**, 477-479.

Gardner, J. A., and Gainsborough, H. (1929). *Lancet* i, 603-606.

Gavin, G., and McHenry, E. W. (1940). *J. Biol. Chem.* **139**, 485.

Gertler, M. M., Garn, S. M., and Bland, E. F. (1950). *Circulation* **2**, 517-522.

Gilbert, J. (1955). *Calif. Med.* **82**, 114-115.

Gildea, E. F., Man, E. B., and Peters, J. P. (1939). *J. Clin. Invest.* **18**, 739-755.

Gitlin, D., and Cornwell, D. (1956). *J. Clin. Invest.* **35**, 756.

Gofman, J. W., Lindgren, F. T., and Elliott, H. A. (1949). *J. Biol. Chem.* **179**, 973-979.

Gofman, J. W., Glazier, F., Tamplin, A., Strisower, B., and De Lalla, O. (1954). *Physiol. Revs.* **34**, 589-607.

Gonalons, G. R. (1916). *Semana méd. (Buenos Aires)* **23**, 639-644.

Goolden, A. W. G. (1956). *Lancet* i, 890-891.

Gould, R. G. (1951). *Am. J. Med.* **11**, 209-227.

Gould, R. G., Lotz, L. V., and Lilly, E. H. (1956). *Federation Proc.* **15**, 264-265.

Graham, D. M., Lyon, T. P., Gofman, J. W., Jones, H. B., Yankley, A., Simonton, J., and White, S. (1951). *Circulation* **4**, 666-673.

Greenbaum, A. L., and McLean, P. (1953). *Biochem. J.* **54**, 407-424.

Groen, J., Kamminga, C. E., Reisel, J. H., and Willebrands, A. F. (1950). *Ned. Tijdschr. Geneesk.* **94**, 728-738.

*Gross, J., and Pitt-Rivers, R. (1953). *Vitamins and Hormones* **11**, 159-172.

Hahn, P. F. (1943). *Science* **98**, 19-20.

Hardinge, M. G., and Stare, F. J. (1954). *Am. J. Clin. Nutrition* **2**, 83-88.

Hershey, J. M. (1930). *Am. J. Physiol.* **93**, 657P.

Hildreth, E. A., Mellinkoff, S. M., Blair, G. W., and Hildreth, D. M. (1951). *Circulation* **3**, 641-646.

Hillyard, L. A., Entenman, C., Feinberg, H., and Chaikoff, I. L. (1955). *J. Biol. Chem.* **214**, 79-90.

Hillyard, L. A., Entenman, C., and Chaikoff, I. L. (1956). *J. Biol. Chem.* **223**, 359-368.

Horlick, L., and Katz, L. N. (1949). *Am. Heart J.* **38**, 336-349.

Howard, R. P., and Furman, R. H. (1956). *J. Clin. Endocrinol. and Metabolism* **16**, 965-966.

Isaksson, B. (1954). *Acta Physiol. Scand.* **32**, 281-290.

Jeavons, S. M., and Ricketts, C. R. (1956). *J. Clin. Pathol.* **9**, 255-256.

Jones, H. B., Gofman, J. W., Lindgren, F. T., Lyon, T. P., Graham, D. M., Strisower, B., and Nichols, A. V. (1951). *Am. J. Med.* **11**, 358-380.

Jones, R. J., Reiss, O. K., and Huffman, S. (1956). *Proc. Soc. Exptl. Biol. Med.* **93**, 88.

Joslin, E. P., Root, H. F., White, P., Marble, A., and Bailey, C. C. (1946). "Treatment of Diabetes Mellitus," 8th ed. Lea and Febiger, Philadelphia.

Katz, L. N. (1952). *Circulation* **5**, 101-114.

Kempner, W. (1948). *Am. J. Med.* **4**, 545-577.

Keys, A. (1949). *Federation Proc.* **8**, 523-529.

Keys, A. (1952). *Circulation* **5**, 115-118.

Keys, A., Mickelsen, O., Miller, E. V. O., and Chapman, C. B. (1950a). *Science* **112**, 79-81.

Keys, A., Mickelson, O., Miller, E. V. O., Hayes, E. R., and Todd, R. L. (1950b). *J. Clin. Invest.* **29**, 1347-1353.

Keys, A., Fidanza, F., Scardi, V., and Bergami, G. (1952). *Lancet* ii, 209-210.

Keys, A., Fidanza, F., Scardi, V., Bergami, G., Keys, M. H., and Di Lorenzo, F. (1954a). *A.M.A. Arch. Internal Med.* **93**, 328-336.

Keys, A., Vivanco, F., Rodriguez Miñon, J. L., Keys, M. H., and Castro Mendoza, H. J. (1954b). *Metabolism, Clin. and Exptl.* **3**, 195.

Keys, A., Anderson, J. T., Fidanza, F., Keys, M. H., and Swahn, B. (1955). *Clin. Chem.* **1**, 34-52.

Keys, A., Anderson, J. T., and Grande, F. (1957a). *Lancet* i, 66-67.

Keys, A., Kimura, N., Kusukawa, A., Bronte-Stewart, B., Larsen, N. P., and Keys, M. H. (1957b). *Federation Proc.* **16**, p. 204 (abstract 875).

Keys, A., Kimura, N., Kusukawa, A., and Yoshimoti, M. (1957c). *Am. J. Clin. Nutrition* **5**, 245-250.

Kinsell, L. W., Partridge, J., Boling, L., Margen, S., and Michaels, G. D. (1952). *J. Clin. Endocrinol. and Metabolism* **12**, 909-913.

Kinsell, L. W., Partridge, J., Boling, L., Margen, S., and Michaels, G. D. (1953). *J. Clin. Nutrition* **1**, 224-231.

Kinsell, L. W., Michaels, G. D., Friskey, R. W., Brown, F. R., Jr., and Maruyama, F. (1956). *Circulation* **14**, 484.

Knobil, E., and Greep, R. O. (1956). *Federation Proc.* **15**, 111.

Koehler, A. E., and Hill, E. (1953). *Federation Proc.* **12**, 232.

Koenig, V. L., Gassner, F. X., and Gustavson, R. G. (1945). *Am. J. Physiol.* **144**, 363-368.

Kornerup, V. (1950). *A.M.A. Arch. Internal Med.* **85**, 398-415.

Kunkel, H. G., and Slater, R. J. (1952). *J. Clin. Invest.* **31**, 677-684.

Lerman, J., and Pitt-Rivers, R. (1955). *J. Clin. Endocrinol. and Metabolism* **15**, 653.

Leveille, G., Fisher, H., and Weiss, H. S. (1957). *Proc. Soc. Exptl. Biol. Med.* **94**, 383-384.

Levin, L. (1945). *Endocrinology* **37**, 34-43.

Levin, L., and Farber, R. K. (1952). *Recent Progr. in Hormone Research* **7**, 399-435.

Lévy, M., and Lévy, M. (Mme.). (1931). *Bull. acad. méd. (Paris)* **105**, 666-675.

Li, C. H., and Papkoff, H. (1956). *Science* **124**, 1293-1294.

Little, J. A., Shanoff, H. M., Van der Flier, R. W., and Rykert, H. E. (1954). *Circulation* **10**, 585-586.

Lorenz, F. W., Entenman, C., and Chaikoff, I. L. (1938a). *J. Biol. Chem.* **122**, 619-633.

Lorenz, F. W., Chaikoff, I. L., and Entenman, C. (1938b). *J. Biol. Chem.* **126**, 763-769.

Ludden, J. B., Bruger, M., and Wright, I. S. (1942). *A.M.A. Arch. Pathol.* **33**, 58-62.

Luden, G. (1916). *J. Biol. Chem.* **27**, 273-297.

Macheboeuf, M. (1929). *Bull. soc. chim. biol.* **11**, 268-293.

Malmros, H., and Wigand, G. (1955). *Minn. Med.* **38**. In Symposium on Arteriosclerosis, University of Minnesota.

Man, E. B., and Gildea, E. F. (1937). *J. Biol. Chem.* **119**, 769-780.

Mann, G. V., and Andrus, S. B. (1956). *Federation Proc.* **15**, 1831.

Mann, G. V., and White, H. S. (1953). *Metabolism* **2**, 47-58.

Mann, G. V., Nicol, B. M., and Stare, F. J. (1955a). *Brit. Med. J.* **ii**, 1008-1010.

Mann, G. V., Teele, K., Hayes, O., McNally, A., and Bruno, D. (1955b). *New Engl. J. Med.* **253**, 349-355.

Mann, G. V., Watson, P. L., and Adams, L. (1952). *J. Nutrition* **47**, 213-224.

Mann, G. V., Andrus, S. B., McNally, A., and Stare, F. J. (1953). *J. Exptl. Med.* **98**, 195-217.

Marx, W., Marx, L., and Deuel, H. J., Jr. (1951). *Am. Heart J.* **42**, 124-128.

Mason, R. L., Hunt, H. M., and Hurxthal, L. M. (1930). *New Engl. J. Med.* **203**, 1273-1278.

Mathivat, A., and Cottet, J. (1953). *Bull. mém. soc. méd. hôp. Paris* **69**, 1030-1048.

Mayer, A., and Schaeffer, G. (1913). *J. physiol. et pathol. gén.* **15**, 984-998.

Melka, J. (1927). *Zentr. inn. Med.* **48**, 704.

Messinger, W. J., Porosowska, Y., and Steele, J. M. (1950). *A.M.A. Arch. Internal Med.* **86**, 189-195.

Mininni, G., Contro, S., and Checchia, C. (1955). *Circulation Research* **3**, 191-193.

Morris, B., and Courtice, F. C. (1955). *Quart. J. Exptl. Physiol.* **40**, 127-137.

Moynihan, B. (1925). *Brit. Med. J.* **i**, 393-398.

Muhlbock, O., and Kaufmann, C. (1938). *Z. ges. exptl. Med.* **102**, 461-468.

Nakanishi, K., Bhattacharyya, B. K., and Fieser, L. F. (1953). *J. Am. Chem. Soc.* **75**, 4415-4417.

Neumann, J., and Herrmann, E. (1911). *Wien. klin. Wochschr.* **24**, 411.

Nikkilä, E. A. (1953). *Scand. J. Clin. & Lab. Invest.* **5**, Suppl. 8.
Offrenkrantz, F. M. (1938). *Am. J. Clin. Pathol.* **8**, 536.
Okey, R., and Boyden, R. E. (1927). *J. Biol. Chem.* **72**, 261-281.
Oliver, M. F., and Boyd, G. S. (1953a). *Clin. Sci.* **12**, 217-222.
Oliver, M. F., and Boyd, G. S. (1953b). *Brit. Heart J.* **15**, 387-392.
Oliver, M. F., and Boyd, G. S. (1953c). *Clin. Sci.* **12**, 293-298.
Oliver, M. F., and Boyd, G. S. (1954). *Am. Heart J.* **47**, 348-359.
Oliver, M. F., and Boyd, G. S. (1955a). *Clin. Sci.* **14**, 15-23.
Oliver, M. F., and Boyd, G. S. (1955b). *Minn. Med.* **38**, 794-799.
Oliver, M. F., and Boyd, G. S. (1956a). *Circulation* **13**, 82-91.
*Oliver, M. F., and Boyd, G. S. (1956b). *Lancet* ii, 1273-1276. Endocrine influences.
Oliver, M. F., and Boyd, G. S. (1957a). *Lancet* i, 124-125.
Oliver, M. F., and Boyd, G. S. (1957b). *Lancet* ii, 829-830.
*Oncley, J. L. (1956). *Harvey Lectures. Ser.* **50**, 71-91. Lipoprotein view.
Oncley, J. L., Gurd, F. R. N., and Melin, M. (1950). *J. Am. Chem. Soc.* **72**, 458-464.
Oncley, J. L., Walton, K. W., and Cornwell, D. G. (1957). *J. Am. Chem. Soc.* **79**, 4666-4671.
Page, I. H., and Brown, H. B. (1952). *Circulation* **6**, 681-687.
Page, I. H., Kirk, E., Lewis, W. H., Jr., Thompson, W. R., and Van Slyke, D. D. (1935). *J. Biol. Chem.* **111**, 613-639.
Page, I. H., Lewis, L. A., and Gilbert, J. (1956). *Circulation* **13**, 675-679.
Parsons, W. B., Achor, R. W. P., Berge, K. G., McKenzie, B. F., and Barker, N. W. (1956). *Proc. Staff Meetings Mayo Clinic* **31**, 377-390.
Pekkarinen, A., Kerppola, I., and Petro, L. (1952). *Acta Endocrinol.* **10**, 212-220.
Perry, H. M., and Schroeder, H. A. (1955). *J. Chronic Diseases* **2**, 520-533.
Peters, J. P., and Man, E. B. (1943). *J. Clin. Invest.* **22**, 715-720.
*Peters, J. P., and Van Slyke, D. D. (1946). "Quantitative Clinical Chemistry," 2nd ed. Interpretations, 1. Williams and Wilkins, Baltimore, Maryland.
Pribram, E. E. (1923). *Arch. Gynäkol.* **119**, 57.
Rafstedt, S. (1955). *Acta Paediat. Suppl.* 102.
Rafstedt, S., and Swahn, B. (1954). *Acta Paediat.* **43**, 221-234.
Robinson, R. W., Higano, N., and Cohen, W. D. (1957). *A.M.A. Arch. Internal Med.* **100**, 739-743.
Russ, E. M., Eder, H. A., and Barr, D. P. (1951). *Am. J. Med.* **11**, 468-479.
Russ, E. M., Eder, H. A., and Barr, D. P. (1955). *Am. J. Med.* **19**, 4-24.
Schettler, G. (1950). *Klin. Wochschr.* **28**, 565-566.
Schettler, G. (1955). *Medizinische No.* **36**, 1247.
Schiller, H. (1919). *Surg. Gynecol. Obstet.* **29**, 450-454.
Schube, P. G. (1937). *J. Lab. Clin. Med.* **22**, 280-284.
Schwarz, O. H., Soule, S. D., and Durie, B. (1940). *Am. J. Obstet. Gynecol.* **39**, 203-213.
Seifter, J., Baeder, D. H., Zilliken, F. W. (1956). *Abstr. 20th Intern. Physiol. Congr., Brussels,* p. 818.
Sellers, E. A., and You, R. W. (1956). *Brit. Med. J.* i, 815-819.
Sherber, D. A., and Levites, M. M. (1953). *J. Am. Med. Assoc.* **152**, 682-686.
Slemons, J. M., and Stander, H. J. (1923). *Bull. Johns Hopkins Hosp.* **34**, 7-10.
Smith, G. van S., and Smith, O. W. (1936). *New Engl. J. Med.* **215**, 908-914.
Sperry, W. M. (1936). *Am. J. Diseases Children* **51**, 84-90.
Sperry, W. M. (1937). *J. Biol. Chem.* **117**, 391-395.

Sperry, W. M., and Webb, M. (1950). *J. Biol. Chem.* **187**, 107-110.

Stamler, J., Pick, R., and Katz, L. N. (1953). *Circulation Research* **1**, 94-98.

Stamler, J., Pick, R., and Katz, L. N. (1954). *Circulation* **10**, 237-246.

Stieger, A., Zaragonatis, C. J. D., Miller, G. M., Seifter, J., and Baeder, D. H. (1956). *Am. J. Med. Sci.* **232**, 605-612.

Steiner, A., and Domanski, B. (1944). *Proc. Soc. Exptl. Biol. Med.* **55**, 236-238.

Steiner, A., and Kendall, F. E. (1946). *A.M.A. Arch. Pathol.* **42**, 433.

Steiner, A., Payson, H., and Kendall, F. E. (1955). *Circulation* **11**, 784-788.

*Swahn, B. (1953). *Scand. J. Clin. & Lab. Invest.* **5**, Suppl. 9. Lipoprotein review.

Tanner, J. M. (1951). *J. Physiol.* **115**, 371-390.

Teilum, G. (1937). *Compt. Rend. soc. biol.* **125**, 577-580.

Terroine, E.-F. (1914). *J. physiol. et pathol. gén.* **16**, 386-397, 408-418.

Tiselius, A. (1930). *Nova Acta Regiae Soc. Sci. Upsaliensis* IV, **7** (4).

Tiselius, A. (1939). *Harvey Lectures Ser.* **35**, 37-70.

Toor, M., Katchalsky, A., Agmon, J., and Allalouf, D. (1957). *Lancet* i, 1270-1273.

Trotter, W. R. (1956). *Lancet* i, 885-889.

Tucker, H. F., and Eckstein, H. C. (1937). *J. Biol. Chem.* **121**, 479-484.

Tucker, R. G., and Keys, A. (1951). *J. Clin. Invest.* **30**, 869-873.

Turner, K. B. (1933). *J. Exptl. Med.* **58**, 115-125.

Turner, K. B., and Steiner, A. (1939). *J. Clin. Invest.* **18**, 45-49.

Walker, W. J., Lawry, E. Y., Love, D. E., Mann, G. V., Levine, S. A., and Stare, F. J. (1953). *Am. J. Med.* **14**, 654-664.

Weiner, N., Milch, L. J., and Shultz, G. E. (1956). *J. Appl. Physiol.* **9**, 88-90.

Weil, R., and Ross, S. (1949). *Endocrinology* **45**, 207.

Weld, C. B. (1944). *Can. Med. Assoc. J.* **51**, 578.

Widal, F., Weill, A., and Landat, M. (1913). *Compt. rend. soc. biol.* **74**, 882-883.

Wiese, H. F., and Hansen, A. E. (1951). Texas *Repts. Biol. Med.* **9**, 516-544.

Wilber, C. G., and Levine, V. E. (1950). *Exptl. Med. Surg.* **8**, 422-425.

Wilkinson, C. F., Jr., Blecha, E., and Reimer, A. (1950). *A.M.A. Arch. Internal Med.* **85**, 389-397.

CHAPTER 6

BIOSYNTHESIS OF CHOLESTEROL*

R. Gordon Gould

---

* Abbreviations used in Chapters 6 and 7: ATP, adenosine triphosphate; ADP, adenosine diphosphate; AMP, adenosine monophosphate or adenylic acid; CoA (or HSCoA), coenzyme A; HMG, β-hydroxy-β-methylglutarate; BMG, β-methylglutaconate; HIV, hydroxyisovalerate; DMA, dimethylacrylate; PP, pyrophosphate; MVA, mevalonic acid (β-methyl-β-hydroxy-δ-valerolactone); DPN, diphosphopyridine nucleotide or coenzyme I; EDTA, ethylenediaminetetraacetic acid; HCC, higher counting companions.

Chemical nomenclature in this chapter follows in general the preferred usage in the United States.

I. Introduction

Even before the introduction of isotopic tracer techniques, it had been established by balance methods that animals are capable of cholesterol biosynthesis (see Chapter 1). Page and Menschick (1932), and Schoenheimer and Breusch (1933), showed that either biosynthesis or degradation could occur, depending on the cholesterol content of the diet fed, but no clear idea of the rapidity of cholesterol biosynthesis nor of the pathway was gained until tracer methods were applied to this problem. Rittenberg and Schoenheimer (1937) found that deuterium (H^2), present in the body water of a mouse, gradually became incorporated into cholesterol in stable, nonexchangeable positions. This was interpreted as proving the total synthesis of cholesterol from small units which acquired deuterium atoms during the course of their chemical transformations, an interpretation which was subsequently confirmed by studies with C^{13}- and C^{14}-labeled precursors. In the deuterium oxide studies, the maximum incorporation observed in whole mice corresponded to approximately 50% of the stable cholesterol hydrogen atoms being derived from body water. Popják and Beeckmans (1950a) have found values of about 63% in a study of cholesterol synthesis in fetal rabbit liver and intestine.

Sonderhoff and Thomas (1937) found that deutero-acetate (CH^2_3-COO^-) was converted by yeast into ergosterol in high yield, and Bloch and Rittenberg (1942) showed it to be utilized by rats and mice for cholesterol synthesis. Later, Bloch *et al.* (1946) found rat liver slices capable of converting acetate-1-C^{14} into cholesterol, an observation which has stimulated an immense amount of work on many aspects of cholesterol biosynthesis. An important contribution has been the development by Bucher (1953) of a method of preparing cell-free fractions of liver capable of synthesizing cholesterol; only the microsomal and the soluble supernatant fractions are required.

II. Pathways in Cholesterol Biosynthesis

A. THE PATTERN OF ACETATE INCORPORATION

The magnitude and complexity of the task of working out the individual steps in cholesterol biosynthesis is apparent from the structural formula of cholesterol. Nevertheless, remarkable progress has been made during the last few years, particularly by Bloch and associates, although many other investigators have made important contributions. The pathway of biosynthesis may now be roughly sketched in, although there is still ample room for speculation by the reader. Total synthesis from acetate can be achieved by soluble extracts of liver, but no enzyme involved in this synthesis beyond the part common to fatty acid and cholesterol biosynthesis has yet been purified or even identified, and many intermediates are still unknown.

Acetate is the principal, and probably the only, common, simple metabolite from which cholesterol is biosynthesized. A number of other substances which have also been shown by isotopic tracer methods to contribute carbon or hydrogen atoms to cholesterol are listed in Table I. The evidence is in general compatible with the hypothesis that these substances are first metabolized to acetate or to an activated form of acetate, presumably acetyl coenzyme A. A few of the substances listed, particularly acetaldehyde, butyrate, and the isopropyl portion of isovalerate, have been reported to be converted into cholesterol with higher efficiency than for acetate. Although the explanation of these observations is not apparent at present, it should be noted that in some cases the results from different laboratories vary considerably in a quantitative sense, suggesting that the explanation may lie in the experimental conditions chosen.

Every carbon in cholesterol may be derived from acetate; this was established by the very extensive studies which have been in progress since about 1949 in several laboratories with the goal of isolating and identifying the origin of each carbon atom in cholesterol. Wuersch et al. (1952) completed the analysis of the side chain, and Popják and Cornforth have recently completed the remarkable feat of a systematic carbon-by-carbon dissection of the whole ring system (Cornforth et al., 1953, 1956, 1957a; Popják, 1955). The pattern of distribution of acetate methyl and carboxyl carbons in cholesterol is shown in Fig. 1. Carboxyl-labeled acetate gives C^{14} only in the positions indicated in the figure, but methyl-labeled acetate gives about 5 to 10% as much C^{14} in carboxyl positions as in methyl positions. The explanation of this partial randomization is evident from a consideration of the Krebs tricarboxylic acid pathway, as shown in Fig. 2. Methyl-labeled acetate may be used directly for sterol biosynthesis, or it may condense with oxalacetate to form citrate and later give rise, via pyruvate, to acetate in which both carbons are labeled; with carboxyl-labeled acetate redistribution will result in loss of C^{14}.

TABLE I

SOME PRECURSORS OF CHOLESTEROL[a]

Compound	Reference
Acetate	1, etc.
Acetaldehyde	12
Ethanol	2, 14
Pyruvate	2, 17, 19
Acetone	5, 8, 12
Acetoacetate	11, 12, 16, 18
Butyrate	3, 10, 16
Isobutyrate	3, 15
Valerate	2
Isovalerate	3, 8, 10, 12, 16, 19
Octanoate	20
Glucose	17
Leucine	3
Valine	10

[a] All these compounds are known to give rise to acetyl groups during metabolism.

References

1. Bloch and Rittenberg (1942)
2. Bloch and Rittenberg (1944)
3. Bloch (1944)
4. Anker (1948)
5. Borek and Rittenberg (1949)
6. Brady and Gurin (1950)
7. Little and Bloch (1950)
8. Zabin and Bloch (1950)
9. Pihl et al. (1950)
10. Bloch (1951)
11. Curran (1951)
12. Brady and Gurin (1951)
13. Brady et al. (1951)
14. Curran and Rittenberg (1951)
15. Kritchevsky and Gray (1951)
16. Zabin and Bloch (1951)
17. Popják et al. (1953)
18. Blecher and Gurin (1954)
19. Lynen (1955)
20. Lyon et al. (1956)

In the course of the degradative studies, a working hypothesis of cholesterol biosynthesis was evolved and many of the salient points firmly established. Bonner and Arreguin (1949) had found that acetate or β,β-dimethylacrylate increases rubber formation in guayule plants; they suggested that three molecules of acetate might condense with the elimination of one carboxyl group to form an isoprenoid unit such as dimethylacrylate from which rubber could be formed by further condensation. Such an isoprenoid unit would have the distribution of methyl and carboxyl carbons shown in Fig. 1. On finding that the side chain of cholesterol has this pattern of distribution of methyl and carboxyl carbons, Bloch and his collaborators suggested that cholesterol might be formed from acetate by (1) condensation to an isoprenoid unit; (2) polymerization to squalene; and (3) cyclization of squalene to give cholesterol (Wuersch *et al.*, 1952; Bloch, 1954). The idea that squalene might be an intermediate in cholesterol biosynthesis was not new. Channon (1926) had noted that feeding rats with squalene produced a large increase in the liver cholesterol concentration, and both he and Heilbronn *et al.* (1926) commented on the possibility that squalene might be a precursor of cholesterol. Robinson (1934) suggested a scheme of cyclization of squalene with the splitting off of 3 methyl groups, but not until 1953 was this problem successfully attacked experimentally. Langdon and Bloch (1953a) showed by means of C^{14} that squalene is an intermediate in cholesterol biosynthesis. The investigations since that time can be conveniently grouped into two categories, those dealing with the steps betwen acetate and squalene, and those concerned with the steps between squalene and cholesterol itself.

B. ACETATE TO SQUALENE

The over-all pathway of acetate to squalene was established by the complete degradation of squalene-C^{14}, prepared by incubation of acetate-2-C^{14} with rat liver mince in the presence of squalene carrier (Cornforth and Popják, 1954). The distribution of methyl and carboxyl carbons, given in Fig. 1, is in full accord with the isoprenoid hypothesis. The identity of the isoprenoid unit is still not certain and many of the steps are still hypothetical.

1. Acetate Activation

The first step in all known reactions of acetate in mammalian tissues is undoubtedly the activation of acetate by combination with coenzyme A to give a high-energy thiolester linkage, $CH_3COSCoA$. The acetate-activating enzyme is widely distributed in animal tissues, plants, and yeast, and has been much studied (e.g. Jones *et al.*, 1953; Beinert *et al.*, 1953; Hele, 1954). ATP and Mg ions are required and pyrophosphate is formed in the reaction. Berg (1955) using a purified acetate-activating enzyme from yeast, showed that this reaction probably involves the intermediate formation of an acid anhydride between acetic acid and adenylic acid:

$$CH_3COO^- + ATP \rightleftharpoons \text{acetyladenylate} + \text{pyrophosphate}$$
$$\text{acetyladenylate} + HSCoA \rightleftharpoons CH_3COSCoA + AMP$$

2. Acetoacetate and Acetoacetyl CoA

Acetoacetyl CoA is generally considered to be an intermediate in both fatty acid and cholesterol biosynthesis and in ketone body formation. The conversion of acetyl CoA to acetoacetyl CoA is catalyzed by β-ketothiolase (Lynen *et al.*, 1952). Both acetate units must be activated as shown by Stadtman *et al.* (1951; also see Stern *et al.*, 1953).

$$CH_3COSCoA + CH_3COSCoA \rightleftharpoons CH_3COCH_2COSCoA + HSCoA$$

In 1951 several groups of investigators put forward evidence suggesting that acetoacetate itself was an intermediate in cholesterol biosynthesis (Brady and Gurin, 1951; Curran, 1951; Zabin and Bloch, 1951), but a reinvestigation by Blecher and Gurin (1954) using acetoacetate-1-C^{14} and -4-C^{14} demonstrated that the acetoacetate molecules must

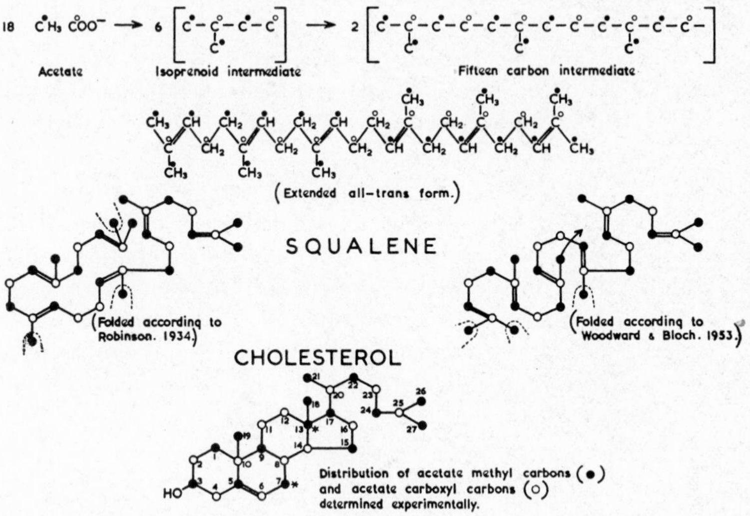

FIG. 1. The pattern of acetate incorporation in cholesterol. The distribution of acetate methyl and carboxyl carbons in squalene and in cholesterol are those experimentally determined. The distribution in the 15-carbon intermediate is hypothetical, based on the isoprenoid theory of biosynthesis. Squalene is shown in three forms, extended all-*trans* form and folded. The sign – – – – indicates removal of a methyl group necessary for cholesterol formation. Carbon atoms 7 and 13 in cholesterol are marked ° to show their relative positions in the squalene molecule (see p. 220).

have been converted into acetate or equilibrated with it before incorporation into cholesterol.

3. Isoprenoid Intermediates

It is highly probable that a branched chain compound with either 5 or 6 carbon atoms is an intermediate in the formation of squalene and cholesterol. A number of branched chain mono- and di-carboxylic acids have been studied, including β-hydroxy-β-methylglutarate or HMG, β-methylglutaconate or BMG, β-hydroxyisovalerate or HIV, and di-

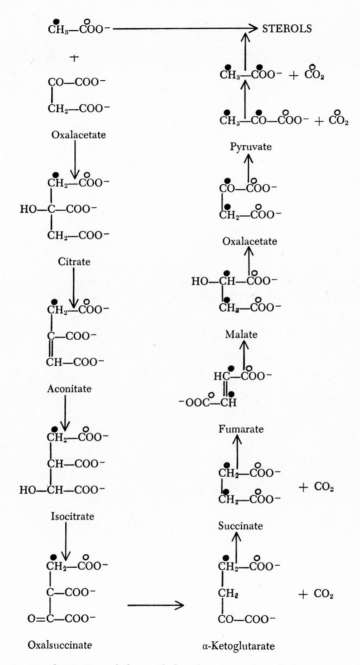

Fᴵɢ. 2. Randomization of the methyl carbon in acetate during passage through the Krebs citric acid cycle.

methylacrylate or DMA (see Fig. 3). By means of C^{14}-labeling, the formation from acetate and conversion to cholesterol have been demonstrated for each. The efficiency of conversion into cholesterol is low in every case and their interconvertibility with each other and with acetate has made it difficult to prove whether any one is actually an intermediate or not. The literature on these compounds is too extensive to list in full but reference is made to the Symposium on Cholesterol Biosynthesis (1955); and to Rabinowitz and Gurin (1954), Rudney (1954), Bloch *et al.* (1954), Lynen (1955), Adamson and Greenberg (1957), and Rudney (1957).

A recently discovered compound of this type, β-hydroxy-β-methyl-δ-valerolactone (see Fig. 3), was shown by Tavormina *et al.* (1956) to

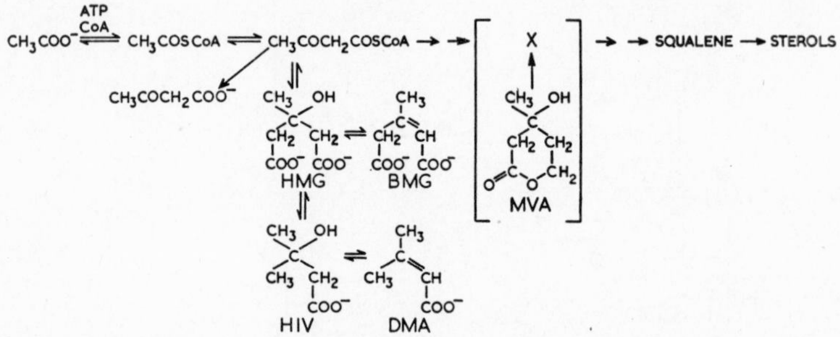

FIG. 3. Some possible intermediates in the pathway from acetate to squalene. MVA, mevalonic acid (β-methyl-β-hydroxy-δ-valerolactone); HMG, β-hydroxy-β-methylglutarate; BMG, β-methylglutaconate; HIV, β-hydroxyisovalerate; DMA, β-dimethylacrylate; ATP, adenosine triphosphate; CoA, coenzyme A.

differ strikingly from the above-mentioned acids in being converted into cholesterol with high efficiency. The name mevalonic acid or MVA has been proposed for this lactone.* This substance was discovered as the result of a search for the "acetate-replacing factor", a growth factor for certain Lactobacilli (Wolf *et al.*, 1956). DL-Mevalonic lactone-2-C^{14} was then synthesized by Tavormina *et al.* (1956), and found to be converted into cholesterol by rat liver homogenate preparations in yields as high as 43%. If only one enantiomorph is utilized, the conversion is almost quantitative.

The carboxyl group of mevalonic acid is eliminated during the con-

---

* The terms mevalonic acid(β,δ-dihydroxy-β-methylvaleric acid) and mevalonic lactone (β-hydroxy-β-methyl-δ-valerolactone) are used interchangeably in this discussion. The lactone is the form customarily employed in experiments but since the lactone ring opens rapidly in the physiological pH range and does not close readily, it is probably the acid form which reacts.

version as was shown by the absence of C^{14} in cholesterol formed from mevalonic acid-1-C^{14} (Tavormina and Gibbs, 1956). Cornforth *et al.* (1957b) showed mevalonic acid to give rise to squalene and determined the pattern of incorporation by complete degradation with results shown in Fig. 4. The position of the C^{14} atoms shows that squalene is built up by the formation of linkages between the 2 and 5 positions in mevalonic acid and invites the speculation that decarboxylation and dehydration of the lactone may occur to produce a bi-radical capable of polymerizing to form polyisoprenoid chains as indicated in Fig. 4.

Mevalonic acid forms a phosphorylated derivative which may represent the first step in the conversion to squalene and sterols; Tchen (1957) has reported that in the presence of a soluble yeast extract fraction, ATP,

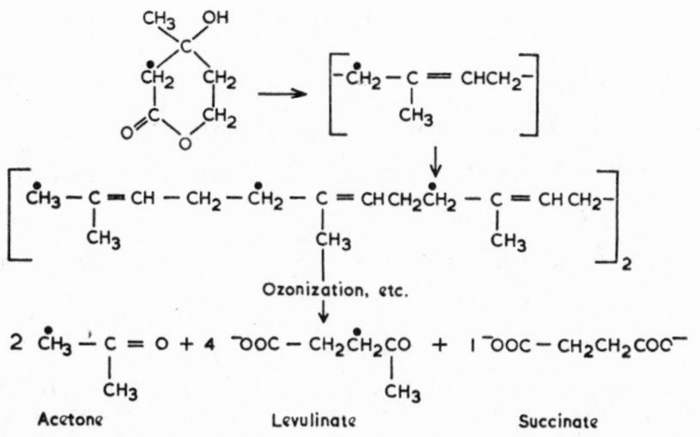

FIG. 4. The pattern of mevalonic acid incorporation in squalene as shown by degradation and identification of each carbon in the products shown (Cornforth *et al.*, 1957b).

Mn^{++}, and fluoride, MVA is converted into a monophosphorylated compound which still contains the carboxyl group but is not a carboxyl phosphate.

Mevalonic lactone-2-C^{14}-5-di-H^3 is converted into squalene with no change in the C^{14}: H^3 ratio, indicating that neither of the hydrogen atoms attached to carbon 5 is lost or labilized during the biosynthetic process (Amdur *et al.*, 1957).

Conversion of squalene into cholesterol should result in the elimination as CO_2 of one C^{14} atom derived from mevalonic acid-2-C^{14} according to the Woodward-Bloch theory discussed below and should give cholesterol labeled in positions 1, 7, 15, 22, 26, and 27. The administration of mevalonic acid-2-C^{14} to intact rats and mice has been reported to result in urinary excretion of almost exactly half the labeled material, and the conversion of up to 37% to cholesterol-C^{14} and about 10% to

$C^{14}O_2$ (Gould and Popják, 1957). Theoretical yields on the assumption that one enantiomorph is quantitatively utilized are 41.7% cholesterol, 8.3% CO_2, and 50% in urine. Mevalonic acid differs significantly from the other 5 and 6 carbon atom branched chain acids in that its conversion into squalene and cholesterol is apparently the only metabolic reaction it undergoes in mammalian tissues.

The biosynthesis of cholesterol from acetate is irreversible, in contrast to that of fatty acids. It is probable, although not yet established by direct proof, that mevalonic acid is an intermediate in cholesterol biosynthesis and that it is formed from acetate; the evidence indicates that at least one step in this biosynthesis must be irreversible.

4. Ten-Carbon Intermediates

Geranic acid, $(CH_3)_2C = CHCH_2CH_2C(CH_3) = CHCOOH$, has been considered as a possible intermediate but no evidence in favor of this view has been reported. Rudney and Farkas (1955) incubated acetate-2-C^{14} with the Rabinowitz and Gurin (1953) liver extract and geranic acid. A C^{14}-acid was formed which was similar to but not identical with geranic acid; chromatographic fractionation of the labeled material containing carrier geranic acid showed separation of the C^{14} and titration peaks. Schwenk et al. (1955a) report that synthetic geranic acid C^{14} was not converted into cholesterol in rats and Sandermann and Stockmann (1956) also reported the same finding.

5. Fifteen-Carbon Intermediates

Farnesenic acid, $(CH_3)_2C = CHCH_2CH_2C(CH_3) = CHCH_2CH_2C$ $(CH_3) = CHCOOH$, has been investigated and some evidence supporting the assumption that it is an intermediate has been reported. Dituri et al. (1956) have reported the isolation of C^{14}-labeled farnesenic acid after incubation of β-hydroxy-β-methylglutarate-C^{14} with the Rabinowitz-Gurin enzyme preparation, but it was apparently not formed from acetate. Unlabeled farnesenic acid reduced the incorporation of HMG-C^{14} into squalene; farnesol did also, but there was no evidence of formation of labeled farnesol. In intact animals, Karvinen and Laakso (1957) have reported that farnesol did not decrease the incorporation of acetate-C^{14} into cholesterol. Langdon and Bloch (1953b) had previously found no effect of farnesol on in vitro cholesterol synthesis from acetate. Sandermann and Stockmann (1956) reported that farnesenic acid-C^{14} of synthetic origin does not give rise to labeled cholesterol but the possibility that the right stereoisomer was absent must be considered. Inhibition of MVA conversion to cholesterol was noted by Wright and Cleland (1957) to be more pronounced from the addition of farnesenic acid than from squalene but these authors concluded that farnesenic acid may be either an intermediate or an anti-metabolite in cholesterol biosynthesis.

6. Squalene

This triterpenoid hydrocarbon first isolated by Tsujimoto in 1906 is now known to have a wide distribution. Langdon and Bloch (1953a) demonstrated the biosynthesis of squalene and simultaneously prepared squalene-C^{14} by feeding rats with unlabeled squalene and acetate-1-C^{14}. Reisolation of the squalene from liver and intestine revealed it to contain C^{14}. On subsequently feeding this squalene to mice, liver cholesterol was obtained which showed a very high incorporation of the C^{14} of the absorbed squalene. Feeding unlabeled squalene together with or immediately before the administration of acetate-C^{14} is advantageous because the amount of squalene in rat liver—the squalene "pool"—is so small that it must have a very rapid turnover time; the carrier squalene acts as a trapping agent. The size of this "pool" has recently been determined by an isotope dilution method to be 50 µg. per gram of liver, of which only about half was believed to be metabolically active (Loud, 1956). An earlier estimate by Langdon and Bloch (1953a, b) was 25 µg. per gram of liver. The rate of synthesis of cholesterol in normal liver slices is about 20 µg. per gram liver per hour (Taylor et al., 1956), suggesting that the turnover half-time of the active squalene is less than 1 hour. Langdon and Bloch (1953a, b) found that squalene-C^{14} reached maximum specific activity within 30 minutes after acetate-C^{14} administration.

The 4 central double bonds of squalene result in 8 possible geometrical isomers, but the naturally occurring form consists of only the all-*trans* isomer (Nicolaides and Laves, 1954). "Purification" of natural squalene through the crystalline hexahydrochloride results in material closely resembling the natural compound in physical properties but differing stereochemically and in being completely inactive as cholesterol precursor (Tomkins et al., 1953a; Langdon and Bloch, 1953a). There is evidence some of the double bonds have shifted as well. Karrer (1953) has reported the synthesis of the all-*trans* isomer of squalene but the conversion of synthetic squalene-C^{14} is yet to be demonstrated. Many confirmations of the role of squalene in cholesterol biosynthesis have since been reported, ranging from its biosynthesis in human skin with 10 times the specific activity of cholesterol (Nicolaides et al., 1955), to biosynthesis by the particle-free fraction of liver homogenate (Dituri et al., 1956).

The technique of demonstrating the occurrence of a suspected inter-

mediate present in trace amounts, by means of a labeled precursor together with the unlabeled intermediate serving as a trapping agent and
a carrier, has been widely and effectively used.

The observation that squalene decreases the incorporation of acetate-
C^{14} into cholesterol has been advanced as evidence that squalene is an
intermediate. It is now clear that this type of information, while useful
as a guide, is not a valid argument in this connection because a number
of substances (e.g. cholestenone, dehydroisoandrosterone, and α-biphenylbutyrate) inhibit acetate incorporation into cholesterol but are
known not to be themselves converted into cholesterol (see Chap. 7).

C. SQUALENE TO CHOLESTEROL

1. Chemical Considerations

Great progress has been made on the elucidation of the cyclization
of squalene and the final steps in cholesterol biosynthesis, largely due to
the investigations of Bloch and his associates. Robinson's (1934) scheme
of cyclization of squalene (Fig. 1) was in agreement with many of the
results on the origin of the individual carbon atoms of cholesterol.
Woodward and Bloch (1953), however, considered the possibility of an
alternative scheme of folding and cyclization of squalene, shown in Fig.
1. The only carbons in cholesterol which differ in their derivation from
acetate carbons and thus permit a choice between the two hypotheses
are 7, 8, 12, and 13. The first clue was obtained by Woodward and Bloch
who, starting with epiandrosterone (derived from methyl-labeled cholesterol), carried out a Kuhn-Roth oxidation and obtained carbons 19
and 10, and 18 and 13 as acetic acid. Further degradation of the acetic
acid showed that 18 and 19 are methyl carbons, as Little and Bloch
(1950) had previously reported, and that either 10 or 13 must also be
a methyl carbon since the mixture had half the specific activity of methyl
carbons. Since Cornforth et al. (1953) had previously established that
10 is a carboxyl carbon, it was inferred that 13 must be a methyl carbon.
This conclusion favors the Woodward-Bloch folding; confirmatory evidence was shortly forthcoming. Carbon 7 was isolated and shown to be
a methyl carbon by Bloch (1953) and by Dauben and Takemura (1953).
Carbon 13 was isolated and its identity confirmed by Cornforth and
Popják (1954), and carbons 11 and 12, the two adjacent carboxyl carbons derived from the center of the squalene molecule according to the
Woodward-Bloch formulation, were separately isolated and identified
as carboxyls by Cornforth et al. (1956).

All the carbons in cholesterol have now been identified, as shown
in Fig. 1, and the pattern of distribution is in complete agreement with
the Woodward-Bloch hypothesis. Although it requires the shift of a

methyl group from position 8 to 13, such shifts are well known in triterpene chemistry and the manner of folding of the chain is much more probable than that in the earlier scheme. Ruzicka (1953) has presented an interesting discussion of mechanisms of ring closure which helps to bring the chemical and biochemical points of view closer together.

2. Cyclization to Lanosterol

Evidence of another kind was also obtained which not only confirmed the Woodward-Bloch cyclization hypothesis, but which enabled an attack to be made on the steps between squalene and cholesterol. Schwenk and Werthessen (1952) had observed that under certain conditions biosynthetic cholesterol-C^{14} was accompanied by digitonin-precipitable materials with higher specific activities which were separable from cholesterol by purification through the dibromide. Dayton et al. (1953) found that rats sacrificed 3 minutes after intravenous injection of acetate-C^{14} yielded liver sterol digitonide containing about 80% of the label as noncholesterol contaminants. These substances, named "higher counting companions", (HCC), by Schwenk, were present in trace amounts, making their identification in the absence of any clues very difficult (Schwenk and Werthessen, 1953; Schwenk et al., 1955a, c).

Bloch and associates found a clue in lanosterol, a constituent of wool fat; its structure was elucidated by Voser et al. (1952) and shown to be a 4,4,14-trimethyl sterol (Fig. 5). It is evident that ring closure of squalene might give lanosterol as the first product. Using the same technique as in the squalene studies, Clayton and Bloch (1956) showed that rat liver synthesizes lanosterol from acetate and that liver rapidly converts lanosterol into cholesterol. Like squalene, lanosterol appears to be a normal constituent in trace amounts of tissues actively synthesizing cholesterol. Tchen and Bloch (1957a, b) have made an experimental attack on the mechanism of enzymatic cyclization of squalene and have shown by means of O^{18} that the oxygen in lanosterol is derived from O_2 and not from H_2O or OH^-. No hydrogen from the medium was incorporated into squalene during cyclization.

3. C_{29} Intermediate

The three methyl groups lost in the transformation of lanosterol to cholesterol (at positions 4 and 14) are oxidized to carboxyl groups and eliminated as CO_2 (Olson and Bloch, 1956). This was demonstrated by preparing lanosterol with all the methyl carbons labeled with C^{14} and incubating this material with rat liver homogenate. For each mole of lanosterol converted into cholesterol approximately 3 moles of $C^{14}O_2$

were formed. Cholesterol prepared from carboxyl-labeled acetate lost virtually no $C^{14}O_2$ under these conditions.

Chromatographic fractionation on deactivated alumina of the non-saponifiable material obtained from liver and intestine of rats sacrificed a few minutes after the injection of acetate-C^{14}, has yielded a compound referred to as X_1 by Gautschi and Bloch (1957). Although only minute amounts were available, they have obtained, by ingenious methods, evidence that X_1 is a C_{29} sterol differing from lanosterol in having lost the methyl group at position 14 (4,4-dimethylcholestadienol). The most significant single finding was that X_1 yielded only about 2/3 as much

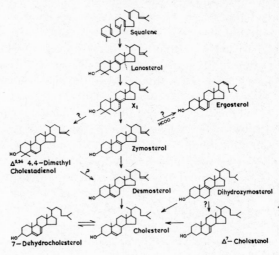

FIG. 5. The pathway from squalene to cholesterol and ergosterol.

$C^{14}O_2$ on incubation with a liver homogenate. Although there is still uncertainty as to the location of the ring double bond in X_1, a probable formula is that in Fig. 5.

4. Zymosterol

$\Delta^{8,24}$-Cholestadienol or zymosterol has been known to be present in yeast and Alexander and Schwenk (1957) have reported evidence indicating that it is also present in pig liver although only in trace amount.

Zymosterol-C^{14} was obtained from yeast by incubation with acetate-C^{14} and shown to be converted into cholesterol-C^{14} in rats (Schwenk et al., 1955a) and in rat liver homogenate (Johnston and Bloch, 1957).

In a discussion of the mechanism of conversion of lanosterol to cholesterol, Bloch (1956a, b) has pointed out that it might be expected that the 8-9 double bond would move to the final 5-6 position before the elimination by oxidation and decarboxylation of the two methyl groups in the 4 position because of the labilizing effect of a β-γ double bond on a carboxyl group. This pathway is indicated in Fig. 5. The experimental evidence at the time of writing, however, favors the view that zymosterol is an intermediate.

5. $\Delta^{5,24}$-Cholestadienol (Desmosterol)

Stokes *et al.* (1956) isolated a new sterol from 12–14-day-old chick embryos by chromatographic fractionation of the *p*-iodobenzoates-I[131]. It was present to the extent of about 2% of the total sterols in chick embryo, but was absent from infertile eggs. The properties and direct comparison with an authentic sample show it to be $\Delta^{5,24}$-cholestadienol (Fig. 5), for which they propose the name desmosterol (*desmo* = link). After 16 hours' incubation of acetate-C[14] with chick embryos, the desmosterol had about 20 times as high a specific activity value as the accompanying cholesterol, suggesting it to be an intermediate in cholesterol biosynthesis. They mention preliminary experiments showing the conversion of "desmosterol-C[14]" to cholesterol-C[14], in rats, a finding which would strengthen this idea.

Evidence that the double bond in the side chain persists until the later stages is discussed by Johnston and Bloch (1957).

6. Unidentified Intermediates

The isolation of a possible intermediate from rat skin has been reported by Frantz *et al.* (1956). This compound has not been identified, but it has been shown to be not identical with any other known precursor and to be readily converted into cholesterol by liver slices.

Stokes *et al.* (1956) reported the isolation of an unidentified intermediate from chick embryo, in addition to desmosterol.

7. Relationship of Cholesterol to Other Tissue Sterols

a. Δ^7-Cholestenol (Lathosterol). Δ^7-Cholestenol is absorbed when fed and appears to be converted into cholesterol by rabbits (Cook *et al.*, 1954; Biggs *et al.* 1954). In fact, it may produce as large an increase in serum cholesterol level as does the feeding of cholesterol itself, and it also produces an increase in liver cholesterol concentration. Davidson *et al.* (1957) have shown liver homogenate capable of transforming Δ^7-cholestenol into cholesterol by the use of tritium-labeled substrate.

The fact that the feeding of Δ^7-cholestenol to rats results in a pronounced inhibition in the ability of liver slices to convert acetate to cholesterol (Langdon and Bloch, 1953b; Tomkins *et al.*, 1953b) cannot be accepted as proof that Δ^7-cholestenol is an intermediate since increased liver cholesterol concentrations are associated with decreased synthetic rates, as discussed in Chapter 7.

b. *7-Dehydrocholesterol.* Cholesterol and 7-dehydrocholesterol appear to be mutually interconvertible in intestine as shown by Glover *et al.* (1952) using nonisotopic methods. 7-Dehydrocholesterol is converted into cholesterol in rabbits with such facility that it is atherogenic (Cook *et al.*, 1954). While there is no direct evidence that 7-dehydrocholesterol is an intermediate, the observation of Page and Menschick (1930) that a substance with the same absorption bands in the ultraviolet as 7-dehydrocholesterol (or ergosterol) is present in the brain of the human fetus and newborn infant, but not in the adult, is of interest. Liver slices from rats fed 7-dehydrocholesterol show an inhibition of cholesterol synthesis (Langdon and Bloch, 1953b; Tomkins *et al.*, 1953b), but this finding is readily explained by conversion to cholesterol and consequent increase in liver cholesterol concentration, and does not indicate 7-dehydrocholesterol to be an intermediate.

c. *Cholestanol.* Little is known about the biosynthesis of this saturated sterol which is present as a constant companion of cholesterol to the extent of 1–3% in normal tissue and in larger amount in atherosclerotic arteries. As the result of a number of observations of Schoenheimer and others, cholestanol was considered for many years to be an end-product of cholesterol metabolism, but it has recently been shown to be metabolized but by a different pathway than cholesterol. Its metabolic relationships with Δ^4-cholestenone and Δ^5-cholestene-3α-ol (epicholesterol) are discussed in Chapter 7, but whether it is formed from cholesterol or as a by-product of cholesterol biosynthesis is uncertain.

d. *Dihydrozymosterol.* Δ^8-Cholestenol has been shown by Johnston and Bloch (1957) to be converted into cholesterol but not as readily as is zymosterol itself; e.g. rat liver homogenate prepared with a blade homogenizer transforms the latter but not the former into cholesterol. It is tempting to postulate the series of reactions: zymosterol → dihydrozymosterol → lathosterol → cholesterol; i.e. $\Delta^{8,24}$-cholestadienol → Δ^8-cholestenol → Δ^7-cholestenol → Δ^5-cholestenol, but the evidence at present does not support this hypothesis.

e. *Alternative pathways.* The above discussion has for simplicity assumed that there is only one pathway in cholesterol biosynthesis. It is of course entirely possible that alternative pathways exist in different tissues, or even in the same tissue. Although it is always difficult to prove a substance to be an intermediate, rigorously and in all species and tissues, the powerful methods now available and the intensive investigations at present in progress promise to extend our knowledge of pathways and intermediates very rapidly and will no doubt make the above discussion quickly out of date.

III. Sites of Sterol Biosynthesis in Animal Tissues

A. Intracellular Sites

The development of a method of homogenization of liver tissue without destruction of the capacity to synthesize cholesterol (Bucher, 1953) has made it possible to attack the problem of cholesterol biosynthesis from an enzymological standpoint. By lysing the small particle fraction containing the mitochondria and large microsomes, combining this extract with the soluble supernatant, and recentrifuging at 100,000 $\times$ g, Rabinowitz and Gurin (1953) obtained a particle-free extract which is capable of synthesizing cholesterol from acetate, and has been much used. Neither the nucleus nor the mitochondria are required, but both the larger microsome and the soluble supernatant (or particle-free) fractions are (Bucher and McGarrahan, 1956). The system requires Mg ions, nicotinamide (presumably to inhibit the breakdown of DPN), DPN, an energy source, and oxygen to convert acetate into cholesterol. Coenzyme A and ATP are necessary but need not be added to this system.

There is evidence suggesting that the soluble supernatant fraction is required primarily for the early stages and both fractions for the final. Rabinowitz et al. (1955) have reported synthesis of squalene from β-hydroxy-β-methylglutarate-C^{14} (HMG) by the soluble fraction alone, and Amdur et al. (1957) have shown that a particle-free preparation from yeast can convert mevalonic lactone into squalene. Johnston and Bloch (1957) find that both fractions are required to convert zymosterol to cholesterol.

The coenzyme requirements of the yeast enzyme system that forms squalene from MVA was reported by Amdur et al. (1957) to include Mn^{++}, ATP, and either DPN or TPN but not CoA. Requirements of the rat liver enzyme system that forms squalene anerobically and sterols aerobically have been found by Popják et al. (1958) to include both DPNH and TPNH, ATP, and an SH compound, present in microsomes, which available evidence indicates is probably CoA. The suggestion that cholesterol synthesis may be regulated by the balance between TPNH and DPNH has been made by Siperstein and Fagan (1957), who found that TPN stimulates cholesterol synthesis from acetate in homogenates containing glucose-6-phosphate far more than DPN and somewhat more than the addition of both these coenzymes. TPN stimulates glucose oxidation by the hexose monophosphate shunt to give TPNH and DPN by the Embden-Meyerhof pathway to give DPNH. Under physiological circumstances, the fraction of glucose metabolism that proceeds by the hexose monophosphate shunt may play a role in the regulation of the rate of cholesterol biosynthesis according to this suggestion.

It is interesting but perhaps not surprising that the microsomes should be the focus of cellular cholesterol biosynthesis as they are also important sites of protein and ribonucleic acid synthesis.

B. Extrahepatic Cholesterol Synthesis

Although most attention has been given to liver, other tissues are capable of cholesterol synthesis. In fact extrahepatic cholesterol synthesis in rats appears to be quantitatively the greater process, as judged from the observation that 30 minutes after the injection of acetate-C^{14}, several times as much cholesterol-C^{14} is found outside the liver as inside.

The methods which have been used to study extrahepatic synthesis are: (1) *in vitro* tissue slice incubation, (2) perfusion of isolated organs, (3) hepatectomized animals, and (4) short-term studies on intact animals. The first two methods give indisputable evidence of the synthetic ability of the tissue under study but the rates are not necessarily representative of those in the intact animal. A comparison of results obtained by several methods is the best way of assessing the relative importance of the various tissues in cholesterol metabolism.

1. Intestine

Srere *et al.* (1950) found that the rat small intestine (when incubated as pieces of 10 to 20 sq. mm. area) showed an incorporation of acetate-1-C^{14} slightly inferior to that of liver slices. In intact rats and rabbits the rate of incorporation is considerably greater than in the liver (Popják and Beeckmans, 1950b). There may be important species differences in intestinal activity since dogs appear to show much less cholesterol biosynthesis in intestine than in liver (Gould, 1952).

2. Blood

Although blood is very active in other aspects of cholesterol metabolism it is apparently not an important site of cholesterol biosynthesis. A small amount of acetate-C^{14} incorporation into cholesterol in fresh, whole blood has been reported by Schwenk *et al.* (1955a), which is probably due to biosynthesis in white cells since neither plasma nor red blood cells show any significant evidence of synthetic activity. After incubating human erythrocytes, washed once with saline, with acetate-C^{14} for 24 hours, London and Schwarz (1953) found activity in cholesterol corresponding to 0.0004% of the acetate as compared with 7% for liver slices. They reported their results as demonstrating a "relatively insignificant degree of synthesis."

3. Aorta

The biosynthesis of cholesterol in arterial tissue is of particular interest because of the possibility that this process might be of importance in atherogenesis. Siperstein et al. (1951) found evidence of in vitro synthesis in aorta of rabbit and chicken. The relative rates of synthesis were estimated by comparing aorta with liver from the same animal. In chickens, the aorta was about 1/40 as active as the liver, and in rabbits 1/500. Species differences appear of importance, since no evidence of a significant rate of synthesis was noted with adult dog aorta (Gould, 1951).

Feller and Huff (1955) found rabbit aortic tissue containing atheromatous lesions to be as active in cholesterol biosynthesis as normal aorta. Hog and turkey aortas have also been reported to be capable of cholesterol synthesis in vitro (Eisley and Pritham, 1955).

Extensive studies of cholesterol biosynthesis in the isolated, perfused swine and calf aorta have been carried out by Werthessen et al. (1954, 1956). These investigators conclude that the aorta not only is actively synthesizing cholesterol, but that it is also capable of supplying cholesterol to the plasma. What fraction of the plasma cholesterol could be derived in this way is not clear at the present time.

The factor of age in relation to cholesterol synthesis in aorta has not often been considered and may well be of importance. It is safe to assume that, during the period of growth, certain tissues will be able to synthesize cholesterol and many other structural constituents of their cells, but that on maturation the rate of synthesis will decrease to low or imperceptible levels. This is clearly the situation in brain, for example. The important consideration for atherogenesis is the question of intracellular cholesterol synthesis in the aorta of the adult, and results obtained on young, rapidly growing animals may be misleading.

4. Adrenal Gland

In vitro biosynthesis in beef adrenal cortex was demonstrated by Srere et al. (1948). It has subsequently been shown to occur in a number of other species, including man, by various techniques. Bolker et al. (1955) demonstrated cholesterol synthesis in guinea pig adrenal slices; and LeRoy et al. (1957) have reported evidence from studies on humans indicating rapid adrenal synthesis after ACTH administration.

Hechter et al. (1953) have shown that bovine adrenal glands synthesize cholesterol and adrenal steroid hormones when perfused *in vitro* with acetate-C^{14} and also that labeled cholesterol is liberated into the perfusing blood.

Further consideration of cholesterol synthesis in the adrenal cortex is given in Chapter 8.

5. *Gonads*

In the rat testis Srere *et al.* (1950) found an activity about a third to a half that of liver in the *in vitro* incorporation of acetate. Brady (1951) found that testis tissue slices from the hog, rabbit, and human synthesized cholesterol and testosterone from acetate-C^{14}. Cholesterol synthesis in rabbit ovary was demonstrated in the intact animal by Popják and Beeckmans (1950b), and in dog ovary by slice and homogenate methods by Rabinowitz and Dowben (1955). Perfusion of sow ovary with acetate-C^{14} resulted in biosynthesis of cholesterol as well as estrogenic hormones (Werthessen *et al.*, 1953). In the dog ovary synthesis was demonstrated in slices and homogenates (Rabinowitz and Dowben, 1955), and perfusion of the sow ovary with acetate-C^{14} resulted in biosynthesis (Werthessen *et al.*, 1953). The subject of steroid hormone formation is described further in Chapter 8.

6. *Brain*

Investigation of cholesterol synthesis in brain of rats at different ages by the deuterium oxide method showed that brain cholesterol is synthesized *in situ* during myelinization at a rapid rate, but stops abruptly and permanently when myelinization is complete (Waelsch *et al.*, 1940). These conclusions were confirmed by the more sensitive acetate-C^{14} method on rat brain slices by Srere *et al.* (1950). Slices of newborn rat brain showed a higher rate of cholesterol synthesis than any other tissue studied.

Brain tumor differs from normal adult brain tissue in showing cholesterol synthesis as Azarnoff *et al.* (1957) have reported.

Brain is the only tissue that shows no evidence of interchange with plasma of cholesterol molecules. All brain cholesterol is synthesized in this tissue and consequently its biosynthesis and turnover can be readily investigated in intact animals. The turnover rate of cholesterol in adult brain is so slow as to be virtually undetectable, suggesting that its function must be structural rather than metabolic.

7. *Skeletal Muscle*

The total musculature of the body contains about 20% of its total cholesterol but very little is known about biosynthesis in muscle tissue. It appears to have a low degree of activity (Gould, 1951).

8. Skin

Srere *et al.* (1950) found that rat skin slices show a rapid rate of sterol biosynthesis *in vitro*. Considering the large amount of this tissue in rats, they concluded that biosynthesis in skin is a major source of extrahepatic cholesterol. The later discovery that a large fraction of rat and mouse skin sterol consists of Δ^7-cholestenol, and the recent observation of Brooks and Baumann (1957) that the Δ^7 isomer has a much higher specific activity than the Δ^5 isomer (12 times as high in mice) after incubation with acetate-C^{14} raises questions as to how much cholesterol is formed in skin and whether Δ^7-cholestenol is an intermediate or not.

Nicolaides and Rothman (1955), and Nicolaides *et al.* (1955) have made extensive studies on the site of sterol and of squalene synthesis in human skin, and conclude *inter alia* that the sebaceous glands produce squalene and convert it very slowly into sterol.

Other aspects of sterol metabolism in the skin are discussed in Chapters 4 and 7.

9. Summary

Cholesterol biosynthesis occurs in all tisssues of the body to a greater or a lesser degree. The most active tissues are apparently the liver, intestine, and skin. Moderate activity is shown by visceral organs such as the kidneys and lungs and by the adrenal cortex and gonads. The activity of skeletal muscle is low, as is that of adipose tissue. The biosynthetic activity in the brain of fetal animals is marked, but in the mature animal it is insignificant if not actually zero.

C. The Hen's Ovary and the Developing Egg

The high cholesterol content of the avian egg has stimulated many investigations on its origin, its changes during incubation, and its subsequent fate in the young fowl. The membranes surrounding the growing ovum in the chicken ovary, the *theca interna* and granulosa, were shown by Popják and Tietz (1953) to be very active in cholesterol biosynthesis.

Although Rittenberg and Schoenheimer (1937) failed to find any evidence of cholesterol biosynthesis in the developing chicken egg by the deuterium oxide method, Bernhard (1941) and Schwenk and Baker (1953) did demonstrate biosynthesis of both cholesterol and fatty acids. Stokes *et al.* (1953) have recently made an extensive investigation and found continuous synthesis from acetate-C^{14} throughout the developmental period, and the apparent rate of synthesis was greatest towards the end of incubation.

IV.   Sterol Biosynthesis in Yeast and Other Organisms

Relatively little has been done on the mechanism of biosynthesis in any cells other than those of mammalian liver and yeast, although much information is available concerning the amounts of various sterols in a wide variety of animals and plants, as discussed in Chapter 4.

Yeast forms ergosterol from acetate in a manner apparently similar to the formation of cholesterol in liver, except for the final stages. At least 26 of the 28 ergosterol carbon atoms in *Neurospora* were shown to be derived from acetate by Ottke *et al.* (1951), who utilized a mutant unable to convert pyruvate or other metabolites into acetate. Ergosterol synthesized by yeast has been found to derive carbons 23 and 25 (Hanahan and Wakil, 1953) and carbons 11 and 12 (Dauben and Hutton, 1956) from the carboxyl carbon of acetate. Coenzyme A has been shown to be required for ergosterol biosynthesis in yeast (Klein and Lipmann, 1953).

Squalene appears to be an intermediate since it is formed in higher specific activity than ergosterol from acetate-C^{14} (Schwenk *et al.*, 1954, 1955b). Squalene-C^{14} obtained in this way has been converted by yeast into ergosterol (Corwin *et al.*, 1956), although some breakdown into smaller fragments, presumably acetate, must have occurred since C^{14} was found in the fatty acids. When yeast homogenates were used almost all the C^{14} was in the fatty acid fraction. They concluded that squalene is not an intermediate in ergosterol synthesis. Their results are analogous to those reported by Popják (1954) on cholesterol synthesis in rat liver slices and on chicken ovary. No explanation of these apparent discrepancies can be offered at present, except the possibility that an activated form of squalene, present in very low concentration, may be the true intermediate.

The carbon atom peculiar to ergosterol, C-28, which is the methyl group on C-24, has been shown to be derived from formate. Hanahan and Wakil (1953) had shown that this carbon is not derived from acetate; Danielsson and Bloch (1957) have now shown that formate contributes this carbon and this carbon only. On chromatographic fractionation of the nonsaponifiable material from yeast incubated with formate-C^{14}, all the known precursors of ergosterol, e.g. squalene, lanosterol, and zymosterol were found to be free of C^{14}, and only a single peak was obtained containing C^{14}-sterol (Johnston and Bloch, 1957). This was found to be ergosterol itself, showing that the C-28 carbon is added as a last step; Figure 5 gives the scheme of ergosterol biosynthesis based on present knowledge.

Eburicoic acid (4,4,14,24-tetramethyl-$\Delta^{8,24(28)}$-cholestadienol-carboxylic acid-21) which is formed by the fungus *P. sulfureus*, has been shown to utilize formate for the carbon atom in position 28 (Dauben *et al.*, 1957), suggesting that a number of plant species may utilize formate in addition to acetate in sterol biosynthesis (see Chapter 14).

V. The Labeling of Sterols

Sterols labeled by a variety of chemical and biosynthetic methods have been employed in studies of sterol metabolism. Cholesterol labeled by chemical methods with C^{14} in ring A or in the side chain, and that labeled biosynthetically by means of acetate-1-C^{14} or -2-C^{14} (in positions indicated in Fig. 1) have been extensively utilized. For many purposes cholesterol labeled with tritium by exchange is useful and is gradually replacing the similarly prepared deuterium-labeled cholesterol. In both, about 53% of the isotopic hydrogens are located in the ring system, largely on carbon-6, and about 47% on the side chain, largely on carbon-25.

The literature on chemical methods of labeling sterols with C^{14}, H^2, and H^3 has been comprehensively surveyed through 1955 by Murray and Williams (1958). Bloch (1957b) has discussed the methodology of labeling sterols and steroids by both chemical and biosynthetic methods. It has recently been discovered that tritium can be introduced into stable positions in sterols, steroids and a great variety of other compounds merely by exposing the compound to high specific activity tritium gas (Wilzbach, 1957).

REFERENCES

(Asterisk denotes review article or monograph)

Adamson, L. F., and Greenberg, D. M. (1957). *Biochim. et Biophys. Acta* **23**, 472-479.

Alexander, G. J., and Schwenk, E. (1957). *Arch. Biochem. Biophys.* **66**, 381-387.

Amdur, B. H., Rilling, H., and Bloch, K. (1957). *J. Am. Chem. Soc.* **79**, 2646-2647.

Anker, H. S. (1948). *J. Biol. Chem.* **176**, 1337-1352.

Azarnoff, D. L., Curran, G. L., and Williamson, W. P. (1957). *Federation Proc.* **16**, 148.

Beinert, H., Green, D. E., Hele, P., Hift, H., Von Korff, R. W., and Ramakrishnan, C. V. (1953). *J. Biol. Chem.* **203**, 35-45.

Berg, P. (1955). *J. Am. Chem. Soc.* **77**, 3163-3164.

Bernhard, K. (1941). *Helv. Chim. Acta.* **24**, 1094-1098.

Biggs, M. W., Lemmon, R. M., and Pierce, F. T., Jr. (1954). *Arch. Biochem. Biophys.* **51**, 155-160.

Blecher, M., and Gurin, S. (1954). *J. Biol. Chem.* **209**, 953-962.

Bloch, K. (1944). *J. Biol. Chem.* **155**, 255-263.

Bloch, K. (1951). *Recent Progr. in Hormone Research* **6**, 111-129.

Bloch, K. (1953). *Helv. Chim. Acta* **36**, 1611-1614.

*Bloch, K. (1954). Biological synthesis of cholesterol. *Harvey Lectures Ser.* **48**, 68-88.

*Bloch, K. (1956a). *In* "Currents in Biochemical Research" (D. E. Green, ed.), pp. 474-492. Interscience, New York.

*Bloch, K. (1956b). *In* "Essays in Biochemistry" (S. Graff, ed.), pp. 22-34. Wiley, New York.

*Bloch, K. (1957a). The biological synthesis of cholesterol. *Vitamins and Hormones* **15**, 119-147.

*Bloch, K. (1957b). *In* "Methods in Enzymology" (S. P. Colowick and N. O. Kaplan, eds.), Vol. 4, pp. 732-751. Academic Press, New York.

Bloch, K., and Rittenberg, D. (1942). *J. Biol. Chem.* **145**, 625-636.

Bloch, K., and Rittenberg, D. (1944). *J. Biol. Chem.* **155**, 243-254.

Bloch, K., Borek, E., and Rittenberg, D. (1946). *J. Biol. Chem.* **162**, 441-449.

Bloch, K., Clark, L. C., and Harary, I. (1954). *J. Biol. Chem.* **211**, 687-699.

Bolker, H. I., Fishman, S., Heard, R. D. H., O'Donnell, V. J., Webb, J. L., and Willis, G. C. (1955). *J. Exptl. Med.* **103**, 199-205.

Bonner, J., and Arreguin, B. (1949). *Arch. Biochem. Biophys.* **21**, 109-124; see also *Federation Proc.* **14**, 765-766.

Borek, E., and Rittenberg, D. (1949). *J. Biol. Chem.* **179**, 843-845.

Brady, R. O. (1951). *J. Biol. Chem.* **193**, 145-148.

Brady, R. O., and Gurin, S. (1950). *J. Biol. Chem.* **187**, 589-596.

Brady, R. O., and Gurin, S. (1951). *J. Biol. Chem.* **189**, 371-377.

Brady, R. O., Rabinowitz, J. L., Van Baalen, J., and Gurin, S. (1951). *J. Biol. Chem.* **193**, 137-144.

Brooks, S. C., Jr., and Baumann, C. A. (1957). *Federation Proc.* **16**, 158-159.

Bucher, N. L. R. (1953). *J. Am. Chem. Soc.* **75**, 498.

Bucher, N. L. R., and McGarrahan, K. (1956). *J. Biol. Chem.* **222**, 1-15.

Channon, H. J. (1926). *Biochem. J.* **20**, 400-408.

*Chevallier, F. (1953). Cholesterol. II. Metabolism as studied with isotopes. *Ann. nutrition et aliment.* **7**, 305-338.

Clayton, R. B., and Bloch, K. (1956). *J. Biol. Chem.* **218**, 305-318; 319-325.

Cook, R. P., Kliman, A., and Fieser, L. F. (1954). *Arch. Biochem. Biophys.* **52**, 439-450.

*Cornforth, J. W. (1955). Biosynthesis of cholesterol. *Revs. Pure and Appl. Chem.* (*Australia*) **4**, 275-302.

Cornforth, J. W., and Popják, G. (1954). *Biochem. J.* **58**, 403-407.

Cornforth, J. W., Hunter, G. D., and Popják, G. (1953). *Biochem. J.* **54**, 590-597; 597-601.

Cornforth, J. W., Youhotsky-Gore, I., and Popják, G. (1956). *Biochem. J.* **64**, 38P.

Cornforth, J. W., Youhotsky-Gore, I., and Popják, G. (1957a). *Biochem. J.* **65**, 94-109.

Cornforth, J. W., Youhotsky-Gore, I., and Popják, G. (1957b). *Biochem. J.* **66**, 10P.

Corwin, L. M., Schroeder, L. J., and McCullough, W. G. (1956). *J. Am. Chem. Soc.* **78**, 1372-1375.

Curran, G. L. (1951). *J. Biol. Chem.* **191**, 775-782.

Curran, G. L., and Rittenberg, D. (1951). *J. Biol. Chem.* **190**, 17-20.

Danielsson, H., and Bloch, K. (1957). *J. Am. Chem. Soc.* **79**, 500.

Dauben, W. G., and Hutton, T. W. (1956). *J. Am. Chem. Soc.* **78**, 2647-2648.

Dauben, W. G., and Takemura, K. H. (1953). *J. Am. Chem. Soc.* **75**, 6302-6304.

Dauben, W. G., Fonken, G. J., and Boswell, G. A. (1957). *J. Am. Chem. Soc.* **79**, 1000-1001.

Davidson, A. G., Dulit, E. G., and Frantz, I. D., Jr. (1957). *Federation Proc.* **16**, 169.

Dayton, S., Mosbach, E. H., and Kendall, F. E. (1953). *Proc. Soc. Exptl. Biol. Med.* **84**, 608.

Dituri, F., Cobey, F. A., Warms, J. V. B., and Gurin, S. (1956). *J. Biol. Chem.* **221**, 181-189.

Eisley, N. F., and Pritham, G. H. (1955). *Science* **122**, 121.

Feller, B. A., and Huff, J. W. (1955). *Am. J. Physiol.* **182**, 237-242.

Frantz, I. D., Jr., Davidson, A. G., and Dulit, E. (1956). *Federation Proc.* **15**, 255.

*Friedman, M., Byers, S. O., and St. George, S. (1956). Cholesterol metabolism. *Ann. Rev. Biochem.* **25**, 613-640.

Gautschi, F., and Bloch, K. (1957). *J. Am. Chem. Soc.* **79**, 684-689.

Glover, M., Glover, J., and Morton, R. A. (1952). *Biochem. J.* **51**, 1-9.

Gould, R. G. (1951). *Am. J. Med.* **11**, 209-227.

Gould, R. G. (1952). In *"Proc. Ann. Meeting, Council for High Blood Pressure Research,"* pp. 1-18. Am. Heart Assoc., New York.

Gould, R. G., and Popják, G. (1957). *Biochem. J.* **66**, 51P.

Hanahan, D. J., and Wakil, S. J. (1953). *J. Am. Chem. Soc.* **75**, 273-275.

Hechter, O., Solomon, M. M., Zaffaroni, A., and Pincus, G. (1953). *Arch. Biochem. Biophys.* **46**, 201-214.

Heilbron, I. M., Kamm, E. D., and Owens, W. M. (1926). *J. Chem. Soc.*, 1630-1644.

Hele, P. (1954). *J. Biol. Chem.* **206**, 671-676.

Johnston, J. D., and Bloch, K. (1957). *J. Am. Chem. Soc.* **79**, 1145.

Jones, M. E., Black, S., Flynn, R. M., and Lipmann, F. (1953). *Biochim. et Biophys. Acta* **12**, 141-149.

Karrer, P. (1953). *Helv. Chim. Acta* **36**, 130-131.

Karvinen, E., and Laakso, P. V. (1957). *Federation Proc.* **16**, 70.

Klein, H. P., and Lipmann, F. (1953). *J. Biol. Chem.* **203**, 95-99; 101-108.

Kritchevsky, D., and Gray, I. (1951). *Experientia* **7**, 183.

Langdon, R. G., and Bloch, K. (1953a). *J. Biol. Chem.* **200**, 129-134; 135-144.

Langdon, R. G., and Bloch, K. (1953b). *J. Biol. Chem.* **202**, 77-81.

Le Roy, G. V., Gould, R. G., Bergenstal, D. M., Werbin, H., and Kabara, J. J. (1957). *J. Lab. Clin. Med.* **49**, 858-869.

Little, H. N., and Bloch, K. (1950). *J. Biol. Chem.* **183**, 33-46.

London, I. M., and Schwarz, H. (1953). *J. Clin. Invest.* **32**, 1248-1252.

Loud, A. V. (1956). *Federation Proc.* **15**, 122.

*Lynen, F. (1955). Lipide metabolism. *Ann. Rev. Biochem.* **24**, 653-688.

Lynen, F., Wessely, L., Wieland, O., and Rueff, L. (1952). *Angew. Chem.* **64**, 687.

Lyon, I., Geyer, R. P., and Marshall, L. D. (1956). *J. Biol. Chem.* **217**, 757-764.

*Murray, A., III, and Williams, D. L. (1958). "Organic Syntheses with Isotopes," Part I, Chapter 13, and Part II, Chapter 3. Interscience, New York.

Nicolaides, N., and Laves, F. (1954). *J. Am. Chem. Soc.* **76**, 2596-2597.

Nicolaides, N., and Rothman, S. (1955). *J. Invest. Dermatol.* **24**, 125-129.

Nicolaides, N., Reiss, O. K., and Langdon, R. G. (1955). *J. Am. Chem. Soc.* **77**, 1535-1538.

Olson, J. A., and Bloch, K. (1956). *Federation Proc.* **15**, 323.

Ottke, R. C., Tatum, E. L., Zabin, I., and Bloch, K. (1951). *J. Biol. Chem.* **189**, 429-433.

Page, I. H., and Menschick, W. (1930). *Naturwissenschaften* **18**, 735.

Page, I. H., and Menschick, W. (1932). *J. Biol. Chem.* **97**, 359-368.

Pihl, A., Bloch, K., and Anker, H. S. (1950). *J. Biol. Chem.* **183**, 441-450.

Popják, G. (1954). *Arch. Biochem. Biophys.* **48**, 102-106.

*Popják, G. (1955). Chemistry, biochemistry, and isotopic tracer technique. *Roy. Inst. Chem.* (*London*), *Lectures, Monographs, Repts.* No. **2**, 23-37.

Popják, G., and Beeckmans, M. L. (1950a). *Biochem. J.* **46**, 547-561.

Popják, G., and Beeckmans, M. L. (1950b). *Biochem. J.* **47**, 233-238.

Popják, G., and Tietz, A. (1953). *Biochem. J.* **54**, Proc. xxxv.

Popják, G., Hunter, G. D., and French, T. H. (1953). *Biochem. J.* **54**, 238-247.

Popják, G., Gosselin, L., Youhotsky-Gore, I., and Gould, R. G. (1958). *Biochem. J.* (in press).

Rabinowitz, J. L., and Gurin, S. (1953). *Biochim. et Biophys. Acta* **10**, 345-346.

Rabinowitz, J. L., and Gurin, S. (1954). *J. Biol. Chem.* **208**, 307-313.

Rabinowitz, J. L., and Dowben, R. M. (1955). *Biochim. et Biophys. Acta* **16**, 96-98.

Rabinowitz, J. L., Dituri, F., Cobey, F., and Gurin, S. (1955). *Federation Proc.* **14**, 760-761.

Rittenberg, D., and Schoenheimer, R. (1937). *J. Biol. Chem.* **121**, 235-253.

Robinson, R. (1934). *J. Soc. Chem. Ind.* (*London*) **53**, 1062.

Rudney, H. (1954). *J. Am. Chem. Soc.* **76**, 2595-2596.

Rudney, H. (1957). *J. Biol. Chem.* **227**, 363-377.

Rudney, H., and Farkas, T. G. (1955). *Federation Proc.* **14**, 757-759.

*Ruzicka, L. (1953). Isoprene rule and the biogenesis of terpenic compounds. *Experientia* **9**, 357-367.

Sandermann, W., and Stockmann, H. (1956). *Naturwissenschaften* **43**, 581.

Schoenheimer, R., and Breusch, F. (1933). *J. Biol. Chem.* **103**, 439-448.

Schwenk, E., and Werthessen, N. T. (1952). *Arch. Biochem. Biophys.* **40**, 334-341.

Schwenk, E., and Baker, C. F. (1953). *Arch. Biochem. Biophys.* **45**, 341-348.

Schwenk, E., and Werthessen, N. T. (1953). *Arch. Biochem. Biophys.* **42**, 91-93.

Schwenk, E., Todd, D., and Fish, C. A. (1954). *Arch. Biochem. Biophys.* **49**, 187-206.

*Schwenk, E., Alexander, G. J., Fish, C. A., and Stoudt, T. H. (1955a). *Federation Proc.* **14**, 752-756.

Schwenk, E., Alexander, G. J., Stoudt, T. H., and Fish, C. A. (1955b). *Arch. Biochem. Biophys.* **55**, 274-285.

Schwenk, E., Alexander, G. J., and Fish, C. A. (1955c). *Arch. Biochem. Biophys.* **58**, 37-51.

Siperstein, M. D., and Fagan, V. M. (1957). *Science* **126**, 1012-1013.

Siperstein, M. D., Chaikoff, I. L., and Chernick, S. S. (1951). *Science* **113**, 747-749.

Sonderhoff, R., and Thomas, H. (1937). *Ann. Chem. Liebigs* **530**, 195-213.

Srere, P. A., Chaikoff, I. L., and Dauben, W. G. (1948). *J. Biol. Chem.* **176**, 829-833.

Srere, P. A., Chaikoff, I. L., Treitman, S. S., and Burstein, L. S. (1950). *J. Biol. Chem.* **182**, 629-634.

Stadtman, E. R., Douderoff, M., and Lipmann, F. (1951). *J. Biol. Chem.* **191**, 377-382.

Stern, J. R., Coon, M. J., and Del Campillo, A. (1953). *Nature* **171**, 28-30.

Stokes, W. M., Fish, W. A., and Hickey, F. C. (1953). *J. Biol. Chem.* **200**, 683-689.

Stokes, W. M., Fish, W. A., and Hickey, F. C. (1956). *J. Biol. Chem.* **220**, 415-430.

*Symposium on Cholesterol Biosynthesis. (1955). *Federation Proc.* **14**, 752-785.

Tavormina, P. A., and Gibbs, M. H. (1956). *J. Am. Chem. Soc.* **78**, 6210.

Tavormina, P. A., Gibbs, M. H., and Huff, J. W. (1956). *J. Am. Chem. Soc.* **78**, 4498-4499.

Taylor, C. B., Nelson, L., Stumpe, M., Cox, G. E., and Tamura, R. (1956). *Federation Proc.* **15**, 534.

Tchen, T. T. (1957). *J. Am. Chem. Soc.* **79**, 6344-6345.

Tchen, T. T., and Bloch, K. (1957a). *J. Biol. Chem.* **226**, 921-930.

Tchen, T. T., and Bloch, K. (1957b). *J. Biol. Chem.* **226**, 931-939.

Tomkins, G. M., Dauben, W. G., Sheppard, H., and Chaikoff, I. L. (1953a). *J. Biol. Chem.* **202**, 487-489.

Tomkins, G. M., Sheppard, H., and Chaikoff, I. L. (1953b). *J. Biol. Chem.* **203**, 781-786.

Tsujimoto, M. (1906). *J. Soc. Chem. Ind., Japan* **9**, 953.

Voser, W., Mijovic, M. W., Heusser, H., Jeger, O., and Ruzicka, L. (1952). *Helv. Chim. Acta* **35**, 2414-2430.

Waelsch, H., Sperry, W. M., and Stoyanoff, V. A. (1940). *J. Biol. Chem.* **135**, 297-302.

Werthessen, N. T., Schwenk, E., and Baker, C. F. (1953). *Science* **117**, 380-381.

Werthessen, N. T., Milch, L. J., Rodman, R. F., Smith, L. L., and Smith, E. C. (1954). *Am. J. Physiol.* **178**, 23-29.

Werthessen, N. T., Nyman, M. A., Holman, R. L., and Strong, J. P. (1956). *Circulation Research* **4**, 586-593.

Wilzbach, K. E. (1957). *J. Am. Chem. Soc.* **79**, 1013.

Wolf, D. E., Hoffman, C. H., Aldrich, P. E., Skeggs, H. R., Wright, L. D., and Folkers, K. (1956). *J. Am. Chem. Soc.* **78**, 4499.

Woodward, R. B., and Bloch, K. (1953). *J. Am. Chem. Soc.* **75**, 2023-2024.

Wright, L. D., and Cleland, M. (1957). *Proc. Soc. Exptl. Biol. Med.* **96**, 219-224.

Wuersch, J., Huang, R. L., and Bloch, K. (1952). *J. Biol. Chem.* **195**, 439-446.

Zabin, I., and Bloch, K. (1950). *J. Biol. Chem.* **185**, 117-130; 131-138.

Zabin, I., and Bloch, K. (1951). *J. Biol. Chem.* **192**, 261-266; 267-273.

CHAPTER 7

THE METABOLISM OF CHOLESTEROL AND OTHER STEROLS IN THE ANIMAL ORGANISM*

R. Gordon Gould and Robert P. Cook

---

* Chemical nomenclature in this chapter follows in general the preferred usage in the United States.

I. Introduction

Knowledge of cholesterol metabolism has increased with extraordinary rapidity since radioactive carbon became available and a considerably more detailed picture may now be given of the pathways of normal cholesterol metabolism than was previously possible. Limitations of space preclude reference to many of the publications in this field; Peters and Van Slyke (1946) covered the literature comprehensively up to 1945, and a number of recent review articles are listed at the end of this Chapter.

We have limited ourselves to certain aspects, stressing particularly the main pathways of cholesterol metabolism in the normal organism. These may be briefly listed as follows: (1) The absorption, esterification, transport, distribution, and ultimate fate of dietary cholesterol and other sterols. (2) The biosynthesis, esterification, equilibration between the various tissues, and ultimate fate of endogenous cholesterol. (3) The role of the liver in supplying and regulating the level of cholesterol in plasma, and in the formation of plasma lipoproteins. (4) The formation of bile acids, their enterohepatic circulation, and the relationship between cholesterol and bile acid metabolism. (5) Finally, consideration is given to some of the many factors which affect these aspects of sterol metabolism.

In experimental animals the concentration of cholesterol in blood plasma and in the tissues is normally relatively constant, i.e. it is homeostatically controlled within a range characteristic for each tissue. The total amount of cholesterol in the body is determined by the balance between the rate of increase due to absorption of cholesterol from the diet plus biosynthesis in tissues and the rate of decrease due to metabolic utilization and excretion. In what follows, we have discussed these four main avenues of cholesterol metabolism in that order.

II. Absorption of Sterols from the Intestine

A. Introduction

Sterols are present in all normal diets and it is agreed that intestinal absorption of cholesterol occurs in mammals and in birds. Absorption in the lower vertebrates is a neglected subject but studies have been made of the process in the larvae of various insects where cholesterol (and other sterols) are growth factors (see Chapter 13).

The current interest centers around the fact that, when cholesterol is fed to certain species of animals, experimental atherosclerosis results. The absorption of other sterols and particularly the effect of their presence in the diet on cholesterol absorption is also an active field of investigation. Some formerly accepted general conclusions concerning the absorbability of sterols other than cholesterol have recently been modified as a result of refinements in methods.

Until the availability of tracers all methods of investigating cholesterol absorption necessitated the feeding of large doses.

B. Methods

1. Balance Method

In this method a known amount of sterol is fed and the excretion in the feces determined (urinary excretion may be generally disregarded in *sterol* studies). The apparent absorption may be expressed as a percentage value, given by

$$\frac{\text{amount ingested} - \text{amount excreted}}{\text{amount ingested}} \times 100$$

or as the maximum absorption per unit body weight. The amount excreted should be corrected for the endogenous excretion which is determined by placing the animal on a sterol-free diet. The method is laborious and time consuming but gives a good general picture of absorption. It does not distinguish between sterols that have been absorbed and then reexcreted, e.g. by the bile.

2. The Examination of Systemic Blood

An increase in the level of plasma cholesterol after its dietary administration is usually taken as evidence of absorption but the administration of relatively large amounts of sterol is usually necessary to show this.

3. Examination of Lymph

The lymph draining from the small intestine or from the thoracic duct may be collected and examined for its cholesterol content. This was described in dogs by Mueller (1915, 1916); a good account of the technique involved in the collection of thoracic duct and hepatic lymph in the rat is given by Bollman *et al.* (1948).

4. Deposition of Excess Cholesterol in the Liver

Increase in cholesteryl esters in liver is a sensitive indicator of cholesterol absorption in the rat (e.g. Ridout *et al.*, 1954). An increase in dietary cholesterol of 0.1% of the dry weight of the diet will produce significant increases in liver cholesteryl esters. In the chicken, Dam *et al.* (1955) found increase in liver cholesterol after feeding 0.1% cholesterol (see Chapter 15).

5. Use of Labeled Sterols

The absorption of labeled sterols may be determined with high specificity and accuracy using a wide range of dosage. Recovery of labeled sterol from thoracic duct lymph, blood, or other tissues provides definite proof of absorption. In small species of experimental animals, total absorption may be determined by analysis of the whole body for labeled sterol and, in larger animals and man, by a balance study on the amounts of labeled material fed and recovered from feces.

C. The Absorption of Dietary Cholesterol

1. Absorption in Man

It is remarkable that the ingestion of large amounts of cholesterol have shown much less effect on the plasma level in human subjects than in the usual experimental animals. Only transient rises in plasma level have been observed (Chapter 5).

Balance experiments have shown very poor absorption. As shown in Table I, the maximum absorption was (as milligrams per kilogram of body weight per day) 10 mg. for added cholesterol and about double this amount when the cholesterol was fed as egg.

Balance experiments utilizing labeled cholesterol (Favarger and Metzger, 1952; Biggs *et al.*, 1952) gave results in agreement with the above value for cholesterol.

2. Comparative Aspects

A large number of animal species have been investigated by the methods described above for their absorption of cholesterol. The data

TABLE I

BALANCE EXPERIMENTS ON THE APPARENT ABSORPTION OF CHOLESTEROL IN MAN

Expt. no.	Form and amount of cholesterol and of fat	Subjects and weight	Period of study (days)	Total dietary sterol (gm.)	Sterol excreted (gm.)	Sterol absorbed			Reference
						Amount (gm.)	As per cent	As mg./kg. body wt./day	
1	Crystalline cholesterol (5 gm.) in oil (100 gm.)	Four adult Germans	3	Range 5.8–6.5 Mean 6.0	1.4–4.2 2.7	— 3.3	— 66	— —	1
2	Cholesterol (9.8 gm.) in oil (50 gm.) and dietary fat (134 gm.)	One adult Scot (71 kg.)	3	11.5	9.9	1.6	16	7.5	2
3	Cholesterol (3 gm. per day) with and without added fat	One adult Bantu (55 kg.)	28	—	Mean 1.4 gm./day	Mean 0.6 gm./day	20	12	3
4	Cholesterol (0.25 gm. to 1 gm. per day)	Three infant or child North Americans	First 6 days After 12 days	—	—	—	Mean 44 Mean 23	—	4
5	Deuterium labeled cholesterol (4.0 gm.) in fat (25 gm.)	Adult Swiss (75 kg.)	3	—	1.7	2.3	57	10	5
	Cholesterol (3.0 gm.) in fat (60 gm.)	Adult Swiss (80 kg.)	3	—	0.7	2.3	75	9	5
6	Trittium labeled cholesterol (0.86 gm.) in fat (85 gm.)	American male (41 yr.) with chronic glomerulonephritis	3 7	—	as % 66 87	—	34 13	—	6

TABLE I (*Continued*)

Expt. no.	Form and amount of cholesterol and of fat	Subjects and weight	Period of study (days)	Total dietary sterol (gm.)	Sterol excreted (gm.)	Sterol absorbed Amount (gm.)	As per cent	As mg./kg. body wt./day	Reference
6	Cholesterol (0.69 gm.) in fat (20 gm.)	American female (51 yr.) with xanthomatosis	3	—	33	—	67	—	6
			7	—	57	—	43	—	
7	*Egg cholesterol* twenty eggs (6.9 gm. cholesterol) and fat (357 gm.)	Same subject as Expt. 2	4	9.2	4.3	4.9	71	17	2
8	Ten eggs per day (3.0 gm. cholesterol) and fat	Same subject as Expt. 3	32	—	Mean 1.7 gm./day	Mean 1.3 gm./day	43	24	3

References

1. Bürger and Winterseel (1929).
2. Cook *et al.* (1956).
3. Bronte-Stewart *et al.* (1956); values given in table have been read from figures.
4. Heymann and Rack (1943).
5. Favarger and Metzger (1952).
6. Biggs *et al.* (1952).

in Table II show clearly that on a body weight basis the smaller experimental animals have a more marked absorption than do the larger species such as the dog and man. The values given for percentage absorption are not so informative and should only be used where the amount of cholesterol is specified. From the results given here and those of others it would appear that the rabbit has an abnormal capacity to absorb cholesterol but in man even under the most favorable conditions it is poorly absorbed.

TABLE II

THE COMPARATIVE ABSORPTION OF CHOLESTEROL

| Species | Typical weight | Amount fed/day (gm.) | Absorption | | Reference |
			As per cent	As gm./kg. body wt./day	
Rat	300 gm.	0.3	40	0.4	1, 2
Guinea pig	400 gm.	0.25	50	0.3	1
Rabbit	1.5 gm.	0.5	75	0.3	1
		0.25	90	0.2	3
Dog	10–12 kg.	1.6	50–80	About 0.1	4
Man	70 kg.	Crystalline, 10	15	0.01	5
		Egg, 6.9	60	0.02	5

References

1. Cook and Thomson (1951).
2. Favarger *et al.* (1955), who give information on the absorption of doses of from 1 to 20% deuterium-labeled cholesterol in rats.
3. Cook *et al.* (1954).
4. Favarger and Metzger (1952) who give information on absorption of deuterium-labeled cholesterol in man.
5. Cook *et al.* (1956).

3. Cholesteryl Esters

Cholesteryl esters present in the diet are hydrolyzed in the intestine before absorption. Free cholesterol was found to be more efficiently absorbed than any of its esters in the chicken (Peterson *et al.*, 1954) and in the rat (Swell *et al.*, 1955b).

D. THE ABSORPTION OF OTHER STEROLS

1. General

There is now a considerable literature on the absorption of sterols other than cholesterol. Some of the older investigations failed to demonstrate absorption of plant sterols, but recent studies show that a slight absorption does occur. The major findings are summarized in Table III, but some amplification is necessary with certain of the more studied compounds.

2. Cholestanol

Schoenheimer et al. (1930) were unable to demonstrate absorption in mice and in dogs, a conclusion also reached by Bürger and Winterseel (1931) and Dam (1934a) in man, and Breusch (1938) in mice. It was generally accepted that cholestanol was not absorbed in any species, in spite of the fact that Dam and Brun (1935) had demonstrated an increased deposition of stanols in the rat liver. In 1954 a number of investigators showed that absorption occurred in a variety of animals (see Table III). Of some interest is the fact that it was found to be as atherogenic as is cholesterol in the rabbit and moreover produced gallstones (Cook et al., 1954). These findings have been confirmed and it has been shown that the gallstones consist of bile salts (Mosbach and Bevans, 1956; Bevans and Kendall, 1956).

3. Sitosterols

The term sitosterol is given to the mixture of C_{29} stenols and stanols found in all higher plants; they constitute the main source of vegetable (or phyto) sterols for man and most animals. The most studied member of the group is β-sitosterol which differs chemically from cholesterol solely in the presence of an ethyl group in position 24.

In Schoenheimer's original experiments he was unable to demonstrate any absorption of sitosterols in a variety of animal species (Schoenheimer, 1929, 1931; Schoenheimer et al., 1930). Recent studies using the sensitive and specific tracer method have shown absorption in rats and humans (Gould, 1955a). The efficiency of absorption of β-sitosterol in rats was about 10% of that for cholesterol, but no increase in the liver sterol concentration was observed in confirmation of Schoenheimer's results. Balance studies by Ivy et al. (1954) showed a disappearance of 35% of the soybean sterol fed to rats and Swell et al. (1956) gave values of 23%. Similar studies in man showed a disappearance of 40% (Bisset and Cook, 1956).

E. FACTORS INFLUENCING STEROL ABSORPTION

1. Bile

For many years it has been axiomatic that bile increases sterol absorption (Deuel, 1955, Vol. II, pp. 260–263), but only since the introduction of labeled sterols has it been shown that the presence of bile is obligatory (Siperstein et al., 1952c). The generally held view is that the bile salts are the active agents in the process. Investigations by Swell et al. (1953) and by Pihl (1955c) on the efficacy of various bile acids on cholesterol absorption in rats, showed that cholic or taurocholic acids are the most active. The mode of action in the presence

TABLE III
THE ABSORPTION OF STEROLS AND OF SQUALENE

I. C_{27} SERIES
   A. *Stanols*

Cholestanol (3β-ol) (dihydrocholesterol)	Absorbed in rats (11, 13, 17); rabbits (7, 11); chickens (27); not absorbed as shown by balance methods in man (4, 12). See text.
Coprostanol	Not absorbed by mice (3) or men (4).

   B. *Stenols*

Δ^5-Cholesten-3α-ol (epicholesterol)	Poorly absorbed in rats (20).
Δ^7-Cholestenol (lathosterol)	Absorbed by rats (38); rabbits (2, 7). Converted to cholesterol after absorption.
Δ^4-Cholestenol	Some absorption in mice, hens and a dog (34). Converted to cholesterol after absorption.
$\Delta^{8(14)}$-Cholestenol	Minimal absorption in rats (16).
7-Dehydrocholesterol	Absorbed by rabbits (7); chickens (29). Converted to cholesterol after absorption.

   C. *Ketones*

7-Ketocholesterol	Slight absorption in rabbits (9).
Δ^4-Cholesten-3-one	Absorbed in rats, 1% in diet has toxic effect and causes adrenal hypertrophy (36).
$\Delta^{3,5}$-Cholestadiene-7-one	Absorbed in rats (21) and chickens (22).

II. C_{28} SERIES

Ergosterol	Some absorption by rats (18); hens (26, 33); absorbed by guinea pig (15).
Irradiated ergosterol	Absorbed by rats (10) and other animals, see (14) Deuel (1955, pp. 323-326).
24-Methylenecholesterol (chalinasterol, ostreasterol)	Absorbed by mice (35).
Brassicasterol	Some absorption by rabbits (8).

III. C_{29} SERIES

Sitosterol	β-Sitosterol absorbed by rat (11, 17, 37); rabbits (11) and man (17). Converted to coprositostanol (31). Its presence decreases the absorption of cholesterol in chickens (28); rats (1, 19, 37) and rabbits (11, 30). It lowers the plasma level of cholesterol in man. See text.
Stigmasterol	No apparent absorption in a variety of mammals (32); mice (3) or rats (31).

IV. SQUALENE

	Absorbed in rat (5, 6); rabbits (23, 24); human (25); and in codfish (6).

TABLE III (*Continued*)

References

1. Best and Duncan (1956).
2. Biggs *et al.* (1954); Lemmon *et al.* (1954).
3. Breusch (1938).
4. Bürger and Winterseel (1931).
5. Channon (1926).
6. Channon and Tristram (1937).
7. Cook *et al.* (1954).
8. Cook and Riddell (unpublished).
9. Cox and Spencer (1949).
10. Cruickshank *et al.* (1954).
11. Curran and Costello (1956a).
12. Dam (1934a).
13. Dam and Brun (1935).
14. Deuel (1955).
15. Glover *et al.* (1957).
16. Gould (unpublished).
17. Gould *et al.* (1956).
18. Hanahan and Wakil (1953).
19. Hernandez *et al.* (1953).
20. Hernandez *et al.* (1954).
21. Kantiengar and Morton (1955b).
22. Kantiengar *et al.* (1955).
23. Kimizuka (1938).
24. Kritchevsky *et al.* (1954).
25. McGuire and Lipsky (1955).
26. Menschick and Page (1932).
27. Nichols *et al.* (1955).
28. Peterson *et al.* (1952).
29. Peterson *et al.* (1954).
30. Pollak (1953a).
31. Rosenheim and Webster (1941b).
32. Schoenheimer (1931).
33. Schoenheimer and Dam (1932).
34. Schoenheimer *et al.* (1935a).
35. Sperry and Bergmann (1937).
36. Steinberg *et al.* (1957).
37. Swell *et al.* (1956).
38. Wells and Baumann (1954).

of dietary fat or fatty acids is still not clear but the main action may be considered as one of dispersion of the cholesterol into a molecular form suitable for absorption.

Bile acids readily form insoluble iron salts and as a method of decreasing cholesterol absorption the administration of ferric chloride has been suggested by Siperstein *et al.* (1953a). Dietary ferric chloride at a level of 3% of the diet was effective in preventing hypercholesterolemia in cockerels but toxic reactions were encountered. Beher and Anthony (1955) found no effect of ferric chloride at levels up to 2% in preventing the accumulation of cholesterol in livers of mice fed a diet containing 1% cholesterol and 0.5% cholic acid (see also Beher *et al.*, 1957).

It is possibly significant that bile contains also phospholipids (see Chapter 4, p. 151) and these as well as the bile salts may affect the process of absorption.

2. Surface-Active Agents

A number of surface-active agents particularly the nonionic detergents such as the "Tweens" and "Tritons" are known to facilitate the absorption of such substances as mineral oil. Wells (1957a) has shown that the addition of Tween 80 to cholesterol diets fed to rats enhances the absorption as shown by increased blood and liver cholesterol levels.

The effect of such agents on the absorption of cholesterol in human diets, although worthy of serious consideration, does not seem to have been investigated.

3. Presence of Dietary Fat and the Physical State of Cholesterol

Although it is generally agreed that the presence of fat is favorable for cholesterol absorption (Cook, 1957), it does not appear to be essential. Popják (1946) demonstrated that amorphous cholesterol fed in aqueous suspension is well absorbed by rabbits. Bollman and Flock (1951) and Pihl (1955a) showed that rats absorbed finely dispersed cholesterol given in a diet with minimal fat content. It has been suggested by Swell et al. (1955a) that dietary fat may act by stimulating the flow of bile, in addition to its actions in dissolving and dispersing of cholesterol. Pihl (1955b) has shown that free fatty acids result in better absorption of cholesterol than do triglycerides.

The nature of the fatty acids in dietary fat has effects on plasma cholesterol levels in man which do not appear to be due to effects on cholesterol absorption; this topic is discussed in Chapter 5. Increased plasma cholesterol levels in man have been reported as a result of feeding large amounts of egg yolk (Okey and Stewart, 1933; Messinger et al., 1950), but it has been found very difficult to produce a significant increase by addition of crystalline or amorphous cholesterol to the diet. How much of the effect of the egg yolk is due to the physical state of the cholesterol contained in it and how much to the phospholipids and fats is not clear.

Recent investigations on the effects of different types of dietary fats on cholesterol absorption and disappearance in the cockerel (Stamler et al., 1957), the rat (Seskind et al., 1957), and the cebus monkey (Portman and Sinisterra, 1957) indicate that unsaturated fats result in better absorption than do more nearly saturated ones.

4. Role of the Pancreas

Pancreatic juice does not appear to be essential for cholesterol absorption. Stamler and Katz (1951) observed higher plasma cholesterol levels in depancreatized than in normal chicks when both were fed cholesterol, and diversion of pancreatic juice was not found to prevent absorption by Byers and Friedman (1955) and Tsung-Min et al. (1954). A stimulating action of pancreatic juice on cholesterol absorption in the presence of bile was noted by Hernandez et al. (1955).

5. Other Sterols

The addition of soy sterols to a high-cholesterol diet was shown by Peterson (1951) to prevent the extreme hypercholesterolemia and the hepatic accumulation in chickens. He suggested that this effect was due to interference with absorption of cholesterol.

Similar protection against alimentary hypercholesterolemia was found to result from adding soy sterols, sitosterol mixture, or pure β-sitosterol to high-cholesterol diets with chickens, rats, rabbits, and mice (see Table III for references).

While the consensus of opinion is that the protective action is due to interference with cholesterol absorption, some of the studies on the absorption of labeled cholesterol have shown a smaller effect on the rate of appearance of the label in thoracic duct lymph than would be expected (Hernandez and Chaikoff, 1954). Some investigators using the amount of cholesterol in the thoracic duct lymph of rats as a measure of absorption failed to find any effect of sitosterol (Rosenman et al., 1954; Friedman et al., 1956a).

In humans, sitosterols have been reported by several groups to lower the plasma cholesterol levels on ordinary diets (e.g. Pollak, 1953b; Joyner and Kuo, 1955; Farquhar et al., 1956; Best and Duncan, 1956). This effect is not observed in all patients and has been reported to be generally most evident in those with the highest initial levels. Interference with absorption of both dietary and biliary cholesterol has been suggested as the mechanism but this has not been proven.

Cholestanol like sitosterol prevents alimentary hypercholesterolemia and atherogenesis in chickens (Siperstein et al., 1953b) and in rabbits (Nichols et al., 1953), but is itself absorbed sufficiently well to produce atheromatous lesions (Nichols et al., 1955).

6. Mineral Oil

The inclusion of mineral oil in the diet of rats increases the fecal excretion of cholesterol (Karvinen et al., 1955).

F. The Pathway of Absorption to the Blood Stream

1. The Intestine

a. Entry to the mucosa. The pioneer experiments of Mueller indicated that absorption was mainly if not entirely by the lymphatic vessels. The use of tritium-labeled cholesterol by Biggs et al. (1951) confirmed this result in rats, and Chaikoff et al. (1952a) using C^{14}-labeled cholesterol showed that of the absorbed sterol in rats, 70–90% was recovered in the lacteal lymph and nearly the whole of it in thoracic duct lymph, half of the cholesterol being in the esterified form. Daskalakis and Chaikoff (1955) consider that the transfer from the gut lumen to the site of esterification is stereospecific and probably enzymatic in nature.

Glover and Green (1956) have made a study of the cellular components (organelles) of the mucosa of the guinea pig intestine during cholesterol absorption and conclude that it becomes associated with the mitochondria, microsomes, etc. They consider that these structures play an active part in the absorption process and possibly mediate the transfer by way of their lipoproteins. These may adsorb (or combine) with the sterol molecules and later release them for transfer to other similar units across the cell. Information on the portal and mode of entry is still scanty. Absorption occurs in the small intestine and apparently only in the distal half (Byers *et al.*, 1953a).

b. The intrinsic sterol metabolism of the intestine. In the early studies on absorption it was generally assumed that all the cholesterol obtained from the chyle was of dietary origin. Experiments with C^{14}-cholesterol have shown this not to be the case; Chaikoff *et al.* (1952a) found that after administering 3.5 mg. of labeled cholesterol to a rat, 15 mg. of cholesterol were obtained in the thoracic duct lymph after 23 hours and of this only about 10% was derived from the labeled cholesterol. The remainder may be derived from the reabsorption of endogenous cholesterol excreted via the bile and intestinal juices, from biosyntheses in the intestine, from lymph coming to the intestine, or all three. Page *et al.* (1953) showed dog thoracic duct lymph to contain cholesterol in lipoprotein form as well as in chylomicrons. They suggested that the bulk of the lymph lipoproteins are derived from blood plasma.

The intestine has the most rapid rate of cholesterol biosynthesis of any tissue in the rat and rabbit but the fate of intestinal cholesterol is not known. No evidence of cholesterol catabolism in intestine has been produced and the excretion of cholesterol into the intestinal lumen appears to be small, as judged by the fecal excretion of injected labeled cholesterol in bile cannulated rats (Siperstein and Chaikoff, 1955). From the available data it may be inferred that in the rat a considerable amount of cholesterol synthesized in intestine may be discharged into intestinal lymph.

2. Appearance in the Chyle

Absorbed cholesterol appears in the chyle (i.e. thoracic duct lymph) as finely emulsified globules, the chylomicrons, which vary in size from 0.5 to 3 µ in diameter. They consist mainly of triglycerides but contain also phospholipid, cholesterol, and protein; it is suggested that they owe their stability to a phospholipid surface layer (Robinson, 1955). Chemical analyses of chylomicrons are shown in Table IV.

TABLE IV

COMPOSITION OF CHYLOMICRA[a,b]

	Dog	Rat	Human
Cholesteryl esters	1.5– 2.0		3.5
Free cholesterol	0.7– 1.0		1.1
Phospholipids	8.2– 8.9	8.5	6.4
Triglycerides	86.3–86.5	ca. 88	87.3
Free fatty acids	0.2		
Protein	2.2– 2.5	2	1.5
Carbohydrate		0.3	0.17

[a] Values as per cent dry weight.

[b] Values for dog chylomicra are quoted from Havel and Fredrickson (1956) and those for rat and human chylomicra are calculated from results of Laurell (1954a, b).

3. Appearance in Systemic Blood

The chyle with the cholesterol-containing chylomicrons is discharged from the thoracic duct into the systemic circulation relatively slowly. This is probably one of the factors limiting the rise in the plasma level of cholesterol after a single oral dose (Chapter 5). The rate of appearance of labeled dietary cholesterol is slow; thus in humans a peak value is reached between 36 and 72 hours (Biggs *et al.*, 1952; Warner, 1952) and only slightly earlier in dogs (Gould, 1952). It is impossible to state as yet the proportion of the ingested dose which enters the liver before appearing in the plasma lipoproteins. When hypercholesterolemia is produced experimentally by the injection of extremely hypercholesterolemic serum or plasma, the cholesterol level in plasma falls rapidly, reaching the normal range in 12 to 24 hours, and the excess cholesterol is deposited in tissues, largely in the liver (e.g. Horlick *et al.*, 1948, in chickens; Oppenheim and Bruger, 1950, in rabbits; and Friedman *et al.*, 1953, in rats). Half-times for this process may be estimated from the data as approximately 2 to 4 hours in chickens and rabbits and 6 hours in rats.

The exchanges between lymph and plasma in dogs, cats, and rabbits have been studied by Courtice and Morris (1955).

4. The Clearing Factor

Some hours after the ingestion of a fatty meal, the blood plasma has a milky or lipemic appearance. This "alimentary hyperlipemia" is largely due to the presence of excess chylomicrons (Deuel, 1955, Vol. II, p. 130). In 1943 Hahn described the *in vivo* clearing of alimentary hyperlipemia after the intravenous injection of heparin; later work has shown that this clearing may be brought about *in vitro* (reviews, Anfinsen, 1955; Bergström and Borgström, 1956).

The clearing factor is now recognized as a plasma esterase which hydrolyzes the neutral fat in the chylomicrons and in the high S_f value (i.e. low density) lipoproteins.

III. Esterification of Cholesterol

A. Concentration of Cholesteryl Esters in Tissues

Cholesterol is found in the tissues both free and esterified with various fatty acids.* The fraction present in esterified form varies greatly among individual tissues, but for any one tissue it is relatively constant under normal conditions. Representative values for various tissues are given in Chapter 4. Constancy of the per cent esterified in blood plasma is well established for man, regardless of variation in the total concentration (Sperry, 1936). A decrease in the per cent esterified is indicative of liver damage.

In general, the functions of cholesterol esterification are not well understood. It may be of significance that brain, with the lowest cholesterol turnover rate of any tissue in the body, has essentially none in esterified form, whereas adrenal cortex, liver, and plasma with rapid turnover rates have relatively large fractions of cholesterol in esterified form.

B. The Fatty Acid Component

Little is known about the fatty acids found in cholesteryl esters due to the lack until recently of satisfactory methods for separating them from triglycerides. Kelsey (1939) developed a method based on the observation that castor bean lipase hydrolyzes triglycerides but not cholesteryl esters, and Kelsey and Longenecker (1941) isolated a cholesteryl ester fraction from beef plasma. Although their preparation contained considerably more fatty acid than could be accounted for on the basis of its cholesterol content, they concluded that the fatty acids consisted of 62% linoleic acid. This method has been investigated by Clément et al. (1954) who report that the hydrolysis of triglycerides from tissues by castor bean lipase is incomplete.

The chromatographic methods for the separation of cholesteryl esters from tissues depend on the use of silicic acid or of acid-washed alumina (Chapter 3). Because of the possibility of hydrolysis and other chemical changes during adsorption on alumina, the silicic acid method is preferred by most workers.

The fatty acids in the plasma cholesteryl ester fraction of lactating

---

* Both free and esterified fractions are normally present in tissues combined with protein. The term "combined" has sometimes been used to mean esterified cholesterol but is not so used in this book.

cows have been characterized by Lough *et al.* (1957), using the silicic acid method. The iodine number of the mixture was 189; fractionation by the reversed phase chromatography method of Howard and Martin (1950) showed linoleic and linolenic acids to be most abundant, constituting 36 and 32%, respectively, of the total. Mono-unsaturated acids made up 17% and arachidonic 6% of the total, and myristic, palmitic, and stearic acids only about 9%. Linoleic acid was present in triglycerides in only very small amount, which supports the hypothesis that this so-called "essential fatty acid" is primarily a constituent of the cholesteryl esters.

It cannot be assumed that these figures apply to other species. In humans, Clément *et al.* (1954) have found iodine numbers of about 130 for the fatty acids present in the plasma cholesteryl esters isolated by the alumina method; and Kinsell *et al.* (1958) have shown that the iodine number may vary over a wide range depending on that of the dietary fat.

C. Cholesterol Esterases

From several tissues, enzyme preparations have been obtained which are active in both esterification of cholesterol with the naturally occurring fatty acids such as oleic, and in hydrolysis of cholesteryl oleate, but it is still not clear whether different enzymes are involved. Most of the studies have been carried out with artificial emulsions of cholesterol and it may be that the low activities reported for many tissues are due to the physico-chemical differences between the artificial substrate and the lipoprotein cholesterol present in the tissues.

1. Pancreas

The most active enzyme preparations have been obtained from pancreas (Klein, 1939; Le Breton and Pantaleon, 1947; Yamamoto *et al.*, 1949; Swell *et al.*, 1950; Swell and Treadwell, 1955; Korzenovsky *et al.*, 1955, 1956). Pancreas homogenate, pancreatic juice (Clément and Clément, 1956), and commercial pancreatin have all been used as sources of the enzyme. The pH optimum for hydrolysis of cholesteryl oleate and other esters was reported as pH 6.6, and that for esterification as pH 6.1 (Swell and Treadwell, 1955). Taurocholate was required according to these authors, although Korzenovsky *et al.* (1956) found cholate to be a specific requirement. The specificity with regard to fatty acids is indicated in Table V. The relative rates of the hydrolysis and esterification reactions for both oleate and linoleate were interpreted as indicating that at equilibrium there would be about two-thirds esterified and one-third free.

Cholesteryl esters present in intestinal contents are hydrolyzed before absorption (Mueller, 1915; Swell *et al.*, 1955b), presumably through the hydrolytic action of the cholesterol esterase in pancreatic juice. Absorbed cholesterol is esterified to 60 to 80% before reaching thoracic duct lymph (Bollman and Flock, 1951), but where this esterification takes place and what enzyme, if any, catalyzes it, is not clear.

TABLE V

RELATIVE RATES OF HYDROLYSIS AND ESTERIFICATION BY PANCREATIC CHOLESTEROL ESTERASE[a]

Compound	Esterification	Hydrolysis
Butyrate	14	905
Oleate	300	154
Linoleate	260	140

[a] Values represent mg. cholesterol reacting per gm. pancreas per hour. From Swell *et al.* (1955b).

The sterol specificity of the pancreatic enzyme has been studied by Swell *et al.* (1954), who found cholestanol to be more rapidly and completely esterified with oleic acid than cholesterol; this is in contrast to the rates of absorption. Other sterols tested were less readily esterified. Per cent esterification at 2 hours was: cholestanol 85; cholesterol 58; β-sitosterol 24; stigmasterol 8.7; ergosterol 6.9.

Pancreatic cholesterol esterase has recently been purified 400-fold by Hernandez and Chaikoff (1957); their results indicate that both esterification and hydrolysis are due to one enzyme and that free sulfhydryl groups are probably involved in the esterification.

2. Intestinal Mucosa

Active preparations have been obtained from this tissue (Nieft and Deuel, 1949; Nieft, 1949). Swell *et al.* (1955c) compared the esterifying activity of rat intestinal mucosa on emulsions of cholesterol and oleic acid, with that of a number of tissues, with results shown in Table VI. These workers also showed that the slight activity of intestinal mucosa was eliminated by pancreatectomy, suggesting that it actually originated in the pancreatic juice (Swell *et al.*, 1950).

TABLE VI

CHOLESTEROL ESTERASE ACTIVITY OF RAT TISSUES[a]

Tissue	Esterification	Hydrolysis
Pancreas	111	75
Intestinal mucosa	1.7	1.3
Liver	0	0

[a] Values in mg. cholesterol reacting per gm. tissue per hour. Other tissues found to be inactive included kidney, testis, spleen, lung, heart, skeletal muscle, serum, adipose, adrenal, and brain. From Swell *et al.* (1955c).

3. Liver

Sperry and Brand (1941) reported that incubation for several days of liver homogenate resulted in esterification of up to 32% of the free cholesterol present. Nieft and Deuel (1949) confirmed this observation with a "lightly centrifuged" liver homogenate, and showed that phosphate ion and a fatty acid source were required. They obtained about 50% esterification with palmitic acid in 21 hours, and obtained evidence supporting the view that esterification and hydrolysis are brought about by different enzymes. Byron et al. (1953) found no esterification of cholesterol-oleic acid-bile acid emulsions with liver homogenates, showing that the conditions for esterification with this enzyme apparently differ from those with the pancreatic enzyme.

Esterification of endogenous cholesterol presumably takes place in liver in vivo, as may be inferred from the rapid appearance of cholesteryl-C^{14} esters in liver after the administration of acetate-C^{14} (Harper et al., 1953; Eckles et al., 1955).

One promising lead in this problem is the observation of Fredrickson (1956) that incubation of mouse liver mitochondria with an emulsion of cholesterol-26-C^{14} resulted in up to 25% of the material becoming esterified.

4. Plasma

Esterification of cholesterol in plasma has been much investigated since Sperry (1935) reported that incubation of human serum for several days produces an increase in the esterified fraction. It is, however, still not clear whether this is the physiological method of formation of these esters. This in vitro reaction has proved to be an extremely complicated phenomenon, and is affected by many factors (Sperry and Stoyanoff, 1937, 1938; Le Breton and Pantaleon, 1947; Swell and Treadwell, 1950; Wagner and Rogalski, 1952; Tayeau, 1955). Tayeau and Nivet (1956) described a change in lipoprotein pattern of serum during incubation which raises a question of the physiological significance of the in vitro esterification process.

Bile acids inhibit the in vitro esterification of cholesterol in serum but are required for esterification of emulsions of cholesterol and higher fatty acids by pancreatic preparations (Swell et al., 1950). The explanation of this striking difference may lie both in differences between the substrates and between the enzymes. Plasma contains cholesterol and phospholipids in soluble lipoprotein form, which need no emulsifier but are highly sensitive to the action of bile acids (Tayeau, 1943, 1944). In the second case, bile acids are needed as an emulsifying agent but may also act as specific activators of the enzyme. Turner et al. (1953) have measured the *in vitro* rate of esterification of serum cholesterol in patients with jaundice and found significantly slower than normal rates. They concluded the inhibitory effect was more likely due to absence of cholesterol esterase than to the presence of bile acids, since the magnitude of the effect could not be correlated with the degree of jaundice.

Both liver and pancreas have been implicated as sources of the cholesterol esterase present in serum. In dogs, pancreatectomy reduces the esterase activity to very low levels (Swell and Kramer, 1953). Gibbs and Chaikoff (1941) reported irregular but marked decreases in the levels of cholesteryl esters in dogs following pancreatectomy. Neither experiment has been confirmed in other species and there are definite differences in the behavior of the dog serum cholesterol esterase and that of other species.

Harper *et al.* (1953) observed a rapid and striking effect of hepatectomy, carried out shortly after the injection of acetate-C^{14}, in preventing the appearance of cholesterol-C^{14} in the sterol ester fraction of several tissues. Their results suggest that liver may be responsible for the appearance of cholesteryl esters in plasma, intestine, kidney, and adrenal, since appearance of free cholesterol-C^{14} in these tissues was not affected.

Isotopic tracer studies have clearly shown that newly synthesized free cholesterol appears rapidly in plasma but is esterified very slowly, reaching as high a specific activity as the free fraction only after about 2 days (Eckles *et al.*, 1955; Hellman *et al.*, 1955). The slow rate of this process suggests the possibility that endogenous plasma cholesterol could be esterified in the plasma but the evidence in general points to the liver as the site of formation of the cholesteryl esters normally present in plasma of endogenous origin (Friedman and Byers, 1955a). Labeled dietary cholesterol becomes largely esterified before appearing in liver or plasma.

IV. Cholesterol Metabolism in the Liver

A. Formation of Plasma Lipoproteins

The cholesterol of the plasma and of the liver may be derived from either hepatic biosynthesis or from dietary sources. Evidence that the liver is the main tissue supplying cholesterol rapidly and in large amount to the blood has been obtained in hepatectomy experiments. Friedman *et al.* (1951) found that the plasma level in the rat, after being lowered by replacement of most of the animal's plasma with human albumin, rose to normal levels within 24 hours, but after partial hepatectomy the return to normal was greatly delayed. Recovery was only about 25% complete after 24 hours and 72 hours were required to reach normal levels. The same conclusion was reached using tracers in dogs; hepatectomy virtually abolished the appearance in the plasma of newly synthesized molecules (Gould, 1951; Harper *et al.*, 1953; Eckles *et al.*, 1955).

On the other hand, cholesterol is being discharged continuously into the blood from the thoracic duct in lipoprotein and chylomicron form. This cholesterol is derived partly from endogenous sources and partly from the diet, and a fraction of it appears ultimately in plasma lipoproteins. It is generally accepted that the liver is required for conversion of chylomicron cholesterol into plasma lipoproteins; evidence to this effect has been reported by Friedman and Byers (1954), and Friedman *et al.* (1956c), who show deposition of chylomicrons in hepatic reticulo-endothelial cells.

As the liver is also the source of the plasma phospholipids (Fishler *et al.*, 1943; Goldman *et al.*, 1950) and of the plasma proteins, including 80% of the globulins (Miller *et al.*, 1951), it is reasonable to assume that plasma lipoproteins are formed in the liver.

B. Turnover of Cholesterol

1. Introduction

The term turnover may be defined as the rate of replacement of the molecules of a body constituent or the rate of disappearance due to excretion and metabolic breakdown or conversion into other substances. In the steady state these two rates will be equal. Cholesterol turnover in individual tissues is complicated by movement of labeled molecules from one tissue to another but whole-body turnover is relatively simple and will be discussed first.

2. Whole-Body Turnover

Rittenberg and Schoenheimer (1937) developed a method of determining whole-body turnover in which mice were maintained with a constant concentration of deuterium in their body water and both the rate of incorporation of deuterium and the maximum attainable isotopic concentration, I_{max}, in whole-body cholesterol were determined. Their data for mice indicated that the I_{max} of deuterium in cholesterol was about half that in body water and that the time required for the cholesterol to reach half the I_{max} value was about 21 days. The presence of inert cholesterol in the brain would not have affected the rate of incorporation but it would decrease the equilibrium value. More recent studies in which any possible effect of inert cholesterol was eliminated have indicated I_{max} to be about 63% of the value in body water (Popják and Beeckmans, 1950).

Data on turnover obtained in this way have usually been found to show a close approximation to the behavior of a simple first-order process, or what is often called exponential behavior. The derivation of equations useful in dealing with such exponential rates of build-up or disappearance of labeled molecules are given in many discussions of the use of tracer methods (e.g. Solomon, 1949; Comar, 1955; Robertson, 1957).

In the present example, the turnover half-time of 21 days may be used to calculate the turnover time and the rate of synthesis, assuming that turnover is exponential. The turnover time (t_t) is $1.44 \times t_{\frac{1}{2}}$ or 30 days. This represents the mean life of a labeled cholesterol molecule and is therefore the time necessary for regeneration of as much cholesterol as is present in the animal. A 25-gm. mouse contains approximately 75 mg. of cholesterol and the rate of synthesis from Rittenberg and Schoenheimer's data corresponds to a regeneration rate of 3.3% or 2.5 mg. per day.

Very few other studies have been done on whole-body turnover but Pihl *et al.* (1950) measured turnover in liver and carcass of the rat. Their estimate of $t_{\frac{1}{2}}$ for carcass cholesterol was 31–32 days. Correcting this value for the more rapid rate of turnover of the small pool of liver cholesterol decreases this value to about 30 days. This corresponds to a rate of synthesis in a 300 gm. rat of about 14 mg. per day.

3. Turnover in Liver and Blood

When the build-up of labeled cholesterol in both liver and the rest of the animal are measured, it is found that labeled cholesterol appears more rapidly in liver but the maximum isotope concentration attainable is approximately the same.

a. Rats. A number of estimates have been made by means of build-up methods. Karp and Stetten (1949) using the deuterium-body water method estimated a $t_{\frac{1}{2}}$ for liver cholesterol of 3 to 4 days. Pihl *et al.* (1950) in a careful study using acetate-C^{14} at a constant level in a fat-free diet and estimating the specific activity of the C_2 pool by following the specific activity of the acetyl group in α-acetamido-γ-phenylbutyrate came to the conclusion that the turnover half-time was about 6 days. Fredrickson *et al.* (1954) have estimated a $t_{\frac{1}{2}}$ of about 4 days based on the incorporation of tritium from H^3OH in liver cholesterol during a 24 hour period, and the assumption that I_{max} is half the body water value.

Methods based on rates of disappearance have also been used. Hotta and Chaikoff (1955) injected cholesterol-C^{14} and followed its disappearance from serum. Between about 17 and 80 hours the decrease in specific activity was exponential with a slope corresponding to a turnover half-time of 42 hours or 1.75 days.

Even more rapid turnover was reported by Landon and Greenberg

(1954) who injected acetate-C^{14} in a series of rats and measured the rate of decrease in specific activity of the cholesterol in serum, liver, and a number of other tissues. Their reported value for liver, $t_{\frac{1}{2}} = 28$ hours, was apparently derived only from animals in which the bile duct had been ligated or cannulated; since both these procedures have been reported to increase the rate of cholesterol synthesis very markedly (Fredrickson et al., 1954; Kelly et al., 1957), faster than normal turnover would be expected. The results of Landon and Greenberg on normal rats are of great interest in showing clearly that, during the first 24 to 36 hours after acetate-C^{14} injection, the specific activity of cholesterol in liver, serum, and intestine falls while that in all other tissues studied rises. The authors pointed out that during this period "turnover of cholesterol in these organs must occur primarily by exchange with cholesterol in the plasma." This will result in a more rapid disappearance of labeled cholesterol from plasma and consequently from liver during the early stages.

If the rates of movement of labeled molecules from one tissue to another are sufficiently rapid, turnover measured for any one tissue after this equilibruim state has been reached will apply to the whole animal. If there is no transfer from one tissue to another, each tissue will have its own turnover rate. In the case of cholesterol we find neither one nor the other, but an intermediate situation, in which interchange of cholesterol molecules between liver and various tissues proceeds at widely varying rates and to varying extents.

The liver and carcass may be considered as a first approximation to be a two-pool, open system, similar to the model systems discussed by Solomon (1949) and by Lax and Wrenshall (1953) (Fig. 1). The liver and blood cholesterol interchange sufficiently fast so that blood does not constitute a separate pool but can be considered to be in equilibrium

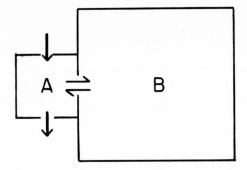

Fig. 1. The liver (A) and carcass (B) considered as a two-pool, open system (see text and Lax and Wrenshall, 1953).

with liver at all times in the measurements under consideration. Equilibration between liver and blood has been studied in dogs and is discussed in the following section.

If the build-up of isotope concentration in A is measured as in the deuterium body-water method, the transfer into B will lengthen the time necessary to reach a maximum concentration in A and thus lengthen the $t_{\frac{1}{2}}$ value. On the other hand, if labeled molecules are initially introduced into A in a single dose as in the single-injection method with either labeled acetate or with cholesterol and the rate of disappearance measured, transfer into B will cause a faster disappearance and result in a shorter $t_{\frac{1}{2}}$ value.

On this basis, it is understandable that build-up methods tend to give longer $t_{\frac{1}{2}}$ values than those based on disappearance following a single dose. It also becomes understandable why the $t_{\frac{1}{2}}$ values for plasma (or liver) cholesterol determined at long time intervals after labeling has been stopped indicate a steadily decreasing turnover rate (Hellman *et al.*, 1954, 1955; McGuire and Lipsky, 1955). Neither method measures directly the rate of regeneration of liver cholesterol or its rate of breakdown and excretion, but both of these rates can be measured by other methods.

The rate of biosynthesis has been determined in liver slices where interchange processes are not a factor. Taylor *et al.* (1956) have found the rate of biosynthesis to be in the range of 0.6 to 3.0 mg. per 100 gm. per hour with a mean of 1.65, corresponding to a $t_{\frac{1}{2}}$ of 4.4 days. While there is no basis for expecting the rate *in vitro* to be the same as in the intact animal it is of interest that the agreement is so close.

The rate of utilization of cholesterol for bile acid formation in the liver has been determined by Bergström and his collaborators. Lindstedt and Norman (1956a) have estimated that the normal rat converts about 1.5 mg. of cholesterol to bile acids per day per 100 gm. body weight. Since a rat has approximately 10 mg. of liver cholesterol per 100 gm. body weight, this value corresponds to a $t_{\frac{1}{2}}$ of 4.6 days, not taking into account any net loss which may result from the enterohepatic circulation of cholesterol. By making use of the recent evidence that almost all of the cholesterol metabolized in the rat is excreted eventually in the feces as bile acid metabolic products or sterols (Bergström, 1952; Siperstein and Chaikoff, 1952), Lindstedt and Norman (1956a) have estimated total body turnover. Taking Pihl's (1954) value of 1.5 to 2.0 mg. per day per 100 gm. of body weight for the fecal excretion of sterols by rats on a cholesterol-free diet, they estimate total body utilization as 3–4 mg. per 100 gm. per day. Assuming the cholesterol content to be 1.8 mg. per gm.

for the whole animal this value corresponds to a $t_{\frac{1}{2}}$ of about 33 days, in good agreement with the value of Pihl *et al.* (1950) of about 30 days.

b. Dogs. Harper *et al.* (1953) found a rapid disappearance of cholesterol-C^{14} from liver immediately after its biosynthesis from acetate-C^{14}. They state "the changes must be accounted for largely on the basis of transport." Eckles *et al.* (1955) in a similar study observed a rapid equilibration between liver free and plasma free cholesterol, and slightly slower equilibration of erythrocyte cholesterol; the esterified plasma cholesterol equilibrated much more slowly. An analysis of these equilibria was made by determining the rate at which the specific activity values for two compartments approach each other, and the following equilibration half-times were estimated: liver free $\rightleftharpoons$ plasma free 0.3 hour; plasma free $\rightleftharpoons$ erythrocyte free 1.4 hours; plasma free $\rightleftharpoons$ plasma ester 7 hours. On the reasonable assumption that all the free cholesterol molecules behave in the same way as the newly formed labeled ones it is apparent that in the dog each molecule of free cholesterol in plasma enters the liver every 30 minutes, on the average, and an equal amount of cholesterol moves from liver into plasma. Additional evidence supporting this view was obtained by measuring the rate of movement of cholesterol-C^{14} from blood into the liver following its injection in normal lipoprotein form (Gould, 1951).

The rate of disappearance of labeled cholesterol from the blood after these rapid equilibrations are completed has a half-time of 8 to 10 days, whether the labeled cholesterol is produced by endogenous biosynthesis or is injected as labeled lipoprotein cholesterol. The rate is reasonably exponential after 2–3 days following injection to the 12th to 15th day, when the curve begins to flatten. During this period there are no doubt some equilibration processes still going on but it is probable that metabolic utilization in the liver is the dominant process.

c. Humans. Equilibration processes occurring in human blood have been studied using radioisotopic tracers, and show qualitatively the same pattern as the dog but some of the rates are slower. The appearance of labeled cholesterol in the plasma and in the erythrocytes following the administration of actate-C^{14} has been investigated by Hellman *et al.* (1954) and by Gould *et al.* (1955), and the pattern of response is illustrated in Fig. 2. Labeled cholesterol appeared first in the plasma free sterol fraction reaching a peak specific activity value in 2 to 4 hours. Equilibration with erythrocyte cholesterol occurred at about the same rate as in dogs, the estimated half-time for the process being between 1 and 2 hours. The plasma ester sterol specific activity curve reaches and usually crosses the plasma free specific activity curve between 48 and 72 hours, and subsequently remains slightly higher. This result would be expected from the continuous dilution of plasma free cholesterol-C^{14} by newly synthesized cholesterol molecules. Kurland *et al.* (1954) injected cholesterol-C^{14} intravenously and found that the specific activity value of erythrocyte cholesterol reached that of the plasma free sterol in from 7 to 14 hours, and that of the plasma ester fraction after 4 to 7 days.

The subsequent disappearance of cholesterol from human plasma has been determined by the workers cited above and there is general agreement that the half-time ($t_{\frac{1}{2}}$) is in the range 8 to 12 days. This value compares well with that of 8 days obtained by London and Rittenberg (1950) for serum cholesterol in a normal man based on the incorporation of deuterium from H^2OH.

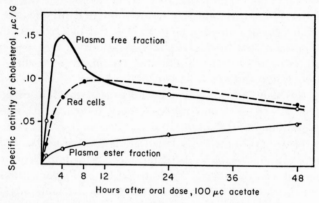

Fig. 2. Composite curves for specific activity of cholesterol after an oral dose of 100 μc. of acetate to human subjects (from Gould *et al.*, 1955).

Oral administration of cholesterol-C^{14} or of cholesterol-H^3 gives a slow rate of appearance in the plasma, the peak specific activity value occurring 24 to 48 hours even after a small dose (e.g. Warner, 1952; Biggs *et al.*, 1952). Either the free or the ester forms may have the higher specific activity during the first two or three days (Biggs and Colman, 1953), but the ester eventually becomes slightly higher, as with the administration of acetate-C^{14}. Hellman *et al.* (1955) have established clearly that cholesterol absorbed from the diet and that biosynthesized in the liver are metabolically interchangeable. This conclusion does not necessarily apply to cholesterol synthesized in other tissues, e.g. brain.

In summary, the cholesterol which is absorbed from the intestine becomes indistinguishable from that produced biosynthetically in the liver. Free cholesterol from the liver equilibrates with that of the plasma which in its turn equilibrates rapidly with that of erythrocytes, but the transformation of free to esterified cholesterol is a relatively slow process. Absorbed cholesterol becomes partially esterified during absorption, presumably in the intestine, whereas endogenous cholesterol becomes esterified in liver and possibly also in plasma or other tissues.

C. Conversion to Bile Acids

1. Bile Acids

The bile acids are steroid monocarboxylic acids related to cholesterol but differing in that (a) the 3-hydroxyl group has the α-configuration (in consequence they are not precipitable by digitonin); and (b) the Δ^5 double bond is absent and the rings A and B have a *cis* configuration to each other. This configuration, designated "normal" for historical reasons, is now denoted as "5β"; it is also present in coprostanol. The bile acids found in mammals usually have 24 carbon atoms and 1, 2, or 3 hydroxyl groups in positions 3, 7, 12, or 6. Many other bile acids are known to occur in nature, particularly in lower vertebrates, and some have 27 to 29 carbon atoms (see reviews by Haslewood, 1955; Tayeau, 1949; Shimizu, 1948; and Sobotka, 1938).

The bile acids found in humans and the common laboratory animals are conjugated with glycine or taurine. Due to species differences, generalizations about bile acid metabolism are of limited validity, as is evident from Table VII, which gives the constitution of the most abundant bile acids in these species.

Bile contains a mixture of the sodium salts of the conjugated bile acids as its principal constituent. The function of bile is the emulsification of fatty materials, which is essential to their enzymatic hydrolysis and is due primarily to the surface-active properties of the bile salts although the lecithin and perhaps other constituents of bile may also contribute. The composition of bile is given in Chapter 4. Isaksson (1954) has isolated a lecithin-bile salt complex from fresh, lyophilized bile which has a remarkable solubilizing effect on cholesterol and he suggests it may play a part in keeping biliary cholesterol from precipitating.

2. Formation of the Bile Acids

The formation of bile acids from cholesterol was first clearly shown by the classic study of Bloch *et al.* (1943) who injected cholesterol-H^2 into a dog and recovered cholic acid with such a high content of deuterium as to prove conversion. In 1952, the quantitative importance of this pathway in cholesterol metabolism in rats was established by Siperstein *et al.* (1952b) and by Bergström (1952) and Bergström and Norman (1953). Results of recent studies in humans, however, indicate that in this species, injected cholesterol-C^{14} is excreted to a much larger extent

TABLE VII
THE BILE ACIDS[a]

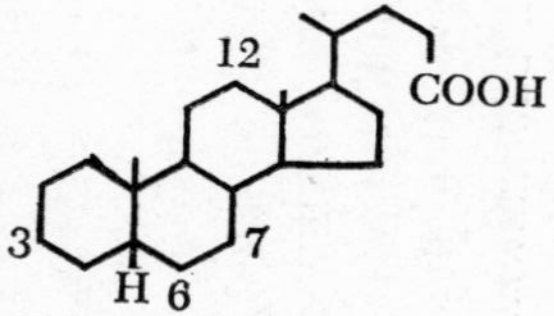

Cholanic acid

$NH_2CH_2CH_2SO_3H$ Taurine
NH_2CH_2COOH Glycine

Trivial name	Cholanic acid derivative	Occurrence in bile of:
Cholic acid	$3\alpha,7\alpha,12\alpha$-trihydroxy	Man and most mammalian species as
Deoxycholic acid	$3\alpha,12\alpha$-dihydroxy	major constituents
Chenodeoxycholic acid	$3\alpha,7\alpha$-dihydroxy	
Lithocholic acid	3α-hydroxy	Man, rat, and other species, as minor constituent
Hyodeoxycholic acid	$3\alpha,6\alpha$-dihydroxy	Hog
Hyocholic acid	$3\alpha,6\alpha,7\alpha$-trihydroxy	Hog
Epimers of hyocholic acid		
Acid I (Hsia et al., 1957)	$3\alpha,6\alpha,7\beta$-trihydroxy (?)	Rat; possibly in other species as well
Acid II (Hsia et al., 1957)	$3\alpha,6\beta,7\alpha$-trihydroxy (?)	

NOTE: Bile acids are present in bile entirely in conjugated form. In rabbits they are conjugated only with glycine, in chickens only with taurine, in rats very largely with taurine, and in man a mixture of tauro- and glyco-acids is present.

[a] The bile acids are given trivial names and also named as derivatives of cholanic acid.

in the fecal sterol fraction than in the fecal steroid acid fraction (Frantz and Carey, 1957).

Cholesterol-C^{14} introduced into the body by feeding, intravenous or intraperitoneal injection, mixes with that in liver and blood, and a little more slowly with that in intestine and other viscera. Its metabolic fate can therefore be considered as indicating the fate of all the cholesterol in rapid equilibrium with blood cholesterol, i.e. in the cholesterol pool, and consists to a very large extent in oxidative removal of the terminal 3 carbon atoms of the side chain and eventual fecal excretion of the remaining 24 carbon atoms as bile acid metabolites.

Subsequent to the intravenous injection of cholesterol-26-C^{14}, rapid oxidation of the 26-C^{14} and excretion as carbon dioxide was found. In the first 24 hours 19% of the dose was recovered in the respiratory CO^2, and in 84 hours about 40% (Chaikoff et al., 1952b). These data correspond to a half-time for this process of about 4 days (uncorrected for other processes), which is close to most of the estimates for the half turnover time of liver-blood cholesterol arrived at by other methods.

The sterol ring system is not broken down to fragments that can be oxidized to carbon dioxide to an appreciable extent, as shown by the observations on the fate of cholesterol-4-C^{14}; no C^{14} has been detected in respiratory carbon dioxide (Chaikoff et al., 1952b) and 95% of the dose was recovered from feces during 15 days subsequent to the intravenous injection in rats of cholesterol-4-C^{14} (Siperstein and Chaikoff, 1955). Of this recovered activity, 10% of the original amount was in the nonsaponifiable fraction and 85% in the steroid acid fraction (Siperstein et al., 1952b). These acidic products were shown by Bergström and Norman (1953) to be a complex mixture of hydroxy and keto acids, no one of which was identical with cholic acid.

Oral administration gave very similar results except for an initial peak of activity in fecal nonsaponifiable fraction due to unabsorbed cholesterol. Figure 3 shows the difference in results due to the route of administration.

Over-all metabolism of cholesterol in rats thus results in the ultimate excretion of about 10% as fecal sterols, 85% as fecal steroid acids, and only 1% in urine, presumably as steroid hormone metabolites.

The rates of conversion into individual bile acids has been studied by means of bile duct fistulas. In rats, Bergström (1952) found that during 10 days after intraperitoneal injection of cholesterol-C^{14}, 22% appeared in cholic acid in rat bile, a small amount in other bile acids, and 7% in the nonsaponifiable fraction. After the intravenous injection of cholesterol-C^{14} in bile fistula rats, Siperstein et al. (1954) observed appearance of C^{14} in taurochenodeoxycholic and lithocholic acids during the first 7 hours. After this time, C^{14} appeared in taurocholic acid and it eventually became the major labeled product. Although these results suggest the possibility that chenodeoxycholic acid or lithocholic acid is an intermediate in cholic acid formation, it is now established, at least in the rat, that neither one is.

In a patient with a bile fistula, 40% of a dose of cholesterol-4-C^{14} was excreted in 50 hours, of which 98.5% was found in bile, only 0.2% in the urine, and 1.3% in the acholic feces (Siperstein and Murray, 1955).

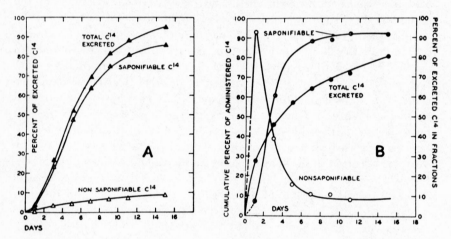

Fig. 3. The fecal excretion of cholesterol-4-C^{14} in rats. A: After intravenous injection; B: After oral administration. (From Siperstein and Chaikoff, 1955, p. 769, with permission of the authors.)

3. Pathways in Bile Acid Formation

The recent application of chromatographic methods to the isolation of bile acids has shown that our knowledge of the bile acids present in bile is still incomplete (e.g. Wootton and Wiggins, 1953; Matschiner *et al.*, 1957a). Figure 4 presents a tentative scheme, representing the present state of knowledge and one which will no doubt need modification in the light of future developments in this very active field. The liver has the ability to cleave only the three terminal carbon atoms on the side chain (Zabin and Barker, 1953), and to introduce numerous alterations in the ring structure of cholesterol and other steroids, but is apparently unable to break down the carbon skeleton beyond the C_{24} stage. Two general pathways in the formation of bile acids may be recognized, apparently depending on whether the side chain is attacked before position 12 is hydroxylated.

a. Cholic acid pathway. Cholic acid may be formed by modification of the ring sytem followed by cleavage of the side chain. As shown by C^{14} or H^3 labeling methods, it is formed from 7α-hydroxycholesterol (Lindstedt, 1957b), 3α,7α-dihydroxycoprostane (Bergström and Lindstedt, 1956), and 3α,7α,12α-trihydroxycoprostane (Bergström et al., 1954); it is not formed from the C_{24} carboxylic acid corresponding to cholesterol, 3β-hydroxy-Δ⁵-cholenic acid (Bergström and Pääbo, 1955), from 25- or 26-hydroxycholesterol (Fredrickson and Ono, 1956), or from any of the known bile acids except deoxycholic acid (Bergström et al., 1953b).

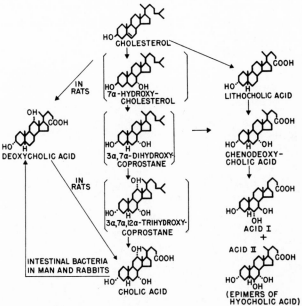

FIG. 4. Pathways in the formation of bile acids.

b. *Alternative pathway.* The second pathway comprises conversion to lithocholic acid (3α), chenodeoxycholic acid (3α,7α), and to various trihydroxycholanic acids which are similar to but not identical with cholic acid. Two of them have recently been studied by Doisy and his associates who have shown that the compound designated acid I is 3α,6α,7-trihydroxycholanic acid (Matschiner et al., 1957a, b; Mahowald et al., 1957a, b; Hsia et al., 1957). It is epimeric with hyocholic acid, the structure of which is probably 3α,6α,7α-trihydroxycholanic acid (Ziegler, 1956). A second new bile acid from rat bile, acid II, is 3α,6β,7α-trihydroxycholanic acid (Hsia et al., 1957). Observations relevant to the alternative pathway include the following: (1) 3β-hydroxy-Δ⁵-cholenic acid, Δ⁴-cholestenone, Δ⁵-cholestenone, 3β-hydroxycoprostane, and 3α-cholesterol have all been found to be converted into acidic products similar to but different from cholic acid (Bergström, 1955; Harold *et al.*, 1955) and they appear to be formed by the alternative pathway. (2) Lithocholic and chenodeoxycholic acids are converted into more polar compounds including substances similar to but not identical with cholic acid (Bergström, 1955). (3) It is possible that both 7α-hydroxycholesterol and 3α,7α-dihydroxycoprostane may be common intermediates of both series since each has been shown to give rise to both cholic and chenodeoxycholic acids (Bergström and Lindstedt, 1956; Lindstedt, 1957b) but there is as yet no proof that either is formed during conversion of cholesterol to bile acids.

The formation of bile acids has been shown to be irreversible, at any rate for cholic acid; Byers and Biggs (1952) showed that cholic acid-H^3 did not give rise to any detectable amounts of cholesterol-H^3 in rats.

It is still uncertain whether cholesterol is an obligatory precursor of bile acids. Some evidence suggesting independent synthesis has been reported; Staple and Gurin (1954) and Dayton *et al.* (1955) found higher specific activity values in bile acids than in biliary cholesterol during the first 3 and 1 days, respectively, after the administration of acetate.

On the other hand, Rosenfeld *et al.* (1955) in an extensive study on human patients with complete bile fistulas using C^{14}- and H^3-labeled acetate and cholesterol, found that the cholic acid specific activity was below that of plasma free cholesterol and of bile cholesterol at all times. The ratio of C^{14}:H^3 was the same in cholesterol and cholic acid, supporting the hypothesis that cholesterol is an obligatory precursor of cholic acid.

c. In vitro formation of bile acids. Oxidation of carbon atom 26 in cholesterol to CO_2 has been demonstrated in liver slices (Meier *et al.*, 1952) and in rat liver homogenates (Anfinsen and Horning, 1953). Δ^{25}-Dehydrocholesterol has been shown to be formed by a solubilized particulate fraction from rat liver homogenate by Lynn *et al.* (1955). On the basis of this finding and other evidence, they suggest the following sequence of reactions:

Fredrickson and Ono (1956) have shown that mouse liver mitochondria convert cholesterol into both 25-hydroxy- and 26-hydroxycholesterol. Administration of these substances to bile fistula rats resulted in the rapid formation of steroid acids similar to but not identical with cholic acid.

d. 7α-Hydroxylation of bile acids. 7α-Hydroxylation of deoxycholic acid by rat liver slices and homogenates has been demonstrated by Bergström *et al.* (1953a) and Bergström and Gloor (1954). Conjugation with taurine occurred concomitantly to give taurocholic acid as the product. Microsomes plus soluble supernatant fractions were found to give 7α-hydroxylation of taurodeoxycholic acid; ATP stimulated the rate of this reaction, and after dialysis addition of DPN and Mg were necessary (Bergström and Gloor, 1955).

4. Conjugation

Enzyme preparations consisting of rat liver microsomes and soluble supernatant fractions are capable of forming both taurocholic and glycocholic acids when ATP is added (Bremer and Gloor, 1955; Siperstein, 1955; Elliott, 1956). Siperstein reported optimal activity after addition of Mg, ATP, CoA, and DPN. Bremer (1956) reported that cholyl CoA is an intermediate in conjugation and is formed in a similar manner to acetyl CoA:

$$\text{Cholic acid} + \text{ATP} + \text{HSCoA} \rightarrow \text{cholyl CoA} + \text{AMP} + \text{PP}$$

The conjugation was brought about by microsomes alone and CoA was an absolute requirement. The enzymes displayed specificity towards the amino compound; in the presence of both taurine and glycine, rabbit liver microsomes gave only glycocholate, chicken microsomes only taurocholate, and rat microsomes gave both, but more tauro- than glycocholate.

Evidence that the liver may not be able to hydrolyze conjugated bile acids has been obtained by Lindstedt and Norman (1957), but there is no doubt that bacteria of the kinds normally present in the large intestine are able to split conjugated bile acids and to cause many changes in bile acids both oxidative and reductive in nature (Schmidt and Hughes, 1942; Norman and Grubb, 1955).

In the intestine the conjugated acids are either reabsorbed or are hydrolyzed through the action of bacteria and metabolized to steroid acids which are not absorbable and are excreted in feces. No conjugated acids have been detected in feces.

D. Enterohepatic Circulation of Bile Acids and of Cholesterol

Bile acids discharged into the intestinal lumen in bile are very rapidly and efficiently absorbed and reutilized. The cholesterol in bile mixes with that present in the intestinal contents and the mixture is partly absorbed and introduced into the systemic circulation via the thoracic duct, as discussed above. A fraction of the biliary cholesterol is returned to the liver where it is reutilized but the enterohepatic circulation of cholesterol is much less rapid and efficient than that of bile acids (Siper-stein *et al.*, 1952a).

Absorbed bile acids are carried in the portal circulation and are ef-ficiently removed from the blood by the liver. Consequently, the bile acids are present in considerably higher concentrations in portal than in peripheral blood (Josephson and Rydin, 1936; see Deuel, 1955, Vol. II, pp. 111–114 for review of enterohepatic circulation). Carey (1956) reported the qualitative identification of cholic and chenodeoxycholic acids in 25 ml. samples of normal human serum; however, Rudman and Kendall (1957) were unable to measure the concentrations of bile acids in normal serum because of the extremely low values. No detect-able amounts of bile acids are present in urine of normal human subjects but in obstructive jaundice, bile acids appear in both peripheral blood and urine in readily measurable amounts.

Most investigations on the synthesis and enterohepatic circulation of bile acids have utilized bile fistula preparations. It should be emphasized that if the bile is completely removed from an animal and the bile salts are neither returned nor replaced, profound changes in the rate of synthesis of bile acids will be produced. Values for bile acid excretion in bile fistula animals represent the maximum capacity of the liver to syn-thesize bile acids rather than the normal rate, as Bergström and Borg-ström (1956) have pointed out. In bile fistula rats the rate of excretion of cholic and chenodeoxycholic acids decreases during the first day and then increases to reach a high, relatively stable value after about 48 hours (Thompson and Vars, 1953; Eriksson, 1956, 1957a). As shown in Fig. 5, about 60 mg. of bile acids are synthesized each day in a 200 gm. rat from the 2nd through the 8th day. This represents the daily conver-sion of about 2 or 3 times the entire cholesterol content of the liver into bile acids and must obviously affect the rate of turnover of hepatic cholesterol as well as the rate of synthesis of bile acids. In normal rats the bile acid production is only about 1.8 mg. per 100 gm. body weight per day (Bergström and Eriksson, 1958).

In bile fistula dogs, Whipple and Smith (1928) found the endogenous production of bile acids to be about 100 mg. per kg. of body weight per day, corresponding to a daily conversion of more than the entire cho-lesterol content of liver. If the collected bile is fed back to the dog, the rate of excretion increases to 800 mg. per kg. per day and can be further increased to about double this figure by feeding additional amounts of bile acids.

It is apparent that there are difficulties in the way of determining the enterohepatic circulation time for bile acids. In the rat, which may not be typical of other species because of the absence of a gall bladder, the enterohepatic circulation is extremely rapid in relation to the size of the bile acid pool. Oral administration of labeled bile acids to bile fistula rats results in the recovery from bile of 80% to 90% of the label in 2 hours (Norman, 1955; Portman and Mann, 1955; Sjövall and Äkesson, 1955). On the basis of other evidence, Bergström *et al.* (1958) have estimated that the bile acids circulate about 15–20 times per day in the rat.

The actual rates of turnover and synthesis of bile acids have been estimated by Bergström and his associates in intact rats and in man by determining the rate of excretion of a small dose of a labeled bile acid,

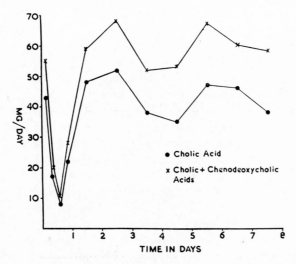

Fig. 5. The rate of excretion of taurocholic and taurodeoxycholic acids in bile fistula rats as a function of time after cannulation (from Eriksson, 1956).

and the size of the pool of that acid by means of the isotope dilution method. Lindstedt and Norman (1956a) injected 1–2 mg. of cholic acid-24-C^{14} into rats and followed the fecal excretion of total activity under normal conditions. The excretion curve was exponential and gave a half-time of 2.3 days; similar values were obtained for chenodeoxycholic acid-24-C^{14} and for lithocholic acid-24-C^{14}.

The amount of cholic acid present in a rat was estimated by Bergström and Eriksson (1958) to be about 5 mg. per 100 gm. body weight by injecting a small amount of labeled cholic acid; after allowing sufficient time for mixing with all the cholic acid in the rat, bile was obtained and cholic acid isolated in pure form. The decrease in specific activity is a measure of the amount of cholic acid in the rat. From the half-time for excretion and the pool size, it was estimated that the daily production is about 1.7 mg. per 100 gm. body weight. Since rat bile acids normally consist of about 90% cholic acid and 10% chenodeoxycholic acid, the figure for total bile acid production may be estimated as about 1.8 mg. per day per 100 gm. body weight.

Lindstedt (1956) has carried out a similar study in humans; 3 subjects were given doses of cholic acid-24-C[14] and samples of bile obtained at various times. The amount of cholic acid in the body was determined by dilution and the turnover half-time determined by the rate of disappearance. The analysis of a sample of bile permitted estimation of the total amount of bile acids in the body. The cholic acid pool ranged from 0.58–1.3 gm. and the $t_{\frac{1}{2}}$ values from 1.2–3 days, corresponding to a rate of cholic acid formation of about 0.3 gm. per day, or close to 1.0 gm. of total bile acids. It may be estimated that about 1 gm. of cholesterol is converted into bile acids per day in normal humans. In patients with bile fistulas, the volume of bile formed has been reported to be about 500 ml. per day (Rundle et al., 1955).

Cholesterol excretion in bile was reported by Friedman et al. (1950) to be about 1.8 mg. per day the first day and somewhat less the second day for bile fistula rats, weighing about 300 gm. Eriksson (1956) found 1.0 mg. per day for the first day and close to 2.0 mg. per day for the next 8 days. As compared with the daily excretion of 40 to 60 mg. of bile acids, the cholesterol loss by this route is clearly of little quantitative significance.

The chief factor affecting the rate of bile acid excretion from the body is the conversion into metabolic products which are not absorbed from the intestine but are excreted in feces. This conversion appears to be due to the action of intestinal bacteria since in their absence, the turnover half-time of bile acids is greatly prolonged. Rats treated with terramycin and phthalylsulfathiazole were shown to have a $t_{\frac{1}{2}}$ for cholic acid of 10–15 days, or 5 to 7 times as long as in normal animals (Lindstedt and Norman, 1956b). In germ-free rats cholic acid had a half-life of 11.4 days and was excreted entirely as taurocholate (Gustafsson et al., 1957). The specific microorganisms responsible for the metabolic alterations of bile acids have not been identified. Clostridium perfringens is capable of hydrolyzing the conjugated bile acids but did not alter the turnover rate when introduced into germ-free rats (Norman and Grubb, 1955).

Deoxycholic acid is apparently not made in the liver but is formed in the intestine from cholic acid by bacterial action and is then absorbed and excreted in bile in conjugated form, in man (Lindstedt, 1957a) and in rabbits (Lindstedt and Sjövall, 1957). Absorption of deoxycholic acid is apparently not as complete as that of cholic acid, however, since free deoxycholic acid has been isolated from human feces (Carey and Watson, 1955). This bile acid occupies an intermediate position; it is a product of bacterial action which is partly utilizable as a bile acid and partly excreted in feces as an end-product of bile acid metabolism.

It was suggested by Sobotka (1938, p. 37) and endorsed by Josephson (1941) that "equilibrium is maintained by synthesis of bile acids paralleling the rate of fecal losses." Bergström and his associates have recently produced experimental support for the concept that the rate of synthesis of bile acids from hepatic cholesterol may be regulated by the amount (or concentration) of circulating bile acids in the rat, perhaps in a manner analogous to the regulation of cholesterol synthesis by its concentration in liver, as discussed on p. 279. Adminstration of taurochenodeoxycholate to bile fistula rats at a rate of 10 mg. per hour depresses the rate of endogenous formation of taurocholate from about 30 mg. per day to a rate of 1–2 mg. per day, which is in the normal range (Bergström *et al.*, 1958).

E. Role of the Liver in Cholesterol Homeostasis

The liver appears to be the chief organ concerned with regulation of both the total body content of cholesterol and the plasma cholesterol level. These two functions are achieved by entirely different methods.

(1) Total body content depends on the balance between the amount of cholesterol formed in the body plus that absorbed from the diet and the amount broken down into other substances plus that excreted in feces. As the amount in the diet increases, cholesterol biosynthesis in liver decreases and may be reduced to very low levels. The efficiency of absorption also decreases at high dietary levels under experimental conditions but it is not clear if the variation in cholesterol content found in different natural diets would be sufficient to result in a change in the efficiency of absorption.

An important pathway of utilization of cholesterol is the conversion of cholesterol to bile acids in the liver. The rate of this process appears to be regulated primarily by the total content of bile acids in the body, and can be increased many fold if the enterohepatic circulation is broken as in bile fistula preparations. The more efficient the reabsorption and reutilization of bile acids, the slower their turnover, and the slower the conversion of cholesterol to bile acids. This may be thought of as a chain of consecutive feed-back controlled reactions:

It is of the first importance to note that the rate of conversion of bile acids to metabolites appears to be controlled by the nature of the intestinal bacteria. Acceleration of this process or of the excretion of bile acids as insoluble salts could be expected to produce an acceleration in the utilization of cholesterol and might possibly be a feasible method of eliminating excessive amounts of cholesterol stored in liver. A secondary increase in the rate of cholesterol biosynthesis would also be expected.

(2) The plasma cholesterol level does not necessarily reflect the concentration of cholesterol in liver, or the rate of hepatic synthesis. It does appear to be influenced by the plasma levels of phospholipids and triglycerides and probably of the specific proteins capable of combining with cholesterol. The distribution of cholesterol between liver and plasma is affected by many factors both dietary and endogenous. Cholesterol feeding in experimental animals first increases the liver cholesterol level, particularly of the esterified fraction, and eventually also the plasma level; hypothyroidism and certain other metabolic derangements produce an elevated plasma level but no or only a slight increase in liver level; a fat-free diet has been reported to produce a decrease in plasma level but an increase in liver level in rats (Alfin-Slater *et al.*, 1954), and there is some recent evidence that corn oil may have a similar effect (Avigan and Steinberg, 1957). Under all conditions examined, a rapid interchange of free cholesterol molecules has been observed to occur between plasma and liver so explanations of changes in distribution of cholesterol must take into account the dynamic equilibrium between these two compartments.

The chief functions of the liver in cholesterol metabolism may be summarized as follows: (1) it supplies the endogenous cholesterol, phospholipids, and probably the specific globulins which, together with triglycerides from various sources, constitute the plasma lipoproteins; (2) it plays a dominant role in the regulation of the plasma cholesterol concentration; (3) through the formation of bile acids it is responsible for 75% or more of the catabolism of cholesterol which occurs in the animal as a whole; and (4) it has a readily variable rate of cholesterol biosynthesis and appears to be the chief tissue concerned with cholesterol homeostasis.

V. Metabolism of Cholesterol in Extrahepatic Tissues

A. Biosynthesis

The relative importance of various tissues in the biosynthesis of cholesterol in the intact animal have been found difficult to determine with accuracy because of the rapidity of transfer of newly synthesized molecules from liver to extrahepatic tissues. *In vitro* methods have been invaluable in establishing the capability of a number of tissues to synthesize cholesterol, as discussed in Chapter 6, but cannot be relied on for determining relative importance *in vivo*. Studies on hepatectomized dogs have been reported by Harper *et al.* (1953) and by Eckles *et al.* (1955). Definite evidence of synthesis was noted in intestine, kidney, adrenal, testis, lung, skeletal muscle, and adipose tissue but it was much slower than in liver in every case in this species.

Very short-term experiments in the normal, intact animal with acetate-C^{14}, or preferably H^3OH, as a cholesterol precursor appear to be a feasible approach to the problem but little has been reported concerning individual extrahepatic tissues. In rats, 1 hour after acetate-C^{14} injection, about 3 to 5 times as much newly synthesized cholesterol was found in extrahepatic tissues as in the liver. Intestine and skin account for some, but by no means all, of this apparent extrahepatic synthesis.

B. Equilibration Between Blood and Tissues

Passage of cholesterol from blood into extrahepatic tissues was studied in dogs subsequent to the introduction of blood containing labeled cholesterol in normal lipoprotein form (Gould, 1952). The specific activity of cholesterol in liver and spleen reached half that of plasma in a few hours; kidney, lung, heart, intestine, and diaphragm in 1 to 2 days; and adrenal, aorta, and skin considerably more slowly. Chevallier (1953) has reported similar results in a study of the tissue distribution of cholesterol-C^{14} fed to rats. After 9 days of feeding, intestine, liver, and serum had high and essentially equal specific activity values; spleen, bone marrow, lung, depot fat, heart, and adrenal glands had between 60 and 80% of the serum value; kidney, skin, and muscle were about 30%, testicle somewhat less, and brain had no detectable activity.

C. Catabolism

The oxidative breakdown of cholesterol-26-C^{14} to $C^{14}O_2$ has been studied in tissue slices prepared from various tissues by Meier *et al.* (1952). Liver was found to be most active but kidney, adrenal, testes, and spleen showed a slight but significant degree of ability to degrade cholesterol; the per cent of substrate C^{14} which was recovered in CO_2 is shown in Table VIII. The evidence of cholesterol catabolism in kidney is of particular interest and is possibly related to the suggestion of Lewis *et al.* (1956) that the kidney has a regulatory function on the plasma cholesterol level.

In general, this evidence supports that given above (p. 000), in indicating that cholesterol catabolism outside of the liver is quantitatively of minor importance. Conversion of cholesterol into steroid hormones is discussed in Chapter 8.

1. Vitamin D₃ Formation

The conversion of cholesterol to 7-dehydrocholesterol in intestine and skin has been demonstrated (Glover *et al.*, 1952; Festenstein and Morton, 1955). Since it is well known that 7-dehydrocholesterol is converted by the action of ultraviolet light into vitamin D_3 *in vitro* and in the skin, it may be concluded that a quantitatively small but important pathway in cholesterol metabolism is the conversion to vitamin D_3 (reviews, Harris, 1954; Dam, 1955).

TABLE VIII

OXIDATIVE BREAKDOWN OF CHOLESTEROL-26-C^{14} TO $C^{14}O_2$

Tissue	%
Liver (rat)	0.27 –0.33
Kidney (rat)	0.11 –0.14
Adrenal (beef)	0.07 –0.08
Testes (rat)	0.06 –0.08
Lung (rat)	0.014–0.016
Spleen (rat)	0.031–0.036
Brain (adult rat)	0.014–0.011
Boiled liver	0.00 –0.012

NOTE: Values as per cent of added C-26 oxidized to CO_2. From Meier *et al.* (1952).

2. Growth Stimulation

Cholesterol has been shown to be a growth factor for certain insects and protozoa (review, Deuel, Vol. III, pp. 378-380). Of outstanding interest is the recent report that cholesterol is required for the growth of single, human cervical carcinoma cells in tissue culture (HeLa, S-3 clonal strain), although it is not required when massive inocula are used (Sato *et al.*, 1957). This observation strengthens the view that cholesterol is an essential cellular constituent.

VI. Factors Influencing Cholesterol Biosynthesis, Turnover, and Distribution in Tissues

The effects of a large number of agents and experimental conditions on the rates of cholesterol biosynthesis and turnover and on cholesterol concentrations in tissues have been investigated. Liver has been most extensively studied and found to exhibit a marked variation in rate of synthesis not shown by most other tissues. It should not, however, be assumed that decreasing the rate of hepatic cholesterol synthesis will necessarily result in a decreased plasma cholesterol level. More often, decreased hepatic synthesis has been found associated with an increased plasma level and may be a result rather than a cause of the hyper-cholesterolemia. The rate of utilization, the distribution between liver and plasma, and the rate of synthesis of cholesterol are all interrelated variables, and all three must be considered in attempting to understand the action of specific experimental or clinical changes on cholesterol metabolism.

A. NUTRITIONAL FACTORS

1. Fasting

Decreased hepatic biosynthesis has been observed in fasted rats both *in vivo* and *in vitro*. Tomkins and Chaikoff (1952), using the rat liver slice method, observed a decrease in synthetic rate to about 10% of the control value after 24 hours of fasting and to even lower values after 72 hours. In the intact rat, however, Van Bruggen *et al.* (1952) found only a slight decrease after 24 hours of fasting, a much smaller decrease than in fatty acid biosynthesis; after 48 hours of fasting the rate of synthesis was half and after 72 hours about one-third of the control value. The difference between *in vivo* and *in vitro* methods in estimating the effect of fasting has been confirmed by direct comparison of the two methods using both acetate-C^{14} and H^3OH incorporation as a measure of synthesis (Gould *et al.*, 1958). Liver homogenates from fasted rats have been reported to show much less ability to synthesize cholesterol from acetate than those from controls. The importance of liver glycogen in cholesterol synthesis is indicated by the fact that incubation of normal liver homogenate with salivary amylase completely abolished synthetic activity but addition of hexose diphosphate restored it (Bucher and McGarrahan, 1956).

The nature of the diet fed before the fasting period appears to be of importance in the synthetic rate measured *in vitro*. Whitney and Roberts (1955) reported that pre-feeding with a high-fat diet largely eliminated the effect of fasting on cholesterol biosynthesis in liver, as measured *in vitro*.

Cholesterol biosynthesis estimation appears to be sensitive to the nutritional state of the animal, particularly by *in vitro* methods, and the possibility that an apparent inhibition due to vitamin deficiencies, disease, etc., may be actually a result of impaired nutrition should always be considered.

2. Cholesterol Content of Diet

A marked inhibition in hepatic cholesterol biosynthesis is produced by feeding cholesterol in several species of experimental animals, as measured by isotopic tracer methods both *in vitro* and *in vivo* (Gould and Taylor, 1950; Taylor and Gould, 1950; Alfin-Slater *et al.*, 1952;

Tomkins *et al.*, 1953a, b; Gould *et al.*, 1953; Langdon and Bloch, 1953; Frantz *et al.*, 1954). A single oral dose of cholesterol given to dogs decreased the *in vivo* rate of hepatic synthesis 16 hours later to a few per cent of the control value (Gould, 1951). In rat liver slices, the rate was found to decrease from about 1.6 mg. per 100 gm. liver per hour to 0.01–0.05 after the feeding of a 2% cholesterol diet for 1 day, 1 week, or 2 months (Taylor *et al.*, 1956). The recovery to near normal rates of synthesis took only about 1 day in the first instance, 6 to 8 days in the second, and about 15 in the third.

Other tissues examined have shown at most slight inhibition in cholesterol biosynthesis due to feeding a high-cholesterol diet, but results on adrenal glands *in vivo* indicate a possible effect in this tissue. In rats and rabbits the intestine normally has a faster rate of cholesterol biosynthesis than liver and it continues to synthesize rapidly even when the liver has many times its normal content of cholesterol and has virtually ceased synthesis.

Taylor and his associates have studied the effect of dietary cholesterol on *in vitro* synthesis in monkeys and humans. In both species the control rates were found to be much lower than in rats and dogs (Cox *et al.*, 1954; Taylor *et al.*, 1955). In monkeys a marked decrease was noted in liver after 4-6 weeks of cholesterol feeding. In humans, however, no relationship to habitual diet was noted and no significant increase in rate after a few days on a cholesterol-free regime. No data are available for normal humans who have been maintained on low-cholesterol diets for prolonged periods. Conversely, when the cholesterol concentration is decreased in liver, cholesterol biosynthesis may be increased to 10 to 20 times the normal rate (see p. 000 and p. 000). Swell *et al.* (1957) have reported that 24 hours after cannulation of the thoracic duct in rats, the rate of synthesis in liver measured *in vivo* was increased almost 10-fold. The amount of cholesterol lost to the animal during the 24-hour period was 8 to 10 mg. but no significant change in liver cholesterol concentration was noted in this study.

Morris *et al.* (1957) have fed rats labeled cholesterol at 0.05% and 2% of the diet for 2-week periods to determine whether dietary cholesterol, by suppresing hepatic synthesis, would completely replace endogenous cholesterol in plasma. At the 0.05% level, 67–80% of the plasma cholesterol was still of endogenous origin and at the 2% level, 10–26%. Dilution of the labeled cholesterol by interchange with the large pools of unlabeled tissue cholesterol may be partly responsible for this effect.

Alfin-Slater *et al.* (1952) suggested that inhibition of cholesterol synthesis seemed to be correlated with a high total cholesterol concentration in liver. Frantz *et al.* (1954) carried this idea a step further and suggested an inverse relationship between total cholesterol concentration in rat liver slices and the logarithm of the rate of biosynthesis. More recent studies in rats and rabbits by both *in vitro* and *in vivo* techniques have shown a more nearly linear relationship if the free cholesterol concentration is considered rather than the total or the esterified (Gould, 1955b). In low and normal concentration ranges, free and total values tend to be nearly proportional but in higher ranges (above about 3 to 3.5 mg. per gm. liver), the esterified fraction rises much faster than the free.

A distinction between free and esterified cholesterol seems necessary in view of present knowledge of the differences in their roles in metabolism and in their location in the liver cell homogenate fractions. The fact that cholesterol biosynthesis requires only the microsome and soluble supernatant fractions, both of which contain very largely free cholesterol, and that the immediate product of synthesis is the free form also lend credibility to the argument. It seems probable that the free cholesterol concentration in liver is a regulatory factor in hepatic cholesterol biosynthesis. In rats an increase in concentration of about 0.10–0.20 mg. per gm. has been found to be associated with a 50% decrease in the rate of biosynthesis over a wide range of synthetic rates (Gould, 1955b). Although considerable scatter is exhibited by values for individual animals, mean values of groups show a regular and reproducible behavior.

Inhibition of cholesterol biosynthesis in homogenates and in the combined microsomal and soluble supernatant fractions from livers of cholesterol-fed rats have been reported but when mevalonic acid-2-C^{14} was used as the substrate rather than acetate-C^{14}, a much smaller effect was produced by cholesterol feeding (Gould and Popják, 1957). It was suggested that the control of cholesterol synthesis in liver must be concerned with one or more of the steps between acetate and mevalonic acid.

3. Fat Content of Diet

The effect of the amount and nature of dietary fat on the human plasma cholesterol levels is discussed in Chapter 5. No significant changes in hepatic cholesterol synthesis in experimental animals as a result of a high-fat diet have been reported (Alfin-Slater *et al.*, 1952). Such diets may increase the cholesterol concentration in liver together with the triglyceride concentration (Peters and Van Slyke, 1946; Whitney and Roberts, 1955), but there is no marked change in plasma levels and no evidence concerning the origin of the excess hepatic cholesterol. It may be derived from the increased amount in intestinal lymph or from a slight increase in hepatic synthesis.

Fat-free diets have been reported by Alfin-Slater *et al.* (1954) to result in decreased cholesterol levels in plasma but increased levels in liver and adrenal glands in rats. After 20 weeks on an almost fat-free diet, the plasma level showed a decrease of 34%, the liver an increase of 110% (which was confined almost exclusively to the ester fraction), and the adrenal glands an increase of 37%.

B. ENDOCRINE FACTORS

The following account deals with the hormonal influences on the biosynthesis and turnover mainly in experimental animals. The effect of the endocrine gland secretions on the level of circulating cholesterol in health and in disease in humans is discussed in Chapters 5 and 10.

1. Thyroid

Much work has been done on the effect of experimentally produced changes in thyroid status on cholesterol synthesis and metabolism, and the general conclusion appears to be that in the thiouracil-induced hypothyroid state all metabolic processes are slowed down, including cholesterol synthesis in liver and in all other tissues (Karp and Stetten, 1949).

Catabolic and excretory processes are, however, also slowed down, so that the total body content is not materially altered. The increase in cholesterol concentration is peculiar to plasma and has not been reported for any other tissue. Conversely, hyperthyroidism produces increases in biosynthetic processes generally, including catabolic and excretory ones. Clinical hypothyroidism is usually associated with hypercholesterolemia and hyperthyroidism is sometimes associated with hypocholesterolemia (as shown by the effect of therapeutic procedures; Peters and Man, 1950).

a. Effect on cholesterol synthesis measured by tracer methods. Karp and Stetten's results on deuterium uptake in rats showed a small but significant decrease in cholesterol turnover in all tissues, including liver, due to thiouracil, but it was smaller than the change in turnover of other constituents. Byers *et al.* (1952) measured the uptake of tritium in visceral cholesterol of hypo- and hyperthyroid rats, and found the incorporation to be: controls 0.7, hypothyroid 0.27, hyperthyroid 1.6. Marx *et al.* (1953) found that surgical thyroidectomy reduced by about 20% the uptake of deuterium in liver cholesterol during a 4-day period. Dayton *et al.* (1954) using constant intravenous infusion of acetate-1-C^{14} and measuring the turnover of acetate, and the synthesis of cholesterol and fatty acids, concluded that the rate of cholesterol biosynthesis was proportional to the basal metabolic rate.

Frantz *et al.* (1954) found no significant decrease in the synthesis of cholesterol in liver slices of hypothyroid rats (I^{131} treated). Individual variability in the rate of synthesis as measured by this method would make it difficult to detect a change as small as the 20–30% to be expected from the H^2OH studies, so these findings are not in significant disagreement with the deuterium studies.

The rate of disappearance of labeled cholesterol from blood is decreased in hypothyroid animals and increased in hyperthyroid (Weiss and Marx, 1955).

b. Effect on biliary excretion of cholesterol and bile acids. Friedman, Byers, and their associates have made extensive studies on the biliary excretion of cholesterol in rats with bile duct cannulas (Byers and Friedman, 1952b; Rosenman *et al.*, 1951, 1952a, b). They have shown that in thiouracil-treated rats the volume of bile excreted decreased from 13.2 ml. per day to 10.1, and the cholesterol from 1.5 to 0.8 mg. per day. Thyroid-fed rats gave a bile volume of 19.6 ml. and a cholesterol excretion of 8 mg. per day (Byers and Friedman, 1952b). They postulate that the biliary excretion rate of cholesterol is an indicator of the rate of hepatic cholesterol synthesis in general. Isotopic tracer techniques give different results than the biliary excretion rate method under many experimental conditions, but both types of methods agree in indicating decreased synthesis in hypothyroid rats.

Thompson and Vars (1953) confirmed the effects of hypo- and hyperthyroidism on bile volume and noted that cholic acid excretion was decreased in both cases. Eriksson (1957b) has confirmed the latter observation, but has found that total bile acid excretion increased in hyperthyroidism because of a large increase in chenodeoxycholic acid. This acid normally constitutes about 15% of the total bile acids, but in hypothyroid rats it is decreased to less than 10% and in hyperthyroid rats is increased to over 50%. Abell *et al.* (1956) have reported that in dogs fecal excretion of sterols and bile acids is not affected by thiouracil administration, but if a high-cholesterol diet and thiouracil are fed, an impaired capacity to convert dietary cholesterol into bile acids was observed.

c. Effect in man. A much greater effect of hypothyroidism on the incorporation of acetate-1-C^{14} into plasma cholesterol has been reported for humans than is found in experimental animals. Gould *et al.* (1955) found that 9 severely myxedematous patients with high plasma cholesterol levels gave no significant C^{14}-activity in plasma cholesterol following a 100 µc. dose of acetate-1-C^{14}, which gave about 0.12 µc. per gm. in normal humans. In a study by Lipsky *et al.* (1955) on 3 myxedema patients there was a five-fold decrease in incorporation (corrected for increased pool size). In both studies, therapy with thyroxine or triiodothyronine produced a rapid return to normal synthetic rates and decrease to lower concentrations.

Kurland and Lucas (1955) injected cholesterol-C^{14} in patients before the induction of myxedema with I^{131} and followed the rate of disappearance. No difference in pool size at 7 days was observed nor any change in rate of disappearance during the first 13 days, but thereafter the disappearance rate was slower in the hypothyroid state. The rate of esterification of the labeled cholesterol was also much slower.

2. Adrenal

The cholesterol in the adrenal cortex is present in a higher concentration and in a more labile form than in any other tissue. Various types of experimentally induced stress, including hemorrhage, burns, tourniquet shock, and fasting, cause a rapid and marked decrease in adrenal cholesterol concentration, due presumably to an accelerated conversion into adrenal cortical hormones. Disappearance of half the adrenal cholesterol in 3 hours has resulted from nonfatal hemorrhage or the injection of ACTH in rats (Sayers, 1950). It is the esterified cholesterol which decreases in amount; at 15 to 24 hour after tourniquet shock, the esterified fraction was less than one-third the control value and the free fraction showed little change (Popják, 1944). By 48 hours, cholesterol levels were again normal.

Decreased plasma cholesterol levels also result from experimental stress in animals and from ACTH injection in animals (Mann and White, 1953; Sayers, 1950) and in man (Conn *et al.*, 1950). The change was primarily in the esterified fraction and was most marked about 1 day after ACTH administration in man, but the return to normal levels required 5 days or longer. It is not clear whether this decrease in plasma level is caused by movement of esterified cholesterol from plasma into adrenal more rapidly than it can be replaced, or to an independent effect of the increased levels of adrenal cortical hormones.

The adrenals themselves show a rapid rate of cholesterol synthesis *in vitro* (Chapter 6), and this rate may be greatly increased as a result of whole body X irradiation (Gould *et al.*, 1958). It is probable that a decrease in cholesterol concentration will stimulate the rate of synthesis in adrenal as it appears to in liver.

Adrenalectomy causes a decrease in hepatic cholesterol synthesis, as measured *in vitro* (Perry and Bowen, 1956). Fatty acid synthesis was also depressed but acetoacetate formation was not affected.

3. Pituitary

Hypophysectomy was found to depress the synthesis in rat liver slices to very low levels (Tomkins *et al.*, 1952; Baruch and Chaikoff, 1955), but Hill *et al.* (1955) have shown that this is a secondary effect due to nutritional status since it was not observed if the rats were fed a diet containing 60% glucose but was evident with 25% glucose. This observation suggests the possibility that decreased synthetic rates reported in hypothyroid and in adrenalectomized animals may also exhibit a similar relationship to diet.

4. Pancreas

Brady and Gurin (1950) found both in alloxan-diabetic rats and in pancreatectomized cats that synthesis of fatty acids from acetate-C^{14} was greatly impaired (in liver slice preparations) but that cholesterol synthesis proceeded normally. Hotta and Chaikoff (1952) have reported a considerably faster rate of synthesis in alloxan-diabetic rat liver slices. Van Bruggen *et al.* (1954) studying intact rats found no significant difference between alloxan-diabetic animals and controls as measured by the fraction of injected acetate-C^{14} incorporated in liver cholesterol. Here again the question of the nutritional status at the time of examination and the differences between *in vitro* and *in vivo* methods of estimation may account for the difference in results.

C. Miscellaneous

1. Radiation

Whole body X irradiation in rats has been found to result in a great increase in hepatic cholesterol biosynthesis, both *in vitro* and *in vivo* methods of estimation (Gould *et al.*, 1958). The response is presumably indirect, since it is not manifested until some time after the irradiation and is much greater at 48 hours than at 24 hours post-irradiation. The dose-response at 48 hours was reported to be linear up to 2400 r. with an increase of 100% of the control synthetic rate for each 100 r. of radiation.

Since this increased synthesis was associated with decreased hepatic cholesterol concentration, it was suggested that the effect is due to an increased utilization or excretion of cholesterol which depleted the liver and stimulated synthesis.

A similar effect was found in adrenal; X irradiation, like other forms of stress, causes a sharp drop in the adrenal cholesterol content. It also produces a rise in the rate of synthesis which may be as high as 20 to 40-fold the normal rate. The increased utilization in this tissue is clearly due to increased conversion of cholesterol into steroid hormones.

The effect of whole body X irradiation of rats is also apparent when liver slices (Gould *et al.*, 1958), homogenate, or the microsome-soluble supernatant fraction of homogenate are incubated with acetate-C^{14} (Bucher *et al.*, 1957; Gould and Popják, 1957).

2. Surface-Active Agents

a. Synthetic compounds. The intravenous injection of a number of surface-active agents has been found to result in a dramatic rise in serum lipids, including cholesterol. Triton WR1339 and Tween 80,* two commercial nonionic detergents, were shown by Kellner *et al.* (1951) to produce increases in cholesterol level in rabbits to many times the normal level in a few days. The hypercholesterolemia persists as long as the surface-active agent remains in the blood stream, which is several days for Triton. Cornforth *et al.* (1951) found that Triton disappeared from blood in mice with a half-time of about 24 hours after the first day.

Friedman and Byers (1953) have shown that 50 mg. of Triton doubled the plasma cholesterol level in 4 hours in rats; 100 mg. gave increases in phospholipids from 81 to 1200 mg.%, in cholesterol from 55 to 363 mg.%, and in total lipids from 159 to 2346 mg.% in 24 hours. During the stage of rapid increase in plasma level, the liver cholesterol concentration appears to fall, according to data of Hirsch and Kellner (1956a, b), from 2.1 mg. per gm. liver for controls to 1.3, 24 hours after the last of a series of 3 injections of Triton WR1339. Frantz and Hinkelman (1955) have shown in the rat by both *in vivo* and *in vitro* methods that there is about a three-fold increase in the rate of synthesis 24 hours after Triton injection. At 72 hours, as the Triton disappears from blood, the cholesterol is deposited in liver, causing an increase in level to about 5 mg. per gm. and a decrease in the rate of synthesis to about 1/15th of normal. In mice, Triton also causes a striking depletion of cholesterol and other lipids in the adrenal as judged by histochemical tests (Cornforth *et al.*, 1951).

Triton appears to mobilize liver lipids by means of its surface-active properties in a manner not well understood at present. Friedman and Byers (1957c) have reported that triglyceride levels rise within minutes following the injection of Triton and that phospholipid and cholesterol

---

* Triton WR1339 is described by its manufacturers (Rohm and Haas Co., Philadelphia) as consisting of arylalkyl polyethers of phenol; Triton A20 is a 25% aqueous solution. Cornforth *et al.* (1951) describe the synthesis of similar compounds. The "Tweens" are a series of esters of polyoxyethylene sorbitan. Tween 20 is the monolaurate, 40 the monopalmitate, 60 the monostearate, and 80 the monooleate. They are manufactured by Atlas Powder Co., Wilmington 99, Delaware. Both groups of compounds are commonly used to disperse sterols and their esters in experimental studies.

levels rise more slowly, suggesting that the rise in neutral fat is the cause of the subsequent hypercholesterolemia. One might speculate that the presence of Triton in plasma stabilizes lipoprotein complexes involving proteins not normally capable of forming lipoproteins, or facilitates the formation of chylomicron-like particles containing all 3 types of lipids. The cholesterol present cannot be regarded as "trapped" or "locked-in" since the individual molecules are as free to interchange with liver cholesterol as in normal plasma (Frantz and Hinkelman, 1955), but the distribution between liver and plasma is altered.

b. Bile acids. The salts of both the conjugated and unconjugated bile acids are ionic detergents, and, as such, have strong surface-active properties, particularly the former. They differ from the Tritons and Tweens in being hemolytic.

Under normal circumstances, only conjugated bile salts are secreted in bile, reabsorbed from the intestine, and carried by the portal circulation to the liver where they are reutilized. When the bile duct is ligated, hypercholesterolemia and hyperphospholipidemia rapidly develop. There is also a large increase in hepatic cholesterol biosynthesis as Frantz and Hinkelman (1955) have shown by means of acetate-C^{14} incorporation *in vivo* and *in vitro,* and by tritium water incorporation *in vivo.* A 19-fold increase was noted in intact rats by the C^{14} method. In this method the relative rate is measured during a period of probably only a few minutes; it is based on the assumption of a similar distribution of injected acetate-C^{14} and similar dilution with endogenous acetate in sham-operated and bile duct-ligated animals. The H^3OH method indicates a 4-fold increase during a 24-hour period; $t_{\frac{1}{2}}$ values were estimated to be 4.1 days for the sham-operated rats and 1.4 for the bile duct-ligated. This difference corresponds to the biosynthesis of about 0.14 mg. per 100 gm. body weight per hour over and above the normal hepatic synthesis, or about 10 mg. per 300 gm. rat per day, sufficient to raise the plasma level by over 100 mg.% per day.

Ligation of the bile duct together with the oral administration of bile salts has been used by Byers and Friedman (1952a), who obtain plasma cholesterol levels of 600 mg.% by feeding 100 mg. of cholic acid daily. Hypercholesterolemia was produced without ligation of the bile duct by continuous perfusion with a cholate solution of unilaterally nephrectomized rats (Byers *et al.,* 1953b). Friedman and associates have suggested that increase in the plasma cholate level is responsible for the hypercholesterolemia in patients with nephrosis, xanthoma, diabetes, myocardial infarct, and hypothyroidism (Friedman *et al.,* 1952). Recently Friedman and Byers (1957a) in a study on rats considered that in biliary obstruction the increase of plasma bile salts increases the level of plasma cholesterol by first causing an increase in the level of phospholipids.

3. Phospholipid and Triglyceride Injection

It has long been known that a change in the plasma levels of any one of the three classes of lipids, triglycerides, phospholipids, and cholesterol, usually is associated with changes in the others. Friedman and Byers (1955b, 1956) have reported that sustained, elevated levels in plasma of triglycerides and phospholipids (produced by injecting about 15 ml. of a 10% emulsion of sesame oil or coconut oil with 0.6–1% of soybean lecithin into a 300 gm. rat during a 12-hour period) increased the plasma cholesterol level from about 50–60 to 80–128 mg.%. In a second study (Byers and Friedman, 1956), similar effects were produced by injection of 27 ml. of a 2% soybean lecithin emulsion during a 24-hour period. In the first paper it was reported that partial hepatectomy abolished the production of hypercholesterolemia, but in later studies it was found that both subtotal and total hepatectomy enhanced the increase in plasma cholesterol levels due to injection of lecithin emulsions. Rabbits also showed hypercholesterolemia as a result of sustained hyperphospholipidemia (Friedman and Byers, 1957b).

4. Nephrosis

In human nephrosis and in the nephrotic condition produced in rats by injection of rabbit antibodies to rat kidney (Masugi nephritis) hyperlipemia and hypercholesterolemia are marked features. There is a considerable amount of evidence that the hyperlipemia is a result of hypoalbuminemia since prevention of the latter also prevents the former (Heymann and Hackel, 1955; Rosenman et al., 1956). After bilateral nephrectomy, rats with Masugi nephritis do not develop hypercholesterolemia.

As in Triton hyperlipemia, mobilization of liver lipids appears to be the source of the excess lipids. No tissues except plasma show elevated cholesterol concentrations.

5. Plant Sterols

Sitosterol mixture and pure β-sitosterol are themselves absorbed to a small extent, as described on p. 245. When fed alone in high concentration, they fail to increase the total sterol level of liver or plasma in rats, and do not appear to have any significant effect on the rate of hepatic cholesterol synthesis (Gould, 1955a).

6. Cholestanol

In rats, dietary cholestanol is capable of replacing a considerable fraction of liver cholesterol, but no marked or consistent effect on hepatic cholesterol synthesis was noted (Gould et al., 1956; Curran and Costello, 1956a).

7. Δ⁴-Cholestenone (Cholest-4-en-3-one)

A strong inhibitory effect on cholesterol synthesis was found by Tomkins et al. (1953b), in liver slices from cholestenone-fed rats. Steinberg and Fredrickson (1956) have confirmed and extended this finding. They report that a single 60 mg. dose of Δ⁴-cholestenone fed to a rat 24 hours before sacrificing sufficed to inhibit cholesterol biosynthesis by 94%, as measured by incorporation of acetate-2-C^{14} into liver slice cholesterol. Only 40% inhibition of fatty acid synthesis was found and no inhibition of acetoacetate formation.

Chronic feeding experiments with 1% cholestenone added to the diet revealed it to have a remarkable ability to decrease the serum cholesterol level to about half of normal in rats, chickens, and dogs, but to have toxic properties as well (Steinberg and Fredrickson, 1956; Tomkins et al., 1957). Adrenal glands were greatly hypertrophied and their cholesterol content reduced. The liver showed little change in cholesterol concentration but a large increase in nonsaponifiable material which gave a digitonide but not the Liebermann-Burchard reaction. This material must be presumed to be cholestanol in view of the known conversion of Δ⁴-cholestenone into cholestanol (Anker and Bloch, 1949; Stokes et al., 1955; Harold et al., 1957). The inhibition of cholesterol synthesis was more pronounced than has been reported to result from cholestanol feeding.

8. α-Phenylbutyrate and Related Compounds

Cottet and associates have reported anti-hypercholesterolemic effects from administration of α-phenylbutyrate and β-phenylvalerate in rats and in hypercholesterolemic humans (Cottet et al., 1953, 1954). Steinberg and Fredrickson (1955a, b) have found a small inhibitory effect of α-phenylbutyrate on in vivo incorporation of acetate-1-C^{14} into liver cholesterol (24% decrease, $p < 0.001$), but could not confirm the results reported by the French workers on serum cholesterol level decreases either in rats or in hypercholesterolemic patients.

α-p-Biphenylylbutyrate has been reported by Annoni (1956) to lower serum cholesterol levels in patients by 40% when fed at a level of 0.3 gm. daily. Garattini et al. (1956) have reported that this compound partially prevents the hyperlipemia (including the hypercholesterolemia) produced by Triton injection. It has been shown by Tavormina and Gibbs (1957) to inhibit conversion of mevalonic acid to cholesterol in rat liver homogenates and to be a far more potent inhibitor than the α-phenyl derivative in cholesterol biosynthesis from either acetate or mevalonic acid.

9. Effect of Metal Ions and Chelating Agents

Curran has made a study of factors affecting the efficiency of cholesterol biosynthesis in rat liver slices in the course of which he has found that K^+, Mg^{++}, and Mn^{++} are necessary for optimal synthesis (Curran and Clute, 1953). Chromium ions increase the efficiency and vanadium and iron decrease it by 50–75% at concentrations of $10^{-4} M$ (Curran, 1954).

Chelating agents also have effects; 8-quinolinol decreased the synthetic rate, but the addition of Mn^{++} counteracted this effect (Curran, 1955). Ethylenediaminetetraacetic acid (EDTA or Versene) increased the rate of synthesis in normal rat liver slices.

A test of the possible therapeutic usefulness of vanadium has been reported by Curran and Costello (1956b). Rabbits were fed cholesterol for several weeks and then half of them put on a diet containing 0.05% of $VOSO_4 \cdot H_2O$ for 6 weeks. Although no difference in liver or serum cholesterol levels was found as a result of the vanadium feeding, the content of cholesterol in the aorta was lower in the treated group (13.8 as compared with 26.6 mg. per gm. of dry weight, $p < 0.01$). The rate of hepatic cholesterol synthesis was lower in liver slices from V-fed animals. Mountain et al. (1956) also investigated this problem and found similar results.

Uhl et al. (1953) studied the effect of injected and fed EDTA on rabbits and found it to aggravate dietary hypercholesterolemia, but to prevent the increased concentration in liver in both cases. They also concluded that EDTA promotes removal of excess hepatic cholesterol. Rosenman and Smith (1956) have found that EDTA fed at a level of 4% of a diet containing 2% cholesterol and 1% cholate increased the hypercholesterolemia strikingly, particularly when the disodium salt was used.

10. Vitamins

A number of vitamin-deficiency states are associated with inanition, and it is often difficult to differentiate between a direct effect of vitamin deficiency and an indirect effect, resulting from the inanition. Migicovsky (1955) observed a decreased rate of cholesterol synthesis in liver homogenates from vitamin A-deficient rats and noted that this effect might be due to the inanition.

Pantothenic acid is a component of coenzyme A and is therefore obviously required for cholesterol synthesis. Klein and Lipman (1953a) showed a relationship between CoA level and both sterol and fatty acid biosynthesis in yeast and also (Klein and Lipman, 1953b) observed a decrease in cholesterol synthesis in liver slices from pantothenic acid-deficient rats. The liver CoA levels were also decreased in the deficient animals. Lata and Anderson (1954), starting with 60-day-old rather than weanling rats, found an increase in liver slice cholesterol synthesis as a result of feeding a pantothenic acid-deficient diet for 4–5 months.

VII. The Excretory Pathways

A. INTESTINAL EXCRETION

The intestinal tract forms the major pathway for the excretion of cholesterol and its major metabolic products which appear finally in the feces.

1. Fecal Sterols

In a normal adult man of 70 kg. on a mixed diet the total excretion of sterols is about 500 mg. per day or about 7 mg. per kg. body weight (Table IX).

TABLE IX
HUMAN FECAL STEROL EXCRETION[a]

	Diet	Range	Mean	Reference
Infants (3–19 months)	Milk	0.11–0.42	—	Gamble and Blackfan (1920); Beumer (1923)
Adults	Mixed	0.26–0.60	0.38	Ellis and Gardner (1913)
	Mainly bread	0.15–0.40	0.25	Gardner and Fox (1921)
	Mixed	0.12–0.90	0.37	Bürger and Winterseel (1929)
	Mixed	—	0.4	Cook et al. (1956)
			0.5	

[a] Values as gm./day.

In man and other omnivores the amount of vegetable stenols and stanols (C_{28} and C_{29} series) depends on the diet. The normal feces of herbivores and of chickens contain mainly vegetable sterols, no C_{27} sterols being demonstrable (Dorée and Gardner, 1908; Schoenheimer, 1929; Marker and Shabica, 1940). The fecal sterol of marine birds is mainly cholesterol (Krueger, 1944).

Of the C_{27} series in the feces of man, rat, and dog the *stenols* present are Δ^5-, Δ^7- and $\Delta^{5,7}$-cholestenols and there is evidence for other "fast acting" sterols (Wells et al., 1955; Coleman and Baumann, 1957b). The effects of age, sex, and diet on the sterol pattern in rat feces have been studied by Coleman and Baumann (1957a). The major *stanol* present in the feces of omnivores including adult man and of the carnivores is coprostanol which is in the unesterified form, but small amounts of esterified sterols are found (e.g. Cook *et al.*, 1956). The 3α-ol epimer (epicoprostanol) has been found in dog feces (Marker *et al.*, 1942), and in ambergris, the intestinal secretion of certain whales (Lederer *et al.*, 1946). A small amount of cholestanol was demonstrated by Windaus and Uibrig (1915) in human feces.

Coprostanone is present in human feces (Rosenfeld *et al.*, 1954), and smaller amounts of other ketones (Robertson, 1955). Various di- and tri-hydroxysterols have also been demonstrated (Cook *et al.*, 1956). In rodents the bile is a major pathway of excretion for the end-products of sex hormone metabolism (e.g. Leblond, 1951).

2. Origin

Unabsorbed sterols derived from dietary vegetable or animal sources may form a considerable part of the total sterol (p. 000). The lymphocytes, mucus, and intestinal secretions contribute; it has been estimated that in dogs about 10% of the lipid (or about the same proportion of sterol) is derived from mucus (Sperry, 1932). The "fast acting" sterols have their origin in the intestinal mucosa (Wells *et al.*, 1955). Most of the biliary cholesterol is reabsorbed (p. 000). The intestinal bacteria while contributing to the total fatty acids do not contain sterols (Chapter 4). The intestinal protozoa presumably make a small contribution.

3. Coprostanol Formation

The reduction of cholesterol to a 3β,5β-stanol has been a subject of interest and the history is described in Chapter 1. The site of conversion is considered to be the large intestine, no coprostanol being found in the intestinal contents discharged from patients with either a terminal ileostomy or a cecostomy (Gardner *et al.*, 1935). That the process of conversion is due to microbial action in the large intestine is suggested because the administration of bacteriostatics such as succinylsulfathiazole or of compounds such as carbarsone which inhibit protozoal growth prevent the reduction (Rosenheim and Webster, 1943b; Wainfan *et al.*, 1952). Moreover the normal human upper intestine has a low bacterial content (Cregan and Hayward, 1953). Recently the *in vitro* conversion of cholesterol to coprostanol with bacterial cultures isolated from feces has been demonstrated conclusively (Rosenfeld *et al.*, 1954; Snog-Kjaer *et al.*, 1956; Coleman and Baumann, 1957c).

The early observations of Ellis and Gardner (1909) suggested that cats needed a meat diet to bring about the transformation. These observations were extended by Rosenheim and Webster (1941a) who concluded that the glycolipid phrenosin was an essential factor. They also showed (Rosenheim and Webster, 1941b) that with rats the conversion of sitosterol to 3β,5β-sitostanol (coprositostanol) occurred in its presence. Diet plays some role in the process because in infants and in adults on a milk diet cholesterol is excreted mainly (Gamble and Blackfan, 1920). In rats and rabbits Wells (1957b) has found that the inclusion of lactose (30%) causes inhibition of coprostanol formation. The addition of decholesterolized brain powder to human diets has been suggested as a method of lessening cholesterol absorption since coprostanol is not absorbed. Jones *et al.* (1953, 1957) have observed an increase in the turnover rate of serum cholesterol in humans as a result of feeding large amounts of such a preparation and suggest that this effect may be due to an increased fecal excretion of endogenous cholesterol.

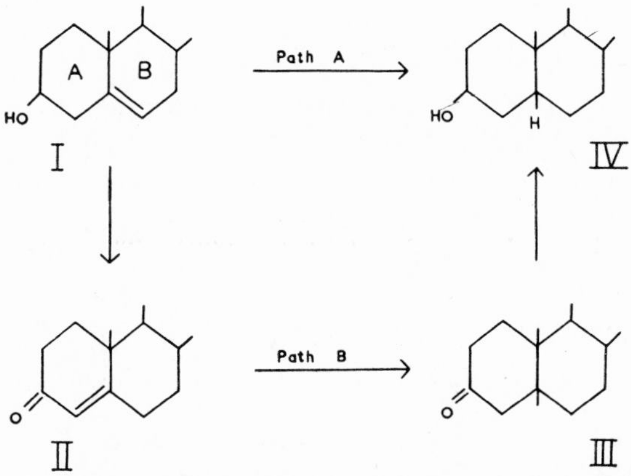

Fig. 6. The conversion of cholesterol to coprostanol. All the compounds have been isolated from feces; it is possible that alternative pathways exist.

Feeding of whole calf brain to chickens resulted in an increased deposition of sterol in liver (Sperry and Stoyanoff, 1935).

The pathways of reduction are shown in Fig. 6. It was long considered that cholestenone (II) was an essential intermediate (Schoenheimer *et al.*, 1935b; Rosenheim and Webster, 1943a, b) and that reduction followed pathway A via coprostanone (III) to coprostanol (IV). Using tracers it has been shown that a direct microbial reduction, not involving a 3-one derivative, occurs as shown in pathway B (Rosenfeld *et al.*, 1954). Confirmatory evidence for the reduction has been given by Snog-Kjaer *et al.*, 1956). Normally the bacterial action ends with the reduction (Dam, 1934b), but cultures of bacteria have been developed which bring about further changes (Wainfan *et al.*, 1954). The bacterial oxidation is enhanced by the presence of thyroxine (Wainfan and Marx, 1955).

4. Fecal Steroid Acids

The fecal excretion of deoxycholic acid by man is described above (p. 273). Carey (personal communication) found an excretion of about 75 mg. per day for a 70 kg. man. The value for the petroleum ether-insoluble fecal acid fraction determined by Cook et al. (1956) was about 250 mg. per day. These values correspond to 2–3 mg. per kg. body weight per day on a mixed diet. In experimental animals the altered bile acids are mainly in the keto form (e.g. Edwards and Cook, 1955). The change is brought about by bacterial action (e.g. Hoehn et al., 1944 and p. 272). The microbial conversions of cholesterol to coprostanol, and of the metabolic changes affecting the bile acids may be important mechanisms in the control of cholesterol metabolism, particularly in omnivorous and carnivorous species.

B. THE SKIN SECRETION (SEBUM)

The occurrence and metabolism of sterols in the skin is discussed in Chapter 4, Chapter 6 and in this Chapter (p. 275). The skin fat or sebum is a constant source of loss of sterols in all animals; the loss shows wide variations but in man about 100 mg. is lost per day and a slightly greater amount of squalene. An interesting study of the human secretion of squalene and of cholesterol has been made by Boughton et al. (1957) who found that the squalene content of sebum is lower and the cholesterol content higher in children than in adults.

VIII. The Metabolism of Other Sterols
A. C_{27} SERIES

Cholestanol was for long considered to be simply an end-product of cholesterol metabolism which was excreted in the feces but not otherwise metabolized in the body. Chaikoff and associates have studied the metabolism of cholestanol with the aid of carbon-14, and have found many of the previous concepts to be in error.

No evidence of the transformation of cholesterol-4-C^{14} into cholestanol has been obtained (Harold et al., 1957) and the origin of this saturated sterol is therefore still unknown. It is present as a constant companion of cholesterol in all tissues where it constitutes about 2% of the total sterol (see Chapter 4). The most probable origin is from a precursor common to cholesterol.

Cholestanol is metabolized to steroid acids which differ slightly but definitely from cholic and chenodeoxycholic acids (Harold et al., 1957) possibly due to the 5α-configuration of the molecule. After being injected intravenously into rats, cholestanol was rapidly excreted in the feces; in 67 hours, 40% of the dose was eliminated as a mixture of neutral sterols (40%) which were largely cholestanol and steroid acids (60%). The bile was shown to be the only important excretory route for both cholestanol and the steroid acids; only 1–2% was excreted in feces in bile duct-cannulated animals.

Δ^4-Cholestenone (cholest-4-en-3-one) is found in small amounts in the tissues (Page and Menschick 1930; Prelog et al., 1947) and in the feces (see above). It is converted into cholestanol (Anker and Bloch, 1949; Stokes et al., 1955). Harold et al. (1955, 1956) have shown that Δ^4-cholestenone-4-C^{14} when injected intravenously into rats is excreted in bile as cholestenone, cholestanol, and a mixture of steroid acids which differ from cholic and chenodeoxycholic acids. In a later publication Harold et al. (1957) showed that the mixture of steroid acids is virtually identical with that formed from cholestanol. Liver homogenates convert Δ^4-cholestenone to cholestanol and to cholestanone; the latter is probably an intermediate.

Epicholesterol (cholest-5-en-3α-ol) has been shown by Harold et al. (1955) to be converted into cholestanol but not into cholesterol. Following intravenous injection, over 50% was excreted in bile in 48 hours, of which 90% was steroid acids and the rest cholestanol. On the basis of the above observations, Harold et al. (1957) suggest the pathway shown in Fig. 7 for the metabolism of these sterols which are not convertible into cholesterol. Δ^5-Cholestenone is so readily converted into Δ^4-cholestenone that its role as an intermediate in this pathway has not been clarified. These authors suggest the Δ^5 isomer may be the true intermediate (cf. Fieser, 1954).

The significance of the dienones, ketols, di- and tri-hydroxysterols which have been isolated from the liver and other tissues (e.g. Cain and Morton, 1955; Haslewood, 1941; Kantiengar and Morton, 1955a; Rattray et al., 1956) is still obscure.

Other C_{27} sterols which have been studied, such as Δ^7-cholestenol, 7-dehydrocholesterol, $\Delta^{5,24}$-cholestadienol (desmosterol), and zymosterol, are converted into cholesterol as discussed in Chapter 6.

B. C_{28} AND C_{29} SERIES

Ergosterol is metabolized by excretion in bile as a mixture of neutral sterols and acidic compounds (Hanahan and Wakil, 1953). After intravenous injection of ergosterol-C^{14} into a bile fistula rat, these workers found that 34% was excreted in bile in 72 hours, of which 64% was in the nonsaponifiable fraction. No ergosterol was present and only about one-third was precipitable by digitonin. After intravenous injection into normal rats, ergosterol-C^{14} was isolated unchanged from various tissues, particularly liver, but no evidence of conversion to cholesterol was found. Glover *et al.* (1957) studied the absorption and metabolism of ergosterol-C^{14} in guinea pigs. The main metabolic products found in the intestine, liver, and adrenals were acidic in nature. The uptake of radioactivity by the adrenals was as high as that by the liver.

Little is known about the catabolism of sitosterols in the body. After absorption from the intestine β-sitosterol-H^3 disappears rapidly from the

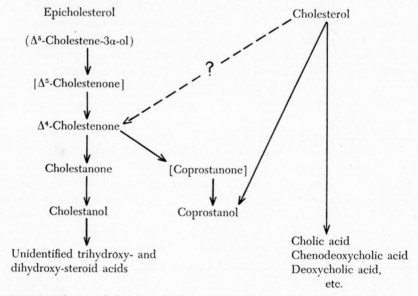

Fig. 7. The metabolism of cholestanol and related compounds. Modified from Harold *et al.* (1957).

blood stream and has been observed to be concentrated in the bile sterol fraction (Gould, 1955a).

C. Antistiffness Factor

Wulzen and his colleagues (e.g. Wulzen and Bahrs, 1941) found that a "stiffness" developed in guinea pigs when they were fed a diet apparently complete in vitamin requirements but containing no added vegetable foodstuffs. The condition was relieved by feeding supplements of kale, grass, etc. It has been suggested that stigmasterol or ergosterol are active agents in alleviating the condition but on account of the practical difficulties in assaying the effect of therapeutic agents it is difficult to assess the results. The pathological changes induced on the deficient diets are quite pronounced (reviews by Dasler, 1950; Dam, 1951; Cheldelin, 1954).

IX. Summary

Figure 8 shows diagrammatically some of the more important pathways in cholesterol metabolism. Tissue cholesterol arises by biosynthesis particularly in liver, intestine, adrenals, and gonads, and by absorption from the intestine.

Plasma cholesterol is derived largely from liver although the molecules may have ultimately been derived from the diet or from biosynthesis

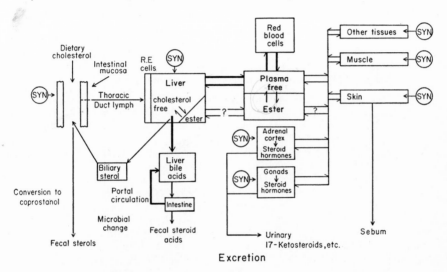

FIG. 8. A generalized diagram of the metabolism of cholesterol in the animal organism. Syn, biosynthesis, R.E. cells, reticulo-endothelial cells.

in liver or other tissues. Unesterified cholesterol molecules in plasma interchange most rapidly with those in liver, and (in order of decreasing rates) with those in erythrocytes, spleen, intestine, adrenals, muscle, fat depots, skin, and arterial walls. As a result of the slow rates of mixing with the large amounts of cholesterol in muscle and skin, the apparent turnover rate of plasma or liver cholesterol decreases with time after the introduction of labeled molecules. Regardless of whether cholesterol is administered in labeled form or is biosynthesized from a labeled precursor, the specific activity will gradually approach the same value in all tissues except the central nervous system.

Catabolism of cholesterol consists primarily in conversion to bile acids in the liver. Although the bile acids are reabsorbed via the enterohepatic circulation and reutilized with great efficiency, they are eventually modified by bacterial action in the intestine and excreted in the feces. In the rat this pathway accounts for about 80% of all cholesterol catabolized. Other pathways include excretion of sterols in the feces and in the skin secretion. Catabolism to steroid hormones also occurs (Chapter 8).

The rate of cholesterol synthesis is more variable in liver and in the steroid hormone-producing tissues than elsewhere. In liver the logarithm of the rate of biosynthesis is usually inversely related to the free cholesterol concentration, suggesting that the rate of biosynthesis plays a role in cholesterol homeostasis. There is evidence that the rate of conversion of cholesterol to bile acids is similarly associated with the rate of turnover of bile acids, and may be controlled by the concentration of bile acids present in liver.

REFERENCES

(Asterisk denotes review article or monograph)

Abell, L. L., Mosbach, E. H., and Kendall, F. E. (1956). J. Biol. Chem. 220, 527-535.
Alfin-Slater, R. B., Schotz, M. C., Shimoda, F., and Deuel, H. J., Jr. (1952). J. Biol. Chem. 195, 311-315.
Alfin-Slater, R. B., Aftergood, L., Wells, G. F., and Deuel, H. J., Jr. (1954). Arch. Biochem. Biophys. 52, 180-185.
*Anfinsen, C. B., Jr. (1955a). In "Symposium on Atherosclerosis," pp. 217-226. National Research Council, Washington, D. C. (Clearing factor.)
*Anfinsen, C. B., Jr. (1955b). Minn. Med. 38, 767-774. (Lipoproteins.)
Anfinsen, C. B., Jr., and Horning, M. G. (1953). J. Am. Chem. Soc. 75, 1511.
Anker, H. S., and Bloch, K. (1949). J. Biol. Chem. 178, 971-976.
Annoni, G. (1956). Farmaco (Pavia) Ed. Sci. 11, 244.
Avigan, J., and Steinberg, D. (1957). Circulation 16, 492.
Baruch, H., and Chaikoff, I. L. (1955). Endocrinology 56, 609-611.
Beher, W. T., and Anthony, W. L. (1955). Proc. Soc. Exptl. Biol. Med. 90, 223-225.
Beher, W. T., Anthony, W. L., and Baker, G. D. (1957). Proc. Soc. Exptl. Biol. Med. 95, 734-736.
Bergström, S. (1952). Kgl. Fysiograf. Sällskap. Lund. Förh. 22(16), 1-5 (In English).
Bergström, S. (1955). Record Chem. Progr. (Kresge-Hooker Sci. Lib.) 16, 63-68.
*Bergström, S., and Borgström, B. (1956). Ann. Rev. Biochem. 25, 177-195. (Absorption of lipids, clearing factor, and bile acid formation.)
Bergström, S., and Eriksson, S. (1958). Acta. Physiol. Scand. (in press).
Bergström, S., and Eriksson, S. (1954). Acta Physiol. Scand. 8, 1373-1377.
Bergström, S., and Gloor, U. (1955). Acta Chem. Scand. 9, 34-38.
Bergström, S., and Lindstedt, S. (1956). Biochim. et Biophys. Acta 19, 556-557.
Bergström, S., and Norman, A. (1953). Proc. Soc. Exptl. Biol. Med. 83, 71-74.
Bergström, S., and Pääbo, K. (1955). Acta Chem. Scand. 9, 699-701.
Bergström, S., Dahlquist, A., and Ljungqvist, U. (1953a). Kgl. Fysiograf. Sällskap. Lund, Förh. 23(12), 1-4 (In English).

Bergström, S., Rottenberg, M., and Sjövall, J. (1953b). Z. physiol. Chem. **295**, 278-285.

Bergström, S., Pääbo, K., and Rumpf, J. A. (1954). Acta Chem. Scand. **8**, 1109.

Bergström, S., Danielsson, H., and Gloor, U. (1958). Acta Chem. Scand. (in press).

Best, M. M., and Duncan, C. H. (1956). Circulation **14**, 344-348.

Beumer, H. (1923). Z. Kinderheilk. **35**, 298-304.

Bevans, M., and Kendall, F. E. (1956). A.M.A. Arch. Pathol. **62**, 112-116.

Biggs, M. W., and Colman, D. (1953). Circulation **7**, 393-402.

Biggs, M. W., Friedman, M., and Byers, S. O. (1951). Proc. Soc. Exptl. Biol. Med. **78**, 641-643.

Biggs, M. W., Kritchevsky, D., Colman, D., Gofman, J. W., Jones, H. B., Lindgren, F. T., Hyde, G. M., and Lyon, T. P. (1952). Circulation **6**, 359-366.

Biggs, M. W., Lemmon, R. M., and Pierce, F. T., Jr. (1954). Arch. Biochem. Biophys. **51**, 155-160.

Bisset, S. K., and Cook, R. P. (1956). Biochem. J. **63**, 13P.

Bloch, K., Berg, B. N., and Rittenberg, D. (1943). J. Biol. Chem. **149**, 511-517.

*Bloor, W. R. (1943). "Biochemistry of the Fatty Acids." Reinhold, New York.

Bollman, J. L., and Flock, E. V. (1951). Am. J. Physiol. **164**, 480-485.

Bollman, J. L., Cain, J. C., and Grindley, J. H. (1948). J. Lab. Clin. Med. **33**, 1949-1952.

Boughton, B., MacKenna, R. M. B., Wheatley, V. R., and Wormall, A. (1957). Biochem. J. **66**, 32-38.

Brady, R. O., and Gurin, S. (1950). J. Biol. Chem. **187**, 589-596.

Bremer, J. (1956). Acta. Chem. Scand. **10**, 56-71.

Bremer, J., and Gloor, U. (1955). Acta Chem. Scand. **9**, 689-698.

Breusch, F. L. (1938). J. Biol. Chem. **124**, 151-158.

Bronte-Stewart, B., Antonis, A., Eales, L., and Brock, J. F. (1956). Lancet i, 521-526.

Bucher, N. L. R., and McGarrahan, K. (1956). J. Biol. Chem. **222**, 1-15.

Bucher, N. L. R., Loud, A. V., and McGarrahan, K. (1957). Federation Proc. **16**, 17.

Bürger, M., and Winterseel, W. (1929). Z. physiol. Chem. **181**, 255-263.

Bürger, M., and Winterseel, W. (1931). Z. physiol. Chem. **202**, 237-245.

Byers, S. O., and Biggs, M. W. (1952). Arch. Biochem. Biophys. **39**, 301-304.

Byers, S. O., and Friedman, M. (1952a). Am. J. Physiol. **168**, 138-139.

Byers, S. O., and Friedman, M. (1952b). Am. J. Physiol. **168**, 297-302.

Byers, S. O., and Friedman, M. (1955). Am. J. Physiol. **182**, 69-72.

Byers, S. O., and Friedman, M. (1956). Proc. Soc. Exptl. Biol. Med. **92**, 459-462.

Byers, S. O., Rosenman, R. H., Friedman, M., and Biggs, M. W. (1952). J. Exptl. Med. **96**, 513-516.

Byers, S. O., Friedman, M., and Gunning, B. (1953a). Am. J. Physiol. **175**, 375-379.

Byers, S. O., Friedman, M., Biggs, M. W., and Gunning, B. (1953b). J. Exptl. Med. **97**, 511-524.

Byron, J. E., Wood, W. A., and Treadwell, C. R. (1953). J. Biol. Chem. **205**, 483-492.

Cain, J. C., and Morton, R. A. (1955). Biochem. J. **60**, 274-283.

Carey, J. B., Jr. (1956). Science **123**, 892.

Carey, J. B., Jr., and Watson, C. J. (1955). J. Biol. Chem. **216**, 847-850.

Chaikoff, I. L., Bloom, B., Siperstein, M. D., Kiyasu, J. Y., Reinhardt, W. O., Dauben, W. G., and Eastham, J. F. (1952a). *J. Biol. Chem.* **194**, 407-412.

Chaikoff, I. L., Siperstein, M. D., Dauben, W. G., Bradlow, H. L., Eastham, J. F., Tomkins, G. M., Meier, J. R., Chen, R .W., Hotta, S., and Srere, P. A. (1952b). *J. Biol. Chem.* **194**, 413-416.

Channon, H. J. (1926). *Biochem. J.* **20**, 400-408.

Channon, H. J., and Tristram, G. R. (1937). *Biochem. J.* **31**, 738-747.

*Cheldelin, V. H. (1954). In "The Vitamins" (W. H. Sebrell and R. S. Harris, eds.) Vol. II, pp. 591-593. Academic Press, New York. (Antistiffness factor.)

*Chevallier, F. (1953). *Ann. nutrition et aliment.* **7**, 305-338. (Cholesterol metabolism.)

Clément, G., and Clément, J. (1956). *Compt. rend. soc. biol.* **150**, 336-339.

Clément, G., Clément, J., and Louedec, A. (1954). *Arch. sci. physiol.* **8**, 233-250.

Coleman, D. L., and Baumann, C. A. (1957a). *Arch. Biochem. Biophys.* **66**, 226-233; 287-292.

Coleman, D. L., and Baumann, C. A. (1957b). *Arch. Biochem. Biophys.* **71**, 287-292.

Coleman, D. L., and Baumann, C. A. (1957c). *Arch. Biochem. Biophys.* **72**, 219-225.

Coleman, D. L., Wells, W. W., and Baumann, C. A. (1956). *Arch. Biochem. Biophys.* **60**, 412-418.

*Comar, C. L. (1955). "Radioisotopes in Biology and Agriculture." McGraw-Hill, New York.

Conn, J. W., Vogel, W. C., Louis, L. H., and Fajans, S. S. (1950). *J. Lab. Clin. Med.* **35**, 504-517.

*Cook, R. P. (1952). *Biochem. Soc. Symposia (Cambridge, Engl.)* **No. 9**, 14-29. (Absorption and excretion of sterols.)

Cook, R. P. (1957). Unpublished observations.

Cook, R. P., and Thomson, R. O. (1951). *Quart. J. Exptl. Physiol.* **36**, 61-74.

Cook, R. P., Kliman, A., and Fieser, L. F. (1954). *Arch. Biochem. Biophys.* **52**, 439-450.

Cook, R. P., Edwards, D. C., and Riddell, C. (1956). *Biochem. J.* **62**, 225-234.

Cornforth, J. W., Hart, P. D. A., Rees, R. J. W., and Stock, J. A. (1951). *Nature* **168**, 150-153.

Cottet, J., Vignalon, J., Redel, J., and Colas-Belcour, J. (1953). *Bull. mém. soc. méd. hôp. Paris* **69**, 903-908.

Cottet, J., Mathivat, A., and Redel, J. (1954). *Presse méd.* **62**, 939-941.

Courtice, F. C., and Morris, B. (1955). *Quart. J. Exptl. Physiol.* **40**, 138-148; 149-160.

Cox, G. E., Nelson, L. G., Wood, W. B., and Taylor, C. B. (1954). *Federation Proc.* **13**, 31.

Cox, R. H., and Spencer, E. Y. (1949). *Science* **110**, 11.

Cregan, J., and Hayward, N. J. (1953). *Brit. Med. J.* **I**, 1356-1359.

Cruickshank, E. M., Kodicek, E., and Armitage, P. (1954). *Biochem. J.* **58**, 172-175.

Curran, G. L. (1954). *J. Biol. Chem.* **210**, 765-770.

Curran, G. L. (1955). *Proc. Soc. Exptl. Biol. Med.* **88**, 101-103.

Curran, G. L., and Clute, O. L. (1953). *J. Biol. Chem.* **204**, 215-219.

Curran, G. L., and Costello, R. L. (1956a). *Proc. Soc. Exptl. Biol. Med.* **91**, 52-56.

Curran, G. L., and Costello, R. L. (1956b). *J. Exptl. Med.* **103**, 49-56.

Dam, H. (1934a). *Biochem. J.* **28**, 815-819.
Dam, H. (1934b). *Biochem. J.* **28**, 820-825.
°Dam, H. (1951). *Ann. Rev. Biochem.* **20**, 295. (Antistiffness factor.)
°Dam, H. (1955). *Progr. Chem. Fats and Other Lipids* **3**, 172-178. (Vitamin D.)
Dam, H., and Brun, G. C. (1935). *Biochem. Z.* **276**, 274-276.
Dam, H., Prange, I., and Søndergaard, E. (1955). *Acta Physiol. Scand.* **34**, 141-146.
Daskalakis, E. G., and Chaikoff, I. L. (1955). *Arch. Biochem. Biophys.* **58**, 373-380.
°Dasler, W. (1950). *Chicago Med. School Quart.* **11**, 70-73. (Antistiffness factor.)
Dayton, S., Dayton, J., Drimmer, F., and Kendall, F. E. (1954). *Circulation* **10**, 595.
Dayton, S., Mosbach, E. H., Drimmer, F., and Kendall, F. E. (1955). *Federation Proc.* **14**, 460.
°Deuel, H. J., Jr. (1955). "The Lipids," Vols. II and III. Interscience, New York.
Dorée, C., and Gardner, J. A. (1908). *Proc. Roy. Soc.* **B80**, 212-226.
Eckles, N. E., Taylor, C. B., Campbell, D. J., and Gould, R. G. (1955). *J. Lab. Clin. Med.* **46**, 359-371.
Edwards, D. C., and Cook, R. P. (1955). *Biochem. J.* **61**, 671-676.
Elliott, W. H. (1956). *Biochem. J.* **62**, 427-433, 433-436.
Ellis, G. W., and Gardner, J. A. (1909). *Proc. Roy. Soc.* **B81**, 505-515.
Ellis, G. W., and Gardner, J. A. (1913). *Proc. Roy. Soc.* **B86**, 13-18.
Eriksson, S. (1956). *Acta Chem. Scand.* **10**, 156-157.
Eriksson, S. (1957a). *Proc. Soc. Exptl. Biol. Med.* **94**, 578-582.
Eriksson, S. (1957b). *Proc. Soc. Exptl. Biol. Med.* **94**, 582-584.
Farquhar, J. W., Smith, R. E., and Dempsey, M. E. (1956). *Circulation* **14**, 77-82.
°Favarger, P. (1956). *Ann. nutrition et aliment.* **10**, 211-236. (Sterol absorption.)
Favarger, P., and Metzger, E. F. (1952). *Helv. Chim. Acta* **35**, 1811-1819.
Favarger, P., Gerlach, J., and Roth, M. (1955). *Helv. Physiol. et Pharmacol. Acta* **13**, 245-248.
Festenstein, G. N., and Morton, R. A. (1955). *Biochem. J.* **60**, 22-25.
Fieser, L. F. (1954). *Science* **119**, 710-716.
Fishler, M. C., Entenman, C., Montgomery, M. L., and Chaikoff, I. L. (1943). *J. Biol. Chem.* **150**, 47-55.
°Frantz, I. D., Jr. (1955). *Minn. Med.* **38**, 779-783. (Control of cholesterol synthesis.)
Frantz, I. D., Jr., and Carey, J. B., Jr. (1957). *J. Lab. Clin. Med.* **50**, 814-815.
Frantz, I. D., Jr., and Hinkelman, B. T. (1955). *J. Exptl. Med.* **101**, 225-232.
Frantz, I. D., Jr., Schneider, H. S., and Hinkelman, B. T. (1954). *J. Biol. Chem.* **206**, 465-469.
Fredrickson, D. S. (1956). *J. Biol. Chem.* **222**, 109-120; *Federation Proc.* **15**, 255.
Fredrickson, D. S., and Ono, K. (1956). *Biochim. et Biophys. Acta* **22**, 183-184.
Fredrickson, D. S., Loud, A. V., Hinkelman, B. T., Schneider, H. S., and Frantz, I. D., Jr. (1954). *J. Exptl. Med.* **99**, 43-53.
Friedman, M., and Byers, S. O. (1952). *Am. J. Physiol.* **168**, 292-296.
Friedman, M., and Byers, S. O. (1953). *J. Exptl. Med.* **97**, 117-130.
Friedman, M., and Byers, S. O. (1954). *Circulation* **10**, 491-500.
Friedman, M., and Byers, S. O. (1955a). *J. Clin. Invest.* **34**, 1369-1374.
Friedman, M., and Byers, S. O. (1955b). *Proc. Soc. Exptl. Biol. Med.* **90**, 496-499.
Friedman, M., and Byers, S. O. (1956). *Am. J. Physiol.* **186**, 13-18.

Friedman, M., and Byers, S. O. (1957a). *Am. J. Physiol.* **188**, 337-351.
Friedman, M., and Byers, S. O. (1957b). *Proc. Soc. Exptl. Biol. Med.* **94**, 452-455.
Friedman, M., and Byers, S. O. (1957c). *Federation Proc.* **16**, 41.
Friedman, M., Byers, S. O., and Michaelis, F. (1950). *Am. J. Physiol.* **162**, 575-578.
Friedman, M., Byers, S. O., and Michaelis, F. (1951). *Am. J. Physiol.* **164**, 789-791.
Friedman, M., Byers, S. O., and Rosenman, R. H. (1952). *Science* **115**, 313-315.
Friedman, M., Byers, S. O., and Gunning, B. (1953). *Am. J. Physiol.* **172**, 309-316.
Friedman, M., Rosenman, R. H., and Byers, S. O. (1956a). *Circulation Research* **4**, 157-161.
°Friedman, M., Byers, S. O., and St. George, S. (1956b). *Ann. Rev. Biochem.* **25**, 613-640. (Cholesterol metabolism.)
Friedman, M., Byers, S. O., and St. George, S. (1956c). *Am. J. Physiol.* **184**, 141-144.
°Fukushima, D. K., and Rosenfeld, R. S. (1954). *In* "Chemical Pathways of Metabolism" (D. M. Greenberg, ed.), Vol. 1, pp. 349-411. Academic Press, New York. (Sterol metabolism.)
Gamble, J. L., and Blackfan, K. D. (1920). *J. Biol. Chem.* **42**, 401-409.
Gardner, J. A., and Fox, F. W. (1921). *Proc. Roy. Soc.* **B92**, 358-367.
Gardner, J. A., Gainsborough, H., and Murray, R. M. (1935). *Biochem. J.* **29**, 1139-1144.
Garattini, S., Morpurgo, C., and Passerini, N. (1956). *Experientia* **12**, 347-348.
Gibbs, G. E., and Chaikoff, I. L. (1941). *Endocrinology* **29**, 877-884; 885-899.
Glover, J., and Green, C. (1956). *In* "Biochemical Problems of Lipids" (G. Popják and E. Le Breton, eds.), pp. 359-364. Academic Press, New York.
Glover, M., Glover, J., and Morton, R. A. (1952). *Biochem. J.* **51**, 1-9.
Glover, J., Leat, W. M. F., and Morton, R. A. (1957). *Biochem. J.* **66**, 214-221.
Goldman, D. S., Chaikoff, I. L., Reinhardt, W. O., Entenman, C., and Dauben, W. G. (1950). *J. Biol. Chem.* **184**, 727-733.
°Gould, R. G. (1951). *Am. J. Med.* **11**, 209-227. (Cholesterol metabolism.)
Gould, R. G. (1952). *In* "Proc. Ann. Meeting Council for High Blood Pressure Research," pp. 3-16. Am. Heart Assoc., New York.
Gould, R .G. (1955a). *Trans. N.Y. Acad. Sci.* [2] **18**, 129-134.
°Gould, R. G. (1955b). *In* "Symposium on Atherosclerosis," pp. 153-168. National Research Council, Washington, D. C. (Cholesterol metabolism.)
Gould, R. G., and Popják, G. (1957). *Biochem. J.* **66**, 51P.
Gould, R. G., and Taylor, C. B. (1950). *Federation Proc.* **9**, 179.
Gould, R. G., Taylor, C. B., Hagerman, J. S., Warner, I., and Campbell, D. J. (1953). *J. Biol. Chem.* **201**, 519-529.
Gould, R. G., Le Roy, G. V., Okita, G. T., Kabara, J. J., Keegan, P., and Bergenstal, D. M. (1955). *J. Lab. Clin. Med.* **46**, 374-384.
Gould, R. G., Lotz, L. V., and Lilly, E. H. (1956). *In* "Biochemical Problems of Lipids" (G. Popják and E. Le Breton, eds.), pp. 353-358. Academic Press, New York.
Gould, R. G., Bell, V. L., and Lilly, E. H. (1958). *Am. J. Physiol.* (In press).
Gustafson, B. C., Bergström, S., Lindstedt, S., and Norman, A. (1957). *Proc. Soc. Exptl. Biol. Med.* **94**, 467-474.
Hahn, P. F. (1943). *Science* **98**, 19-20.
Hanahan, D. J., and Wakil, S. J. (1953). *Arch. Biochem. Biophys.* **44**, 150-158.
Harold, F. M., Jayko, M. E., and Chaikoff, I. L. (1955). *J. Biol. Chem.* **216**, 439-447.

Harold, F. M., Abraham, S., and Chaikoff, I. L. (1956). *J. Biol. Chem.* **221**, 435-447.

Harold, F. M., Chapman, D. D., and Chaikoff, I. L. (1957). *J. Biol. Chem.* **224**, 609-620.

Harper, P. V., Jr., Neal, W. B., Jr., and Hlavacek, G. R. (1953). *Metabolism, Clin. and Exptl.* **2**, 69-80.

*Harris, R. S. (1954). *In* "The Vitamins" (W. H. Sebrell and R. S. Harris, eds.), Vol. III, pp. 132-209. Academic Press, New York. (Vitamin D.)

Haslewood, G. A. D. (1941). *Biochem. J.* **35**, 708-711.

*Haslewood, G. A. D. (1955). *Physiol. Revs.* **35**, 178-196. (Bile acids.)

Havel, R. J., and Fredrickson, D. S. (1956). *J. Clin. Invest.* **35**, 1025-1032.

Hellman, L., Rosenfeld, R. S., and Gallagher, T. F. (1954). *J. Clin. Invest.* **33**, 142-149.

Hellman, L., Rosenfeld, R. S., Eidenoff, M. L., Fukushima, D. K., Gallagher, T. F., Wang, C. I., and Adlersberg, D. (1955). *J. Clin. Invest.* **34**, 48-60.

Hernandez, H. H., and Chaikoff, I. L. (1954). *Proc. Soc. Exptl. Biol. Med.* **87**, 541-544.

Hernandez, H. H., and Chaikoff, I. L. (1957). *J. Biol. Chem.* **228**, 447-457.

Hernandez, H. H., Peterson, D. W., Chaikoff, I. L., and Dauben, W. G. (1953). *Proc. Soc. Exptl. Biol. Med.* **83**, 498-499.

Hernandez, H. H., Chaikoff, I. L., Dauben, W. G., and Abraham, S. (1954). *J. Biol. Chem.* **206**, 757-765.

Hernandez, H. H., Chaikoff, I. L., and Kiyasu, J. Y. (1955). *Am. J. Physiol.* **181**, 523-526.

Heymann, W., and Hackel, D. B. (1955). *Proc. Soc. Exptl. Biol. Med.* **89**, 329-332.

Heymann, W., and Rack, F. (1943). *Am. J. Diseases Children* **65**, 235-246.

Hill, R., Bauman, J. W., and Chaikoff, I. L. (1955). *Endocrinology* **57**, 316-321.

Hirsch, R. L., and Kellner, A. (1956a). *J. Exptl. Med.* **104**, 1-13.

Hirsch, R. L., and Kellner, A. (1956b). *J. Exptl. Med.* **104**, 15-24.

Hoehn, W. M., Schmidt, L. H., and Hughes, H. B. (1944). *J. Biol. Chem.* **152**, 59-66.

Horlick, L., Feldman, M., Jr., and Katz, L. N. (1948). *Proc. Soc. Exptl. Biol. Med.* **68**, 243-245.

Hotta, S., and Chaikoff, I. L. (1952). *J. Biol. Chem.* **198**, 895-899.

Hotta, S., and Chaikoff, I. L. (1955). *Arch. Biochem. Biophys.* **56**, 28-37.

Howard, G. A., and Martin, A. J. P. (1950). *Biochem. J.* **46**, 532-538.

Hsia, S. L., Matschiner, J. T., Mahowald, T. A., Elliott, W. H., Doisy, E. A., Jr., Thayer, S. A., and Doisy, E. A. (1957). *J. Biol. Chem.* **225**, 811-823.

Isaksson, B. (1954). *Acta Soc. Med. Upsaliensis* **59**, 277-306.

Ivy, A. C., Lin, T. M., and Karvinen, E. (1954). *Am. J. Physiol.* **179**, 646-647.

Jones, R. J., Kraft, S. C., Huffman, S., Balter, E. L., and Gordon, R. B. (1953). *Circulation Research* **1**, 530-533.

Jones, R. J., Reiss, O. K., Balter, E. L., and Cohen, L. (1957). *Proc. Soc. Exptl. Biol. Med.* **96**, 442-446.

*Josephson, B. (1941). *Physiol. Revs.* **21**, 463-486. (Bile acids.)

Josephson, B., and Rydin, A. (1936). *Biochem. J.* **30**, 2224-2228.

Joyner, C., Jr., and Kuo, P. T. (1955). *Am. J. Med. Sci.* **230**, 636-647.

Kantiengar, N. L., and Morton, R. A. (1955a). *Biochem. J.* **60**, 28-29.

Kantiengar, N. L., and Morton, R. A. (1955b). *Biochem. J.* **60**, 30-34.

Kantiengar, N. L., Lowe, J. S., Morton, R. A., and Pitt, G. A. J. (1955). *Biochem. J.* **60**, 34-39.

Karp, A., and Stetten, D., Jr. (1949). *J. Biol. Chem.* **179**, 819-830.
Karvinen, E., Lin, T. M., and Ivy, A. C. (1955). *Am. J. Physiol.* **181**, 439-440.
*Katz, L. N., and Stamler, J. (1953). *"Experimental Atherosclerosis."* C. C Thomas, Springfield, Illinois.
Kellner, A., Correll, J. W., and Ladd, A. T. (1951). *J. Exptl. Med.* **93**, 373-398.
Kelly, F. B., Jr., Economou, S. G., Stumpe, M., Taylor, C. B., and Cook, G. E. (1957). *Federation Proc.* **16**, 71.
Kelsey, F. E. (1939). *J. Biol. Chem.* **130**, 187-193.
Kelsey, F. E., and Longenecker, H. E. (1941). *J. Biol. Chem.* **139**, 727-740.
Kimizuka, T. (1938). *J. Biochem. (Tokyo)* **27**, 469-488.
Kinsell, L. W., Michaels, G. D., Dailey, J. P., Splitter, S., and Talpers, S. J. (1958). *Proc. Soc. Exptl. Biol. Med.* (In press).
Klein, H. P., and Lipmann, F. (1953a). *J. Biol. Chem.* **203**, 95-100.
Klein, H. P., and Lipmann, F. (1953b). *J. Biol. Chem.* **203**, 101-108.
Klein, W. (1939). *Z. physiol. Chem.* **259**, 268-281.
Korzenovsky, M., Rust, A. C., and Diller, E. R. (1955). *Federation Proc.* **14**, 239.
Korzenovsky, M., Vesely, B. M., and Diller, E. R. (1956). *Federation Proc.* **15**, 292.
Kritchevsky, D., Moyer, A. W., Tesar, W. C., Logan, J. B., Brown, R. A., and Richmond, G. (1954). *Circulation Research* **2**, 340-343.
Krueger, J. (1944). *J. Am. Chem. Soc.* **66**, 1795-1797.
Kurland, G. S., and Lucas, J. L. (1955). *J. Clin. Invest.* **34**, 947.
Kurland, G. S., Lucas, J. L., and Freedburg, A. S. (1954). *J. Clin. Invest.* **33**, 950.
Landon, E. J., and Greenberg, D. M. (1954). *J. Biol. Chem.* **209**, 493-502.
Langdon, R. G., and Bloch, K. (1953). *J. Biol. Chem.* **202**, 77-81.
Lata, G. F., and Anderson, E. (1954). *Arch. Biochem. Biophys.* **53**, 518-520.
Laurell, C. B. (1954a). *Scand. J. Clin. & Lab. Invest.* **6**, 22-24.
Laurell, C. B. (1954b). *Acta Physiol. Scand.* **30**, 289-294.
Lax, L. C., and Wrenshall, G. A. (1953). *Nucleonics* **11**, 18-20.
Leblond, C. P. (1951). *In* "Ciba Foundation Conference on Isotopes in Biochemistry," pp. 4-13. Churchill, London.
Le Breton, E., and Pantaleon, J. (1947). *Arch. sci. physiol.* **1**, 63-80, 199-217.
Lederer, E., Marx, F., Mercier, D., and Perot, G. (1946). *Helv. Chim. Acta* **29**, 1354-1365.
Lemmon, R. M., Pierce, F. T., Jr., Biggs, M. W., Parson, M. A., and Kritchevsky, D. (1954). *Arch. Biochem. Biophys.* **51**, 161-169.
*Lewis, L. A. (1955). *Minn. Med.* **38**, 775-778. (Lipoproteins.)
Lewis, L. A., Kolff, W. J., and Page, I. H. (1956). *Federation Proc.* **15**, 119.
Lindstedt, S. (1956). *Acta Chem. Scand.* **10**, 1051.
Lindstedt, S. (1957a). *Arkiv Kemi* **11**, 145-150.
Lindstedt, S. (1957b). *Acta Chem. Scand.* **11**, 417-420.
Lindstedt, S., and Norman, A. (1956a). *Acta Physiol. Scand.* **38**, 121-128.
Lindstedt, S., and Norman, A. (1956b). *Acta Physiol. Scand.* **38**, 129-134.
Lindstedt, S., and Norman, A. (1957). *Acta Chem. Scand.* **11**, 414-416.
Lindstedt, S., and Sjövall, J. (1957). *Acta Chem. Scand.* **11**, 421-426.
Lipsky, S. R., Bondy, P. K., Man, E. B., and McGuire, J. S., Jr. (1955). *J. Clin. Invest.* **34**, 950.
London, I. M., and Rittenberg, D. (1950). *J. Biol. Chem.* **184**, 687-691.
Lough, A. K., Garton, G. A., and Duncan, W. R. H. (1957). *Biochem. J.* **65**, 31-32P.
Lynn, W. S., Jr., Staple, E., and Gurin, S. (1955). *Federation Proc.* **14**, 783-785.

McGuire, J. S., Jr., and Lipsky, S. R. (1955). *J. Clin. Invest.* **34**, 704-710.

Mahowald, T. A., Matschiner, J. T., Hsia, S. L., Richter, R., Doisy, E. A., Jr., Elliott, W. H., and Doisy, E. A. (1957a). *J. Biol. Chem.* **225**, 781-793.

Mahowald, T. A., Matschiner, J. T., Hsia, S. L., Doisy, E. A., Jr., Elliott, W. H., and Doisy, E. A. (1957b). *J. Biol. Chem.* **225**, 795-802.

Mann, G. V., and White, H. S. (1953). *Metabolism, Clin. and Exptl.* **2**, 47-58.

Marker, R. E., and Shabica, A. C. (1940). *J. Am. Chem. Soc.* **62**, 2523-2525.

Marker, R. E., Wittbecker, E. L., Wagner, R. B., and Turner, D. L. (1942). *J. Am. Chem. Soc.* **64**, 818-822.

Marx, W., Gustin, S. T., and Levi, C. (1953). *Proc. Soc. Exptl. Biol. Med.* **83**, 143-146.

Matschiner, J. T., Mahowald, T. A., Elliott, W. H., Doisy, E. A., Jr., Hsia, S. L., and Doisy, E. A. (1957a). *J. Biol. Chem.* **225**, 771-779.

Matschiner, J. T., Mahowald, T. A., Hsia, S. L., Doisy, E. A., Jr., Elliott, W. H. and Doisy, E. A. (1957b). *J. Biol. Chem.* **225**, 803-810.

Meier, J. R., Siperstein, M. D., and Chaikoff, I. L. (1952). *J. Biol. Chem.* **198**, 105-109.

Menschick, W., and Page, I. H. (1932). *Z. physiol. Chem.* **211**, 246-252.

Messinger, W. J., Porosowska, Y., and Steele, J. M. (1950). *A.M.A. Arch. Internal Med.* **86**, 189-195.

Migicovsky, B. B. (1955). *Can. J. Biochem. Physiol.* **33**, 135-138.

Miller, L. L., Bly, C. G., Watson, M. L., and Bale, W. F. (1951). *J. Exptl. Med.* **94**, 431-453.

Morris, M. D., Chaikoff, I. L., Felts, J. M., Abraham, S., and Fansah, N. O. (1957). *J. Biol. Chem.* **224**, 1039-1045.

Mosbach, E. H., and Bevans, M. (1956). *Arch. Biochem. Biophys.* **63**, 258-259.

Mountain, J. T., Stockwell, F. R., and Stockinger, H. E. (1956). *Proc. Soc. Exptl. Biol. Med.* **92**, 582-587.

Mueller, J. H. (1915). *J. Biol. Chem.* **22**, 1-9.

Mueller, J. H. (1916). *J. Biol. Chem.* **27**, 463-480.

Nichols, C. W., Jr., Siperstein, M. D., and Chaikoff, I. L. (1953). *Proc. Soc. Exptl. Biol. Med.* **83**, 756-758.

Nichols, C. W., Jr., Lindsay, S., and Chaikoff, I. L. (1955). *Proc. Soc. Exptl. Biol. Med.* **89**, 609-613.

Nieft, M. L. (1949). *J. Biol. Chem.* **177**, 151-156.

Nieft, M. L., and Deuel, H. J., Jr. (1949). *J. Biol. Chem.* **177**, 143-150.

Norman, A. (1955). *Kgl. Fysiograf. Sällskap. Lund, Förh.* **25**(2), 19-25. (In English.)

Norman, A., and Grubb, R. (1955). *Acta Pathol. Microbiol. Scand.* **36**, 537-547. (In English.)

Okey, R., and Stewart, D. (1933). *J. Biol. Chem.* **99**, 717-727.

Oppenheim, E., and Bruger, M. (1950). *Proc. Soc. Exptl. Biol. Med.* **75**, 636-638.

Page, I. H., and Menschick, W. (1930). *Naturwissenschaften* **18**, 585.

Page, I. H., Lewis, L. A., and Plahl, G. (1953). *Circulation Research* **1**, 87-93.

Perry, W. F., and Bowen, H. F. (1956). *Am. J. Physiol.* **184**, 59-62.

Peters, J. P., and Man, E. B. (1950). *J. Clin. Invest.* **29**, 1-11.

*Peters, J. P., and Van Slyke, D. D. (1946). "Quantitative Clinical Chemistry: Interpretations," 2nd ed., Vol. 1. Williams and Wilkins, Baltimore, Maryland.

Peterson, D. W. (1951). *Proc. Soc. Exptl. Biol. Med.* **78**, 143-147.

Peterson, D. W., Nichols, C. W., Jr., and Shneour, E. A. (1952). *J. Nutrition* **47**, 57-65.

Peterson, D. W., Shneour, E. A., and Peek, N. F. (1954). *J. Nutrition* **53**, 451-460.

Pihl, A. (1954). Eksogent og Endogent Cholesterol. Ph.D. Thesis, Akademisk Trykningssentral, Oslo (summary in English).

Pihl, A. (1955a). *Acta Physiol. Scand.* **34**, 183-196.

Pihl, A. (1955b). *Acta Physiol. Scand.* **34**, 197-205.

Pihl, A. (1955c). *Acta Physiol. Scand.* **34**, 206-217.

Pihl, A., Bloch, K., and Anker, H. S. (1950). *J. Biol. Chem.* **183**, 441-450.

Pollak, O. J. (1953a). *Circulation* **7**, 696-701.

Pollak, O. J. (1953b). *Circulation* **7**, 702-706.

Popják, G. (1944). *J. Pathol. Bacteriol.* **55**, 485-496.

Popják, G. (1946). *Biochem. J.* **40**, 608-621.

Popják, G., and Beeckmans, M. L. (1950). *Biochem. J.* **47**, 233-238.

Popják, G., and Le Breton, E., eds. (1956). "Biochemical Problems of Lipids." Academic Press, New York.

Portman, O. W., and Mann, G. V. (1955). *J. Biol. Chem.* **213**, 733-743.

Portman, O. W., and Sinisterra, L. (1957). *Federation Proc.* **16**, 397.

Prelog, V., Tagmann, E., Lieberman, S., and Ruzicka, L. (1947). *Helv. Chim. Acta* **30**, 1080-1090.

Rattray, J. B. M., Cook, R. P., and James, A. T. (1956). *Biochem. J.* **64**, 10P.

Ridout, J. H., Lucas, C. C., Patterson, J. M., and Best, C. H. (1954). *Biochem. J.* **58**, 297-301.

Rittenberg, D., and Schoenheimer, R. (1937). *J. Biol. Chem.* **121**, 235-253.

Robertson, D. M. (1955). *Biochem. J.* **61**, 681-688.

*Robertson, J. S. (1957). *Physiol. Revs.* **37**, 133-154.

Robinson, D. S. (1955). *Quart. J. Exptl. Physiol.* **40**, 112-126.

Rosenfeld, R. S., Fukushima, D. K., Hellman, L., and Gallagher, T. F. (1954). *J. Biol. Chem.* **211**, 301-311.

Rosenfeld, R. S., Hellman, L., and Gallagher, T. F. (1955). *Federation Proc.* **14**, 271.

Rosenheim, O., and Webster, T. A. (1941a). *Biochem. J.* **35**, 920-927.

Rosenheim, O., and Webster, T. A. (1941b). *Biochem. J.* **35**, 928-931.

Rosenheim, O., and Webster, T. A. (1943a). *Biochem. J.* **37**, 513-514.

Rosenheim, O., and Webster, T. A. (1943b). *Biochem. J.* **37**, 580-585.

Rosenman, R. H., and Smith, M. K. (1956). *J. Clin. Invest.* **35**, 11-19.

Rosenman, R. H., Friedman, M., and Byers, S. O. (1951). *Science* **114**, 210-211.

Rosenman, R. H., Friedman, M., and Byers, S. O. (1952a). *Circulation* **5**, 589-593.

Rosenman, R. H., Byers, S. O., and Friedman, M. (1952b). *J. Clin. Endocrinol. and Metabolism* **12**, 1287-1299.

Rosenman, R. H., Byers, S. O., and Friedman, M. (1954). *Circulation Research* **2**, 160-163.

Rosenman, R. H., Friedman, M., and Byers, S. O. (1956). *J. Clin. Invest.* **35**, 522-532.

Rudman, D., and Kendall, F. E. (1957). *J. Clin. Invest.* **36**, 530-537.

Rundle, F. F., Cass, M. H., Robson, B., and Middleton, M. (1955). *Surgery* **37**, 903-910.

Sato, G., Fisher, H. W., and Puck, T. T. (1957). *Science* **126**, 961-964.

*Sayers, G. (1950). *Physiol. Revs.* **30**, 241-320. (Adrenal cholesterol.)

Schmidt, L. H., and Hughes, H. B. (1942). *J. Biol. Chem.* **143**, 771-783.

Schoenheimer, R. (1929). *Z. physiol. Chem.* **180**, 1-37. Studies on the absorption of plant sterols. With Yuasa, D., pp. 19-23, is described the absorption of sitosterol.

*Schoenheimer, R. (1931). *Science* **74**, 579-584. (Sterol absorption.)

Schoenheimer, R., and Dam, H. (1932). *Z. physiol. Chem.* **211**, 241-245.

Schoenheimer, R., von Behring, H., Hummel, R., and Schindel, L. (1930). *Z. physiol. Chem.* **192**, 73-111. Studies on the saturated sterols of organisms. Absorption, pp. 97-102; excretion, pp. 102-111.

Schoenheimer, R., Dam, H., and von Gottberg, K. (1935a). *J. Biol. Chem.* **110**, 667-671.

Schoenheimer, R., Rittenberg, D., and Graff, M. (1935b). *J. Biol. Chem.* **111**, 183-192.

Seskind, C. R., Schroeder, M. T., Rasmussen, R., and Wissler, R. W. (1957). *Federation Proc.* **16**, 371.

*Shimizu, T. (1948). *J. Japan. Biochem. Soc.* **20**, 118-130. (Bile acids.)

Siperstein, M. D. (1955). *Federation Proc.* **14**, 282.

Siperstein, M. D., and Chaikoff, I. L. (1952). *J. Biol. Chem.* **198**, 93-104.

*Siperstein, M. D., and Chaikoff, I. L. (1955). *Federation Proc.* **14**, 767-774. (Formation of bile acids.)

Siperstein, M. D., and Murray, A. W. (1955). *J. Clin. Invest.* **34**, 1449-1453.

Siperstein, M. D., Hernandez, H. H., and Chaikoff, I. L. (1952a). *Am. J. Physiol.* **171**, 297-301.

Siperstein, M. D., Jayko, M. E., Chaikoff, I. L., Dauben, W. G. (1952b). *Proc. Soc. Exptl. Biol. Med.* **81**, 720-724.

Siperstein, M. D., Chaikoff, I. L., and Reinhardt, W. O. (1952c). *J. Biol. Chem.* **198**, 111-114.

Siperstein, M. D., Nichols, C. W., Jr., and Chaikoff, I. L. (1953a). *Science* **117**, 386-389.

Siperstein, M. D., Nichols, C. W., Jr., and Chaikoff, I. L. (1953b). *Circulation* **7**, 37-41.

Siperstein, M. D., Harold, F. M., Chaikoff, I. L., and Dauben, W. G. (1954). *J. Biol. Chem.* **210**, 181-191.

Sjövall, J., and Äkesson, I. (1955). *Acta Physiol. Scand.* **34**, 273-278, 279-286.

Snog-Kjaer, A., Prange, I., and Dam, H. (1956). *J. Gen. Microbiol.* **13**, 256-260.

*Sobotka, H. (1938). "Physiological Chemistry of the Bile." Williams and Wilkins, Baltimore, Maryland.

Solomon, A. K. (1949). *J. Clin. Invest.* **28**, 1297-1307.

Sperry, W. M. (1932). *J. Biol. Chem.* **96**, 759-768.

Sperry, W. M. (1935). *J. Biol. Chem.* **111**, 467-478.

Sperry, W. M. (1936). *J. Biol. Chem.* **114**, 125-133.

Sperry, W. M., and Bergmann, W. (1937). *J. Biol. Chem.* **119**, 171-176.

Sperry, W. M., and Brand, F. C. (1941). *J. Biol. Chem.* **137**, 377-387.

Sperry, W. M., and Stoyanoff, V. A. (1935). *J. Nutrition* **9**, 157-161.

Sperry, W. M., and Stoyanoff, V. A. (1937). *J. Biol. Chem.* **117**, 525-532.

Sperry, W. M., and Stoyanoff, V. A. (1938). *J. Biol. Chem.* **126**, 77-89.

Stamler, J., and Katz, L. N. (1951). *Circulation* **4**, 255-261.

Stamler, J., Pick, R., and Katz, L. N. (1957). *Federation Proc.* **16**, 123.

Staple, E., and Gurin, S. (1954). *Biochim. et Biophys. Acta* **15**, 372-376.

Steinberg, D., and Fredrickson, D. S. (1955a). *Circulation* **12**, 493-494.

Steinberg, D., and Fredrickson, D. S. (1955b). *Proc. Soc. Exptl. Biol. Med.* **90**, 232-236.

Steinberg, D., and Fredrickson, D. S. (1956). *Ann. N.Y. Acad. Sci.* **64**, 579-589.

Steinberg, D., Fredrickson, D. S., and Liddle, G. W. (1957). *Federation Proc.* **16**, 255.

Stokes, W. M., Fish, W. A., and Hickey, F. C.   (1955).   *J. Biol. Chem.* **213**, 325-328.

Swell, L., and Kramer, N. C.   (1953).   *Proc. Soc. Exptl. Biol. Med.* **82**, 197-198.

Swell, L., and Treadwell, C. R.   (1950).   *J. Biol. Chem.* **185**, 349-355.

Swell, L., and Treadwell, C. R.   (1955).   *J. Biol. Chem.* **212**, 141-150.

Swell, L., Byron, J. E., and Treadwell, C. R.   (1950).   *J. Biol. Chem.* **186**, 543-548.

Swell, L., Flick, D. F., Field, H., Jr., and Treadwell, C. R.   (1953).   *Proc. Soc. Exptl. Biol. Med.* **84**, 428-431.

Swell, L., Field, H., Jr., and Treadwell, C. R.   (1954).   *Proc. Soc. Exptl. Biol. Med.* **87**, 216-218.

Swell, L., Flick, D. F., Field, H., Jr., and Treadwell, C. R.   (1955a).   *Am. J. Physiol.* **180**, 124-128.

Swell, L., Boiter, T. A., Field, H., Jr., and Treadwell, C. R.   (1955b).   *Am. J. Physiol.* **180**, 124-128.

Swell, L., Boiter, T. A., Field, H., Jr., and Treadwell, C. R.   (1955c).   *Am. J. Physiol.* **181**, 193-195.

Swell, L., Boiter, T. A., Field, H., Jr., and Treadwell, C. R.   (1956).   *J. Nutrition* **58**, 385-398.

Swell, L., Trout, E. C., Jr., Field, H., Jr., and Treadwell, C. R.   (1957).   *Science* **125**, 1194-1195.

*Symposium on Atherosclerosis.   (1955).   *Natl. Acad. Sci. Natl. Research Council, Publ. No.* **338**, Washington, D. C.

Tavormina, P. A., and Gibbs, M. H.   (1957).   *J. Am. Chem. Soc.* **79**, 758-759.

Tayeau, F.   (1943).   *Compt. rend. soc. biol.* **137**, 239.

Tayeau, F.   (1944).   *Bull. soc. chim. biol.* **26**, 295-298.

*Tayeau, F.   (1949).   *Exposés ann. biochem. med.* **10**, 251-308.   (Bile acids.)

Tayeau, F.   (1955).   *Arch. sci. biol.* (*Bologna*) **39**, 545-553.

*Tayeau, F., and Nivet, R.   (1956).   *In* "Biochemical Problems of Lipids" (G. Popják and E. Le Breton, eds.), pp. 365-370. (Serum cholesterol esterase.)

Taylor, C. B., and Gould, R. G.   (1950).   *Circulation* **2**, 467-468.

Taylor, C. B., Cox, G. E., Nelson, L. G., Davis, C. B., Jr., and Hass, G. M.   (1955).   *Circulation* **12**, 489.

Taylor, C. B., Nelson, L. G., Stumpe, M., Cox, G. E., and Tamura, R.   (1956).   *Federation Proc.* **15**, 534.

Thompson, J. C., and Vars, H. M.   (1953).   *Proc. Soc. Exptl. Biol. Med.* **83**, 246-248.

Tomkins, G. M., and Chaikoff, I. L.   (1952).   *J. Biol. Chem.* **196**, 569-573.

Tomkins, G. M., Chaikoff, I. L., and Bennett, L. L.   (1952).   *J. Biol. Chem.* **199**, 543-545.

Tomkins, G. M., Sheppard, H., and Chaikoff, I. L.   (1953a).   *J. Biol. Chem.* **201**, 137-141.

Tomkins, G. M., Sheppard, H., and Chaikoff, I. L.   (1953b).   *J. Biol. Chem.* **203**, 781-786.

Tomkins, G. M., Nichols, C. W., Jr., Chapman, D. D., Hotta, S., and Chaikoff, I. L.   (1957).   *Science* **125**, 936-937.

Tsung-Min, L., Karvinen, E., and Ivy, A. C.   (1954).   *Am. J. Physiol.* **179**, 680.

Turner, K. B., McCormack, G. H., Jr., and Richards, A.   (1953).   *J. Clin. Invest.* **32**, 801-806.

Uhl, H. S. M., Brown, H. H., Zlatkis, A., Zak, B., Myers, G. B., and Boyle, A. J.   (1953).   *Am. J. Clin. Pathol.* **23**, 1226-1233.

Van Bruggen, J. T., Hutchens, T. T., Claycomb, C. K., Cathey, W. J., and West, E. S. (1952). *J. Biol. Chem.* **196**, 389-394.

Van Bruggen, J. T., Yamada, P., Hutchens, T. T., and West, E. S. (1954). *J. Biol. Chem.* **209**, 635-640.

Wagner, A., and Rogalski, L. (1952). *J. Lab. Clin. Med.* **40**, 324-334.

Wainfan, E., and Marx, W. (1955). *J. Biol. Chem.* **214**, 441-445.

Wainfan, E., Henkin, G., Rice, L. I., and Marx, W. (1952). *Arch. Biochem. Biophys.* **38**, 187-193.

Wainfan, E., Henkin, G., Rittenberg, S. C., and Marx, W. (1954). *J. Biol. Chem.* **207**, 843-849.

Warner, I. (1952). *Federation Proc.* **11**, 306.

Weiss, S. B., and Marx, W. (1955). *J. Biol. Chem.* **213**, 349-353.

Wells, W. W. (1957a). *Arch. Biochem. Biophys.* **66**, 217-225.

Wells, W. W. (1957b). *Federation Proc.* **16**, 402.

Wells, W. W., and Baumann, C. A. (1954). *Proc. Soc. Exptl. Med.* **87**, 519-521.

Wells, W. W., Coleman, D. L., and Baumann, C. A. (1955). *Arch. Biochem. Biophys.* **57**, 437-444.

Whipple, G. H., and Smith, H. P. S. (1928). *J. Biol. Chem.* **80**, 697-707.

Whitney, J., and Roberts, S. (1955). *Am. J. Physiol.* **181**, 446-450.

Windaus, A., and Uibrig, C. (1915). *Ber.* **48**, 857-863.

Wootton, I. D. P., and Wiggins, H. S. (1953). *Biochem. J.* **55**, 292-294.

Wulzen, R., and Bahrs, A. M. (1941). *Am. J. Physiol.* **133**, 500.

Yamamoto, R. S., Goldstein, N. P., and Treadwell, C. R. (1949). *J. Biol. Chem.* **180**, 615-621.

Zabin, I., and Barker, W. F. (1953). *J. Biol. Chem.* **205**, 633-636.

Ziegler, P. (1956). *Can. J. Chem.* **34**, 523-529.

CHAPTER 8

CONVERSION OF CHOLESTEROL TO STEROID HORMONES*

Oscar Hechter

I. Introduction

A decade ago the major questions in steroid hormone biosynthesis were relatively simple. Is cholesterol actually the precursor of steroid hormones, as most believed? If so, what are the routes of conversion to the various steroid hormones in the secretory product of the adrenal cortex, ovary, testis, and placenta? The work of the past few years has, in large part, answered these questions. Cholesterol has now been definitely established as a key precursor of the steroid hormones; the *major* steps which are presumably involved in the conversion of cholesterol to the various steroid hormones have been outlined in terms of the successive intermediary compounds formed and the enzymes responsible for the individual steps. From this advance, however, a host of new questions and problems have arisen in a manner reminiscent of the struggle between Hercules and the Hydra.

---

* Chemical nomenclature in this chapter follows in general the preferred usage in the United States.

309

The new problems in steroid biosynthesis are manifold and in diverse fields. A new field of enzymology involving steroids as substrates has developed from the study of the individual enzymes involved in steroid hormone biosynthesis (cf. Dorfman and Ungar, 1953; Dorfman, 1955). With the recognition that microorganisms possess enzymes which modify the steroid nucleus and side chain at the same positions as those observed with mammalian tissues (cf. the exhaustive review of Eppstein et al., 1956), this enzymological field has proliferated beyond its original confines. Subsequent work has revealed that the oxygen used for steroid hydroxylations, whether achieved by enzymes from mammalian sources or microorganisms, comes directly from molecular oxygen rather than via water (Hayano et al., 1956b). From this finding it has become apparent that steroid oxidations resemble other oxygen-requiring systems, among which should be included certain dealkylating enzymes (Brodie et al., 1955), pyrocatechol oxidase (Hayaishi et al., 1955), p-hydroxyphenylpyruvic oxidase (Zamoni and LaDuc, 1956). Several of these enzymes resemble the adrenal and testicular hydroxylating enzyme systems in that they require, in addition to oxygen, a reductant such as reduced triphosphopyridine nucleotide (TNPH) and a heavy metal. Working with enzymes obtained from both molds and mammals, inquiries are being directed toward elucidating the mechanisms of these enzyme actions in fundamental terms.

The elucidation of biosynthetic sequences for steroid hormones has clearly posed certain key problems important at a physiological level; these relate to the manner of regulation of the biosynthetic sequences in the living cell. In one aspect, this involves questions of "intracellular geometry" wherein the individual steps in the sequence are integrated in terms of organized intracellular structures (cf. Saba and Hechter, 1955; Hayano et al., 1956a). In its larger aspect, however, the problem of regulation of steroid hormone production concerns the mode of action of certain pituitary trophic hormones (of protein or polypeptide nature) upon specific target cells, wherein activation of cell function is expressed in terms of increased steroid hormone production. While our knowledge of the mechanism of any hormone action, in fundamental terms, is obscure (cf. Hechter, 1955), some progress has been made in defining the problem of ACTH action (cf. Hechter, 1952, 1953a, 1955, 1957; Hayano et al., 1956a).

Finally, there remains to be mentioned the impact of the newer knowledge of steroid hormone biosynthetic sequences upon clinical endocrinology, wherein it has long been held that certain defects of steroid hormone biogenesis may be related to characteristic clinical disturbances in man. With respect to certain disorders of the adrenal cortex, notably in the case of the adrenogenital syndrome, it now appears that we may be close to an understanding of a disease process at a molecular level (cf. Jailer, 1953; Jailer *et al.*, 1955; Bongiovanni and Eberlein, 1955; Dorfman, 1953, 1955).

Where the range of inquiry is so wide, it is not possible to review these diverse and expanding fields. Indeed, in the space allotted, it will only be possible to present the basic data concerning the metabolic routes operative in the biosynthesis of the various steroid hormones from cholesterol, together with some discussion of the question as to whether cholesterol is an obligatory intermediary in steroid hormone formation. Fortunately, compilation and discussion of the immense body of work relating to the diverse aspects of steroid hormone biosynthesis not covered in this discussion are available in various review articles; reference will be made to these wherever possible in an effort partially to repair the deficiencies of the present paper. An Italian monograph of 400 pages entitled "Sindromi Cliniche da Alterato Metabolismo Ormonico Steroideo" (Antognetti *et al.*, 1955) may represent the most complete treatment presently available of the field in its diverse aspects.

II. Historical Reflections

The idea that cholesterol might be a precursor of the steroid hormones developed as the chemical structures of the hormones isolated from the ovary, corpus luteum, testis, and adrenal cortex were found to be perhydrocyclopentenophenanthrene derivatives, bearing an obvious chemical relationship to cholesterol. On the assumption that the biosynthetic mechanisms utilized to form complex molecules *in vivo* are implicit in the chemical structures involved, as evidenced by reactivity in the organic reactions of the chemistry laboratory, the pioneers in steroid chemistry hypothesized biogenetic relationships between cholesterol and the various steroid hormones then known. These efforts were particularly popular before 1940 and a typical scheme of this era is illustrated in Fig. 1, taken from Karrer's text (1938) which embodies hypothetical relationships derived primarily from Ruzicka and Butenandt. It will be seen that one of the hypothetical routes envisaged involved the degradation of the cholesterol side chain to form pregnenolone; this upon oxidation gave rise to progesterone, the hormone of the corpus luteum; progesterone in turn was hypothesized as a precursor of testosterone, the hormone of the testis, which in turn was regarded as the precursor of the ovarian hormones, estrone and estradiol. It will be shown later in this paper that it is precisely these reactions, demonstrated only in the past few years, which are now regarded as basically involved in the biosynthesis of steroid hormones.

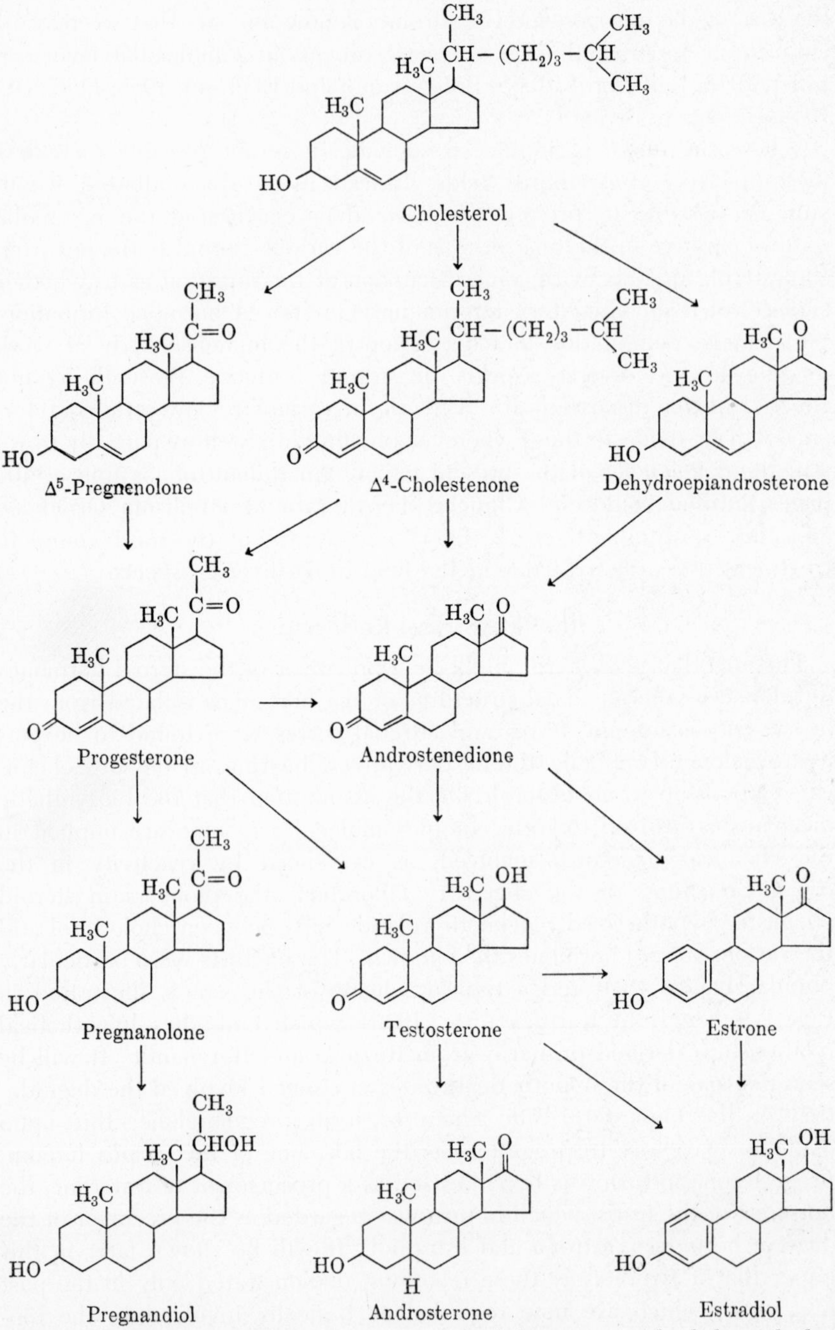

FIG. 1. Relationship between various steroid hormones and cholesterol, hypothesized by Karrer (1938). Similar schemes were proposed by Koch, Fieser, Butanandt, and Ruzicka in this period.

The history of the subsequent developments has been previously discussed (cf. Dorfman and Ungar, 1953); here we may consider why a puzzle visualized *conceptually* so completely required almost two decades before it could be solved. The answer, in largest part, was due to an insufficient interest, and related to this an inability to develop techniques capable of deciding between the various and diverse alternative pathways all equally plausible in terms of paper chemistry.* These factors combined to create a relative "impasse" which lasted until 1949, although in the preceding years, the view that cholesterol was the prime steroid hormone precursor was strengthened to a point of general acceptance by suggestive evidence obtained by the indirect methodology characteristic of steroid biochemistry in the period 1940–1949. In the most definitive of these experiments, Bloch (1945) demonstrated that isotopically labeled cholesterol was converted in a pregnant woman to pregnandiol (the characteristic urinary metabolite of progesterone), strongly suggesting cholesterol transformation to progesterone in the placenta.

In 1949 the ingredients necessary for direct and active prosecution of

---

* This, however, is not the whole story; doubts of a considerable magnitude were soon to be leveled against the early biogenetic relationships postulated by the steroid chemists. One came from biochemistry as it developed from 1940 onward, with enzymology as its dominant theme; this led to a succession of completely unexpected discoveries of enzymatic reactions which appeared to be completely at variance with the background of chemical knowledge. The discovery of the role of acetate in sterol biosynthesis and of succinate and glycine in porphyrin formation are but two of many examples, which at the time appeared to be completely unpredictable from any of the particular chemical features of the end products. The reaction of the biochemist was empiricism; it appeared that the enzymes in the living cell did not "know" the "chemistry" of the organic chemist. This attitude has subsequently changed, but this change is a relatively recent occurrence of the past few years; it is not surprising that in this ideological background the speculative efforts of chemists to chart biosynthetic pathways were regarded with a high degree of scepticism, if not indifference. The second was perhaps less substantial, but it played some part. When the fractionation of adrenal cortex tissue resulted in the culmination of the isolation and identification of some 28 steroids, 6 possessing typical adrenocortical activity by the assays then employed, in addition to progesterone, estrone, as well as 3 C_{19} steroids possessing androgenic activity, the number of permutations and combinations of plausible biogenetic relationships became so large that it no longer seemed profitable to speculate in the absence of direct evidence. Finally, the work on the adrenal cortex steroids introduced another source of doubt. Having isolated a multiplicity of hormonally active steroids from a tissue, it became clear that under physiological conditions all need not necessarily be secreted into the blood stream. A cardinal assumption of classical endocrinology was challenged in that it was no longer certain that the isolation of a hormonally active product from a glandular extract was sufficient to establish that the isolated substance was actually a hormone secreted by the gland.

the puzzle of steroid hormone biogenesis were introduced. The "interest," which had been missing, developed from the dramatic discovery that cortisone possessed completely unexpected therapeutic activity in rheumatoid arthritis and related diseases (Hench *et al.*, 1949); the impact of this discovery, at a time when the world supply of cortisone was just a few grams, was such that large numbers of scientists entered the field of steroid hormone biosynthesis and the tempo of work in those laboratories already committed was tremendously accelerated. Methodology developed during the apparent "dormant" period of steroid biogenesis was simultaneously available (or was soon to be developed) and ready for the Mayo Clinic discovery.

In methodology, the basic shift was from the study of over-all reactions in the intact organism to *in vitro* systems, where it became possible to study the individual steps of a process. The breakthrough in this area came first with the isolated perfused cow adrenal. Having previously defined conditions where the perfused adrenal produced corticosteroid from endogenous precursors, and where this production could be enhanced by the addition of ACTH to the perfusion medium (Hechter, 1949), it became possible to perfuse possible steroid precursors through an *in vitro* preparation and determine the enzymatic transformations by characterizing the product formed. On the basis of studies involving the isolation and chemical characterization of the major products formed as the result of perfusion of various exogenous steroids through the adrenals, a tentative outline of the route of corticosteroidogenesis was soon to be put forward; Fig. 2 is the outline presented at the Laurentian Hormone Conference in 1950 (Hechter *et al.*, 1951). The perfusion technique, developed at a time (1944 to 1949) when methods for the isolation and characterization of steroids in microgram amounts were not available, attempted to circumvent these difficulties by presenting 100–200 mg. steroid substrate to a large gland (weighing 20 gm. or so), so that the steroidal products formed in the 5–50 mg. range could be isolated by column chromatography and identified by classical chemical techniques (melting point, mixed melting point, optical rotation); indeed, the reactions demonstrated in Fig. 2 were all based on classical procedures. While adsorption column chromatography, introduced by Reichstein to steroid biochemistry had been a powerful tool in isolation studies, further progress in corticosteroid biosynthesis toward simpler systems (slices, homogenates, enzyme extracts) clearly depended upon micromethods for fractionation and identification of steroids at a microgram level; these were almost immediately available in the tool of filter paper chromatography (Zaffaroni and Burton, 1951; Burton *et al.*, 1951; Bush, 1952). Coupled with C^{14}-labeled steroids, soon to be made available, and the powerful tool of infrared spectroscopy, paper chromatography literally gave "wings" to steroid biochemistry; isolation and identification no longer were the rate-determining factors in biochemical progress. With analytical advance, progress was rapid; cholesterol was shown to be converted to adrenocortical hormones in the perfused adrenal; the enzymes predicted by the perfusion data became an active field of investigation, soon to be crowned by success. Simultaneously, the new analytical methods made it possible directly to attack the problem of the chemical nature of the adrenocortical secretory product by isolating and identifying the steroids in the adrenal vein of living animals, a technique pioneered by Vogt (1943), but which could not be

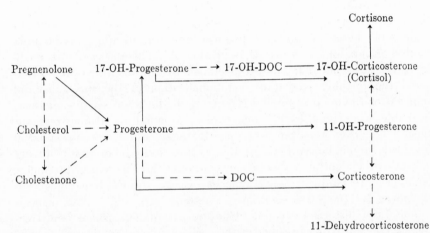

Fig. 2. The tentative scheme of corticosteroidogenesis presented at the Laurentian Hormone Conference (1950), where it was assumed that cholesterol was a primary precursor of corticosteroids (Hechter et al., 1951). The solid lines represent reactions established at that time; the dotted lines, reactions which seemed possible in 1950.

fully exploited until the new micro-methods were available almost a decade later. Finally, the new concepts and methods in adrenal biosynthesis facilitated the development of microbiological screening projects set up to exploit microorganism enzymatic systems for specific transformations of steroids added to culture media, which was to revolutionize the commercial production of steroids (cf. Eppstein et al., 1956).

The work on adrenal cortex proceeding at three levels concurrently (i.e. in vivo studies of adrenal venous blood, perfusion, and the study of the enzymatic reactions of adrenal homogenates) soon combined to give a remarkably consistent outline of corticoid biosynthetic sequences consistent with Fig. 2. The implications of the steroidogenic sequence in the adrenal cortex for other endocrine glands were clear. If in the adrenal cortex, progesterone was, in fact, an intermediary in the production of cortisol and corticosterone, might it not be an end product in the corpus luteum due to the absence of appropriate hydroxylation systems and thus constitute the hormone from this tissue? Similarly, in the testis, where Ruzicka and Prelog (1943) had isolated Δ^5-pregnenolone, it became possible to envisage progesterone as the precursor of testosterone and androstenedione (Δ^4-androstene-3,20-dione), if the testis contained enzymes which could remove the progesterone side chain. The area of profitable work was thus clearly drawn and developments were soon to be forthcoming in this area. There remained the problem of the biosynthesis of estrogens, long postulated to be derived from C_{19} androgens; here the problem involved removal of the C-19 angular methyl group and aromatization of ring A. The discovery of a 19-hydroxylation system for androstenedione by Meyer (1955a, b) constituted the opening wedge to a rationalization of the mechanism of removal of the angular methyl group. With the stage set, the methods available were soon to be successfully exploited to demonstrate the definitive conversion of testosterone to estrogens. While the puzzles involved in the biosynthesis of the various steroid hormones are not solved in their entirety, the various "patterns" are beginning to emerge and merge; techniques are available for discovery of the remaining missing pieces and the puzzle seems near solution.

This brief historical account illustrates in striking fashion how completely concept is the prisoner of the technology and motivations of the period in which it develops. Danby (1940), for example, foresaw the possibilities inherent in the study of biosynthetic reactions in an *in vitro* perfusion system as early as 1940. Her interesting results, which included the demonstration that the perfusion of dehydroepiandrosterone and Δ^5-androstene-3β,17β-diol through bull testis led to the production of more potent androgens (probably androstenedione and testosterone), came historically "too soon" to be successfully exploited. Similarly, in the area of microbiological transformation of steroids, the pioneer work of Mamoli, Ercoli, and their collaborators (cf. Eppstein *et al.*, 1956) attracted minor attention, until the economic possibilities associated with the manufacture of steroid hormones in bulk gave impetus to this major development.

III. Corticoids

A. NATURE OF ADRENOCORTICAL SECRETORY PRODUCT

Although more than 30 steroids have been isolated from extracts of adrenocortical tissue (cf. Hechter and Pincus, 1954; Dorfman and Ungar, 1953), it is generally agreed from studies of the steroid content of adrenal venous blood that the adrenocortical secretion contains only a limited number of steroids (Bush, 1953; Hechter and Pincus, 1954; Nelson, 1955). The best known cortical steroids are shown in Table I.

TABLE I
SOME CORTICAL STEROIDS

Substituents at C—			Names as derivatives	Other trivial
11	17	18	of corticosterone[a]	names
H	H	CH_3	11-Deoxycorticosterone	Cortexone (DOC)
O	H	CH_3	11-Dehydrocorticosterone	Compound A
β-OH	H	CH_3	Corticosterone	Compound B
H	α-OH	CH_3	17α-Hydroxy-11-deoxy-corticosterone	
O	α-OH	CH_3	17α-Hydroxy-11-dehydro-corticosterone	Cortisone, compound E
β-OH	α-OH	CH_3	17α-Hydroxycorticosterone	Cortisol, hydro-cortisone, compound F
β-OH	H	$H—C=O$	Aldosterone	Electrocortin

[a] The compound names are those of Kendall; see also Reichstein and Shoppee (1943).

The secretory product of *normal* animals of diverse species uniformly contains either cortisol or corticosterone (or a mixture of both) as the predominant component(s); also observed are a variety of trace substances, one of which is aldosterone, now established as the principal adrenocortical regulator of electrolyte metabolism (Simpson and Tait, 1955; Luetscher, 1956a, b; Gaunt *et al.*, 1955). On the basis of our present information, these three corticosteroid hormones appear to be the "principal" corticoids, *considered physiologically*, in the secretion of normal animals, and it will be our task to account for their biosynthesis.

This is not to say that cortisol, corticosterone, and aldosterone represent the only steroids in the adrenocortical secretion. In the secretory product of normal animals there is evidence for trace amounts of DOC (deoxycorticosterone), 17-hydroxy-DOC, as well as yet unidentified corticosteroids, whose biological activity is unknown,[*] and for certain 19-carbon 17-ketosteroids (the so-called adrenal androgens), whose biosynthesis will be considered in a later section. Moreover, as will be discussed later, there is substantial evidence that in certain diseases of the adrenal gland, the nature of the steroid mixture secreted by the adrenal is markedly altered, so that the major components are no longer cortisol or corticosterone.

B.   Conversion of Cholesterol to Cortisol and Corticosterone

The definitive demonstration that cholesterol is converted in the adrenal cortex to cortisol and corticosterone was first achieved in the isolated cow adrenal perfused with cholesterol-4-C^{14} (Zaffaroni et al., 1951; Hechter et al., 1953); later this conversion was demonstrated in cell-free homogenates of cow adrenal cortex tissue and in fractions thereof (Saba and Hechter, 1955; Hayano et al., 1956a). The conversion of cholesterol-C^{14} to cortisol and corticosterone, as well as a multiplicity of other products, has likewise been reported in hog adrenal homogenates (Heard et al., 1956). In vivo, it has been shown in man that following the administration of cholesterol labeled doubly with C^{14} and tritium, characteristic urinary metabolites of cortisol labeled with both tritium and C^{14} were isolated: the metabolites included tetrahydrocortisol, tetrahydrocortisone, as well as certain 17-ketosteroids (Werbin and LeRoy, 1954, 1955).

Our present knowledge of the reactions involved in the conversion of cholesterol to cortisol and corticosterone, in the main, is derived from in vitro studies of the cow adrenal cortex. Using various steroids as substrates, in systems ranging in complexity from the isolated perfused cow gland to cell-free homogenates and fractions thereof, certain reactions have been shown to occur, whereas others do not. Based upon these studies, possible sequences of the reactions involved in the production of cortisol and corticosterone have been proposed (Hechter and

---

[*] It should, however, be noted that one or another of the "trace" components indicated may yet be added to the list of physiologically important adrenocortical hormones. The recent history of aldosterone has shown that the concentration of a substance in the adrenocortical secretion need bear no necessary relationship to its physiological importance. When it is considered that bioassay procedures have not as yet been devised to assess the full spectrum of biological effects influenced by the adrenal cortex, it is possible to conjecture that the "last" adrenocortical hormone to be discovered may not be aldosterone.

Pincus, 1954; Dorfman, 1953, 1955; Samuels, 1955; Staudinger, 1955). The sequence illustrated in Fig. 3 appears to the author best to fit the available information on the cow adrenal. All of the reactions shown in Fig. 3 have now been definitively demonstrated in cell-free homogenates and are consistent with the results obtained by perfusing various substrates through cow adrenals.

The scheme envisions an initial cleavage of the cholesterol (C_{27}) side chain to form isocaproic acid (Lynn et al., 1955; Staple et al., 1956) and the C_{21} steroid, pregnenolone (Saba et al., 1954; Solomon et al., 1954; Saba and Hechter, 1955; Staple et al., 1956). A system capable of catalyzing this cleavage reaction has been described (Lynn et al., 1955; Staple et al., 1956) in adrenal tissue, as well as in testis and ovary. While the system has been purified and obtained free of particulate components of adrenal homogenates and certain of the cofactor requirements have been established (notably adenosinetriphosphate (ATP) and diphosphopyridine nucleotide (DPN), it is probable that several enzymes are operative in the over-all cleavage reaction. The suggestion that 20-hydroxycholesterol is an intermediary in the reaction from cholesterol to pregnenolone (Lynn et al., 1955) finds support in the recent studies of Solomon et al. (1956a). Incubation of cow adrenal homogenates with cholesterol-4-C^{14} resulted in the formation of 20β-hydroxycholesterol-C^{14}, and the following cholesterol derivatives were found not to be intermediaries: 22α-hydroxy, 22β-hydroxy, 22-keto, 24β-hydroxy, and 24-keto. The cleavage step thus involves, as a minimum, a C-20 hydroxylating enzyme system and a system which splits the bond between C-20 and C-22, which may be designated as a C-20,22 desmolase. If Dorfman's recent speculation (1957) should prove to be tenable, three enzymes may be envisaged as participating: a C-20 hydroxylating system, plus a C-22 hydroxylating system, which yields the C-20,22 dihydroxycholesterol, then split by a C-20,22 desmolase to yield pregnenolone. The findings that C-22 hydroxy- or ketocholesterol do not appear to be intermediaries (Staple et al., 1956; Solomon et al., 1956a) might merely be an expression of the possibility that preliminary hydroxylation at C-22 precludes subsequent hydroxylation at C-20, but not the reverse. Further work is necessary to elucidate the detailed enzymology of the "cleavage system" whereby cholesterol is converted to pregnenolone.

Pregnenolone, in turn, is oxidized to progesterone through the action of an enzyme, designated as 3β-hydroxy dehydrogenase, the properties of which have been described (Samuels, 1953; Beyer and Samuels, 1956; Hayano et al., 1956a). This enzyme, found in adrenal tissue, but also in corpus luteum, testis, and placenta, not only catalyzes the conversion of pregnenolone to progesterone, but the analogous reaction in the C_{19}

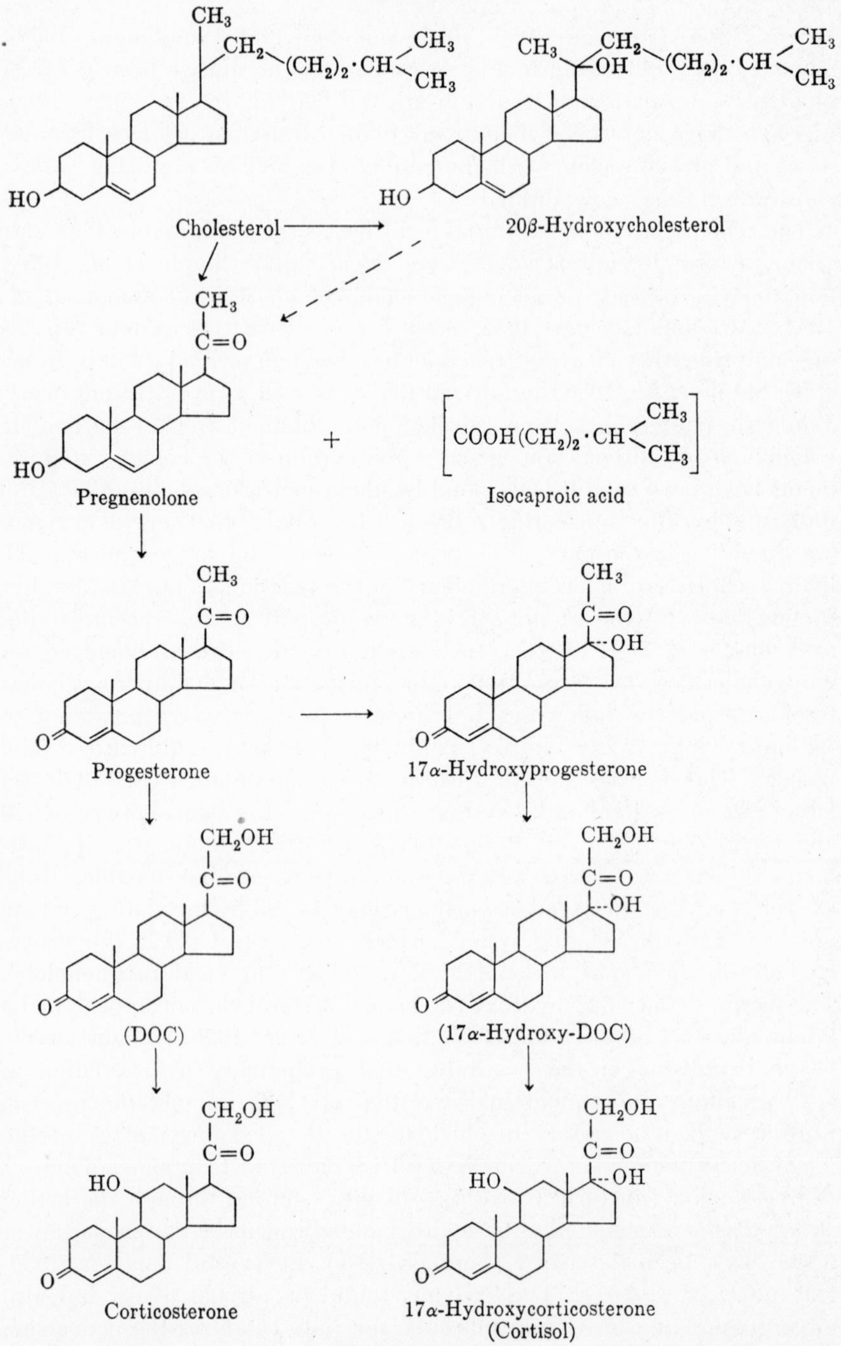

Fig. 3. Present sequence of cholesterol conversion to cortisol and corticosterone in bovine adrenal cortex tissue. The solid lines represent reactions which have been established definitively.

series, dehydroepiandrosterone (DHA) to androstenedione. In addition, the enzyme acts upon a variety of 3β-hydroxysteroids (in the C_{19} and C_{21} series) but is without effect upon 3α-hydroxysteroids. The 3β-hydroxy dehydrogenase, which requires DPN as cofactor, is noteworthy among dehydrogenases in that it does not promote a reversible reaction; thus the conversion of Δ^4-3 ketosteroids to Δ^5-3β hydroxy compounds is not achieved with this enzyme and DPNH.

As Fig. 3 indicates, progesterone is postulated to be a key intermediary. A bifurcation in the biosynthetic pathways occurs depending upon whether or not progesterone is hydroxylated at the C-17α position, so that cortisol and corticosterone, the end products, arise from separate pathways. If progesterone is 17-hydroxylated, sequential hydroxylations at C-21 and C-11β catalyzed by specific hydroxylating systems lead to the production of cortisol; alternatively, in the absence of 17-hydroxylation, sequential hydroxylations at C-21 and C-11β lead to the production of corticosterone. The evidence for a sequential order of hydroxylations for cortisol and corticosterone production in bovine tissue has previously been reviewed (Hechter and Pincus, 1954; Samuels, 1955) and need not be detailed here.

Since the adrenal enzyme systems which specifically introduce hydroxyl groups into C-11β, C-17α, and C-21 of the progesterone molecule have been recently reviewed (Hayano *et al.*, 1956a; Grant, 1956), we shall here only briefly summarize the salient details.* The conversion of progesterone to 17-hydroxyprogesterone is catalyzed by a 17-hydroxylase system, first demonstrated in the adrenal (Plager and Samuels, 1954, 1955) but subsequently found in testis (Slaunwhite and Samuels, 1956; Lynn, 1956; Lynn and Brown, 1956; Savard *et al.*, 1956) and ovary (Solomon *et al.*, 1956b). The conversion of 17-hydroxyprogesterone to 17-hydroxy-DOC, and of progesterone to DOC is mediated by a C-21 hydroxylase system. Recent evidence (Ryan, 1956; Ryan and Engel, 1956) indicates that at least two enzymes are involved in the C-21 hydroxylase system. Unlike the enzyme systems previously discussed, the C-21 hydroxylase system appears to be specific for adrenal tissue.

Finally, the conversion of 17-hydroxy-DOC to cortisol and of DOC to corticosterone is carried out by way of a C-11β hydroxylase system which also acts upon certain C_{19} steroids such as androstenedione (cf. Hayano *et al.*, 1956a). This hydroxylation system is rather specific for the adrenal

---

* In this discussion the enzyme systems which introduce hydroxyl groups into specific points of the steroid nucleus or side chain will be referred to as "hydroxylase systems"; no theoretical implications are involved in this designation which is employed merely for convenience, since it appears that these specific hydroxylations are complex processes involving at least two enzymes, if not more.

and has not been observed in other hormone-producing tissues from normal animals. Recent work has shown that the C-11β-hydroxylase system in the adrenal contains at least two enzymes, one of which can be replaced by an, as yet, unidentified enzyme also present in liver (Tomkins, 1956). The variable requirements of the C-11 hydroxylase system, studied at varying levels of organization ranging from intact mitochondria to purified preparations, have been the subject of discussion (cf. Hayano et al., 1956a). Here it will suffice to point out that as the enzyme system is successively purified, the nature of its requirements for activity is altered, and its specificity for steroids modified. Thus, using disrupted mitochondrial preparations, the system is relatively specific for DOC and 17-hydroxy-DOC; 17-hydroxyprogesterone, progesterone, and pregnenolone are not detectably converted to 11-hydroxylated products. Using intact mitochondria, where the enzyme system is localized, progesterone is 11-hydroxylated at rates far beyond those observed with disrupted mitochondrial preparations (Brownie et al., 1954), though the rates observed are still markedly less than those observed with DOC or 17-hydroxy-DOC as substrate (cf. Hayano et al., 1956a). Finally, Tomkins et al. (1957) has found that, as the C-11β hydroxylase system is further purified, differences in reactivity with DOC and 17-hydroxy-DOC begin to appear, suggesting that there may be separate enzymes for the 11-hydroxylation of each individual steroid.

Certain recent findings have indicated that pathways other than those of Fig. 3 may be operative in biosynthesis of corticosterone and cortisol; specifically, when it was reported that DOC could be converted to cortisol, the postulated sequence no longer became obligatory. The original report that DOC could give rise to cortisol came from the publication of Dorfman et al. (1953). After incubating C^{14}-DOC with bovine adrenal homogenates, these workers added carrier corticosterone and cortisol and found radioactivity not only in the isolated and purified corticosterone, but in the cortisol as well. While details concerning the radiochemical homogeneity of the cortisol isolated were not given, the yield of DOC conversion to cortisol was estimated to be about 2%, whereas the conversion of DOC to corticosterone in this system was of the order of 90–95%. More recently Heard et al. (1956) have reported that C^{14}-DOC is converted to cortisol in yields almost equivalent to those obtained for corticosterone in rat, rabbit, hog, as well as bovine preparations, (primarily tissue sections but including cell-free homogenates as well). Based, in part, upon these findings, an alternative sequence has been put forward by Dorfman (1955), strongly supported by Heard et al. (1956), wherein all possible orders of hydroxylations are considered likely.

In considering these findings, it must be emphasized that insufficient details are given in the publications of Heard and his associates (1956) to determine whether the radioactive zones isolated as cortisol from DOC incubation experiments were radiochemically homogeneous. From the details available in their publications, it would appear that the "cortisol" was isolated by paper chomatography in the propylene glycol–toluene system (20 hr., where it remained near the starting line); the subsequent failure of this eluted zone, in both free and acetylated state, to separate from authentic cortisol and its acetate on admixture chromatography was accepted as identity. While the technique described may be useful in delineating "tentative" identity, it is completely unsatisfactory as a method for establishing radiochemical homogeneity. The possibility thus arises that C^{14}-DOC was converted to a radioactive product of mobility similar to cortisol both in its free and acetylated forms in the limited systems employed, *but which is not cortisol*. That this may be the explanation for the results of Heard *et al.* (1956), is strongly indicated by the recent studies of Eichhorn and the author (1957). We have reinvestigated this problem by incubating trace quantities of DOC-4-C^{14} and progesterone-4-C^{14} with cell-free homogenates of cow adrenal cortex, prepared in three different media, which have the capacity to form sizable quantities of both cortisol and corticosterone from endogenous precursors. It was observed with these diverse media that whereas C^{14}-progesterone was incorporated into both the corticosterone and cortisol formed, C^{14}-DOC was not incorporated to a detectable extent into the cortisol formed, although its conversion to C^{14}-corticosterone was readily evident. Upon fractionation of the C^{14}-DOC incubation products, a considerable amount of radioactivity was observed during the preliminary paper chromatographic separation, which had mobility similar to cortisol. With further purification, however, the radioactivity associated with the cortisol zone disappeared; in marked contrast, the radioactivity of the cortisol zone derived from incubation with C^{14}-progesterone remained constant during these same fractionation procedures. While these experiments are not directly comparable to those of Heard *et al.* (1956), the studies cited raise the strong possibility that the "cortisol" isolated following incubation with DOC-21-C^{14} by Heard *et al.* may have been contaminated with C^{14} polar products other than cortisol.[*] Until it has been shown, using unequivocal techniques for the

---

[*] This explanation might help to explain another feature of the *in vitro* data of Heard and his associates (1956) which is completely at variance with *in vivo* results. From the analysis of adrenal vein blood of rats and rabbits it has been conclusively demonstrated that the principal corticosteroid secreted is corticosterone, with barely detectable amounts of cortisol. Nevertheless, Heard *et al.* have reported

demonstration of radiochemical homogeneity, that DOC is actually converted to cortisol, there would appear to be no need to postulate an alternative pathway of cortisol production via DOC.

Another point of uncertainty concerns the role of 11β-hydroxyprogesterone as an intermediary in the biosynthesis of cortisol and corticosterone. Originally it was considered not to be a *major* intermediary on the basis of adrenal perfusion experiments, wherein 11β-hydroxyprogesterone failed to give rise to significant amounts of cortisol or corticosterone (cf. Hechter and Pincus, 1954). Recent findings that 11β-hydroxyprogesterone is a major product of progesterone metabolism in adrenal mitochondria (Brownie *et al.*, 1954; Saba and Hechter, 1955) have served to reopen the possibility of its precursor role. The possibility exists that 11β-hydroxyprogesterone formed *intracellularly* functions as an intermediary, whereas on perfusion it is not readily transferred into the cells, hence its apparent inability to function as a precursor. To investigate this possibility, Eichhorn and the author (1958) have incubated *trace* amounts of 11β-hydroxyprogesterone-4-C^{14} with cell-free adrenal homogenates which produce corticoids from endogenous precursors and have studied the degree of incorporation of this steroid into the cortisol and corticosterone formed, relative to trace amounts of DOC-21-C^{14} and progesterone-4-C^{14}, studied in aliquots of the same homogenate. The results of these studies have demonstrated that while 11β-hydroxyprogesterone is capable of being converted to both cortisol and corticosterone by bovine adrenal tissue, the rate of 11β-hydroxyprogesterone conversion to cortisol is much slower than the rate of progesterone conversion to cortisol; similarly, the rate of corticosterone production from either progesterone or DOC is much greater than with 11β-hydroxyprogesterone. The conclusion, therefore, emerges that 11β-hydroxyprogesterone is not a *major* intermediary in the biosynthetic sequence in bovine glands.

With regard to 11,17-dihydroxyprogesterone (21-deoxycortisol), also postulated to be a possible intermediary in cortisol biosynthesis (Dorfman, 1955), our information is more limited. Until the rates of cortisol production from progesterone, 17-hydroxy-DOC, and 21-deoxycortisol are compared in systems of diverse organizational complexity, the significance of 21-deoxycortisol as a *major* intermediary in the biosynthesis of cortisol, while possible, remains questionable.

While the sequence illustrated in Fig. 3 is derived from studies in

---

that tissue sections of rabbit glands and quartered adrenals of rats incubated *in vitro* produce sizable amounts of "cortisol" as well as corticosterone. Identification of the cortisol by more definitive techniques than those employed would appear to be requisite before this conclusion can be accepted.

bovine glands, it may represent the major route of normal biosynthesis of cortisol and corticosterone in the adrenals of all species (cf. Hechter and Pincus, 1954), since certain major *in vivo* findings in other species can be best accounted for in terms of this sequence. Thus the *in vivo* findings (cf. Hechter and Pincus, 1954) that the adrenals of some species secrete cortisol almost exclusively (e.g. man, sheep, and monkey), while others secrete predominantly corticosterone (e.g. rat and rabbit), while still others (cow, dog, cat, and ferret) secrete mixtures of both cortisol and corticosterone, are explicable in terms of the sequence outlined, if the single assumption be made that in the competition for progesterone between the C-17α and C-21 hydroxylase systems, the C-17 hydroxylation system has a greater affinity for progesterone than does the C-21 hydroxylation system (Hechter, 1953b; Hechter and Pincus, 1954; Hayano *et al.*, 1956a). When the 17-hydroxylating system is present in high concentration, intracellular progesterone, formed at rates insufficient to saturate the 17-hydroxylating system, is converted primarily to 17-hydroxyprogesterone and then via 17-hydroxy DOC to cortisol (as in man, monkey, and sheep). If the rate of progesterone formation exceeds the capacity of the 17-hydroxylating system, then the remainder of the progesterone will be 21-hydroxylated and give rise to corticosterone in addition to cortisol (dog, cat, etc.). Finally, if the 17-hydroxylating system is absent (or inactive) the progesterone will be exclusively transformed through DOC to corticosterone (rat and rabbit). It has been suggested that the preferential hydroxylation of progesterone at C-17 (relative to C-21) may be due to spatial arrangements of the enzymes at the surface of a multienzyme sequence (Hayano *et al.*, 1956a).

Striking evidence that the sequence in Fig. 3 may be generalized is derived from recent studies in man. In 1950, when the consequences of the corticosteroidogenic sequence were discussed, it was predicted by Hechter *et al.* (1951) that certain diseases might involve specific adrenal hydroxylation systems, so that cortisol and/or corticosterone need not necessarily be the major end products present in the adrenocortical secretion. Specifically, it was pointed out that if the C-11β hydroxylase system were absent (or inhibited), 17-hydroxy-DOC and DOC would be the major corticosteroids released into the circulation, and the consequences of other "blocks" were clearly indicated. It now has been unequivocally established that in patients exhibiting the adrenogenital syndrome, such well-defined "blocks" in the corticosteroid biosynthetic sequence actually exist. In man, cortisol is normally the predominant steroid in the adrenocortical secretion; corticosterone is present in much lower amount (Pincus and Romanoff, 1955). Cortisol, thus, may be regarded as the "key hormone" involved in maintaining the normal feed-

back mechanism operative in the regulatory relationship between pituitary ACTH and the adrenal cortex, although other factors undoubtedly
play a role. In the adrenogenital syndrome defined by Wilkins (1952)
as a congenital adrenocortical hyperplasia, there is a deficiency in the
biosynthesis of cortisol, as evidenced by a variety of findings including
the markedly diminished excretion of the urinary metabolites of cortisol,
tetrahydrocortisol, and tetrahydrocortisone (cf. Eberlein and Bongiovanni, 1955a). Associated with this deficiency there appears to be an
excessive production of androgens, as reflected by high excretion of
urinary 17-ketosteroids. When it was established that the administration
of cortisone (or cortisol) to these patients reduced the elevated excretion of urinary 17-ketosteroids and produced a remission of the disease,
the concept developed that, as a consequence of inadequate production
of cortisol, the secretion of ACTH by the anterior pituitary was no
longer regulated and ACTH stimulated the adrenal gland to produce
and release steroids other than cortisol which give rise to circulating
androgens. Subsequent studies have revealed that the "block" in cortisol biosynthesis may involve either the C-21 or C-11β hydroxylation
steps, so that steroids which normally function as intermediaries in cortisol biosynthesis, are released into the circulation where they are, in
part, excreted in the urine as tetrahydro derivatives (cf. Fig. 4), and
in part, are secondarily metabolized by extra-adrenal systems to androgens. Thus, in many patients with the adrenogenital syndrome, large
quantities of pregnanetriol (pregnane-3α,17α,20α-triol) are character-
istically excreted in the urine (Bongiovanni et al., 1954; Eberlein and
Bongiovanni, 1955a); pregnanetriol is the tetrahydro derivative of 17α-
hydroxyprogesterone, and its abnormally large amounts present in urine
has been taken to suggest a C-21 hydroxylase system deficiency in the
conversion of 17α-hydroxyprogesterone to cortisol in these patients (cf.
Jailer, 1953; Jailer et al., 1955, as well). In still other patients, however,
when the disease is complicated by hypertension, large amounts of
tetrahydro-17-hydroxy-DOC (pregnane-3α,17α,21-triol-20-one) and smaller amounts of tetrahydro-DOC (pregnane-3α,21-diol-20-one) have been
found in the urine of these persons (Eberlein and Bongiovanni, 1955b).
Tetrahydro derivatives of 17-hydroxy-DOC and DOC are normally not
detected in the urine; their abnormal presence has led to the conclusion that, due to a deficiency of adrenal C-11β hydroxylase system in
these patients, 17-hydroxy-DOC and DOC are the major end products
of corticosteroidogenesis. The hypertension described as a complication
of the adrenogenital syndrome has been tentatively ascribed to the
secretion of DOC by the adrenal cortex (Bongiovanni and Eberlein,
1955). For other aspects of the disturbance in steroid metabolism related

to the adrenogenital syndrome, particularly the possibility that an excess of DHA production may be involved, the reader is referred to review articles of Dorfman (1953, 1955).

The sequence illustrated in Fig. 3 is also in accord with the basic finding that, *in vivo*, ACTH administration in the dog and cat rapidly increases the production of *both* cortisol and corticosterone without markedly influencing the ratio of cortisol to corticosterone (Bush, 1953),

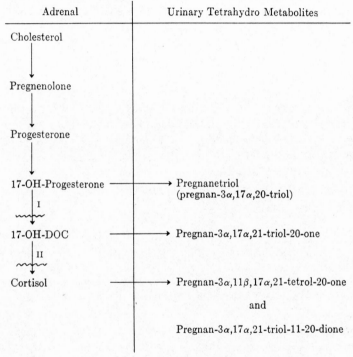

Adrenal	Urinary Tetrahydro Metabolites
Cholesterol	
↓	
Pregnenolone	
↓	
Progesterone	
↓	
17-OH-Progesterone ⟶	Pregnanetriol (pregnan-3α,17α,20-triol)
I	
17-OH-DOC ⟶	Pregnan-3α,17α,21-triol-20-one
II	
Cortisol ⟶	Pregnan-3α,11β,17α,21-tetrol-20-one
	and
	Pregnan-3α,17α,21-triol-11-20-dione

FIG. 4. Two possible sites of "block" in the biosynthetic pathway from cholesterol to cortisol; I is a "block" involving the C-21 hydroxylase system, II involving the C-11β hydroxylase system. Based upon alterations in the excretion of certain urinary metabolites in the adrenogenital syndrome, "blocks" in the biosynthetic sequence have been assumed to occur at either I or II in this disease (see text).

which is consistent only with a theory that both compounds are derived from a common intermediary and that ACTH acts on some point of the reaction sequence *before* the production of this common intermediary. In terms of our sequences, the last intermediary common to both cortisol and corticosterone is progesterone and the suggestion arises that ACTH must activate some step in the sequence between cholesterol and pregnenolone; the *in vitro* data on the point of action of ACTH in the perfused cow adrenal (Stone and Hechter, 1954; and cf. Hayano *et al.*, 1956a) independently point to the same conclusion.*

While the studies cited in the adrenogenital syndrome constitute striking support for the postulated biosynthetic sequence, further work in other species at both *in vitro* and *in vivo* levels is necessary to establish the general validity and the exclusiveness of the sequence illustrated. The finding in bovine adrenal homogenates that 11β-hydroxy-progesterone can be converted to both cortisol and corticosterone, albeit at minor rates relative to the "normal" intermediaries, indicates that alternative pathways are possible; in certain disease processes these may be operative. Thus, the finding of pregnane-3α-ol-11,20-dione (the tetra-hydro derivative of 11-ketoprogesterone) in the urine of patients with the adrenogenital syndrome (Lieberman and Dobriner, 1950) indicates that 11β-hydroxyprogesterone may be produced and released in rela-tively high amount from the adrenals of certain patients with this disease. Similarly, the finding of the tetrahydro derivative of 17-hydroxy-11-ketoprogesterone in the urine of certain patients receiving ACTH and cortisone (Dobriner and Lieberman, 1952) indicates the possibility that 21-deoxycortisol (11,17-dihydroxyprogesterone) may be released by the adrenals as well. Thus, in disease processes, the alternative possi-

---

* The view of Heard *et al.* (1956) that ACTH activates hydroxylation reactions, more particularly the conversion of DOC to "cortisol" is in direct contrast to the concept stated here. From a variety of considerations, both *in vivo* and *in vitro*, Heard's conclusion regarding ACTH action seems unsatisfactory. Thus, the data cited in the present paper concerning the metabolic alterations in the adrenogenital syndrome are consistent with only the theory that ACTH action upon the corticoid biosynthetic sequence must involve a step *prior* to hydroxylation at C-21 and C-11. Similarly, the data of Farrell *et al.* (1955) who showed that, following hypophysec-tomy in the dog, the rate of *in vivo* cortisol and corticosterone production fell propor-tionately to the same extent as their 11-deoxy intermediaries, 17-hydroxy-DOC and DOC, are consistent only with a theory that ACTH does not activate the 11-hydroxylation step. Without respect to *in vitro* data, the conclusion is clear that, in both the perfused gland and in homogenates, ACTH does not significantly in-fluence hydroxylations at C-17, C-21, or C-11 (cf. Hechter and Pincus, 1954; Stone and Hechter, 1954). There remains to be considered the significance of the ACTH effect upon DOC conversion to a more polar product, designated by Heard *et al.* (1956) as cortisol, which we have previously indicated is probably not cortisol. In the studies of Heard *et al.*, wherein ACTH effects are reported, sections of adrenal tissue were employed (not thin slices); the authors comment upon the marked inefficiency of this system to provide effective contact of enzyme and substrate. It seems clear that in preparations of this type the penetration of DOC into the cell, where the intracellular enzymes are located, might well be the rate-limiting reaction in DOC "hydroxylation"; if ACTH increased the entry of DOC into the cells of the thick adrenal section through one mechanism or another, the effect of ACTH re-ported upon hydroxylation enzymes might be explicable in terms which are con-sistent with other data in this field.

bilities of sequential hydroxylations indicated by Dorfman (1955) may well be operative; to what degree remains for future investigation.

C. CONVERSION OF CHOLESTEROL TO ALDOSTERONE

Recently it has been demonstrated that cholesterol is a precursor of aldosterone. The author, N. Saba, and J. Eichhorn in this laboratory, in association with P. J. Ayres, S. A. S. Tait, and J. T. Tait at the Middlesex Hospital, London, have demonstrated that cholesterol-4-C^{14} incubated with a mitochondrial preparation of cow adrenal cortex tissue, contaminated with adsorbed microsomal and supernate enzymes yields radioactive aldosterone; in this case the aldosterone was isolated and rigorously purified until it was radiochemically homogeneous.

Since aldosterone is corticosterone with an aldehyde function at the angular methyl group at C-18, it is reasonable to consider the biosynthesis of this mineralocorticoid as an offshoot of the sequence in Fig. 3 for corticosterone and cortisol production. On this view, following hydroxylation at C-18, and subsequent oxidation to an 18-aldehyde (by a suitable dehydrogenase), aldosterone could arise from corticosterone, DOC (C-11β hydroxylation following C-18 oxidation) or progesterone (hydroxylations at both C-11β and C-21 following C-18 oxidation).

The available studies undertaken to differentiate between these possible routes indicate only that *all* may be involved. Thus, Kahnt *et al.* (1955a) reported that DOC could be converted to aldosterone by fortified bovine adrenal homogenates, but no evidence for similar conversion of progesterone or corticosterone was obtainable under these conditions (Wettstein and Anner, 1954). In later studies, Kahnt *et al.* (1955b) after incubation of DOC with bovine adrenal homogenates, isolated 18-hydroxy-DOC, a logical intermediate in the conversion of DOC to aldosterone. However, in experiments involving the perfusion of an artificial medium through calf adrenals, Rosemberg *et al.* (1956) reported that progesterone, but not DOC or corticosterone, was converted to aldosterone. To complete the cycle of possibilities Ayres *et al.*, (1957) found with incubation of *trace* quantities of various C^{14}-labeled substrates and capsule strippings of ox adrenals (previously shown by Ayres *et al.*, 1956) to produce corticosterone and aldosterone but little or no cortisol) that progesterone-4-C^{14}, DOC-21-C^{14}, and corticosterone-4-C^{14} were *all* converted to aldosterone; the specific activities of the aldosterone and corticosterone isolated at the end of the experiment with each substrate were of the same order of magnitude. In these capsule stripping experiments, much smaller quantities of substrates were employed than in other studies and radiochemically homogeneous aldosterone was isolated by microchemical procedures rather than by measuring increases produced by steroid addition over the aldosterone produced from endogenous sources.

The available *in vitro* work summarized in Fig. 5 indicates that progesterone, DOC, and corticosterone may all serve as precursors of aldosterone but does not permit any conclusions regarding the precise sequence involved. Studies in progress involving a comparison of specific activities of the aldosterone and corticosterone formed, studied on a kinetic basis, should provide data to differentiate between the various possible routes. Moreover, if the enzymology of the "C-18 oxidase" system could be unraveled in terms of the individual enzymes involved, this might help to clarify the problem of which of these alternative pathways is primarily operative.

There remains to be considered the regulation of aldosterone production in relation to the pathways illustrated in Fig. 5. In contrast to the production of cortisol and corticosterone which has clearly been shown to be under the influence of ACTH (cf. Hechter and Pincus, 1954), the regulation of aldosterone production is completely dissimilar in that it appears to be largely independent of pituitary control (cf. Luetscher, 1956a, b). Regulation of aldosterone production by electrolytes, as well as changes in extracellular fluid volume (EFV), have been suggested (cf. Luetscher, 1956a, b); such regulatory factors may either be operative upon the adrenal cortex directly as has been suggested in the case of ions (Rosenfeld *et al.*, 1956; Giroud *et al.*, 1956; but cf. Luetscher, 1956a, in this regard), or involve the intermediary of a humoral factor, elaborated by the diencephalon, which appears to act as a trophic hormone with regard to aldosterone production (Rauschkolb and Farrell, 1956).

The interesting studies of Muller *et al.* (1956a, 1956b) afford an alternative view of ACTH action to regulate aldosterone secretion. A homeostatic mechanism related to changes in EFV, but independent of ACTH, is believed to be an important factor in regulating aldosterone production; as the EFV expands, the urinary excretion of aldosterone is decreased; contrariwise, EFV contraction stimulates aldosterone excretion. According to Muller *et al.* (1956b), ACTH does stimulate aldosterone production as evidenced by urinary studies, but this effect is often masked by the operation of the homeostatic mechanism referred to. In any case, it is clear that, if the views of Muller *et al.* (1956b) are correct in their essentials, the apparent lack of influence of ACTH upon aldosterone production is explicable without resort to any modifications of the biosynthetic sequences proposed.

A second feature of aldosterone biosynthesis may be related to the "apparent" independence of aldosterone production to ACTH stimulation. This arises from the fact that aldosterone is a "trace" component relative to cortisol and/or corticosterone. If the "C-18 oxidase" system involved in aldosterone production has a *low capacity and is easily saturated with steroid substrate* (whether operative upon progesterone, DOC, or corticosterone is not pertinent to this discussion), it is easy to visualize how trace amounts of aldosterone could be produced relatively independent of ACTH. The production of aldosterone would be little influenced in the absence of ACTH because even when progesterone, DOC, and corticosterone are formed at a decreased rate, the 18-

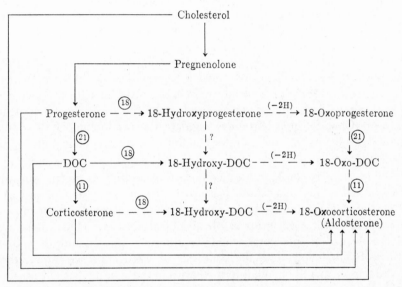

FIG. 5. Some possible routes of cholesterol conversion to aldosterone. The solid lines represent reactions which have been definitively established; the dotted lines without question marks represent probable reactions which have not been demonstrated; the dotted lines with question marks, represent reactions which though possible are regarded as unlikely.

oxidase system might still tend to be saturated. Alternatively, when these substrates are increased as the result of ACTH action, the 18-oxidase system, being nearly saturated, would not respond with a marked increase in the formation of aldosterone. Whether the views of Muller *et al.* (1956b) or the alternative suggested here is the primary explanation of the apparent lack of effect of ACTH upon aldosterone regulation remains for future investigation. On the other hand, the question as to how the diencephalon factor of Farrell (or changes in EFV) influences aldosterone production is less clear. Ultimately, the influence of these factors would appear to be directed at the 18-oxidase system in the cells of the zona glomerulosa, since this is the site where aldosterone is produced (cf. Ayres *et al.*, 1956); there the regulatory factors presumably control the rate of aldosterone production by influencing either the *availability, capacity,* or *synthesis* of the 18-oxidase system.

IV. Androgens

A. NATURE OF THE ANDROGENS SECRETED BY TESTIS AND ADRENAL

The testis is the classic source of "masculinity," although androgens are produced in other organs, because the testis androgens secreted into the circulation normally constitute the major portion of the pool of circulating "androgenic activity." Testosterone, the most active androgen, together with androstenedione, another potent androgen, have been demonstrated in the venous effluent of the dog testis (West *et al.*, 1952) and testosterone has been identified in spermatic vein blood of humans (Lucas *et al.*, 1957); present information is consistent with the view that testosterone is a major secretory product of the testis in other species as well. Gonadotropic hormones regulate the production of the androgens by influencing the secretory activity of the Leydig cells of the testis (Leach *et al.*, 1956).

While there is considerable evidence that androgens are produced in the adrenal cortex, ovary, and perhaps in the placenta, as well as in the liver, the contribution of these sources to the circulating "androgen pool" is normally limited in terms of physiological activity. Thus, in the case of the ovary and placenta, where testosterone and/or androstenedione are probably involved in the synthesis of estrogens (see later), these androgens are, in the main, intermediaries in the synthesis of C_{18} phenolic end products. In the case of the adrenal cortex, there is direct evidence for trace amounts of androstenedione, 11β-hydroxyandrostenedione, and DHA in the adrenal venous blood of humans (Romanoff *et al.*, 1953; Pincus and Romanoff, 1955; Bush *et al.*, 1956) and in the case of the dog, analysis of adrenal vein blood reveals evidence for the first two of these steroids and adrenosterone (Hechter *et al.*, 1955). Since 11-oxygenated 17-ketosteroids (17KS) are "weak androgens" relative to 11-deoxy 17KS (cf. Dorfman and Shipley, 1956), the direct physiological contribution by the adrenal to the circulating androgen pool is normally minimal. In addition to the C_{19} steroids released directly into the circulation, the adrenal cortex may contribute indirectly to the androgen pool; this arises because certain C_{21} steroids, which do not of themselves possess androgenic activity may be converted (in large part by the liver) to androgenic steroids (cf. Dorfman, 1955). In this group are cortisol (and its metabolite, cortisone) and other 17-hydroxylated products which might be released, such as 17-hydroxyprogesterone and 17-hydroxy-DOC; the 17 KS resulting from the latter two steroids are potent 11-deoxy androgens, whereas cortisol (or cortisone) degradation would give rise to the "weak" 11-oxygenated androgens. Normally, these latter steroids are released in trace amount. However, under certain conditions, e.g. adrenogenital syndrome, the release of 17-hydroxyprogesterone and 17-hydroxy-DOC from the adrenal into the circulation may be excessive; in such cases these C-21 steroids might be secondarily converted into active androgens (cf. Jailer, 1953; Dorfman, 1955). In adrenal hyperplasia or in adrenal tumors, there may be sufficient production of adrenal androgens contributed directly to the circulation, particularly DHA, to cause overt masculinization in females (cf. Dorfman and Shipley, 1956). Although it is difficult precisely to define the regulatory factors in adrenal androgen production in view of both its direct and indirect contribution to the androgen pool, the evidence available suggests that ACTH may be the primary regulator of the adrenal androgen production, since inhibition of exogenous ACTH in the adrenogenital syndrome by cortisone reduces the elevated androgen titers (Wilkins, 1952).

B. Conversion of Cholesterol to Androgens in Adrenal

The direct conversion in the adrenal of cholesterol to androgens (androstenedione and 11β-hydroxyandrostenedione) has been demonstrated in bovine adrenal tissue (E. Bloch, private communication). Moreover, progesterone, demonstrated to be derived from cholesterol in the corticosteroidogenic sequence previously discussed, has unequivocally been shown to be converted to androgens in the adrenal. Thus, following the perfusion of progesterone-4-C^{14} through bovine adrenals, radioactive 11β-hydroxyandrostenedione was isolated (Kushinsky, 1955); upon incubation of C^{14}-progesterone with cell-free adrenal homogenates, C^{14}-androstenedione was detected (Rao and Heard, 1957). The scission of the side chain by a C-17,20 desmolase system probably involves preliminary 17-hydroxylation, as has been shown in androgen biosynthesis by testis (to be discussed in the next section).

In addition to the pathway via C_{21} intermediaries, Dorfman (1953, 1955, 1956, 1957) has suggested an alternative route wherein cholesterol is cleaved directly to form DHA, the C_{19} equivalent of pregnenolone. DHA, in turn, could be converted to the remaining adrenal androgens by enzymes known to be present in the adrenal. While no definite statements can be made as to whether both of these pathways are operative, Fig. 6 is a scheme illustrating these alternative sequences. The key to the problem involves DHA. If pregnenolone and 17-hydroxypregnenolone are not precursors of DHA (while such reactions have not been demonstrated this does not mean that this may not eventually be achieved), then the key precursor role postulated by Dorfman is almost certainly correct. Meanwhile, Dorfman and Shipley (1956) have summarized an impressive list of indirect evidence consistent with the view that DHA arises independently of C_{21} intermediaries.

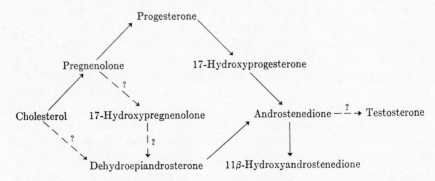

FIG. 6.   Conversion of cholesterol to adrenal androgens. The solid lines represent reactions which have been definitively established. The reactions illustrated as dotted lines with a question mark are regarded as possible.

C. Conversion of Cholesterol to Androgens in Testis

A pathway for the biosynthesis of testicular androgens in rat and human testis has been established (Fig. 7). The route is similar to that found in the adrenal and consists of the formation of testosterone and androstenedione by way of pregnenolone, progesterone, and 17α-hydroxyprogesterone (Slaunwhite and Samuels, 1956; Lynn, 1956; Savard et al., 1956). Lynn and Brown (1956) have shown that rat testicular particles, which convert progesterone via 17-hydroxyprogesterone to androgens plus acetic acid, do not cleave the side chain of 17-hydroxy-DOC.

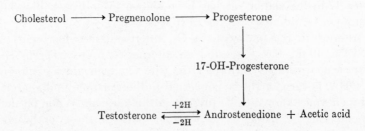

FIG. 7.   Conversion of cholesterol to testis androgens. All of the reactions have now been demonstrated (see text).

V. Estrogens

A. Nature of Estrogens Produced

The ovary is the principal site of estrogen production in the non-pregnant female; the cyclic production of estrogens is dependent in largest part upon the ovarian response to the pituitary gonadotropins, follicle-stimulating hormone (FSH), and luteinizing hormone (LH). Although the nature of the estrogens released from the ovary into the circulation has not been definitely identified, it is generally agreed that the hormones involved are 17β-estradiol and/or estrone which have been isolated from ovarian tissue and the urine from various species (for reference cf. Dorfman and Ungar, 1953; Dorfman, 1955). The weaker estrogen, estriol, isolated from urine is known from metabolic studies in intact animals to arise from estradiol and estrone as follows:

$$17β\text{-estradiol} \rightleftarrows \text{estrone} \rightarrow \text{estriol}.$$

Estrogens have been isolated from bovine adrenal and while small amounts may be produced by the adrenal cortex in the female as well as the male, the amount released from the adrenal into the circulation is normally insufficient to overcome estrogen deficiency following oopherectomy. In the male, the testis seems unquestionably to be a source of estrogens; indeed, stallion testis is the richest tissue source of 17β-estradiol and estrone. In pregnancy the principal source of estrogens is the placenta, and the ovary, in certain species at least, is of secondary importance. In the urine of the pregnant mare certain ring B unsaturated phenols, which are very weak estrogens, have been isolated: these include equilin and equilenin (for references, cf. Dorfman and Ungar, 1953).

B. Conversion of Cholesterol to Estrogens

On the basis of recent studies, it is now established that cholesterol is a precursor of estrogens.[*] Recently, it has been shown in humans that cholesterol is converted to estrone, *in vivo* (Werbin et al., 1957). Previously, it had been shown in ovarian tissue that cholesterol is converted to progesterone (Solomon et al., 1956b); that progesterone is converted by bovine ovarian tissue homogenates to 17-hydroxyprogesterone and androstenedione (Solomon et al., 1956b); and that androstenedione is converted to estrogen in various tissues including ovary, placenta, and the adrenal (Meyer, 1955a, b). Testosterone, which can be oxidized to

---

[*] Although it was first claimed by Heard et al. (1954) that cholesterol is not a precursor of the estrogens, as evidenced by the failure of C^{14}-cholesterol administered in the pregnant mare to be incorporated into the urinary estrogens, subsequent reconsideration of the data has led to the retraction of this view (Heard et al., 1955).

androstenedione, was shown in another study to be converted to estradiol in human ovarian tissue, stallion testis (a known source of estrogenic steroids), and in a feminizing adrenal tumor (Baggett *et al.*, 1955, 1956). Heard *et al.* (1955) have added confirmatory *in vivo* evidence of the latter reaction and West *et al.* (1956) have shown that this conversion can occur in humans even in the absence of the ovaries and adrenals. These results are consistent with sequence illustrated in Fig. 8.

The key to the mechanism of the conversion of androgens to estrogens came from Meyer's study (1955a, b) wherein it was demonstrated that

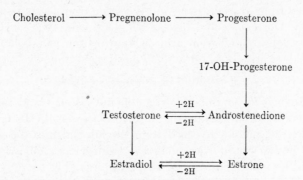

Fig. 8. Conversion of cholesterol to estrogens. All of the reactions shown have now been demonstrated in ovarian tissue (see text).

androstenedione was converted to 19-hydroxyandrostenedione, thus opening the way for the removal of the angular carbon at position 19. Meyer found in addition that the 19-hydroxy derivative was converted to estrogens more rapidly than Δ^4-androstenedione, whereas the rates with 19-nortestosterone or $\Delta^{1,4}$-androstadien-3,17-dione were lower than with androstenedione. Whereas Heard *et al.* (1956) consider the most likely scheme of aromatization to be the removal of C-19 (following oxidation of 19-hydroxy to 19-oxo) as formaldehyde, Dorfman (1956) believes that the results of Meyer are consistent with another pathway, wherein the angular methyl group is oxidized further to a carboxyl (removed as CO_2) and an additional dehydrogenation (believed to involve hydroxylation at C-1 or 2, followed by dehydration) is postulated to occur prior to removal of the CO_2.

VI. The Problem of Alternative Pathways Involved in Steroid Hormone Biosynthesis

As the precursor role of cholesterol in steroid hormone biosynthesis was being established, the question was immediately raised: is cholesterol an obligatory intermediate in steroid hormone formation? In the case of corticosteroids (Hechter, 1952, 1953a; Hechter *et al.*, 1953; Stone and Hechter, 1954), androgens (Brady, 1951; Hellman *et al.*, 1952; Dorfman, 1955), and estrogens (Heard *et al.*, 1956), suggestive data were obtained which indicated that cholesterol need not be an obligatory intermediate in steroid hormone biosynthesis from acetate-C^{14}. While these preliminary suggestions are open to alternative explanations, stronger suggestive evidence in favor of an alternative pathway of corticosteroid biosynthesis has been recently obtained by Heard and his associates (1956). They have reported that cell-free homogenates of hog adrenals convert acetate-1-C^{14} to various corticosteroids, including cortisol and corticosterone, under conditions wherein acetate is not converted to C^{14}-cholesterol in detectable amount (i.e. the cholesterol of the adrenal system is not detectably labeled, though it is easily isolatable); the same homogenate, however, converts cholesterol-to-4-C^{14} to corticosteroid products. The alternative (noncholesterol) pathway, suggested by these studies, although not definitively established in any single case,[*]

---

[*] The major evidence which has been taken to indicate that an alternative (noncholesterol) pathway might exist arises from experiments wherein following C^{14}-acetate, the steroids formed had a higher specific activity (SA) than the cholesterol isolated. The homogenate experiments of Heard *et al.* cited, wherein radioactive steroids are obtained from C^{14}-acetate without detectable labeling of the cholesterol in the system, are not fundamentally different in principle from the previous studies, but merely represent the most clear-cut differentiation between the SA of the steroid hormones and cholesterol yet reported. Two basic problems arise in considering the significance of this type of data as regards the existence of a separate pathway (previously discussed in Hechter, 1953a): the first relates to the fact that comparison of the SA of cholesterol and steroid hormones, in all the studies cited, was not examined on a kinetic basis. This type of comparison is requisite, since it is known from theoretical considerations that the SA of a reaction product under certain conditions may be significantly higher than that of its precursor; this depends upon the point in the SA curve of precursor and its immediate reaction product which is chosen for analysis (Zilversmit *et al.*, 1943). The second is more difficult to evaluate; it arises from the possibility that while there may be diverse metabolic "pools" of cholesterol, only one of which is operative in steroid hormone biosynthesis, our present methods of fractionating tissue cholesterol separate it only into two major fractions—"free" and "esterified." Since the SA of the cholesterol isolated is thus operationally limited, it is apparent that the SA of a cholesterol fraction need bear no necessary quantitative relationship to the "active" cholesterol pool postulated. These considerations may be applied to the work of Heard *et al.* Thus, it is possible that C^{14}-acetate could condense to form trace amounts of radioactive cholesterol

is of sufficient probability to invite speculation as to its possible nature. At the outset, it may be mentioned that the possibility of an alternative pathway in bile acid formation has been considered by Staple and Gurin (1954).

If we postulate that acetate might be converted both to cholesterol and to corticoids (without involving cholesterol as intermediary) it is apparent that at some point in these biosynthetic sequences, an intermediary common to both pathways is involved, which we may designate as X. Thus:

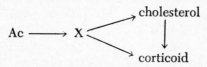

The question next arises whether X may not be involved in a generalized way in the synthesis of diverse steroid hormones and in bile acids as well, in the following manner:

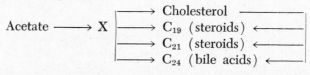

This speculation gives rise to the question of the nature of X, and more particularly to the question of the specific intermediaries between C_2 and X. For the answer to this, it is necessary to consider the recent concepts of the biosynthesis of cholesterol.

It is now established that all of the carbons of cholesterol, isolated from liver, may be derived from acetate carbon. The generally accepted scheme of cholesterol biosynthesis, in its essence, involves the condensation of three C_2 units (derived from acetate) to form a branched-chain intermediate of 5 (or 6) carbon atoms related to isoprene, which may be mevalonic acid (Tavormina *et al.*, 1956); the condensation of these "isoprene" units to form a triterpene chain, squalene; the formation of

---

at specific sites, wherein it was directly converted to steroid hormones. Under these circumstances the C^{14}-cholesterol would not accumulate or "mix" with nonlabeled cholesterol in the system. Cholesterol when analyzed would not be detectably labeled in this hypothetical case even if cholesterol, formed from acetate, had been the immediate precursor of the radioactive hormone synthesized. The foregoing remarks are introduced merely to illustrate the difficulties involved in establishing the definitive existence of an alternative (noncholesterol) pathway. The author feels that the alternative pathway is likely, despite the reservations indicated. This is a prejudice on his part which arises from a biological background which suggests that, given an important function for survival, Nature does not appear to rely on a unitary pathway.

the steroidal ring system by folding and cyclization of the aliphatic hydrocarbon to form lanosterol, and the elimination of three methyl groups to form cholesterol (C_{27}) (cf. Chapter 6). We may accept as established the fact that squalene and lanosterol do go to cholesterol; the question whether squalene need be considered an obligatory intermediary is another problem, and the answer to this is not clear. Popják (1954) for example, has put forth strong suggestive evidence that squalene may not be an obligatory intermediary in cholesterol synthesis; moreover, the fact that squalene content of similar tissues in different species is so markedly dissimilar, raises the question as to whether squalene may not serve some biological role in addition to acting as a sterol precursor. The high squalene content of fish liver relative to mammalian liver is paralleled by the fact that yeast contains large amounts of squalene and ergosterol, whereas *Neurospora*, which also synthesizes ergosterol, contains only traces (or no) squalene at all (Stone, Nussbaum and Hechter, unpublished work). This gives rise to the possibility, as Popják has suggested, that when high squalene levels are encountered in tissues, squalene may be primarily an end product, and not just an intermediary in sterol synthesis.

With these considerations in mind, it is possible to approach the problem of our hypothetical unit X by inquiring first whether the "isoprene unit" need necessarily condense to form squalene, presumably by a head to head condensation of two 15-carbon isoprenoid units. The literature of terpenes isolated from natural sources indicates that, in Nature, the isoprene unit can condense in innumerable ways (e.g. C_{10}, C_{15}, C_{20}). Since the active C_5 (or C_6) unit is presumably formed as a result of the following reactions:

$$
\begin{aligned}
&(1) \ \text{Acetate} &&\longrightarrow C_2 \\
&(2) \ C_2 + C_2 &&\longrightarrow C_4 \\
&(3) \ C_4 + C_2 &&\longrightarrow C_6 \\
&(4) \ C_6 &&\longrightarrow C_5 + C_1
\end{aligned}
$$

it is likely that C_5 (or C_6) starts to condense in the presence of C_2 and C_4 units, and that these units might participate in the condensation at some point. For example, let us consider the condensation of 4 isoprene units head to tail, head to tail, head to head (as in abeitic acid, 1-pimaric acid, ferruginol, etc.), to give the C_{20} isoprenoid unit illustrated in Fig. 9. As illustrated, this structure might condense with C_2 to form a structure (C_{22}) which after removal of three methyl carbons, and shifting of the methyl to form the angular methyl at C-18 (steroid series), could give rise to a C_{19} steroid. With C_4 it could give a C_{24} unit, and through a similar mechanism give C_{21} steroids; with C_5, then C_2 to give rise to a C_{27} hydrocarbon which gives rise to bile acids (C_{24}). In each case the distribution of carbon, whether from methyl or carboxyl of acetate, would be identical with that predicted from the known distribution of acetate carbon in cholesterol and squalene. It is apparent that comparison of the specific activity of specific carbons of biosynthetically produced steroid hormones or bile acids with the distribution of the comparable carbon in cholesterol would not differentiate between product synthesized via X (independent of cholesterol) or as a result of degradation of cholesterol. In this connection the finding that C-20 and C-21 in the corticoid side chain of cortisol, corticosterone, and $3\alpha,17\alpha,21$-

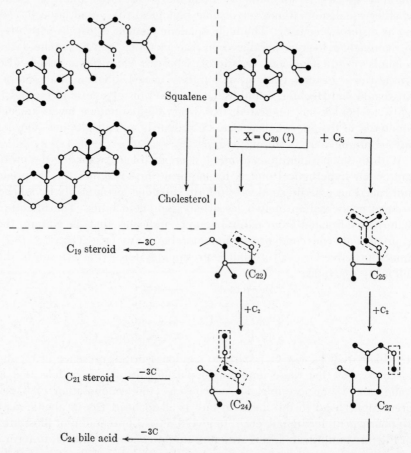

Fig. 9. A speculative sequence for alternative (noncholesterol) routes of synthesis of steroid hormones and bile acids from acetate, wherein a key intermediary X is postulated to be a C_{20} isoprenoid unit. The distribution of acetate carbon in squalene (Woodward-Bloch scheme) and in X is illustrated: Methyl carbons (●), carboxyl carbon (O).

trihydroxypregnane-20-one produced biosynthetically from acetate-C^{14} (Caspi *et al.*, 1956, 1957), as well as the C-24 of biosynthetic cholic acid (Staple and Gurin, 1954), are identical to that predicted from the Woodward-Bloch scheme for incorporation of acetate into cholesterol does not distinguish between these possibilities.

There is another feature of this speculative sequence which bears discussion. This relates to the postulation of condensation of small units (C_2) upon a polyisoprenoid unit (C-20); it may be mentioned that the adherents of the squalene-cholesterol hypothesis have shown that to form ergosterol, a one-carbon unit is utilized (Chapter 6), and to give rise to the C_{29} phytosterols the condensation of a C_2 unit or two C_1 units would be necessary. Thus, in principle, some mechanism of this type would appear to be obligatory to account for the biosynthesis of sterols generally. If condensations of small units (C_1 or C_2) may occur at a C-30 stage, there would appear to be no special difficulty in visualizing this at an earlier C-20 stage.

The scheme wherein an unknown is postulated as a key intermediary in steroid synthesis is completely speculative, and the available data are open to alternative explanations. Nevertheless, if progress is to be made concerning the alternative pathways suggested in the biosynthesis of steroid hormones, some concept should be put forward to serve as an inflammatory stimulant, if nothing more. It is of some interest that from a consideration of the available data on the biosynthesis of estrogens, Dorfman (1956) has been led to the independent suggestion that the ring B unsaturated estrogens (equilin and equilenin) may be derived from the condensation of an ethyl toluene residue plus a C_{10} isoprenoid unit.

VII. Concluding Remarks

Within the past few years a problem which had resisted solution for several decades, has in large part been dispatched, thanks to the development of powerful new tools. With a well-developed concept available, it may safely be predicted that the remaining gaps in our knowledge concerning the route of cholesterol conversion to steroid hormones will be filled in. With the application of modern techniques of enzyme chemistry, detailed understanding of the enzymology of each of the individual steps in the various biosynthetic sequences may be expected as has been achieved notably in the case of the C-11β hydroxylation reaction. Though still short of the final goal, the partial successes achieved in understanding the enzymology of this step indicate that no special difficulties at a conceptual level are present. Concerning the postulated alternative pathway of steroid hormone biosynthesis which does not involve cholesterol, although the present picture is vague, here again there would appear to be no conceptual barrier which cannot be hurdled if the available techniques are exploited.

When, however, we come to the question of how steroid biosynthetic sequences are regulated in living cells by specific trophic hormones, our forecast is less certain. In this area our understanding is limited not only by insufficient data, but the need for new unifying ideas and concepts. The available data indicate only that "something more" than is encompassed by the chemical reactions of a sequence (despite the detailed inclusion of enzymes and cofactors) is involved in the *regulation* and *direction* of metabolic pathways in the living cell. Consider in this connection the various steroid hormone biosynthetic sequences in the adrenal cortex, testis, corpus luteum, and ovary, which produce as end products, corticosteroids, androgens, progesterone, and estrogens, respectively. Our inquiry has revealed that in the various sequences most of the enzyme steps present in each of these endocrine tissues are basically similar; the differences in end products depend on the presence or absence of a few specific hydroxylating or oxidative systems. How, then, is specificity of trophic hormone action achieved? More particularly, how does ACTH specifically activate corticosteroid hormone production without influencing progesterone secretion from the corpus luteum or testosterone (and androstenedione) secretion from the testis, or estrogen secretion from the ovary? Similar questions arise in the case of gonadotropic hormone action directed only at the testis and ovary, and for luteotropin hormone action specifically upon the corpus luteum. There is no evidence that hormone specificity is the result of hormone action upon enzymes specific to the target organ. Indeed, in the case of ACTH action, where our knowledge is most advanced, it is clear that ACTH activates an early step in the sequence between cholesterol and pregnenolone, which normally is the rate-limiting reaction, and this is precisely the area that is common to all of the sequences of steroid hormone biosynthesis. Nor is this our only difficulty. Each of the pituitary trophic hormones discussed, in addition to activating specific steroid biosynthetic sequences, also promotes cell *growth* in its respective target organ. At a minimum, growth may be defined as the synthesis of each of the characteristic components of specifically differentiated cells (we are aware, of course, that growth involves more than merely a collection of biosynthetic reactions). This must mean that in each target organ, the trophic hormone activates every biosynthetic sequence characteristic for the cell (i.e. nucleoproteins, proteins, carbohydrates, lipoids, etc.), and it must do this specifically for cells in one endocrine organ but not in the closely related cells of another organ. If I have chosen to emphasize our conceptual ignorance of the fundamental mechanism of action of hormones, this is because, in my opinion, the first step toward knowledge in this area is to recognize our need for a concept of sufficient breadth to encompass the problem in its entirety.

Since this volume is concerned with cholesterol, this discussion should not close without mention of the possible relationship of the findings reviewed in this chapter to the problem of the physiological role of cholesterol in steroid hormone-producing cells. The question arises whether cholesterol in these tissues primarily plays a precursor role, wherein it functions as a storage form of preformed steroid nuclei to supply trace amounts of hormones as needed, or whether it serves some other function as well. There are sufficient data in the case of the adrenal cortex to indicate that cholesterol may do more than serve as a precursor of steroid hormones. The content of adrenal cholesterol in the rat is about 4%; following maximal doses of ACTH, this value declines 50% (or more) in 3 hours (Long, 1947). Let us assume that a pair of rat adrenals weighs 30 mg.; ignoring any possible contribution of blood cholesterol to the adrenal content, the rate of cholesterol disappearance in a pair of adrenals due to ACTH is of the order of 200 µg. or 5.0×10^{-4} mM. per hour. According to Vogt (1955), the production of corticosteroids (primarily corticosterone) by rat adrenals *in vivo*, maximally stimulated by ACTH, is about 32 µg. per min. per gram adrenal (corrected for losses due to extraction). Assuming that the corticoid formed is derived exclusively from adrenal cholesterol, this corresponds to the production of about 50 µg. or 1.4×10^{-4} mM per hour per pair of adrenals. In other words, only about a quarter of the cholesterol which disappears in the rat adrenal as the result of ACTH action is accounted for in terms of conversion to corticosteroid. What happens to the other three-quarters of the adrenal cholesterol which disappears? This question is raised to indicate that while one aspect of cholesterol function in certain specific steroid hormone-producing cells has been solved, much remains to be learned concerning other possible functions of cholesterol in these cells. Perhaps elucidation of these "other functions" in the adrenal cortex will help to clarify the role which cholesterol must play in generalized cellular function, if the ubiquitous distribution of this sterol in mammalian cells is to become meaningful in biological terms.

References

(*Asterisk denotes review article or monograph*)

*Antognetti, L., Adezati, L., Pende, G., and Scopinaro, D. (1955). "Sindromi Cliniche da Alterato Metabolismo Ormonico Steroides" N.16 Collana di Monografie dell' Archivio. "E. Maragliano," Genova.

Ayres, P. J., Gould, R. P., Simpson, S. A., and Tait, J. F. (1956). *Biochem. J.* **63**, 19 p.

Ayres, P. J., Hechter, O., Saba, N., Tait, S. A. S., and Tait, J. F. (1957). *Biochem. J.* **65**, 22 p.

Baggett, B., Engel, L. L., Savard, K., and Dorfman, R. I. (1955). *Federation Proc.* **14**, 175.

Baggett, B., Engel, L. L., Savard, K., and Dorfman, R. I. (1956). *J. Biol. Chem.* **221**, 931.

Beyer, K. F., and Samuels, L. T. (1956). *J. Biol. Chem.* **219**, 69.

Bloch, K. (1945). *J. Biol. Chem.* **157**, 661.

Bongiovanni, A. M., and Eberlein, W. R. (1955). *Pediatrics* **16**, 628.

Bongiovanni, A. M., Eberlein, W. R., and Cara, J. (1954). *J. Clin. Endocrinol. and Metabolism* **14**, 409.

Brady, R. O. (1951). *J. Biol. Chem.* **193**, 145.

Brodie, B. B., Axelrod, J., Cooper, J. R., Gaudette, L. T., La Du, B. N., Mitoma C., and Udenfriend, S. (1955). *Science* **121**, 603.

Brownie, A. C., Grant, J. K., and Davidson, D. W. (1954). *Biochem. J.* **58**, 218.

Burton, R. B., and Zaffaroni, A. (1951). *J. Biol. Chem.* **188**, 763.

Bush, I. E. (1952). *Biochem. J.* **50**, 370.

Bush, I. E. (1953). *Ciba Colloquia Endocrinol.* **7**, 210.

Bush, I. E., Swale, L., and Patterson, J. (1956). *Biochem. J.* **62**, 168.

Caspi, E., Rosenfeld, G., and Dorfman, R. I. (1956). *J. Org. Chem.* **21**, 814.

Caspi, E., Ungar, F., and Dorfman, R. I. (1957). *J. Org. Chem.* **22**, 326.

Danby, J. (1940). *Endocrinology* **27**, 236.

Dobriner, K., and Lieberman, S. (1952). *Ciba Colloquia Endocrinol.* **2**, 381.

Dorfman, R. I. (1953). *Trans. 5th Josiah Macy Jr. Conf. on Adrenal Cortex,* p. 27.

*Dorfman, R. I. (1955). *In* "The Hormones" (G. Pincus and K. V. Thimann, eds.), Vol. 3, p. 293. Academic Press, New York. Steroid Metabolism.

*Dorfman, R. I. (1956). *Am. J. Med.* **21**, 679. Steroid Metabolism.

Dorfman, R. I. (1957). *Cancer Research* **17**, 535.

*Dorfman, R. I., and Shipley, R. A. (1956). "Androgens." Wiley, New York.

*Dorfman, R. I., and Ungar, F. (1953). "Metabolism of Steroid Hormones," Burgess, Minneapolis, Minnesota.

Dorfman, R. I., Hayano, M., Haynes, R., and Savard, K. (1953). *Ciba Colloquia Endocrinol.* **7**, 191.

Eberlein, W. R., and Bongiovanni, A. M. (1955a). *J. Clin. Invest.* **34**, 1337.

Eberlein, W. R., and Bongiovanni, A. M. (1955b). *J. Clin. Endocrinol. and Metabolism* **15**, 1531.

Eichhorn, J., and Hechter, O. (1957). *Proc. Soc. Exptl. Biol. Med.* **95**, 311.

Eichhorn, J., and Hechter, O. (1958). *Proc. Soc. Exptl. Biol. Med.* (in press).

*Eppstein, S. H., Meister, P. D., Murray, H. C., and Peterson, D. H. (1956). Microbiological transformations of steroids and their applications to the synthesis of hormones. *Vitamins and Hormones* **14**, 359.

Farrell, G. L., Rauschkolb, E. W., and Royce, P. C. (1955). *Am. J. Physiol.* **182**, 269.

*Gaunt, R., Renzi, A. A., and Chart, J. J. (1955). Aldosterone—a review. *J. Clin. Endocrinol. and Metabolism* **15**, 621.

Giroud, C. J. P., Saffran, M., Schally, A. V., Stachenko, J., and Venning, E. H. (1956). *Proc. Soc. Exptl. Biol. Med.* **92**, 855.

*Grant, J. K. (1956). Enzymic hydroxylation of steroids. *Annual Repts. on Progr. Chem. (Chem. Soc. London)* **52**, 316.

Hayaishi, O., Katagivi, M., and Rothberg, S. (1955). *J. Am. Chem. Soc.* **77**, 5450.

*Hayano, M., Saba, N., Dorfman, R. I., and Hechter, O. (1956a). *Recent Progr. in Hormone Research* **12**, 79. Biogenesis of adrenal steroid hormones.

Hayano, M., Saito, A., Stone, D., and Dorfman, R. I. (1956b). *Biochim. et Biophys. Acta* **21**, 380.

*Heard, R. D. H., Jacobs, R., O'Donnell, V. J., Peron, F. G., Saffran, J. C., Solomon, S. S., Thompson, L. M., Willoughby, H., and Yates, C. H. (1954). *Recent Progr. Hormone Research* **9**, 383. C^{14} in steroid metabolism.

Heard, R. D. H., Jellinck, P. H., and O'Donnell, V. J. (1955). *Endocrinology* **57**, 200.

*Heard, R. D. H., Bligh, E. G., Cann, M. C., Jellinck, P. H., O'Donnell, V. J., Rao, B. G., and Webb, J. L. (1956). Biogenesis of the sterols and steroid hormones. *Recent Progr. in Hormone Research* **12**, 45.

Hechter, O. (1949). *Federation Proc.* **8**, 70.

*Hechter, O. (1952). *Trans. 3rd Josiah Jr. Conf. on Adrenal Cortex*, p. 115.

*Hechter, O. (1953a). *Ciba Colloquia Endocrinol.* **7**, 161. Biogenesis of Corticoids.

Hechter, O. (1953b). *Rev. can. biol.* **12**, 123.

*Hechter, O. (1955). Concerning possible mechanisms of hormone action. *Vitamins and Hormones* **13**, 293.

Hechter, O. (1957). *Cancer Research* **17**, 512.

*Hechter, O., and Pincus, G. (1954). Genesis of the adrenocortical secretion. *Physiol. Revs.* **34**, 459.

Hechter, O., Macchi, I. A., Korman, H., Frank, E., and Frank, H. (1955). *Am. J. Physiol* **182**, 29.

Hechter, O., Solomon, M. M., Zaffaroni, A., and Pincus, G. (1953). *Arch. Biochem. Biophys.* **46**, 201.

*Hechter, O., Zaffaroni, A., Jacobsen, R. P., Levy, H., Jeanloz, R. W., Schenker, V., and Pincus, G. (1951). The nature and the biogenesis of the adrenal secretory product. *Recent Progr. Hormone Research* **6**, 215.

Hellman, L., Rosenfeld, R. S., Fukushima, D. K., Gallagher, T. F., and Dobriner, K. (1952). *J. Clin. Endocrinol. and Metabolism* **12**, 934.

Hench, P. S., Kendall, E. C., Slocumb, C. H., and Polley, H. F. (1949). *Proc. Staff Meetings Mayo Clinic* **24**, 181.

Jailer, J. W. (1953). *Bull. N.Y. Acad. Med.* **29**, 377.

Jailer, J. W., Gold, J. J., VandeWiele, R., and Lieberman, S. (1955). *J. Clin. Invest.* **34**, 1639.

Kahnt, F. W., Neher, R., and Wettstein, A. (1955a). *Experientia* **11**, 446.

Kahnt, F. W., Neher, R., and Wettstein, A. (1955b). *Helv. Chim. Acta* **38**, 1237.

*Karrer, P. (1938). "Organic Chemistry." Elsevier, Amsterdam.

Kushinsky, S. (1955). Ph.D. Thesis, Dept. Chem., Boston Univ., Boston.

*Leach, R. B., Maddock, W. O., Tokuyama, I., Paulsen, C. A., and Nelson, W. O. (1956). *Recent Progr. in Hormone Research* **12**, 377. Testicular hormone production.

Lieberman, S., and Dobriner, K. (1950). *Proc. Am. Chem. Soc. 117th Meeting*, p. 19c.

*Long, C. N. H. (1947). *Recent Progr. in Hormone Research* **1**, 99. Adrenal cholesterol and ascorbic acid.

Lucas, W. M., Whitmore, W. F., Jr., and West, C. D. (1957). *J. Clin. Endocrinol. and Metabolism* **17**, 465.

*Luetscher, J. A., Jr. (1956a). *Advances in Internal Med.* **8**, 155.

*Luescher, J. A., Jr. (1956b). *Recent Progr. in Hormone Research* **12**, 175. Studies of aldosterone.

Lynn, W. S., Jr. (1956). *Federation Proc.* **15**, 305.

Lynn, W. S., Jr., and Brown, R. (1956). *Biochim. et Biophys. Acta* **21**, 403.

Lynn, W. S., Jr., Staple, E., and Gurin, S. (1955). *Federation Proc.* **14**, 783.

Meyer, A. S. (1955a). *Experientia* **11**, 99.

Meyer, A. S. (1955b). *Biochim. et Biophys. Acta* **17**, 441.

Muller, A. F., Riondel, A. N., and Mach, R. S. (1956a). *Lancet* i, 831.

Muller, A. F., Riondel, A. N., and Manning, E. L. (1956b). *Lancet* ii, 1021.

*Nelson, D. H. (1955). *In* "5th Ann. Report on Stress" by H. Selye and G. Heuser, p. 169. MD Publications, New York.

Pincus, G., and Romanoff, E. B. (1955). *Ciba Colloquia Endocrinol.* **8**, 97.

Plager, J. E., and Samuels, L. T. (1954). *Arch. Biochem. Biophys.* **42**, 477.

Plager, J. E., and Samuels, L. T. (1955). *J. Biol. Chem.* **211**, 21.

Popják, G. (1954). *Arch. Biochem. Biophys.* **48**, 102.

Rao, B. G., and Heard, R. D. H. (1957). *Arch. Biochem. Biophys.* **66**, 504.

Rauschkolb, E. W., and Farrell, G. L. (1956). *J. Clin. Endocrinol. and Metabolism* **16**, 915.

Reichstein, T., and Shoppee, C. W. (1943). *Vitamins and Hormones* **1**, 345-413.

Romanoff, E. B., Hudson, P., and Pincus, G. (1953). *J. Clin. Endocrinol. and Metabolism* **13**, 1546.

Rosemberg, E., Rosenfeld, G., Ungar, F., and Dorfman, R. I. (1956). *Endocrinology* **58**, 708.

Rosenfeld, G., Rosemberg, E., Ungar, F., and Dorfman, R. I. (1956). *Endocrinology* **58**, 255.

Ruzicka, L., and Prelog, V. (1943). *Helv. Chim. Acta* **26**, 975.

Ryan, K. J. (1956). *Federation Proc.* **15**, 344.

Ryan, K. J., and Engel, L. L. (1956). *J. Am. Chem. Soc.* **78**, 2654.

*Saba, N., and Hechter, O. (1955). Cholesterol-4-C^{14} metabolism in adrenal homogenates. *Federation Proc.* **14**, 775.

Saba, N., Hechter, O., and Stone, D. (1954). *J. Am. Chem. Soc.* **76**, 3862.

Samuels, L. T. (1953). *Ciba Colloquia Endocrinol.* **7**, 176.

*Samuels, L. T. (1955). *Progr. in Chem. Fats Lipids* **3**, 395. Steroid hormone metabolism.

Savard, K., Dorfman, R. I., Baggett, B., and Engel, L. L. (1956). *J. Clin. Endocrinol. and Metabolism* **16**, 1629.

*Simpson, S. A., and Tait, J. F. (1955). *Recent Progr. in Hormone Research* **10**, 204. Isolation, chemistry, and physiology of aldosterone.

Slaunwhite, W. R., Jr., and Samuels, L. T. (1956). *J. Biol. Chem.* **220**, 341.

Solomon, S., Lenz, A. L., Vande Wiele, R., and Lieberman, S. (1954). *Proc. Am. Chem. Soc. N.Y.*, p. 29c.

Solomon, S., Levitan, P., and Lieberman, S. (1956a). *Proc. Can. Physiol. Soc. 20th Meeting, Montreal*, p. 54.

Solomon, S., Vande Wiele, R., and Lieberman, S. (1956b). *J. Am. Chem. Soc.* **78**, 5453.

Staple, E., and Gurin, S. (1954). *Biochim. et Biophys. Acta* **15**, 372.

Staple, E., Lynn, W. S., Jr., and Gurin, S. (1956). *J. Biol. Chem.* **219**, 845.

*Staudinger, H. J. (1955). "Hormone und ihre Wirkungsweise," p. 192. Springer, Berlin.

Stone, D., and Hechter, O. (1954). *Arch. Biochem. Biophys.* **51**, 457.

Tavormina, P. A., Gibbs, M. H., and Huff, J. W. (1956). *J. Am. Chem. Soc.* **78**, 4498.

Tomkins, G. M. (1956). Proceedings of the American Chemical Society, Atlantic City, p. 57c.

Tomkins, G. M., Michael, P. J., and Curran, J. F. (1957). *Biochim. et Biophys. Acta* **23**, 655.

Vogt, M. (1943). *J. Physiol.* **102**, 341.

Vogt, M. (1955). *J. Physiol.* **130**, 161.

Werbin, H., and Le Roy, G. V. (1954). *J. Am. Chem. Soc.* **76**, 5260.

Werbin, H., and Le Roy, G. V. (1955). *Federation Proc.* **14**, 303.

Werbin, H., Plotz, J., Le Roy, G. V., and Davis, E. M. (1957). *J. Am. Chem. Soc.* **79**, 1012.

West, C. D., Damast, B. L., Sarro, S. D., and Pearson, O. H. (1956). *J. Biol. Chem.* **218**, 409.

West, C. D., Hollander, V. P., Kritchevsky, T. H., and Dobriner, K. (1952). *J. Clin. Endocrinol. and Metabolism* **12**, 915.

Wettstein, A., and Anner, G. (1954). *Experientia* **10**, 397.

Wilkins, L. (1952). *J. Pediat.* **41**, 860.

Zaffaroni, A., and Burton, R. B. (1951). *J. Biol. Chem.* **193**, 749.

Zaffaroni, A., Hechter, O., and Pincus, G. (1951). *J. Am. Chem. Soc.* **73**, 1390.

Zannoni, V. G., and La Du, B. N. (1956). *Federation Proc.* **15**, 391.

Zilversmit, D. B., Entenman, C., and Fishler, M. C. (1943). *J. Gen. Physiol.* **26**, 325.

CHAPTER 9

MICROSCOPICAL LOCALIZATION OF CHOLESTEROL IN CELLS AND TISSUES

Geoffrey H. Bourne

I. Introduction

A. GENERAL TECHNIQUES

A short account of the usual techniques employed in histology is needed to understand the difficulties involved in localizing cholesterol (and other steroids) in tissues. Briefly the processes used are: (1) Fixation or stabilizing the component parts of the cell by stopping intracellular enzyme activity and precipitating structural proteins. (2) Embedding in a suitable medium so that: (3) Sectioning of the tissue into thin slices may be made with a microtome. (4) Removal of the embedding material, followed by: (5) Staining with a dyestuff or suitable chemical reagent so that the component parts are differentiated. Alternatively unstained sections may be examined by optical methods (see later).

The routine procedure is to fix the tissue in formalin, dehydrate in aqueous solutions of ethanol, then in pure ethanol, clear with xylene, embed in paraffin wax, section, remove the paraffin wax with solvents, by a process essentially the reverse of that followed in the dehydration procedure, and finally stain. In this procedure the lipid components including the sterols are removed and appear as blank spaces in the finished preparation. This "negative" approach is useful for demonstrating total lipid but for the localization of the component lipids the fixed tissue is embedded in a suitable nonfatty medium and sectioned while in the frozen state so as to conserve the lipid. The sections so obtained are then mounted and examined under the microscope by the procedures to be described.

B. DEMONSTRATION OF LIPID IN TISSUE SECTIONS

1. Birefringence

This property, known also as double refraction or anistropy, is shown by certain crystals (solid and "liquid"). Birefringence is manifested in a compound when it is viewed under the crossed nicols of a polarizing microscope, the birefringent material appearing "light" against a dark background. The property is well shown by cholesterol and its esters and is of value in scanning tissues but its results should be viewed with caution (see later).

Other optical properties, e.g. fluorescence, are also used. The ovary after fixation shows a natural fluorescence, the so-called autofluorescence (Dempsey and Bassett, 1943). This reaction is given apparently by certain steroids but it is also shown by a variety of unsaturated lipids, and by other compounds (cf. Pearse, 1953).

2. The Staining of Cellular Lipids

A variety of methods are used to study the nature and distribution of cellular lipids and for a complete account special texts should be consulted (e.g. Gomori, 1952; Pearse, 1953). The account given here concerns cholesterol and its esters in relation to the other lipids and this is shown in Table I where the commonly used lipid stains are given.

TABLE I

SOME PROCEDURES FOR STAINING AND DEMONSTRATING LIPID CONSTITUENTS[a]

Procedure	Tissue component stained preferentially	Free cholesterol	Cholesteryl esters
Sudan dyes, e.g. Sudan III,	Neutral fat, i.e. triglycerides;	Slight or no reaction	Some staining
Sudan black, acetylated Sudan black[b]	Sudanophil material		
Osmium tetroxide	Unsaturated fatty acids, e.g. in phospholipids and higher unsaturated glycerides	Negative	Some reaction with highly unsaturated esters
Hematoxylin after fixation with dichromate	"Myelin," i.e. the mixture of phospholipids, glycolipids, and free cholesterol found, e.g. in the myelin sheath	?	?
Birefringence	See text	Marked	Marked

[a] Based on personal observations and those of Aschoff (1909).

[b] See Casselman (1954) for review, also Bermes and McDonald (1957).

Aschoff in 1909 gave a review, which is still of great interest, of the morphology of the "lipoid" substances found in normal and pathological tissues. He studied tissues and a number of chemical compounds both by the polarizing microscope and with the then used lipid stains and found that the following substances show birefringence (1) phosphatides, (2) oleic acid soaps, (3) cholesterol esters, and (4) solutions of cholesterol in phosphatides, oleic acids, and fats. The most constant birefringence was shown by the cholesterol esters and moreover the staining reactions of the birefringent droplets or globules was identical with that of the cholesterol esters. Biedl (1912, p. 291) made chemical analyses of the adrenal cortex and reached a similar conclusion.

Because of these and similar observations birefringence was (and still often is) taken as a specific means for the localization of cholesterol in tissue preparations. The view was criticized by Lison (1936; see also Cain, 1950) who showed that neutral fats and fatty acids, which are liquid in the fresh warm state and in this condition are isotropic, may set in a crystalline form and become birefringent when they cool or are fixed. Only cholesterol, its esters, and phosphatides when in the form of spherocrystals show, however, the black (Maltese) cross of polarization. Even with liver cells known to be rich in cholesterol, Okey (1944) found that birefringence was not observed.

It must therefore be concluded that birefringence, though a useful indication of the presence of cholesterol and its esters, is not a specific nor a constant test. It is possible, however, that technical developments will make the method of greater applicability. An account of the many applications of the polarizing microscope is given by Hartshorne and Stuart (1950).

C. EARLY OBSERVATIONS

The necessarily short historical summary given here is concerned mainly with tissues rich in cholesterol such as the adrenal cortex and the tissues of the reproductive system which have been studied the most extensively.

According to Biedl (1912) in his informative account of the subject, Ecker in 1846 was the first to demonstrate the presence of lipid (or lipoid) granules in the adrenal cortex, Leydig in 1850 (Review, 1857) to show their presence in cells of the testis, and His in 1865 to draw attention to their existence in the ovary. At first these droplets were considered to consist only of fat, i.e. glycerides, but in 1872 von Brunn showed that their properties were different. Thus they did not react strongly with osmium tetroxide and, moreover, Rabl in 1891 found that after treatment of the tissues with this reagent that although "true fat" becomes insoluble in fat solvents, the "fat" of the adrenal cortex, etc., was still soluble. The birefringent nature of the cortical fat droplets was demonstrated by Kaiserling and Orgler in 1902 who showed that there were also present granules or droplets of an isotropic nature.

In a study on the adrenal cortex of a large variety of animals Elliott and Tuckett (1906) concluded that "of the secretory products of the cortex the fat must be clearly distinguished from the doubly refractive substance" and "as the store of the latter in any area grows, that of the fat, which might be regarded as a sign of its formation, sinks."

The chemical nature of the fat droplets was (and still is) in dispute. Virchow in 1857 had claimed that it was mainly the then newly discovered lecithin. Rosenheim and Tebb in 1908 were the first to show the complex nature of the adrenal cortical lipids which they found to consist of the glycolipid phrenosin, phosphatides, triglycerides, and a variety of cholesterol esters, a conclusion substantiated by Biedl (1912).

II.   Histological Demonstration of Cholesterol

From what has been described in Section I it is obvious that to rely on the optical property of birefringence and on simple staining reactions is not sufficient to demonstrate its presence specifically and so more distinctive methods have been sought. These methods depend essentially on a chemical reaction between cholesterol and some reagent. In principle the methods are based on the reactions described in Chapters 2 and 3.

A.   DIGITONIN METHOD

The principle of this method due to Windaus is given in detail in Chapter 2. The digitonin reacts only with cholesterol (or other 3β-hydroxysterol) which is precipitated, the esters are unaffected and for their demonstration special methods must be used. The cholesterol digitonide is seen in sections as colorless birefringent crystals.

1. Differentiation of Free and Esterified Cholesterol

The first use of digitonin as a histological reagent was made by Brunswick (1922) as a simple test. Elaborations of the method to distinguish free and esterified cholesterol were introduced by Leulier and Revol (1930). In their method after precipitation of the free cholesterol, the esters are stained with a Sudan dye and when colored lose their birefringence. Bennett (1940) gives a good account of a method which he used in his study of the cholesterol distribution in the lipids of the cat adrenal.

   a. *Bismuth Trichloride Method.* This method, adapted by Grundland *et al.* (1949) from a color reaction for steroids proposed by Pincus (1943; see also Clark and Thompson, 1948), may be used to differentiate free and esterified cholesterol. The tissues are fixed in an ethanolic solution of digitonin and treated with a solution of nitrobenzene containing bismuth chloride and acetyl chloride. Esterified cholesterol gives no reaction but the free sterol gives a brown color which is retained for a considerable period of time. The advantages of the method are that it is not so destructive to the tissues and a more permanent preparation is obtained than with the methods involving the use of the Liebermann-Burchard reaction (see later). Its disadvantage is that it is not specific (see Chapter 3).

   b. *Feigin's Method (1956).* In this method digitonin precipitation is combined with the Schultz reaction (to be described in detail later) and used to differentiate free and esterified cholesterol in the adrenal gland. The esters are soluble in alchohol-ether but the digitonide is insoluble in the solvent mixture.

Briefly, the technique consists in preparing frozen sections of the formalin-treated gland, one section is retained as a control and the second is immersed in 40% ethanolic solution of digitonin for 3 hours, after which it is then immersed in mixture of ethanol-ether (1:1) for a further 3 hours. The control section and the treated section are then immersed in a solution of iron alum for 2–4 days and the color developed with a mixture of acetic anhydride and sulfuric acid (see under Schultz test). Both the cholesterol esters and the digitonide react to give a blue color. The control slide demonstrates both free and combined cholesterol while in the treated slide only the digitonide from the free sterol is present, the esters having been removed by the ethanol-ether solvent. The method is of great value in the histochemical differentiation of free and esterified sterols.

B. LIEBERMANN-BURCHARD METHOD

A detailed account of this reaction is given in Chapter 3 (p. 128). The method can be applied directly to tissues but it is unsatisfactory in the presence of water. Moreover the cholesterol dissolves in the color reagent, the diffusion of the reaction confusing the accurate localization of the cholesterol-containing entities.

Cavanaugh and Glick (1952) describe an interesting technique based on the Schoenheimer-Sperry method (Chapter 3) for determining the free and total sterol on microgram quantities of tissue such as that present in microtome sections. In this method an extract is made of the tissue so that control sections made by conventional methods are necessary to locate the portion of the tissue under study. The method should be of value in studying the zones of the adrenal gland.

C. SCHULTZ REACTION

Schultz adapted the Liebermann-Burchard reaction to the examination of tissues (Schultz, 1924-25; Schultz and Löhr, 1925) by the following method. Sections of frozen formalin-fixed tissue were exposed to sunlight for some days and then stained with a drop of a mixture of acetic anhydride (and he added "oder besser Eisessig," i.e. or better acetic acid) and sulfuric acid when the cholesterol-containing lipids gave a deep blue color. The preparation was stable only for an hour. Schultz recognized that the reaction was intensified if the sections were exposed for a short time to a solution of ferric chloride. The method has undergone a number of modifications principally in the use of iron alum, and a simple procedure is: (1) Cut frozen sections of the formalin-fixed tissue at 10 to 15 µ. (2) Leave in sunlight for at least 1 week. (3) Treat with 2.5% iron alum for 2 days. (4) Allow nearly to dry on slide and treat with a *drop* of equal parts of concentrated sulfuric acid and acetic anhydride (or acetic acid). (5) Seal the cover slip with paraffin.

The appearance of a blue-green color indicates that cholesterol either free or esterified is present in the sections. It should be emphasized that

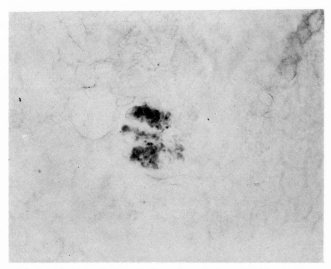

FIG. 1. Schultz cholesterol preparation of contralateral kidney of rat which has developed hypertension following partial clipping of one renal artery. Cholesterol is seen to be deposited in the glomerulus.

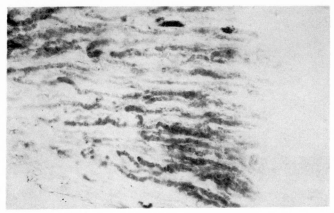

FIG. 2. Schultz cholesterol preparation of clipped kidney from rat which has developed hypertension following partial clipping of this kidney.

variations of color are often observed in the Schultz test; these may be related to the extent of oxidation brought about, or to the presence of other steroids. The occurrence of bubbles commonly occurs and has been one of the drawbacks to the method. Weber *et al.* (1956) have made a detailed study of the technique and point out three undesirable features: (1) Frequent precipitation of ferric ammonium sulfate on tissue sections during incubation; (2) the formation of bubbles; and (3) variations in color from one area to another especially when the amount of cholesterol is small.

1. Specificity and Sensitivity of the Reaction

The specificity of the reaction has often been questioned and one recent study is that by Kent (1952) who made a comparative study of the Liebermann-Burchard and the Schultz reactions. His procedure was to use sections of the acetone-extracted aorta and to soak these in solutions of the compound under test. The treated sections were then used for the staining reactions with the results shown in Table II. The positive reaction obtained with carotene is of great interest but is unlikely to be confused with cholesterol except under special circumstances. The results shown should be compared with those given in Table I, Chapter 3.

Reiner (1953) simulated tissue conditions by making sterol-olive oil-gelatin models containing known amounts of the compound under test. The gelatin blocks were fixed with formalin and handled thereafter exactly as gelatin-embedded tissues, including frozen sectioning and distilled water flotation. Incorporated in the models were cholesterol, 7-dehydrocholesterol, 7-hydroxycholesterol, aerated cholesterol, ergosterol, cholesterol with spleen, adrenal lipids, and carotene. Spot plate tests of these substances were also carried out with results comparable to those of Kent. Reiner concludes that 7-hydroxycholesterol is the substance or one of the substances to which sterols must be convertible before a positive Schultz test is obtained and that at least 50% of Liebermann-Burchard positive material should be present in the lipid phase of the tissue under study. He considers that the reaction is very insensitive but nevertheless useful with tissues such as the adrenal cortex.

2. Mechanism

Schultz states that Windaus suggested that the reaction was due to the presence of oxycholesterol, that is the complex mixture of compounds produced on the aerial oxidation of cholesterol (Chapter 2). One of the main components of this mixture is 7-hydroxycholesterol and Reiner's conclusion (see above) is justified. It is known that autoxida-

TABLE II
COMPARISON OF LIEBERMANN-BURCHARD REACTION AND SCHULTZ TEST

	Liebermann-Burchard reaction[a]		Schultz test in tissue[a]
	in test tube	in tissue	
Controls			
Aorta (atherosclerotic)	−	++	++
Aorta (acetone extracted)	−	Faint purple	Faint purple
Adrenal cortex	−	++	++
Cholesterol	++	+	+
Cholesterol palmitate	++	+	+
Cholesterol oleate	++	+	+
Other Steroids			
Estrone	Eosin red	Eosin red	Yellow-brown
Estradiol	Light yellow	Light yellow	Light yellow
Testosterone	Eosin red	Eosin red	Yellow-red
Dehydroisoandrosterone acetate	Deep red	Medium red	Deep red
Progesterone	Light yellow	Light yellow	Light brown
Deoxycholic acid	Orange	Light yellow	Light purple
Cholic acid	Yellow-red	Light yellow-red	Yellow-brown
Ergosterol	++	+	+
Nonsteroids Giving Positive Reaction			
Carotene	++	++	++
Vitamin A	Blue-purple	Blue-purple	Blue-purple
Linoleic acid	++	+	O
Hydroxylated Benzene Derivatives			
Phenol	Light violet	O	Light purple
Guaiacol	Light yellow	Light yellow	Golden brown
Anethole	Deep red	Light blue	Light purple
Eugenol	Dark red-brown	Red-brown	Light brown
Isoprenoid Compounds			
l-Linalool	Brown-black	Light yellow-brown	Light yellow
d-Limonene	Light brown	Light brown	Medium orange
d-Pinene	Yellow-brown	Light yellow-brown	Light pink
Terpinol	Violet	Light violet	Light purple
Resin Acid			
Abietic acid	Yellow-red	Yellow-red	Yellow-red
	Stearic acid gave negative results		

NOTE: The tests were carried out on the substances *in vitro* in acetone solution, and after sections of acetone-extracted aorta had been soaked in solutions of the compounds (see text). Modified from results of Kent (1952).

[a] ++, intense blue green reaction; +, somewhat less intense.

tion of cholesterol is brought about by exposure to air in the light and that presence of iron catalyzes the process; these conditions all forming part of the Schultz test. Of interest is the use of acetic acid in preference to acetic anhydride. It can be demonstrated that while pure cholesterol gives no reaction with glacial acetic acid and sulfuric acid, 7-hydroxycholesterol gives an immediate and intense color.

The Schultz reaction therefore depends on the oxidation of cholesterol and it is worth speculating whether the process could be catalyzed by some simple method thus shortening the long time needed for its performance.

D. Specificity of Techniques

From what has been written it is clear that the existing techniques all have their limitations. The digitonin method is useful for demonstrating the presence of free sterols and the Liebermann-Burchard reaction is of value in demonstrating the presence of total (free and combined) sterols. It can be used to differentiate "fast" and "slow" acting sterols in skin (see Section III). The Schultz test now has an established place in histochemistry and if the results are viewed with caution it is of great value particularly with tissues rich in cholesterol such as the adrenal cortex. The subject of specificity of the histochemical (as with in vitro tests) is still debatable. A relatively nonspecific method is the bismuth trichloride technique which, however, has the advantage of stability of the preparation.

Refinements in technique particularly in detecting the presence of the steroid hormones are of considerable interest and the reader is referred to the critical review of Deane and Seligman (1953) on procedures for the cytological localization of ketosteroids. The reaction of Camber (1949) and Seligman and Ashbel (e.g. 1952) for the histochemical demonstration of carbonyl (keto) groups in tissues has found wide acceptance. With regard to the subject of the demonstration and localization of the sterol metabolites mentioned in other chapters it is probable that histochemical methods will be combined with separation of cellular components and the use of chromatographic methods adopted for thin sections of tissues.

III. Distribution of Cholesterol in Cells, Organs, and Tissues

A. Cells

An early study of the application of histochemical methods to the localization of the cellular lipid components was by Mayer et al. (1914-15) who after studying the mitochondria of the liver cells concluded that phospholipids were the most important component. Bourne in 1935 demonstrated a marked Schultz-positive reaction in the mitochondria of adrenal cortical cells and a fainter reaction in those of the liver but none in other organs. More recently he has found that the sarcosomes (mitochondria) in the heart muscle of an aged man (90 years) gave a strong Schultz reaction (see p. 368).

Following the pioneer studies of Bensley and Hoerr (1934) on the lipid composition of liver mitochondria in which they showed the presence of cholesterol, there have been a number of chemical investigations on the composition of the cell "organelles" and in particular those of the liver cell; the subject is discussed in Chapter 4.

It must be confessed, however, that apart from cholesterol-rich cells such as the adrenal cortex, existing histochemical tests have not a sufficient degree of sensitivity to demonstrate its presence in cellular components (for exceptions see above). This is well illustrated by the observations of Friedman et al. (1956) who showed that, in a rat after injection of C^{14}-labeled cholesterol, the labeled material could be detected in the reticulo-endothelial cells of the liver but tests for cholesterol by birefringence and by histochemical methods were generally negative.

B. Tissues and Organs

Most studies have been made on organs rich in cholesterol such as the adrenal cortex, and on reproductive glands, and in the following account most attention is given to these organs.

1. The Adrenal Gland

This relatively small but physiologically important structure is covered with a capsule under which lies the cortex, the center of the gland forming the medulla. It is beyond the scope of this chapter to discuss the manifold activities of this gland which are described in special treatises on the subject (e.g. Hartman and Brownell, 1949; Yoffey, 1953; Jones, 1957). The account given is centered around the histochemical demonstration of cholesterol but a general morphological account is a necessary prelude.

Two main types of adrenal gland may be differentiated. The first, a relatively nonfatty type found in the ox and sheep, where the cortex and medulla may be separated relatively easily. The second or fatty type is found inter alia in the rat, guinea pig, and rabbit, and a mechanical separation of cortex and medulla is difficult to make although they are histologically distinct. In man there is a large fetal cortex of the nonfatty type which with increasing age becomes "fatty." Typical chemical analyses of the types of adrenal gland are given in Chapter 4, Table XI.

a. The Adrenal Cortex. Three main zones are differentiated which are from without inwards:

(1) Zona glomerulosa. This occupies about one-sixth of the total area and is composed of cells arranged in short columns which bend over to form arches when they come into contact with the capsule. The other ends of the column continue into the zona fasciculata.

(2) Zona fasciculata. This occupies about two-thirds of the total area, the cells are larger and are usually loaded with lipoid droplets. An outer and an inner layer of this zone are sometimes distinguished (e.g. Yoffey, 1953).

(3) Zona reticularis. This occupies normally about one-sixth of the area and is in contact with the medulla. In this zone the cell columns branch and have a reticular form.

The methods described in Sections I and II, namely, birefringence, lipid stains, Schultz reaction, and tests for carbonyl compounds have all been used in studying the localization of cholesterol and related steroids in the component parts of the gland. Of some interest is the curious and unexplained fact of the presence of ascorbic acid in the adrenal gland (see review by Pirani, 1952 and Bourne, 1957). The amount and distribution is apparently affected by the same factors that influence the amount of cholesterol (e.g. Bahn and Glick, 1954). This statement may have, however, to be modified in view of the observations of Stenger *et al.* (1955), who postulate separate hormones.

(i) *Studies in experimental animals.* The adrenal cortex has been the subject of numerous investigations in a variety of animal species and references to some representative observations are given in Table III. It is difficult to summarize briefly the results of these observations (and those of others) but it is agreed that the zona fasciculata is the portion richest in cholesterol and its esters, and the pattern of this and of the other zones is affected by the age, sex, and physiological state of the animal.

(ii) *Endocrine control.* It is now well established that the activity of the cortex is influenced by the secretions of the thyroid gland and above all by the pituitary (see Sayers and Sayers, 1949). One such morphological and histochemical study of the hormonal effects on the adrenal cortex of the rat was made by Feldman (1951) and a summary of his results is given in Table IV.

(iii) *Effects of feeding excess cholesterol.* A good study on the effect of dietary cholesterol on the rabbit adrenals was made by Kay and Whitehead (1935), who review the earlier literature. They used combined chemical and histochemical methods and found a gross increase in weight, volume, and cholesterol content. The cortical cells were enlarged due to accumulation of cholesterol-containing material but some cells showed degeneration and in them cholesterol crystals were deposited. With the Schultz reagent the lipid droplets gave a deep blue reaction but the crystals gave a lighter shade. They observed also that the deposition of cholesterol was more marked with the males than with the females. A well-illustrated account of the histochemical changes

TABLE III

SOME STUDIES ON THE ADRENAL CORTEX OF EXPERIMENTAL ANIMALS

| Species | Investigation | |
	Histochemical	Chemical
Mouse	Development: Moog *et al.* (1954)	
Rat	Fetal: Josimovich *et al.* (1954)	
	Female: Anderson and Kennedy	
	(1932) (cf.)	Andersen and Sperry (1937)
	Male: Yoffey and Baxter (1949)	Popják (1944)[*]
	Male and female: Harrison and	
	Cain (1947)	Sayers *et al.* (1946)
	Hormonal effects: Feldman (1951)	
Guinea pig	Sex and age: Whitehead (1934b)	Knouff *et al.* (1941)[*]
	Age: Whitehead (1936b)	Sayers *et al.* (1946)
	Unilateral adrenalectomy: White-	
	head (1937)	
	Fasting: Whitehead (1942) (cf.)	Oleson and Bloor (1941)
Rabbit	Sex and age: Whitehead (1936b)	
	Fasting: Whitehead (1942) (cf.)	MacLachlan *et al.* (1941)
Cat	Development: Bennett (1940)	
General studies	Elliott and Tuckett (1906)	
	Whitehead (1934a)	
	Yoffey and Baxter (1947)	
	Greep and Deane (1949)	

NOTE: In the investigations marked [*] the histochemical and chemical methods were matched; cf. the separate investigations were done on the same glands but by different workers.

in the adrenals (and other tissues) of the rabbit after cholesterol feeding is given by McMillan *et al.* (1954).

Okey in 1944 found that in the guinea pig, which develops an anemia on feeding cholesterol, there was no increase in the deposition of cholesterol but in some of the older animals the inner zone of the cortex was invaded by groups of endothelial cells. The rat adrenal is apparently little affected by excess dietary cholesterol (e.g. Sperry and Stoyanoff, 1935).

(iv) *Human adrenals.* The studies of Plecnik (1902) on the changes
in the granules during fetal and infant development are of interest. In
the 5-cm. embryo all the cells contained granules but these were smaller
in size and number until a maximal number was reached at about a year
after birth. Thereafter the number was subject to an unexplained variation. Plecnik's staining method was based on the Weigert bichromate-
hematoxylin stain used for the medullary sheath of nerves. It may
therefore be presumed that he was demonstrating compounds of related
type to those found in nerve, namely, cholesterol, phospholipids, and

TABLE IV

ENDOCRINE EFFECTS ON THE ADRENAL GLAND OF RATS[a]

	No additional hormone	Administration of	
		ACTH	Thyroxine
Normal animal	Control	Causes enlargement of gland and loss of lipid, birefringent material, and carbonyl compounds	Increase in size
Hypophysec-tomized animal	Atrophy of gland, loss of lipid, birefringent ma-terial, and carbonyl compounds	Enlargement of gland, accumulation of bire-fringent material, and carbonyl compounds	Gland un-affected
Thyroidec-tomized animal	Decrease in size, loss of lipid, birefringent ma-terial, and carbonyl compounds	Not done	Not done

Growth hormone had no influence on the adrenal gland macro- or microscopically
[a] From Feldman (1951).

glycolipids. Fex (1920) made a careful study comparing the results of
histological examination with the determination of free and ester cholesterol. He studied not only the adrenals but also the liver and kidney
in normal and pathological tissues. Rogers and Williams (1947) made
an extensive study of human normal and "lipid depleted" adrenal glands
by a variety of histochemical techniques and compared the results with
quantitative determinations of cholesterol content. They conclude that
although the methods used demonstrate the localization and shift of the
lipid pattern "there is no proof that they indicate the distribution of active
adrenal hormones."

(v) *Localization of the sites of hormone production.* The adrenal
gland has received study from the steroid chemist, endocrinologist, biochemist, and histologist because in it are manufactured important hor-

mones and because it is of importance in that vague but suggestive term "stress." These activities all bear some apparent relation to the cholesterol.

The sites of conversion to the steroid hormones are not as yet "pinpointed," but Swann (1940) has suggested that the zona glomerulosa elaborates the electrolyte hormones and zona fasciculata the steroid hormones concerned in carbohydrate metabolism. See also Deane and Greep (1946). Eränko (1955) has shown that if rats are injected with potassium or sodium chloride or with ACTH the zona glomerulosa enlarges but shows no histochemical change, whereas the zona fasciculata shows a loss of birefringent material and substances giving a carbonyl reaction.

There is more evidence for the function of the zona reticularis which is considered to be responsible for the production of androgens (see review by Parkes, 1945). In normal states it contains less lipid and cholesterol than the zona fasciculata but the extent of the reticularis is increased greatly in virilizing tumors in humans (see, e.g. Yoffey, 1953).

An account of the biochemical formation of the adrenal steroid hormones is given in Chapter 8, but their exact sites of formation in the cortex must await refinements of histochemical technique. The functional zonation of the adrenal cortex has been studied and reviewed recently by Race et al. (1957).

b. Adrenal Medulla. The presence of fat cells in the medulla was shown by Elliott and Tuckett (1906) and they concluded that in some species these indicated a cortical admixture. The fat globules were not, however, birefringent. More recently Hillarp and Nilson (1954) have shown the presence of granules in the ox adrenal medulla which are rich in phospholipids and cholesterol.

2. Reproductive System

a. The Testis. The glandular portion of this tissue is divided into lobules which consists of two parts: the interstitial tissue and the seminiferous tubules. The interstitial tissue lies in a network of fibroelastic connective tissue and varies considerably in amount in different species. It contains fibroblasts and the interstitial cells (of Leydig), of which the lipid granules have already been mentioned. These cells are generally considered the source of the androgenic steroids and would thus be expected to contain cholesterol. The seminiferous tubules contain the cells that produce eventually the spermatozoa and lining the epithelium are the supporting cells (of Sertoli) which are considered to have a nutritive function for the developing sperms.

A number of comparative studies in animal species have been made, e.g. in the cat by Pollock (1942); in the rat, mouse, guinea pig, dog, and stallion by McEnery and Nelson (1950); the observers are agreed that cholesterol is present in the cells which might be expected to produce the steroid hormones. In an extensive comparative study Melampy and Cavazos (1954) found a positive Schultz reaction in the interstitial cells of the bull, boar, ram, guinea pig, rat, horned lizard, and frog, but not in those of roosters and certain fish. It is suggested however, that in the latter case this may be related to the breeding season (cf. the studies of Wislocki (1949) on the deer during periods of sexual activity).

In the human testis Montagna and Hamilton (1951) have investigated in some detail the distribution of birefringent and Schultz-positive lipids. The interstitial cells contained lipid which was reactive to the Schultz test but was only occasionally birefringent. Schultz-positive material was found also in the interstitial fibroblast cells and in the Sertoli cells. The seminiferous tubules contained peripheral lipids which were isotropic and did not give a Schultz reaction but the other intratubular lipids are Schultz positive and birefringent. The work is well illustrated and Montagna and Hamilton conclude "that the histological criteria used for the demonstration of the testicular hormones in other animals are not tenable for human testes . . . the presumptive sites of hormones should include the interstitial fibroblast-like cells and the seminiferous epithelium as well as the cells of Leydig."

b. The Ovary. This small but complex tissue shows variations of structure with species, age, menstruation, and pregnancy, for the detailed structure specialized texts should be consulted. In a sexually mature animal it consists essentially of a fibro-cellular stroma surrounded by the germinal epithelium. From this layer develops the Graafian follicle which is lined with cells forming the zona glomerulosa and embedded in one part of this is the ovum. After extrusion of the ovum the follicle develops into the corpus luteum, the large lutein cells of which contain lipids including cholesterol; these cells are considered to be responsible for forming the progesterone hormones. The stromal connective tissue adjacent to the follicle becomes grouped around it forming the theca interna and it is probable that estrogens are manufactured in its cells.

The ovary has been investigated by histochemical methods in a variety of experimental animals (for review see Deane and Seligman, 1953).

From the studies of the various investigators the general conclusion may be drawn that, when the amount of cholesterol (Schultz-positive and birefringent material) is most abundant, the apparent physiological state of the animal shows that at most only slight amounts of hormones are being produced. When the amount of cholesterol declines there is evidence for the formation of the ketosteroid hormones.

An interesting study by McKay *et al.* (1949) on the histochemistry of a variety of human ovarian tumors relates the lipids to the functional activity of the tumors. Thus in tumors with estrogenic activity the reactive lipids were confined to the thecal cells and in tumors with progestational activity the lipids were mainly in the lutein cells.

c. *Placenta.* An account of the early observations on the histochemistry of the lipoids in the placenta is given by Deane and Seligman (1953). The placentas of a wide variety of animal species, and from normal and pathological human subjects, have been studied by Wislocki and his associates, and by others (e.g. Wislocki and Dempsey, 1948).

This short summary of some of the parts of the reproductive system show that the histochemical approach is of great potential value in elucidating the sites of formation of the sex hormones. It is of interest to remark that chemical analyses of the whole tissues (Chapter 4, Table X) show in general a relatively low lipid and cholesterol content. It may therefore be inferred that there is a marked localization of cholesterol in the cells where an active conversion to steroid hormones is occurring.

3. Nervous System

The chemical analyses of the nervous system given in Chapter 4, Table IX, show that it has a high lipid composition consisting of free cholesterol, phospholipids, and cerebrosides (glycolipids) with only very small amounts of neutral fat and cholesterol esters. The greatest concentration of cholesterol is found in the white matter or myelin sheath of the nerves; Brante (1949) gives a detailed account of the distribution of the various lipids in the parts of the nervous system.

Myelin gives only slight reactions with the Sudan dyes, but as might be expected it gives a marked Schultz reaction. The color appears to be diffused in the myelin, no particulate matter being seen.

In the young developing animal there is an active deposition of myelin and it has been shown that there is an active sterol metabolism associated with this process but once deposition is completed the cholesterol is apparently static (see Chapter 7).

If, however, a peripheral nerve is severed it undergoes the process known as Wallerian degeneration in which the structure is completely altered. The histology of this process has been reviewed (e.g. Young, 1948). The chemical processes involved have been studied by Rossiter and his colleagues (Johnson *et al.*, 1949, for review see Johnson *et al.*, 1950). Cholesterol esters make their appearance at the moment of myelin destruction, presumably due to the formation of an enzyme or group of enzymes responsible for the complex chemical changes which occur. Seligman and Ashbel (1951) applied their reaction for the detection of carbonyl compounds to normal and neoplastic nervous tissues and showed that aldehydes and/or ketones were present in the normal myelin of various animal species but not in degenerating myelin. In certain types of tumor affecting the nervous system there were present compounds with reactions suggestive of ketosteroids.

These rather casual observations on this important and cholesterol-rich tissue show the lack of real knowledge. Some speculations on the role of cholesterol in the myelin sheath are given in Section IV.

4. The Retina

The main layers of this important tissue are, following the path of a ray of light entering the eye: (1) optic nerve fibers, (2) optic nerve cells, the branchings of which form (3) *the inner synaptic layer* by union with the ends of (4) the bipolar cells. The branchings from the other ends of these cells form (5) *the outer synaptic layer* by uniting with the arborizations from (6) the layer of outer ganglion cells (outer nuclear layer). This latter layer consists mainly of the nuclei of (7) the rods and cones which are covered by (8) a layer of pigment cells. Francis (1955) has made a histochemical study of the lipids of this complex tissue in a wide variety of vertebrates; using the Schultz test for cholesterol he demonstrated that this substance was present in greatest concentration in the inner synaptic layer. He points out that it is in this layer where cholinesterase is also found. Francis quotes the experiments of Beutner and Barnes (1945) in which they showed that the addition of acetylcholine to a saline solution in contact with cholesterol dissolved in an inert solvent such as benzyl alcohol gives rise to a negative electrical potential—"this electrical negativity may play an important role in the origin of the negative variation associated with the nerve impulse." The presence of cholesterol (and phospholipids) was also demonstrated in the optic nerve fibers and Francis considers that "the function of cholesterol here is probably only that of acting as an insulator, since no cholinesterase is found here." Francis' well-documented and illustrated communication is of great interest.

5. Blood Vessels

The walls of the normal blood vessels show little reaction with lipid stains but in atheromatous vessels there is a considerable deposition of cholesterol and its esters which can be readily demonstrated by the methods described. It is beyond the scope of this chapter to describe and discuss the considerable literature on atherosclerosis (i.e. the lipid deposition in the intimal layer of the artery); this process is described in Chapter 10. Of some interest, however, on account of the histochemical techniques used and the variety of tissues examined, are the observations of Baker and Selikoff (1952). These workers made a study of hyaline arteriolosclerosis (i.e. a translucent or hyaline degeneration affecting chiefly the collagenous connective tissue and fibrous tissue of the smallest arteries) occurring in humans after hypertension. They found that in a total of 47 cases, 46 gave a Sudanophil deposit and 43 a positive Schultz reaction. The reaction was shown in the hyaline regions of the arteries of the kidneys, spleen, adrenals, and striated muscle. No reaction was shown in cardiac muscle, brain, testes, skin, or adipose tissue.

A recent study of presumed normal human arteries is that of Henderson (1956) who examined a series of arteries (left middle cerebral, left coronary, splenic, the aorta at four levels, and the brachial) from subjects free from obvious arterial diseases and representing each decade from 0 to 90 years. Various histochemical techniques were used on frozen sections. It was found that with increasing age the total lipid increased in the apparently normal artery. Cholesterol and its esters, demonstrated by the digitonin method and by the Schultz reaction, appeared in the 20 to 29 decade in the intima of the aorta. Subsequent decades showed a deposition in the intima of other vessels and in the media of the aorta.

The deposition of phospholipid followed a similar pattern to that of the cholesterol. Studies were also made on frankly atheromatous arteries and paper partition chromatography was used to demonstrate cholesterol metabolic products.

6. Muscle

The chemical analyses of muscle given in Chapter 3 show that it has a low content of cholesterol, and unless this was localized, its histological demonstration would be difficult, and such has proved to be the case. It is presumably diffused throughout the tissue but it is of interest to remark that Perry (1952) found lipid in his myofibril preparations. Bloor (1936) has suggested that there is a relation between the amounts of phospholipid and cholesterol (P:C ratio) and the functional activity of muscles. The P:C ratios are high (16:1) for voluntary and cardiac muscles in all animals and low (3.5:1) for smooth muscle. Bloor postulated an apparent correlation between cholesterol content and automaticity.

The lipid component of muscle is a neglected aspect of its physiology and it is possible that refinements of histochemical technique will find a role for this widespread constituent.

7. Skin

The chemical analyses of skin given in Chapter 4, Table XIII show that the epidermal layers are richer in cholesterol and its esters than the deeper layers of corium. Following the pioneer studies of Unna and Golodetz in 1909, this has often been demonstrated (Chapter 4). The histochemistry of the skin has been studied extensively by Montagna and his associates, whose work, and that of others, is the subject of a well-illustrated monograph (Montagna, 1956). A difficulty in studying the lipid pattern of the skin is that the secretion of the sebaceous glands covers and permeates the outer layers thus rendering the results of equivocal value as regards the presence of lipid in the cellular layers.

Histochemical studies have been made on the sebaceous glands of a variety of animals. Montagna and Norback (1947) demonstrated histochemically the presence of esterified sterols in the glands of rat skin, and Montagna and his colleagues (1952) studied the glands in the skin of the hairless mouse, in which they are particularly abundant (see also Kandutsch et al., 1956a).

Baumann and his associates have shown clearly that the main sterol in the epidermal skin of rats and mice is Δ^7-cholestenol and this "fast acting" sterol has been demonstrated histochemically in the sebaceous glands of mice by Brooks et al. (1956). Fast-acting sterols (Chapter 3) have apparently a wide distribution in a variety of skin glands, e.g. preputial, etc., of the rodents. In addition to Δ^7-cholestenol a small amount of 7-dehydrocholesterol is also present (Kandutsch et al., 1956b).

In man Suskind (1951) made a histochemical study of the sebaceous gland and concluded that the cholesterol was present mainly in the esterified form. Chemical analyses of human skin (see Chapter 4) show that fast-acting sterols are present only in small amounts. The significance of the biological distribution of the fast-acting sterols is still obscure.

8. Cholesterol Distribution in an Aged Man

The opportunity was presented of studying the cholesterol distribution in the tissues of a man aged 90 years, dead from "natural causes." The results are so striking that they are described briefly. The Schultz reaction was used throughout. In the adrenal gland only a few isolated patches of cortical cells gave a positive reaction. In the anterior pituitary, groups of cells were outlined by "ropes" of connective tissue which gave a very strong positive reaction; the gland cells gave a light pink color and some of them were arranged in vesicles which contained colloid giving a bright rose-pink color. In the pineal gland which consisted largely of connective tissue there were isolated patches of reacting material. The liver cells gave a light pink diffuse reaction but there were groups of bright pink-staining granules, occasional cells showing a single large globule of green; the Kupfer cells showed some green granules. In the heart most of the fibers of the ventricle had a cloud of bright pink granules dotted with smaller green ones near the nucleus; in the auricle the sarcosomes gave an intense dark green reaction. The kidney tubules gave a bright pink reaction which was most marked in the walls of blood vessels; in the kidney pelvis there was an intracellular reaction with the green color diffused through the cytoplasm of the cells and dark green granules were scattered throughout it. In the skin of the scalp a positive reaction was found only in the sweat glands.

The significance of these observations is difficult to interpret as chemical determinations were not made, but in view of the fact that the Schultz reaction depends basically on an oxidation of cholesterol it is possible that with extreme age the form and nature of the cholesterol distribution in the body's tissues undergoes a radical change.

IV. Some Suggested Structural Roles of Cholesterol

It will have been seen that, using the current histochemical methods, it is possible to localize the cholesterol and other lipids relatively clearly in tissues such as the adrenal cortex and in the sex glands. In the nervous system cholesterol is readily demonstrated in the myelin sheath in which it is, however, widely scattered suggesting a structural role.

Finean (1953; 1956) from his studies on the X-ray diffraction pattern of myelin suggests that it is composed of alternate layers of lipid and of nonlipid (probably protein). The lipid molecules appear to be curled or tilted so that their full length is not extended and there is probably a stable complex formed between the cholesterol molecule and the larger phospholipid molecules. It is postulated that the free hydroxyl group of the cholesterol is important in binding the molecule by associating with the polar end of the lipid chain which it curls around. The "hydrocarbon" part of the cholesterol molecule is bound to the phospholipid by van der Waals forces (see Fig. 3). It will be interesting to follow developments of this work because of the teleological role assigned to the large amount of cholesterol in the nervous system. The theory proposed originally was that because cholesterol has a high dielectric constant it acts as an insulating agent, presumably preventing leakage of the electric charge accompanying the nerve impulse (see e.g. Bills, 1935). This passive role is in contrast to the active one proposed by Francis for the inner synaptic layer of the retina, basing his views on the physico-chemical model experiments of Beutner and Barnes (see above, p. 366). The elucidation of the function(s) of cholesterol (and of the other lipids) in the nervous system will certainly take some intensive study.

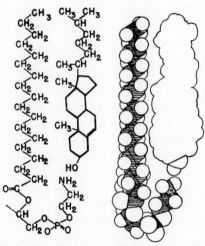

Fig. 3. Suggested method of incorporation of cholesterol in the lipid layer of the myelin sheath (from Finean, 1953). He suggests that the cholesterol molecule in the position shown would be capable of formation of a stabilizing complex with the phospholipid molecule, presumably due largely to the —OH group. The hydrocarbon chain of the cholesterol would be bound to the parallel portion of the phospholipid chain by van der Waals forces.

A. THE CELL MEMBRANE

The relation of lipid to the structure of the cell membrane has aroused much speculation. It is known from analyses of red cell "ghosts" that relatively large amounts of cholesterol and other lipids, mainly phospholipids, are present (see Chapter 5, p. 183). An interesting theory concerning the structure of the red cell membrane was proposed by Winkler and Bungenberg de Jong in 1941. This theory gives to the free cholesterol in the red cell the role of "stabilizer" to the charged phospholipid molecules thus giving form to the membrane. Digitonin has its destructive effect on the cell membrane presumably by combining with the free sterol to form a digitonide (Chapter 1). The essential features of the suggested structure are shown in Fig. 4.

The concept has been elaborated by Frey-Wyssling (1953) whose studies on submicroscopic morphology and its relation to the chemical constituents of the cell are of fundamental importance.

It is of interest to observe that, in the two tissues where cholesterol has been assigned the major role of a structural component, it is present mainly if not entirely in the free unesterified form. There is one striking difference, however, in the "turnover" of the cholesterol in the myelin sheath and in the red cell. In the myelin sheath it is apparently stable and once deposited, under normal conditions remains static for life, but in the red blood cell there is a steady "turnover" and exchange with the plasma cholesterol (Chapter 7).

In general in the tissues where there is active metabolism of cholesterol, esterified cholesterol is found, the amount varying from tissue to tissue, e.g. in the liver about 25% is esterified and about 90% in the

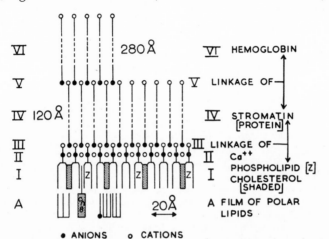

• ANIONS o CATIONS

Fig. 4. Suggested molecular structure of the membrane of the red blood corpuscle (modified from Winkler and Bungenberg de Jong, 1941). Layer A is an incomplete layer of polar lipids: fat, fatty acids, and possibly cholesterol, with the lipophilic ends turned towards the monomolecular layer I of phospholipids, the cholesterol being considered to act as a "stabilizer" to the structure. The cationic groups of the phospholipid due to the positively charged component, e.g. choline, enter into the relation with anionic groups of the stromatin protein. In layer II Ca++ (or possibly other cations) is allocated the negatively charged phosphoric acid of the phospholipid molecule. A good survey of the ultrastructure of the envelope of the erythrocyte is given by Waugh (1950), see also Ponder (1954).

adrenal cortex. Andersen and Sperry (1937) made the interesting observation that when the adrenal cortex is depleted of cholesterol, the smaller amount remaining was mainly in the free form and this they considered as the structural component. We can thus argue that there are two forms of cholesterol in the cell. One a dynamic form which is easily esterified, taking part in the transfer of fatty acids and which is eventually converted into other compounds. The other structural form is part *inter alia* of the cell membrane(s) and for unknown reasons behaves statically in myelin and dynamically in the red cell.

It is to be hoped that the newer techniques being evolved in cytochemistry and cytophysics will elucidate some of the structural roles of this enigmatic compound.

REFERENCES
(Asterisk indicates review article)

Andersen, D. H., and Kennedy, H. S. (1932). *J. Physiol.* (*London*) **76**, 247-260.

Andersen, D. H., and Sperry, W. M. (1937). *J. Physiol.* (*London*) **90**, 296-302.

Aschoff, L. (1909). *Beitr. pathol. Anat. u. allgem. Pathol.* **47**, 1-50.

Bahn, R. C., and Glick, D. (1954). *Endocrinology* **54**, 672-684.

Baker, R. D., and Selikoff, E. (1952). *Am. J. Pathol.* **28**, 573-581.

Bennett, H. S. (1940). *Am. J. Anat.* **67**, 151-228.

Bensley, R. R., and Hoerr, N. L. (1934). *Anat. Record* **60**, 449-455.

Bermes, E. W., and McDonald, H. J. (1957). *Arch. Biochem. Biophys.* **70**, 49-57.

Beutner, R., and Barnes, T. C. (1945). *Proc. Soc. Exptl. Biol. Med.* **58**, 337-338.

Biedl, A. (1912). "The Internal Secretory Organs: their Physiology and Pathology," transl. by A. Forster [from Biedl, A. "Innere Sekretion. Ihre physiologischen Grundlagen und ihre Bedeutung für die Pathologie." Urban und Schwarzenberg, Berlin and Wien, 1910], J. Bale Sons and Danielsson, London. An edition dated 1913 published by W. Wood, New York is cited by Deane and Seligman (1953).

*Bills, C. E. (1935). *Physiol. Revs.* **15**, 1-97.

Bloor, W. R. (1936). *J. Biol. Chem.* **114**, 639-648.

Bourne, G. H. (1935). *Australian J. Exptl. Biol. Med. Sci.* **13**, 239-249.

Bourne, G. H. (1957). "Vitamin C in the animal cell," *Protoplasmatologia.* II,B,2,b,α.

Brante, G. (1949). *Acta Physiol. Scand.* **18**, Suppl. **63**, 189 pp.

Brooks, S. C., Jr., Lalich, J. J., and Baumann, C. A. (1956). *Am. J. Pathol.* **32**, 1205-1213.

Brunswick, O. (1922). *Z. wiss. Mikroskop.* **39**, 316-321.

*Cain, A. J. (1950). *Biol. Revs. Cambridge Phil. Soc.* **25**, 73-112. (Lipid staining.)

Camber, B. (1949). *Nature* **163**, 285.

Casselman, W. G. B. (1954). *Quart. J. Microscop. Sci.* **95**, 321-322.

Cavanaugh, D. J., and Glick, D. (1952). *Anat. Chem.* **24**, 1839-1841.

Clark, L. C., Jr., and Thompson, H. (1948). *Science* **107**, 429-431.

Deane, H. W., and Greep, R. O. (1946). *Am. J. Anat.* **79**, 117-121.

*Deane, H. W., and Seligman, A. M. (1953). *Vitamins and Hormones* **11**, 173-204. (Cytochemistry of ketosteroids.)

Dempsey, E. W., and Bassett, D. L. (1943). *Endocrinology* **33**, 384-401.

Ecker, A. (1846). "Die feinere Bau der Nehennieren beim Menschen und den vier Wirbeltierklassen." Braunschweig. (Quoted by Biedl.)

Elliott, T. R., and Tuckett, I. (1906). *J. Physiol.* (*London*) **34**, 332-369.

Eränko, O. (1955). *Acta Endocrinol.* **18**, 189-200.

Feldman, J. D. (1951). *Anat. Record* **109**, 41-69.

Feigin, I. (1956). *J. Biophys. Biochem. Cytol.* **2**, 213-214.

Fex, J. (1920). *Biochem. Z.* **104**, 82-174.

Finean, J. B. (1953). *Experientia* **9**, 17-19.

Finean, J. B. (1956). *In* "Biochemical Problems of Lipids" (G. Popják and E. Le Breton, eds.), pp. 127-131. Butterworth, London.

Francis, C. M. (1955). *J. Comp. Neurol.* **103**, 355-383.

*Frey-Wyssling, A. (1953). "Submicroscopic Morphology of Protoplasm and Its Derivatives," 2nd ed. Elsevier, Amsterdam.

Friedman, M., Byers, S. O., and St. George, S. (1956). *Am. J. Physiol.* **184**, 141-144.

*Gomori, G. (1952). "Microscopic Histochemistry." Univ. Chicago Press, Chicago, Illinois.

Greep, R. O., and Deane, H. W. (1949). *Ann. N.Y. Acad. Sci.* **50** (Art. 6) 596-615.

Grundland, I., Bulliard, H., and Maillet, M. (1949). *Compt. rend. soc. biol.* **143**, 771-773.

Harrison, R. G., and Cain, A. J. (1947). *J. Anat.* **81**, 286-299.

*Hartman, F. A., and Brownell, K. A. (1949). "The Adrenal Gland." Lea and Febiger, Philadelphia, Pennsylvania.

*Hartshorne, N. H., and Stuart, A. (1950). "Crystals and the Polarising Microscope." Arnold, London.

Henderson, A. E. (1956). *J. Histochem. and Cytochem.* **4**, 153-158.

Hillarp, N. A., and Nilson, B. (1954). *Acta Physiol. Scand.* **32**, 11-18.

His, W. (1865). *Arch. mikroskop. Anat. u. Entwicklungsmech.* **1**, 151-202. (Quoted by Biedl.)

Johnson, A. C., McNabb, A. R., and Rossiter, R. J. (1949). *Biochem. J.* **45**, 500-508.

*Johnson, A. C., McNabb, A. R., and Rossiter, R. J. (1950). *A.M.A. Arch. Neurol. Psychiat.* **64**, 105-121. (Wallerian degeneration.)

*Jones, I. C. (1957). "The Adrenal Cortex." Cambridge Univ. Press, London and New York.

Josimovich, J. B., Ladman, A. J., and Deane, H. W. (1954). *Endocrinology* **54**, 627-639.

Kaiserling, C., and Orgler, A. (1902). *Arch. pathol. Anat. u. Physiol. Virchow's* **167**, 296-310.

Kandutsch, A. A., Murphy, E. D., and Dreisbach, M. E. (1956a). *Cancer Research* **16**, 63-66.

Kandutsch, A. A., Murphy, E. D., and Dreisbach, M. E. (1956b). *Arch. Biochem. Biophys.* **61**, 450-455.

Kay, W., and Whitehead, R. (1935). *J. Pathol. Bacteriol.* **41**, 293-301.

Kent, S. P. (1952). *A.M.A. Arch. Pathol.* **54**, 439-442.

Knouff, R. A., Brown, J. B., and Schneider, B. M. (1941). *Anat. Record* **79**, 17-38.

Leulier, A., and Revol, L. (1930). *Bull. histol. appl. physiol. et pathol. et tech. microscop.* **7**, 241-250.

Leydig, F. (1857). "Lehrbuch der Histologie der Menschen und der Tiere." Frankfurt. (Quoted by Biedl.)

*Lison, L. (1936). "Histochimie animale." Gauthier Villars, Paris.

McEnery, W. B., and Nelson, W. O. (1950). *Anat. Record* **106**, 221-222.

McKay, D. G., Robinson, D., and Hertig, A. T. (1949). *Am. J. Obstet. Gynecol.* **58**, 625-639.

MacLachlan, P. L., Hodge, H. C., and Whitehead, R. (1941). *J. Biol. Chem.* **139**, 185-191.

McMillan, G. C., Klatzo, I., and Duff, G. L. (1954). *Lab. Invest.* **3**, 451-468.

Mayer, A., Rathery, F., and Schaeffer, G. (1914-15). *J. physiol. et pathol. gén.* **16**, 581-596; 606-622.

Melampy, R. M., and Cavazos, L. F. (1954). *Proc. Soc. Exptl. Biol. Med.* **87**, 297.

*Montagna, W. (1956). "The Structure and Function of Skin." Academic Press, New York.

Montagna, W., and Hamilton, J. B. (1951). *Anat. Record* **109**, 635-659.

Montagna, W., and Norback, C. R. (1947). *Am. J. Anat.* **81**, 39-61.

Montagna, W., Chase, H. B., and Melargagno, H. P. (1952). *J. Invest. Dermatol.* **19**, 83-94.

Moog, F., Bennett, C. J., and Dean, C. M., Jr. (1954). *Anat. Record* **120**, 873-891.

Okey, R. (1944). *J. Biol. Chem.* **156**, 179-190.

Oleson, M. C., and Bloor, W. R. (1941). *J. Biol. Chem.* **141**, 349-354.

*Parkes, A. S. (1945). *Physiol. Revs.* **25**, 203-254. (Adrenal gonad relationship.)

*Pearse, A. G. E. (1953). "Histochemistry." Churchill, London.

Perry, S. V. (1952). *Biochim. et Biophys. Acta* **8**, 499-509.

Pincus, G. (1943). *Endocrinology* **32**, 176-184.

*Pirani, C. L. (1952). *Metabolism Clin. and Exptl.* **1**, 197-222. (Adrenals and ascorbic acid.)

Plecnik, J. (1902). *Arch. mikroskop. Anat. u. Entwicklungsmech.* **60**, 414-427.

Pollock, W. F. (1942). *Anat. Record* **84**, 23-29.

Ponder, E. (1954). *Blood* **9**, 227-235.

Popják, G. (1944). *J. Pathol. Bacteriol.* **55**, 485-496.

Rabl, H. (1891). *Arch. mikroskop. Anat. u. Entwicklungsmech.* **38**, 492-523.

Race, G. J., Nickey, W. M., Wolf, P. S., and Jordan, E. J. (1957). *A.M.A. Arch. Pathol.* **64**, 312-323.

Reiner, C. B. (1953). *Lab. Invest.* **2**, 140-151.

Rogers, W. F., and Williams, R. H. (1947). *A.M.A. Arch. Pathol.* **44**, 126-137.

Rosenheim, O., and Tebb, M. C. (1909). *J. Physiol (London)* **38**, Proc. liv.

*Sayers, G., and Sayers, M. A. (1949). *Ann. N.Y. Acad. Sci.* **50** (Art. 6) 522-539. (Pituitary-adrenal system.)

Sayers, G., Sayers, M. A., Liang, T. Y., and Long, C. N. H. (1946). *Endocrinology* **38**, 1-9.

Schultz, A. (1924-25). *Zentr. allgem. Pathol. u. pathol. Anat.* **35**, 314-317.

Schultz, A., and Löhr, G. (1925). *Zentr. allgem. Pathol. u. pathol. Anat.* **36**, 529-533; *Verhandl deut. pathol. Ges.* (20th Meeting) pp. 120-123.

Seligman, A. M., and Ashbel, R. (1951). *Cancer* **4**, 579-596.

Seligman, A. M., and Ashbel, R. (1952). *Endocrinology* **50**, 338-349.

Sperry, W. M., and Stoyanoff, U. A. (1935). *J. Nutrition* **9**, 131-155.

Stenger, E. G., Morsdorf, K., and Dornenjoz, R. (1955). *Arzneimittel-Forsch.* **5**, 489-90.

Suskind, R. R. (1951). *J. Invest. Dermatol.* **17**, 37-54.

*Swann, H. G. (1940). *Physiol. Revs.* **20**, 493-521. (Adrenals.)

Unna, P. G., and Golodetz, L. (1909). *Biochem. Z.* **20**, 469-502.

Virchow, R. (1857). *Arch. pathol. Anat. u. Physiol. Virchow's* **12**, 15.

von Brunn, A. (1872). *Arch. mikroskop. Anat. u. Entwicklungsmech.* **8**, 618-638.

Waugh, D. F. (1950). *Ann. N.Y. Acad. Sci.* **50** (Art. 8) 835-851.

Weber, A. F., Philips, M. G., and Bell, J. T., Jr. (1956). *J. Histochem. and Cytochem.* **4**, 308-309.

Whitehead, R. (1934a). *J. Pathol. Bacteriol.* **39**, 443-447.

Whitehead, R. (1934b). *J. Anat.* **69**, 72-77.

Whitehead, R. (1936a). *J. Anat.* **70**, 123-125.

Whitehead, R. (1936b). *J. Anat.* **70**, 380-385.

Whitehead, R. (1937). *J. Pathol. Bacteriol.* **45**, 441-446.

Whitehead, R. (1942). *J. Pathol. Bacteriol.* **54**, 169-176.

Winkler, K. C., and Bungenberg de Jong, H. G. (1941). *Arch. néerl. physiol.* **25**, 431–466, 467–508.

Wislocki, G. B. (1949). *Endocrinology* **44**, 167-189.

Wislocki, G. B., and Dempsey, E. W. (1948). *Am. J. Anat.* **83**, 1-30.

*Yoffey, J. M. (1953). *In* "The Suprarenal Cortex" (J. M. Yoffey, ed.), pp. 31-38, Academic Press, New York.

Yoffey, J. M., and Baxter, J. S. (1947). *J. Anat.* **81**, 335-342.

Yoffey, J. M., and Baxter, J. S. (1949). *J. Anat.* **83**, 89-98.

*Young, J. Z. (1948). *Symposia Soc. Exptl. Biol.* **2**, 57-74. (Nerves.)

Chapter 10

PATHOLOGICAL MANIFESTATIONS OF ABNORMAL CHOLESTEROL METABOLISM

David Adlersberg and Harry Sobotka

I. Introduction

Our knowledge of the biochemistry of cholesterol forms a strange mosaic. The rather accurate methods of quantitative cholesterol analysis have produced a wealth of data on the concentration of cholesterol in the body fluids and tissues of man and other mammals under physiological and pathological conditions. Tracer techniques using radioactive carbon have permitted a selection among the numerous pathways of synthesis, which may be devised on paper; we have more or less well-established concepts of the synthesis of cholesterol from acetic acid and from certain branched C_5 and C_6 compounds which contain the isopentane or isoprene skeleton (see Chapter 6). Between the two domains of knowledge there are wide stretches of unknown territory. Nothing is known of the purpose of cholesterol in the metabolic economy, in contrast to e.g. the bile acids, whose signal physico-chemical properties permit to attribute to them a well-circumscribed physiological function, a concept substantiated by the facts of evolution. Even aside from teleological considerations, one does not know the significance of the increases and decreases of cholesterol in the body and its organs, and very little about the mechanisms by which cholesterol influences metabolic processes. Like lanolin and like the phosphatids whose metabolic functions are equally puzzling, cholesterol is not water soluble in the strict sense of the word, but without forming a visible opaque or lactescent emulsion, it is found in the body fluids in dispersed form, kept in solution by complex formation with protein and phosphatides. This dual character, intermediary between water solubility and lipid solubility, often causes cholesterol to seek a position on boundaries between two phases and to arrange itself on such interfaces in monomolecular layers.

The combined surface of the red blood corpuscles in 1 ml. of blood amounts to 7000 cm.^{2} (8 sq. ft.). To cover this area with a monomolecular layer requires approximately as much cholesterol as is contained in the corresponding volume of blood plasma, namely, about 2 mg./1 ml. Considering the protective action of cholesterol against hemolysis, this relationship may be important in nephrosis, where an increase in the plasma cholesterol goes hand in hand with enhanced resistance of the red blood cells to hemolysis.

The anomalies in the cholesterol content of blood and organs will be discussed in the following order: (1) hypercholesteremia, essential and in various diseases, (2) hypocholesteremia, and (3) cholesterol deposition.

The blood cholesterol values cannot tell us the whole story of a disease, but give a sometimes distorted cross-section. Cholesterol exerts a carrier function for fatty acids, which explains its rise in the blood during inanition, when it helps in transporting mobilized peripheral fat. There are also superimposed the individual variations of the basic level, which depend not only on sex and age, but also on genetic factors, which will be discussed in the following section.

Because of the interrelation of cholesterol and of its solubility with other colloidal serum constituents, globulins and phospholipids, it may appear desirable to consider cholesterol saturation and capacity rather than actual cholesterol content of the blood. The tendency of cholesterol to form pathological deposits may depend on the capacity of the blood to carry smaller or larger amounts of cholesterol and on the proportion of the cholesterol actually so carried to this capacity.

Insight into the physiology of cholesterol metabolism has accumulated and more will be gained by the study of pathological conditions involving the steroids. The belief that the investigation of the normal should precede that of the pathological has been called erroneous by an author who continues "As a matter of fact the investigation of the abnormal in scientific research precedes that of the normal. The investigation of the abnormal is one of the most potent instruments for new discoveries. The method of experimentation . . . is in fact the creation of artificial conditions, in other words, the effecting of abnormal states" (Sidis, 1939).

II. Normal Cholesterol Levels in Serum

It has been shown that age and sex affect serum lipid levels in man (Keys et al., 1950; McMahon et al., 1951; Adlersberg et al., 1956a). Diet and particularly dietary fat are probably related to serum lipid concentrations (Keys, 1953, 1955, 1956; Brock and Bronte-Stewart, 1955). The role of other factors, such as ethnic origin, occupation, stress, physical activity, smoking, and alcohol is questionable (Walker and Arvidsson, 1954; Keys, 1955). An important genetic component appears to be concerned with the determination of serum cholesterol and phospholipid levels. A brief summary of the available information will be given in the subsequent text.

Observations on serum cholesterol levels in various population groups have been reported by Page et al. (1935), Barker (1939), and Kornerup (1950). More recently Keys et al. (1950) studied 2056 men of ages 17–78 in a middle-income group in Minnesota. McMahon et al. (1951) performed 822 serum cholesterol determinations in 554 normal persons of ages 10–90. Epstein and Boas (1955) included cholesterol studies in their observations on prevalence of manifest atherosclerosis in a working population in New York that consisted mainly of Jews and Italians. Keys and co-workers extended their cholesterol studies to population groups in England (Keys and Keys, 1954); Southern Italy (Naples; Keys et al., 1954a) and Spain (Madrid; Keys et al., 1954b). Oliver and Boyd (1954, 1955a) performed plasma cholesterol determinations in control groups of men and women aged 30 to 70+ in Scotland. Walker and Arvidsson (1954) studied the changes with age in serum cholesterol levels in the South African Bantu. Adlersberg et al. (1956a) examined approximately 1200 healthy males and females between the ages of 2 and 77 years of low-middle income in New York. The almost completely white population was otherwise moderately heterogenous, with a distinct predominance of families of Italian and Irish origin. The total serum cholesterol level of the males remained constant from age 2 through 19. From age 20 through 33 there was a significant increase of total cholesterol level, averaging 3.6 mg. per 100 ml. per year. Thereafter, until age 60, there was no further change. The total serum cholesterol level of the females did not change significantly from age 2 through 32, although there appeared to be a slight decrease from age 2 through 20. From age 33 through 58 a significant rate of increase of 3.2 mg. per 100 ml. per year occurred (Tables IA and B and Fig. 1).

TABLE IA

SERUM CHOLESTEROL LEVELS BY AGE IN MALES AND FEMALES[a]

	Males			Females		
Age group, (yr.)	No.	Mean[b]	$\sigma(x)$	No.	Mean[b]	$\sigma(x)$
3–7[c]	34	179.8	6.48	36	209.0	7.13
8–12[c]	54	180.4	3.98	55	196.4	4.40
13–17	46	175.5	5.10	53	182.9	4.77
18–22	22	185.2	11.76	24	192.6	8.78
23–27	16	194.5	9.74	40	201.9	6.27
28–32[c]	38	243.1	8.02	50	200.1	4.60
33–37[c]	53	231.0	6.14	72	206.9	4.52
38–42[c]	57	246.9	6.11	64	224.5	4.94
43–47	77	237.2	5.30	56	238.9	6.93
48–52	63	238.8	5.73	34	249.5	9.13
53–57[c]	45	239.7	7.43	28	285.8	8.38
58–62	34	236.2	9.08	20	263.8	14.82
63–67	19	249.7	13.05	14	259.9	—
68–72	6	242.5	—	3	241.8	—
73 and 77	2	200.5	—	—		
Total	566			549		

[a] From Adlersberg et al. (1956a).

[b] In mg./100 ml.

[c] The probability that these differences between males and females would arise by accidents of sampling is less than 1 in 1,000.

The changes in serum phospholipid levels with age were similar to the changes in serum cholesterol levels in the two sexes (Fig. 2, Table IC). There were no significant differences between the sexes and between any age groups in the ratio of free to total cholesterol. The cholesterol-phospholipid ratio appeared to be a function of the change in the serum cholesterol level and was independent of age. For each increase in the serum cholesterol level of 1 mg. per 100 ml., there was a 0.71 mg. increase of phospholipid in the serum in the females and a

TABLE IB

CHANGES IN SERUM CHOLESTEROL LEVEL WITH AGE IN MALES AND FEMALES[a]

Age-interval (yr.)	No.	b[b]	P[c]
Males			
2–19	154	—0.278	>0.20
20–33	74	3.622	0.01>P>0.001
34–50	213	—0.445	>0.20
51–60	96	—0.821	>0.20
Females			
2–13	100	—1.478	>0.20
14–20	58	—2.065	>0.20
21–32	104	—1.077	>0.20
33–58	263	3.181	<0.001

[a] From Adlersberg et al. (1956a).

[b] The average annual change of total serum cholesterol in mg./100 ml. is represented by the coefficient b in the regression equation $Y = a + bX$, where X = age in yr. and Y = serum cholesterol level.

[c] Probability that the true value of the average annual change may be zero.

TABLE IC

SERUM PHOSPHOLIPID LEVELS BY AGE IN MALES AND FEMALES[a]

Age group (yr.)	Males			Females		
	No.	Mean[b]	$\sigma(x)$	No.	Mean[b]	$\sigma(x)$
3–7 [c]	29	227.1	8.35	31	261.9	7.96
8–12	50	233.2	4.94	51	241.7	5.10
13–17	40	220.6	5.98	46	235.5	6.54
18–22	20	217.0	13.40	21	243.7	9.35
23–27	16	249.4	12.99	38	249.0	7.33
28–32[c]	34	285.3	8.71	45	241.4	4.56
33–37	45	270.0	6.63	67	255.0	4.24
38–42[c]	49	289.4	5.93	61	270.2	4.46
43–47	61	280.9	6.47	50	275.2	6.22
48–52	47	287.5	8.43	31	290.9	7.79
53–57	41	282.8	8.75	26	313.7	9.91
58–62	30	275.3	9.54	18	298.3	11.84
63–67	19	298.4	11.19	14	317.1	—
68–72	6	279.8	—	3	279.3	—
73 and 77	2	244.0	—	—		
Total	489			502		

[a] From Adlersberg et al. (1956a).

[b] In mg./100 ml.

[c] The probability that these differences between males and females would arise by accidents of sampling is less than 1 in 1,000.

0.67 mg. increase in the males. In other words, as the serum cholesterol level increased, the ratio of cholesterol to phospholipid became greater. The differences between males and females in the changes of lipid levels with age are worthy of note. The period of marked increase of serum

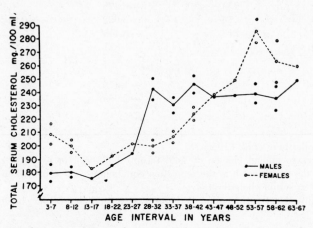

Fig. 1.   Graphic presentation of serum cholesterol levels by age in both sexes (from Adlersberg *et al.*, 1956).

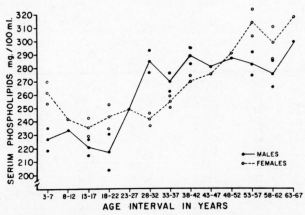

Fig. 2.   Graphic presentation of serum phospholipid levels by age in both sexes (from Adlersberg *et al.*, 1956).

lipid levels, which occurs physiologically in both sexes, starts 13 years later in women than in men and lasts 12 years longer.

A survey of the available data reveals marked differences in the cholesterol levels of the various population groups. There are also differences in α- and β-lipoproteins and in the cholesterol-phospholipid ratio

(Walker and Arvidsson, 1954; Higginson, 1956). In certain populations, e.g., in the South African Bantu, the high incidence of malnutrition, liver disease (cirrhosis, hepatoma), and parasitic infestation may also affect the average serum lipid levels. Therefore, it must be concluded that each survey of serum lipid levels is valid for the specific population only and that comparisons between populations living under different geographical, cultural, economic, and social conditions are of relative value only. (See Chapter 5.)

Studies, to be described later, suggest that genetic factors are important in the etiology of hypercholesteremia. There is, in addition, evidence that the genotype (genetic constitution) of an individual is of primary importance in determining serum cholesterol levels of healthy

TABLE II
SERUM CHOLESTEROL; CORRELATION COEFFICIENTS[a, b]

Item	N	r	P
Father-Mother	201	0.0056	>0.2
Father-Child	373	0.2101	<0.001
Mother-Child	373	0.3646	<0.001
Sib-Sib	123	0.3701[c]	<0.001
Father-Son	181	0.1558	<0.01
Father-Daughter	192	0.2616	<0.001
Mother-Son	181	0.3402	<0.001
Mother-Daughter	192	0.3903	<0.001

[a] From Schaefer et al. (1957).

[b] All cholesterol levels were converted to equivalent levels for males aged 20 to eliminate factors of age and sex.

[c] Intraclass r based on first two sibs only.

persons. This observation is based on a study of 201 families composed of 201 fathers, 201 mothers, 197 daughters, and 167 sons (Adlersberg et al., 1954a; Schaefer et al., 1957). The average age of the fathers was 44.2, of the mothers 40.5 years, of the daughters 13.1 years, and of the sons 12.7 years.

If the genotype of an individual is important in determining serum cholesterol levels, the serum cholesterol levels of the fathers and mothers should not be correlated while those of the fathers and their children, and the mothers and their children, and of sibs should be positively correlated. Alternately, if environmental factors are of primary importance in determining serum cholesterol levels, the levels in the parents' sera should be correlated with each other as well as with those in their children.

In accordance with expectation based on the hypothesis that the genotype is of primary importance in determining serum cholesterol levels, the correlation coefficient between the parents is essentially zero, while those between father and child, mother and child, and sibs are positive and significantly different from zero (Table II). The probability that the difference (0.1545) between the correlation coefficient for the mother-child pairs (0.3646) and that for the father-child pairs (0.2101) may be chance is approximately 0.02.

Thus the data derived from correlation coefficient analyses are consistent with the hypothesis that there is an important genetic component in determining serum cholesterol levels in healthy persons.

III. Hypercholesteremia

A. PRIMARY HYPERCHOLESTEREMIA

1. Essential Hypercholesteremia and Essential Hyperlipemia

Hypercholesteremia may be considered a common finding in most patients with early coronary atherosclerosis (Boas and Adlersberg, 1945; Boas et al., 1948; Adlersberg, 1951). Familial xanthomatosis appears to be the most severe form of this inborn error of lipid metabolism, and coronary atherosclerosis is frequent in this disorder. Uncomplicated coronary atherosclerosis in young persons probably represents a milder form of this metabolic disturbance, the elevated serum cholesterol levels, often found in these individuals, being only one important aspect of a disturbed lipid or lipoprotein metabolism (Adlersberg et al., 1949; Barr et al., 1951; Barr, 1953, 1955).

Until recently, studies of this subject dealt only with a single family (Bloom et al., 1942) or with families of persons known to have either xanthomatosis (Müller, 1938; Wilkinson et al., 1948) or early coronary artery disease (Boas and Adlersberg, 1945; Boas et al., 1948). In a previous investigation the incidence of hereditary hypercholesteremia was estimated in a sample of the population of Mount Sinai Hospital in New York City (Adlersberg et al., 1952; Schaefer et al., 1953). Five hundred persons, 250 men and 250 women, consecutive admissions to the medical wards, as well as the families of 59 of the probands, who proved to have essential idiopathic hypercholesteremia, were studied. The frequency of this disorder was found to be 12%, considering hypercholesteremia to be present in those whose serum cholesterol level was greater than the upper 5% level of the standards of Keys et al. (1950). The frequency of hypercholesteremia among the siblings and children of the hypercholesteremic probands was 36.2% and 34.0%, respectively, by these same standards. The assumption, based on these data, was that hypercholesteremia, in the families of hypercholesteremic probands, is determined by a dominant gene with incomplete penetrance, a hypothesis in accord with that of others (Wilkinson *et al.*, 1948; Adlersberg *et al.*, 1949).

Idiopathic hyperlipemia differs from idiopathic hypercholesteremia in the milky or creamy appearance (lactescence) of the serum and in decided elevation of serum neutral fats and total lipids in the fasting state. Although both abnormalities resemble each other to a certain extent, there are distinct clinical and biochemical differences between them.

Adlersberg (1955) studied 25 persons (index patients) with idiopathic hyperlipemia and 84 members of the families of 20 of these patients. Together with the 5 patients with idiopathic hyperlipemia whose families were not available for study, this group included 89 persons, 58 males and 31 females. Another series included 77 index patients with idiopathic hypercholesteremia with 341 family members and 49 individual patients, a total of 390 persons, 224 males and 166 females. A comparison of idiopathic hyperlipemia and idiopathic hypercholesteremia in their clinical and chemical manifestations is given in Tables III and IV. Among the index patients with either disorder and among their family members there was a high incidence of coronary artery disease; 34% among those with idiopathic hyperlipemia and 43% among those with idiopathic hypercholesteremia. The difference in incidence of coronary artery disease might be in part caused by differences in selection of the patients in the two groups. While a considerable number of the index patients with idiopathic hyperlipemia came under medical care for noncardiac disorders such as pancreatitis and diabetes, those with idiopathic hypercholesteremia were treated almost exclusively for cardiac disease. The incidence of 33% of coronary artery disease among the families with idiopathic hyperlipemia supports the concept that this error of lipid metabolism represents a predisposition to coronary artery disease not too different from that found in idiopathic hypercholesteremia (Soffer and Murray, 1954; Adlersberg, 1955). The observations justify a revision of the old premise that idiopathic hyperlipemia is simply an innocuous abnormality of the blood.

While some information is at hand concerning the incidence of idiopathic hypercholesteremia in the population at large (Schaefer *et al.*, 1953; Adlersberg *et al.*, 1954a), no corresponding data on idiopathic hyperlipemia are available. Based on a rough estimate, idiopathic hypercholesteremia appears to be 5 to 6 times as frequent as idiopathic hyperlipemia. Both idiopathic hyperlipemia and idiopathic hypercholesteremia were encountered more frequently among men. In idiopathic hypercholesteremia men represented 57% of the total number observed. In idiopathic hyperlipemia the preponderance of men was even

TABLE III
COMPARISON OF IDIOPATHIC HYPERLIPEMIA AND IDIOPATHIC HYPERCHOLESTEREMIA
(CLINICAL DATA)[a]

	Idiopathic hyper- lipemia	Idiopathic hyper- choles- teremia
Number of index patients with family study	20	77
Number of persons in the families	84	341
Number of individual patients without family study	5	49
Total number of persons	89	390
Males	58	224
Females	31	166
Xanthelasma of the eyelids	2(2%)	88(23%)
Xanthoma tendinosum	1(1%)	19(10%)[b]
Xanthoma tuberosum	12(14%)	3(2%)[b]
Coronary artery disease	30(34%)	168(43%)
Recurrent pancreatitis	5(6.6%)	1(0.25%)
Diabetes	6(7%)	5(3%)[b]
Asymptomatic index patients	4	8

[a] From Adlersberg (1955).
[b] This number is based on the study of 189 persons of the "new" group.

TABLE IV
COMPARISON OF IDIOPATHIC HYPERLIPEMIA AND IDIOPATHIC HYPERCHOLESTEREMIA
(CHEMICAL DATA)[a]

	Idiopathic hyperlipemia	Idiopathic hypercholesteremia[b]
Lactescence of serum	28	0
Lipemia retinalis	3	0
Average serum total cholesterol		
Index patients	623 mg.%	366 mg.%
All persons	412 mg.%	319 mg.%
Average serum esterified cholesterol		
Index patients	377 mg.%	263 mg.%
All persons	260 mg.%	231 mg.%
Average serum phospholipids		
Index patients	588 mg.%	342 mg.%
All persons	420 mg.%	314 mg.%
Average serum neutral fat		
Index patients	2387 mg.%	436 mg.%
All persons	2541 mg.%	468 mg.%
Average total serum lipids		
Index patients	3598 mg.%	1144 mg.%
All persons	3373 mg.%	1101 mg.%

[a] From Adlersberg (1955).
[b] The chemical data presented in this column are based on the study of 189 persons of the "new" group.

more pronounced: 65% were men and 35% women. The sex differences are further illustrated by the figures obtained in the index patients of the two series. Among those with idiopathic hyperlipemia there were 18 men and 7 women (72% male). In the idiopathic hypercholesteremia group there were 74 men and 52 women (59% male).

Of the 25 index patients with idiopathic hyperlipemia, 6 had diabetes mellitus of the mild variety usually associated with moderate or severe obesity. Only two of these patients required insulin; in the others good diabetic control could be achieved by diet regulation alone. In five of these patients there was evidence of vascular disease; four, two of whom had mild hypertension, exhibited evidence of coronary artery disease, and the fifth had thrombosis of the central retinal vein with loss of vision in one eye. The syndrome of idiopathic hyperlipemia, diabetes mellitus, and vascular disease has been described elsewhere, based on observation of these patients over a period of many months to many years (Adlersberg and Wang, 1955). Among 62 index patients with idiopathic hypercholesteremia, 3 had mild diabetes. Based on this small number, it appears that diabetes occurs more frequently in families with idiopathic hyperlipemia (7%) than in those with idiopathic hypercholesteremia (3%).

Five of the 25 index patients with idiopathic hyperlipemia presented evidence of relapsing pancreatitis. The diagnosis was established by clinical observations, chemical analysis of the blood, urine, and pancreatic enzymes, roentgen studies of the gastrointestinal tract, and, in one instance, by operation. Poulsen (1950) and Klatskin and Gordon (1952) stressed the occurrence of relapsing pancreatitis in patients with idiopathic hyperlipemia. Among other pathogenetic possibilities, that of fat emboli in the pancreatic vessels was considered. In each of the patients with recurrent pancreatitis of this series considerable additional elevation of all serum lipids but especially of triglycerides and total lipids was noted during the attacks and shortly thereafter. One of these patients had diabetes mellitus of the mild variety described above. One may reason that diabetes mellitus in these patients may be secondary to associated pancreatitis in idiopathic hyperlipemia in some instances, even if a definite history of the former is not obtained (Adlersberg and Wang, 1955).

Although both abnormalities of lipid metabolism may be associated with xanthomatosis, there were distinct differences in the variety of clinical manifestations. In the index patients and families with idiopathic hyperlipemia, xanthelasma of the eyelids was noted in 2.2%, xanthoma tendinosum in 1.1%, and xanthoma tuberosum in 13.5%. In contrast, in the group of idiopathic hypercholesteremia, xanthelasma of

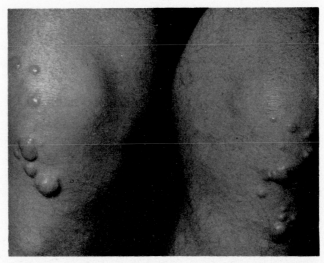

FIG. 3. Xanthoma tuberosum in a patient with idiopathic hyperlipemia (from Adlersberg, 1955).

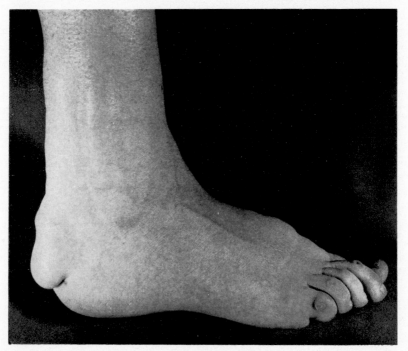

FIG. 4. Xanthoma tendinosum of Achilles tendon in a patient with idiopathic hypercholesteremia (from Adlersberg et al., 1949).

the eyelids was present in 23%, xanthoma tendinosum in 10%, and xanthoma tuberosum in 1.6%. The data indicate that xanthomatosis in idiopathic hyperlipemia was usually of the tuberosum type (Fig. 3) while that seen in idiopathic hypercholesteremia was usually of the tendinosum variety (Figs. 4 and 5). Xanthelasma of the lids was rare in the former and was often seen in the latter. In contrast, xanthoma of the eruptive type was seen in a few instances in the xanthoma tuberosum

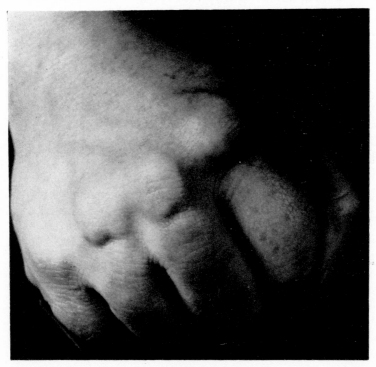

Fig. 5. Xanthoma tendinosum of finger tendons in a patient with idiopathic hypercholesteremia (from Adlersberg *et al.*, 1949).

variety only. These findings are in accord with those of other observers (Lever *et al.*, 1954, 1955).

A number of index patients with idiopathic hyperlipemia and idiopathic hypercholesteremia and their close blood relatives remained asymptomatic despite marked abnormalities of their serum lipid pattern over periods of many years. Certain similarities between the clinical behavior of idiopathic hypercholesteremia and gout have been mentioned elsewhere (Adlersberg, 1949, 1955). In gout, several members within one family may exhibit elevation of serum uric acid, but only one or two may show clinical manifestations of gout or exhibit uric acid deposition in the tissues (tophi). This analogy may be extended to idiopathic hypercholesteremia. For manifest symptoms to appear in either disorder additional mechanisms must be operating, perhaps at the tissue level. The basic metabolic disturbance in idiopathic hypercholesteremia, like that in gout, acts only as a conditioning factor. Many additional factors involved in the genesis of atherosclerosis have been considered in extensive reviews recently published (Gubner and Ungerleider, 1949; Katz and Dauber, 1945). Among them the time factor must be consideerd. The concentration as well as the duration of the metabolic defect of lipid metabolism may influence the deposition of these substances in the tissues (Anitchkow, 1933; Wang *et al.*, 1954).

2. Genetic Aspects

The hereditary nature of idiopathic hypercholesteremia (familial xanthomatosis) has been emphasized repeatedly (Bloom *et al.*, 1942; Müller, 1938; Wilkinson *et al.*, 1948; Adlersberg, 1951, 1955). The mode of transmission of this metabolic fault has been debated but not fully established. This has been due in part to the use of the cutaneous lesions instead of the serum cholesterol levels as a characteristic sign of the disorder. A detailed discussion of the problem was presented elsewhere (Adlersberg *et al.*, 1949; Stecher and Hersh, 1949).

Investigation of families of patients with idiopathic hyperlipemia revealed the interesting fact that among these families both errors of lipid metabolism, i.e. idiopathic hyperlipemia and idiopathic hypercholesteremia, may be seen. Figure 6 presents such a mixed family.

The index patient was a mild diabetic who showed marked lactescence of the serum and the typical chemical findings of idiopathic hyperlipemia. Three of his sons, all in perfect health, had evidence of idiopathic hypercholesteremia, but no hyperlipemia, and their sera were always clear. A fourth son was known to have diabetes but was not available for study. The study of families with idiopathic hyperlipemia suggested that this disorder and idiopathic hypercholesteremia are closely related. One may be considered a variant of the other and may be transmitted by a dominant trait with incomplete penetrance.

3. Biochemical Aspects

The biochemical differences between idiopathic hyperlipemia and idiopathic hypercholesteremia were reflected in the serum lipid partition estimated by chemical analysis and in the serum lipoproteins determined by paper electrophoresis or by starch electrophoresis.

Serum lipid partitions of both groups are compared in Table IV. The lactescence of the serum which characterizes idiopathic hyperlipemia as an entity is associated with profound elevation of neutral fat and total lipid as well as an increase in serum cholesterol and phospholipids far above the levels encountered in idiopathic hypercholesteremia. Only in the mildest instances was there an elevation of neutral fat and total lipids

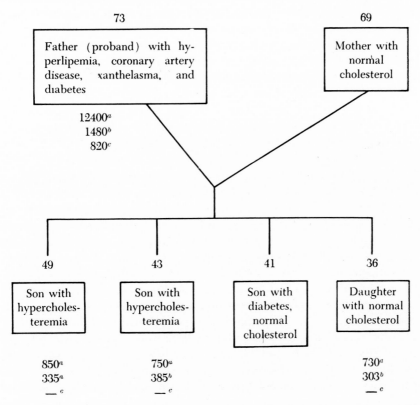

73

Father (proband) with hyperlipemia, coronary artery disease, xanthelasma, and diabetes

69

Mother with normal cholesterol

12400[a]
1480[b]
820[c]

49

Son with hypercholesteremia

43

Son with hypercholesteremia

41

Son with diabetes, normal cholesterol

36

Daughter with normal cholesterol

850[a]
335[a]
— [c]

750[a]
385[b]
— [c]

730[a]
303[b]
— [c]

Fig. 6. The index patient (proband) had idiopathic hyperlipemia; three of his children exhibited idiopathic hypercholesteremia ("mixed" family). Numbers above boxes indicate age in years. Numbers below boxes indicate: [a] serum total lipids; [b] serum cholesterol; [c] serum phospholipid (from Adlersberg, 1955).

with normal levels of cholesterol and phospholipids. If the defective fat clearance of the serum was controlled by dietary adjustment (low-fat diet), the lipid pattern of patients with idiopathic hyperlipemia closely resembled that of idiopathic hypercholesteremia in many instances. The serum turbidity cleared up to a great extent, or even completely. There was a precipitous fall in serum neutral fat and total lipid and a concomitant decrease of serum cholesterol and phospholipid.

Studies of serum lipoproteins by paper electrophoresis were performed in 14 patients with idiopathic hyperlipemia, 11 men and 3 women, average age 47 years. Compared with a series of normal men and women, patients in this group exhibited marked elevation of the O-fraction (lipid adsorbed at the point of application of the serum and representing mainly neutral fat), while β-lipoprotein concentration was unaltered. Similar studies in 29 patients with idiopathic hypercholesteremia (14 women and 15 men), average age 47 years, revealed only moderate depression of α-lipoprotein, moderate elevation of β-lipoprotein, and slight increase in the O-fraction. However, in all instances inspection of the patterns revealed the β-lipoprotein peak to be in the form of a sharp spike which appeared characteristic of idiopathic hypercholesteremia. The data obtained in both groups are summarized in Table V. They shed additional light on the metabolic differences that exist between the two errors of lipid metabolism (Lever et al., 1954, 1955).

Comparative analysis of cholesterol and phospholipid in the various serum lipoproteins, separated simultaneously by starch and paper electrophoresis (Kunkel and Slater, 1952; Nikkilä, 1953; Ackermann et al., 1954; Schettler, 1955), revealed additional differences when normal serum and serums from patients with idiopathic hypercholesteremia and with idiopathic hyperlipemia were analyzed (Paronetto et al., 1956).

In idiopathic hypercholesteremia, regardless of the method of electrophoresis used, the cholesterol and phospholipid contents were markedly increased in the β-lipoprotein fraction and decreased in the α-lipoprotein fraction (Fig. 7). In idiopathic hyperlipemia, marked differences in the distribution of cholesterol and phospholipid were observed with the two methods of electrophoresis. When starch was used as the supporting medium, elevation of cholesterol and phospholipid in the α$_2$-lipoprotein fraction was the prominent feature, whereas when paper was used the elevation of these lipids was seen in the β-lipoprotein (Fig. 7). By both methods, decrease of these lipids was observed in α-lipoprotein.

Considerable adsorption of serum triglycerides (chylomicrons) to the paper was noted at the point of application. A comparison of the distribution curves of cholesterol and phospholipid by the two methods of electrophoresis showed that large amounts of cholesterol and phospholipid were present in both α$_2$ and β-lipoprotein when starch electrophoresis was used, while the major pattern of these lipids was found in the β-lipoprotein by paper electrophoresis.

The adsorption of serum lipids at the point of application in paper electrophoresis interfered with the migration of some of the cholesterol and phospholipid molecules. When starch was used as supporting

TABLE V

LIPOPROTEIN PROFILE (BY PAPER ELECTROPHORESIS) AND LIPID PARTITION (BY CHEMICAL ANALYSIS) OF THE SERUM IN PATIENTS WITH IDIO-PATHIC HYPERLIPEMIA AND IDIOPATHIC HYPERCHOLESTEREMIA[a]

| Group | No. | Age | Lipoproteins, % of total stainable lipid | | | | Lipids, mg./100 ml. | | | |
			α	β	O-Fraction	β + O	Cholesterol/esters	Phospholipids	Neutral fat	Total lipid
Idiopathic hyperlipemia	13	47	7.5 ± 5.1	50.7 ± 8.1	41.7 ± 8.9	92.4 ± 5.1	605/393 ± 222 ± 123	624 ± 203	1935 ± 394	3164 ± 1620
Idiopathic hypercholesteremia	29	48	20.0 ± 7.8	63.0 ± 6.8	17.0 ± 6.5	80.0 ± 7.8	370/262 ± 79 ± 61	351 ± 49	355 ± 124	1079 ± 187
Normal	10	37	35.3 ± 6.7	52.4 ± 7.2	12.3 ± 3.8	64.7 ± 6.7	211/157 ± 31 ± 25	242 ± 38	176	629

[a] From Adlersberg (1955).

medium, no accumulation and adsorption of triglycerides was observed at the point of origin. The triglycerides migrated freely and the cholesterol and phospholipid molecules migrated with them. This observation is probably related to the easier extractability of cholesterol "enmeshed in lipids" (Byers and Friedman, 1956).

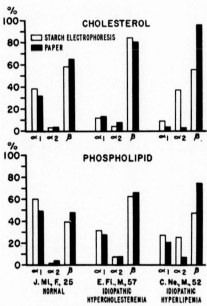

Fig. 7. Cholesterol and phospholipid contents in α_1-, α_2-, and β-lipoprotein fractions separated by starch and paper electrophoresis. No significant differences were observed between the two methods of electrophoresis in a normal person or in persons with idiopathic hypercholesteremia. In idiopathic hyperlipemia, marked increase of cholesterol and phospholipid was seen in the α_2-lipoprotein by starch electrophoresis, whereas, by paper electrophoresis, these lipids were mainly increased in the β-lipoprotein (from Paronetto et al., 1956).

B. Secondary Hypercholesteremia and Hyperlipemia

1. Diabetes

In uncomplicated, clinically controlled diabetes mellitus hypercholesteremia is rarely seen. If present, it is usually due to other causes such as biliary obstruction, renal complications, hypothyroidism, or to association with idiopathic hyperlipemia or hypercholesteremia. In uncontrolled diabetes associated with keto-acidosis elevation of all serum lipid fractions is a regular occurrence. After adequate therapy, a gradual decrease to normal levels takes place.

It is of interest that complications of diabetes in absence of ketosis or acidosis may be associated with well-defined changes in serum lipids and polysaccharides (Adlersberg et al., 1956b). Four groups of patients with diabetes are presented for comparison (Table VI).

TABLE VI

CHEMICAL DATA OF NORMAL CONTROLS AND OF DIABETIC PATIENTS WITH AND WITHOUT COMPLICATIONS[a]

Group	I Normal controls (N)	II Uncomplicated diabetes (D)	III Diabetes and retinopathy (DR)	IV Diabetes and Kimmelstiel- Wilson syndrome (DKW)
No. of cases	11	38	12	16
Cholesterol, mg.%				
Total	245 ± 54	236 ± 49	256 ± 41	318 ± 64
Esterified		174 ± 37	187 ± 22	221 ± 59
Phospholipids, mg.%	214 ± 38	259 ± 47	290 ± 33	326 ± 61
Total lipids, mg.%	629 ± 136	804 ± 182	958 ± 160	1195 ± 268
Neutral fats, mg.%	231	310	411	550
Glucosamine, mg.%	97 ± 8	106 ± 16	136 ± 18	168 ± 30
Polysaccharide, mg.%	146 ± 11	139 ± 11	158 ± 20	181 ± 23

	Probability values (P)		
	D vs. DR	D vs. DKW	DR vs. DKW
Cholesterol			
Total	0.23	0.0001	0.02
Phospholipids	0.035	0.0001	Not significant by inspection
Total lipids	0.018	0.0001	0.023
Glucosamine	0.0001	0.0001	0.0025
Polysaccharide	0.00015	0.0001	0.013

[a] From Adlersberg et al. (1956b).

Group I consisted of persons who were found to be in good health and were examined as controls during the time of study. Their ages were comparable with those of the following groups. Group II consisted of 38 patients with uncomplicated diabetes. Group III included 12 specially selected patients with early diabetic retinopathy and no evidences of hypertensive retinopathy, proteinuria, or renal inadequacy. Group IV consisted of 16 patients with the fully developed Kimmelstiel-Wilson syndrome. Severe retinopathy, hypertension, edema, proteinuria and doubly refractile lipids in the urine were the outstanding features.

It is evident that Groups I and II exhibit no striking differences. The average levels of serum cholesterol, esterified cholesterol, neutral fats, and total lipids as well as those of serum glucosamine and polysaccharides are quite similar in the nondiabetic controls and in the patients with uncomplicated diabetes of similar age. A striking abnormality in both serum lipids and complex carbohydrates is seen in Group IV. The patients of this group show marked elevation of all serum lipid fractions as well as of complex serum carbohydrates. Patients in Group III with early retinopathy without any evidence of renal involvement present apparently statistically significant differences in comparison with patients having uncomplicated diabetes and with nondiabetics. The increases are noted chiefly in neutral fat, total lipids, serum glucosamine, and total serum polysaccharides. In contrast, serum cholesterol and phospholipids remain in normal limits.

One must consider, therefore, that the blood changes perhaps precede the degenerative alteration of the tissue and the deposition of protein-carbohydrate and protein-lipid compounds in the retina and in the renal glomerulus. Thus, the increases of serum lipid and carbohydrate components which have been observed may both be pathogenetically related in the development of diabetic retinopathy and diabetic glomerulosclerosis. Whether both the lipids and carbohydrate fractions increase in parallel fashion or one precedes the other remains to be investigated.

2. Hypothyroidism

The role of the thyroid in the control of serum lipids is better established than that of other endocrine glands. Total thyroidectomy in man and experimental animals results in decided elevation of serum lipids including serum cholesterol (Hurxthal, 1933, 1934; Fleischmann et al., 1940). Cholesterol levels ranging to 700 mg.% have been observed. The diagnostic importance of hypercholesteremia in patients with hypothyroidism is limited in adults. It is perhaps of greater practical importance in hypothyroidism in children (Peters and Man, 1943; Foldes and Murphy, 1946). It may best be used as a guide in substitution therapy of hypothyroidism, again, especially in children (Soffer, 1951).

There appear to be species differences in the response of serum lipids to surgical or nonsurgical thyroidectomy in animals. Our own observations in rabbits and dogs revealed marked elevations of serum cholesterol and phospholipids in the dog in contrast to only moderate elevation of these fractions in the rabbit. Serum triglycerides and total lipids were more increased in the rabbit than in the dog (Table VII).

3. Nephrosis

In lipid nephrosis and also in the nephrotic edematous phases of nephritis, we find a syndrome of albuminuria, hypoproteinemia and hyperlipemia; much of the latter consists in hypercholesteremia. The albumin in proteinuria is not identical with serum albumin. Too little is known about the chemical composition and the physico-chemical properties of urinary protein to decide whether it represents one of the fractions of serum albumin or a product, modified during passage through the kidney. The primary cause of nephrosis was originally considered to be a disorder of the kidney, but following A. A. Epstein one ascribes the condition nowadays to an abnormality of the systemic protein metabolism. In many instances, urinary protein contains less sulfur than serum albumin. Some urinary protein has been reported to possess globulin characteristics (Luetscher *et al.*, 1956). In any event, proteinuria is accompanied by a depletion of circulating albumin, leading to an inversion of the albumin:globulin ratio from values around 1.3–1.5 to values of less than 1. Proteinuria of 1%, i.e. 10–15 gm. per

TABLE VII

EFFECT OF THYROIDECTOMY ON PLASMA LIPIDS IN DOGS AND RABBITS

The elevation of the lipid fractions is more extensive in the dogs for plasma cholesterol and phospholipids and in the rabbits for total lipids and triglycerides.

Species	No.	Procedure of thyroid-ectomy	Plasma lipids, mg./100 ml.					
			Before			After		
			Cholesterol/esters	P.L.[a]	T.L.[a]	Cholesterol/esters	P.L.	T.L.
Dogs	3	Surgical	144/112	290	708	338/238	443	1133
Dogs	6	I-131						
Rabbits	30	Surgical	41/32	87	240	63/47	113	487

[a] P.L. = Phospholipids; T.L. = Total Lipids.

day, would completely exhaust the circulating albumin (4% of 5000 ml. = 200 gm.) within 2–3 weeks. This process of depletion must be counteracted by formation of serum albumin probably from the globulins, currently furnished by the liver. In fact in hypoproteinemia, the tyrosine and tryptophan content of the serum albumin, which may serve for its chemical characterization, approaches the higher tyrosine-tryptophan content of the globulins, a sign of the accelerated and, thus, less thorough transformation of globulin into albumin (Tuchman and Sobotka, 1932). In order to maintain as high as feasible a colloid-osmotic pressure and to prevent the sucking of liquid into the edematous tissue, globulin, or some of its fractions, is converted into fragments of about 4 times smaller molecular weight, which are not given enough time to change their chemical complexion under the existing stress. The globulins, especially the β- and α-variety contain substantial amounts of lipids which are released in the process and thus produce lipemia including hypercholesteremia (Fishberg, 1929).

An analogous mechanism operates to produce lipemia and hypercholesteremia following substantial withdrawal of blood or of plasma; the latter is accomplished by plasmapheresis, where the blood corpuscles of the removed blood volume are reinjected into the animal without the plasma. Here, too, the globulin is regenerated, but must be in part converted into albumin to maintain the colloid-osmotic pressure, thus releasing bound lipids during this transformation (Fishberg and Fishberg, 1927, 1928). In this experimental situation as well as in nephrosis one could assume as an alternative explanation that the serum globulin is not actually ever formed in the chain of events, but that a similarly constituted precursor is directly transformed into albumin plus lipid.

Lipemia in pregnancy also appears to be caused by the greater hydration of the mother's blood in adaptation to the lower protein content of the fetal blood (Novak and Lustig, 1947).

4. Biliary Obstruction

We meet an essentially different situation in biliary obstruction. This may be brought about by extrahepatic causes such as gallstones in the hepatic or in the common bile duct or by neoplasms, e.g. of the papilla of Vater. Intrahepatic obstruction is due to a narrowing or occlusion of the biliary canaliculi in the course of various pathological processes. In both instances the free flow of bile is interrupted and the regurgitated bile is pressed into the only remaining outlet of the liver, the vena hepatica, causing as most visible symptom the appearance of bile pigment in the circulation, the skin, and sclera. Obstructive jaundice is accompanied by hypercholesteremia, but it would be a wrong conception to ascribe this phenomenon to the simple regurgitation of biliary cholesterol (Sobotka, 1941a). The bile, as it is secreted in the liver, contains between 0.5 and 2.0% bile acids, but less than 0.1% cholesterol (Sobotka, 1937). Figuring on a daily secretion of 1000–1500 ml. of bile, the total amount of cholesterol would then be 1–1.5 gm. as against 5–30 gm. of bile acids. We know that the actual production of biliary constituents is much smaller, since they are reabsorbed in the intestine and returned to the liver; about one-seventh of the bile acids that pass through the sphincter of Oddi are lost in the feces and it is this amount, which must be synthesized in the liver to maintain a steady state. But even the full amount of biliary cholesterol could raise the level in the serum by not more than 25 mg. per 100 ml. in a day. At the same time within 1 day bile acids would appear in quantities 5–30 times as high. In fact at the onset of obstruction bile acids reach the blood stream, causing peripheral itching, and hence the urine where their quantity may be determined. Actual amounts in serum and in urine are minimal compared to the productive capacity of the liver. We know that bile acids are such powerful hemolytic and cytotoxic agents that amounts of more than 20–40 mg.%* in the circulation produce a variety of grave and lethal symptoms. One may often observe a rise of serum cholesterol from 200 mg.% to 3 and 4 times this value in a short time on the acute onset of biliary obstruction. As soon as the bile cannot reach the intestine and presses back into the liver, the output of bile acids stops abruptly. The rapid increase of the serum cholesterol reflects its vicarious production, providing a homeostatic mechanism, in this case to avoid the accumulation of toxic bile acids, signaled by their surface-active effects. The switch from bile acid production to cholesterol production involves the stereochemical position on carbon atom 3, a double bond $\Delta_{5,6}$, 1 to 2 hydroxyl groups on C-7 and C-12 and the side chain (see Chapter 7). The oxidative degradation of the side chain with introduction of a carboxyl group on C-24, and the addition of the hydroxyl groups will not take place in obstruction. Whether a configurational change at C-3 and unsaturation on C-5–C-6 be included in the altered steroid metabolism of obstruction depends on the structure of the unknown common precursor of bile acids and cholesterol.

The additional quantities of cholesterol in the circulation will be esterified to the usual extent as long as the liver itself functions normally; a typical analytical result of acute biliary obstruction will thus be, e.g. 800 mg. total cholesterol of which 600 mg. are esterified. The total cholesterol in obstructive jaundice may reach values of 1500 mg.% per 100 ml.

IV. Hypocholesteremia

A. Cachectic States

In cachectic states produced by prolonged starvation such as was observed in the inmates of concentration camps or by consuming diseases such as carcinoma or tuberculosis, low serum lipid levels are observed. Cholesterol concentrations as low as 100 mg.% or less may be encountered, associated with correspondingly low levels of serum phospholipids, triglycerides, and total lipids. The mechanism of these changes is not clear although it is related to the prolonged diminished food and fat intake. Reduced synthesis or increased loss of cholesterol, e.g. by diminished reabsorption of the sterol excreted with the bile into the bowel, are other possibilities to be considered.

---

* mg.% = mg./100 ml.

B. Hyperthyroidism

In contrast to hypothyroidism, hyperthyroidism exhibits the tendency to lower serum lipid levels including hypocholesteremia (Peters and Man, 1943). However, this trend is of no reliable diagnostic value in the diagnosis of hyperthyroidism in a given case. It is also of less practical value as a guide in the therapy of clinical hyperthyroidism than the opposite finding of hypercholesteremia seen in hypothyroidism (Soffer, 1951).

C. Addison's Disease

In chronic adrenocortical insufficiency (Addison's disease) a tendency to low serum cholesterol levels has been seen in contrast to adreno-cortical hyperfunction which is often associated with hypercholesteremia (Soffer et al., 1955). In the animal experiment, ketonuria and fatty in-filtration of the liver produced by anterior pituitary extracts, by pan-createctomy, or by starvation, can be prevented by adrenalectomy (MacKay and Barnes, 1937; Fry, 1937). Administration of one of the cortisones in large doses in man and experimental animal produces decided elevation of serum lipids and sometimes gross lactescence (Ad-lersberg et al., 1950a, b, 1951, 1954b). These changes are less pro-nounced after ACTH administration (Adlersberg et al., 1951).

D. Parenchymatous Liver Disease

In parenchymatous liver disease, especially in acute yellow atrophy, in severe catarrhal jaundice, also in the acute episodes of liver cirrhosis, the synthesis of cholesterol in the liver is impaired and hypocholesteremia results. This is accompanied by a drop of the percentage of esterified cholesterol, the so-called "Ester-sturz," which was observed by Thann-hauser (Thannhauser and Schaber, 1926; cf. Feigl, 1918) and studied by E. Z. Epstein et al. (Epstein, 1931, 1932; Epstein and Greenspan, 1936). Enzymatic esterification in the liver or by a hepatogenic enzyme becomes inoperative. The resulting drop of esterified cholesterol below 30–40 mg.% with a total cholesterol below 100 mg.% is a most unfavor-able symptom.

In obstructive jaundice of extrahepatic origin of long standing and of intrahepatic origin by a primary affection of liver metabolism one finds a combination of high total cholesterol levels with low esterification, e.g. 600 mg.% total with 150 mg. of esterified cholesterol. It is these cases, in which the determination of esterified cholesterol gains the greatest significance for diagnosis and therapy.

V. Diseases Characterized by Cholesterol Deposition

We have dealt so far with the reflection of disease on the cholesterol level of the blood. We must now consider disturbances of cholesterol metabolism that are not always mirrored by changes in its blood level, or where these changes are of minor amount and lack pathognomonic significance. Cholesterol is deposited in a variety of tissues under diverse pathological conditions. Depending on their site, the depositions of cholesterol may or may not disturb the normal functioning of the organism.

Cholesterol is deposited in atheromatous lesions, in xanthomatous lesions, in cholesteatoma, in certain types of lipidosis, and in gallstones. With the exception of the latter, which are based on an entirely different mechanism and which will be discussed separately, the deposition of cholesterol is usually accompanied by the deposition of carotene, whose biological function—except for its role as provitamin A—is as obscure as that of cholesterol. There is a connection between sterols and carotenoids, which must lie deeper than the mere similarity of their solubility properties. The fact strikes us that the algae contain simultaneously the greatest variety of sterols and of carotenoids, while only a few representatives of both groups are found in animals and higher plants.

A. Atherosclerosis in Man

Atherosclerosis is the most frequent and important pathological alteration of the intima and subintima in the arteries and particularly in the coronary arteries. The changes consist in the early stages of deposition of lipid and mucopolysaccharides in the intima; in later stages, fibrous tissue and calcium appear in various proportions in addition to larger quantities of lipid, especially cholesterol (Windaus, 1910). The atherosclerotic lesion represents a subgroup of a wider pathological entity defined as arteriosclerosis. Such pathological conditons as medial calcification (Mönckeberg's sclerosis) and arteritis obliterans (Burger's disease) are often included in the entity of arteriosclerosis. These conditions, however, are not primarily related to atherosclerosis and thus will not be discussed here.

The biochemical aspects of atherosclerosis have been the subject of extensive investigative work (Weinhouse and Hirsch, 1940; Steiner and Domanski, 1943; Hueper, 1945; Katz and Dauber, 1945; Adlersberg et al., 1949; Gofman et al., 1950; Gould, 1951; Steiner et al., 1952; Page, 1954). Evidence is accumulating that atherosclerosis represents a metabolic disorder involving particularly lipids and lipoproteins, especially cholesterol (Morrison et al., 1948). This concept is based on well-documented clinical and experimental observations. There is a higher incidence of atherosclerosis in conditions associated with abnormally high serum cholesterol levels, such as familial hypercholesteremia, myxedema, nephrosis, and Cushing's syndrome. On the other hand, clinical states associated with abnormally low cholesterol levels, such as prolonged consuming diseases, cirrhosis of the liver, and hyperthyroidism, are known to be associated with a low incidence of atherosclerosis (Wilens, 1947). Population groups with very low serum cholesterol levels exhibit low incidence of atherosclerosis, especially coronary atherosclerosis. Recent observations in the South African Bantu, in Guatemala, in Japan, and in certain population groups in Europe are suggestive of such a relationship (Keys and White, 1956; Kusakawa, 1956). It is generally believed that these low serum lipid levels are related to the dietary habits of these people, especially to the low consumption of (animal) fat, although other dietary factors such as low protein and high carbohydrate, especially cereal, intake, high proportion of cellulose, and such variables as ethnic differences, parasitic infestation, climatic influence, different social and economic environment, etc. cannot be overlooked as possible causes of differences in epidemiology. Experimental atherosclerosis can be produced by one technique only and this is feeding of cholesterol to experimental animals with or without additional factors affecting the function of the thyroid or of the adrenals (see later).

Much effort has been spent on measurements of plasma lipid fractions. It was mentioned above that these studies included serum cholesterol, phospholipids, triglycerides, and total lipids. Special attention was given to the α- and β-lipoproteins separated by various techniques (Russ et al., 1951; Adlersberg et al., 1955) and to the ultracentrifuge method separating low density molecules from those with higher density (Gofman et al., 1950). All of these studies suggest a decided alteration of serum lipids and lipoproteins in patients with proven coronary atherosclerosis as a group, although this change is not invariably encountered in each individual patient with this disease. According to recent studies, none of these indices of abnormal lipid metabolism permits prediction of the subsequent clinical course (Gofman et al., 1956). The relatively simple determination of serum total cholesterol is not surpassed by the new, more complicated, and expensive techniques.

The effects of age and sex upon serum lipids have been discussed above. There is clinical and experimental evidence that endocrine factors are instrumental in determining serum lipid levels, and through this mechanism, perhaps atherogenesis. The role of the thyroid in controlling serum lipid levels was discussed before. Whereas hypothyroidism, associated with hypercholesteremia, enhances experimental atherosclerosis, the opposite effect of hyperthyroidism and hypocholesteremia is less well established (Peters and Man, 1943). The adrenal cortex appears to be involved in the regulation of serum lipids. Patients and experimental animals treated with large doses of corticosteroids develop hypercholesteremia and a corresponding increase of other lipid fractions (Adlersberg et al., 1950a, b, 1951, 1954b, 1957). Patients with Cushing's syndrome often show elevation of serum lipids, especially higher cholesterol levels whereas patients with Addison's disease often exhibit hypocholesteremia. There is suggestive evidence that all these alterations are not caused by changes of exogenous cholesterol but are the result of increased or impaired lipid (cholesterol) synthesis or diminished degradation.

The role of the gonads in controlling serum lipid levels is based on clinical and experimental work (Lerman and White, 1946; Eilert, 1949, 1953; Barr, 1953; Oliver and Boyd, 1954, 1955b; Adlersberg, 1957). In the western countries, females in the reproductive stage show marked protection against coronary atherosclerosis as compared with males of similar age. This difference diminishes decidedly after the menopause although the prevalence in the male still persists. The role of estrogens in reversing lipid and lipoprotein changes associated with atherosclerosis has been well established in man and experimental animals (Pick et al., 1951, 1952a, b; Barr, 1953; Oliver and Boyd, 1955b), although long-term studies of the effect of estrogens on the course of atherosclerosis in man are still missing. It is well established, however, that oophorectomized women lose the protection of the female against atherosclerosis.

Many other factors, such as possible effects of the aging process, of hypertension, of occupation, of climate, of the stress and strain of modern living, and especially the role of body build and body weight upon the incidence of atherosclerosis cannot be discussed here. The reader is referred to extensive reviews of this subject published recently (Lerman and White, 1946; Anfinsen, 1955; Keys, 1955; Keys and White, 1956; Adlersberg, 1957). Chemical analyses of the lipid from atheromatous human aortas show the complexity of the composition (see Table VIII). It may be presumed also that there are changes in the composition of the structural protein.

B. Experimental Atherosclerosis

Atherosclerosis is the most important degenerative disease of man. Although this condition can be produced experimentally in many species (see Table IX), the rabbit still retains its leading role in this field of research (Anitschkow, 1933; Davidson, 1951; Mann, 1956).

Wang *et al.* (1954) studied systematically the plasma lipid partition in rabbits during feeding of cholesterol without the addition of fat and without the use of a stomach tube. The steady rise in all lipid fractions

TABLE VIII

THE COMPOSITION OF AND SOME CONSTITUENTS OF THE LIPIDS FROM ATHEROMATOUS HUMAN AORTAS

	As % dry intima	As % of lipid
Lipid	25	100
Steryl esters	14	55
Free sterol	6	23
Phospholipids	1	4
Glycerides, etc.	4	18

Representative values (± 10%) of those given for pooled aortas by Schoenheimer (1928) and McArthur (1942).

Sterols

Schoenheimer *et al.* (1930) found that the total sterol contained about 5% cholestanol or other stanol; McArthur found about 12%.

Ketones and Di- and Tri-hydroxysterols

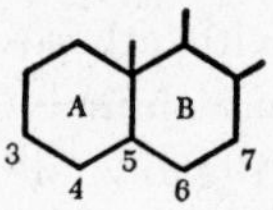

= H, double bond
O, keto
OH, hydroxyl, α or β

3	4	5	6	7	
O	= H	H	= H	H	
= H	H	= H	H	O	Dienones
β-OH	H	= H	H	α-OH	
β-OH	H	= H	H	β-OH	Diols
β-OH	H	α-OH	β-OH	H	Triol

A diol (? 24- or 25-hydroxycholesterol) is also present.

From results of Hardegger *et al.* (1943); Kantiengar and Morton (1955); Henderson (1956).

Other Constituents

Hardegger *et al.* (1943) report the presence of batyl alcohol and of other non-steroidal compounds in the unsaponifiable matter. The lipids are "peroxidized" (Glavind *et al.*, 1952).

Acids Present in Steryl Esters (as % Total)

Palmitic 15, stearic 3, oleic 65, linoleic 9, arachidonic 2, petroleum ether-insoluble 6 (McArthur, 1942).

which occurred for the first 3 months and the subsequent leveling off at slightly lower levels is shown in Table X. Again there were considerable variations in all lipid fractions from animal to animal. After 3 months of cholesterol feeding the average total plasma cholesterol

TABLE IX

SOME STUDIES ON CHOLESTEROL AND VASCULAR DISEASE IN EXPERIMENTAL ANIMALS

Rats	"Middle aged, obese:" Wissler *et al.* (1952)
Guinea pig and hamster	Altschul (1950a, b)
Dogs	Treated with thiouracil: Steiner and Kendall (1946); on pyridoxine deficient diet: Mushett and Emerson (1956); cf. Shull and Mann (1957) for study of normal dogs
Miniature pigs	Peifer and Lundberg (1957)
Cebus monkey	On sulfur amino acid-deficient diet: Mann *et al.* (1953)
Rhesus monkey	On pyridoxine-deficient diet: Rinehart and Greenberg (1949); see also Mann and Andrus (1956)
Chicken	Dauber and Katz (1942); effect of stilbestrol: Horlick and Katz (1948); see also Lindsay *et al.* (1955)
Geese	Wolffe *et al.* (1952)

Comparative studies on rat, guinea pig and rabbit (Cook and McCullagh, 1939).

Reviews: Monograph edited by Cowdry (see Anitschkow, 1933); Katz and Stamler (1953); Keys and White (1956).

TABLE X

EFFECT OF CHOLESTEROL FEEDING ON PLASMA LIPIDS OF THE RABBIT[a]
(All values expressed in mg./100 ml.)

	Control	1 Month	2 Months	3 Months	4 Months	5 Months	6 Months
Total Cholesterol							
Mean	49	641	914	1476	1179	1149	1213
S.D.[b]	± 24	± 329	± 441	± 768	± 455	± 358	± 768
Esterified Cholesterol							
Mean	37	458	669	1141	885	854	896
S.D.	± 18	± 230	± 356	± 594	± 357	± 451	± 551
Phospholipids							
Mean	103	330	413	460	462	460	512
S.D.	± 27	± 126	± 137	± 155	± 196	± 206	± 230
Neutral Fats							
Mean[c]	198	741	893	1094	1048	853	842
Total Lipids							
Mean	350	1712	2219	3030	2689	2462	2567
S.D.	± 206	± 788	± 925	± 1457	± 1313	± 1157	± 1448

[a] From Wang *et al.* (1954).
[b] S.D., Standard deviation.
[c] Since this is a calculated figure no S.D. is done.

rose to 30 times normal; free plasma cholesterol and esterified cholesterol increased similarly. The elevation of plasma phospholipids fell far behind that of plasma cholesterol. After 3 months of cholesterol feeding the average phospholipids reached 4.6 times the control; an additional moderate elevation was seen after 6 months. The differences observed

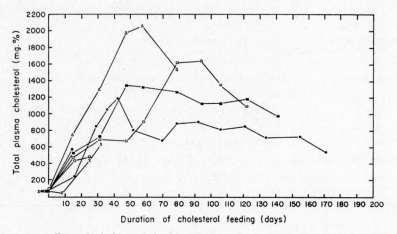

FIG. 8. Effect of cholesterol feeding (1 gm./day) on plasma cholesterol levels in 7 rabbits (from Wang *et al.*, 1954).

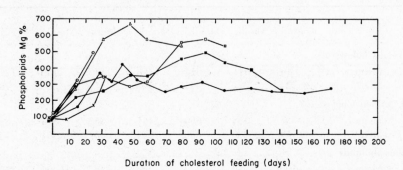

FIG. 9. Effect of cholesterol feeding (1 gm./day) on plasma phospholipid levels in 7 rabbits (from Wang *et al.*, 1954).

during cholesterol feeding between plasma cholesterol and phospholipid elevation are best expressed by the phospholipid-cholesterol ratio which showed a striking change from 2.1:1 during the control period to 0.3:1 during the period of cholesterol feeding. The average total plasma lipids rose to 8.7 times the control after 3 months of cholesterol feeding. After 4 to 6 months the level decreased moderately. The elevation of neutral fat was associated with lactescence of the plasma. Figures 8 and

9 illustrate the alterations of plasma cholesterol and phospholipids in cholesterol-fed animals.

In general, no gross atherosclerotic plaques were found after two weeks of cholesterol feeding. At the end of one month, tiny but definitely yellowish white plaques could be demonstrated at the ascending part and the arch of the aorta, especially around the orifices of the innominate artery and the other branching arteries. Similar small plaques were noticed in the pulmonary artery, especially over the bifurcation.

With continuation of cholesterol feeding atheromatous plaques became larger, more numerous, and confluent with longitudinal orientation. New plaques appeared at the orifices of the intercostal and the branching arteries of the abdominal aorta (Fig. 10). Thickening and beading of the mitral and aortic valves were usually present after 2–3 months of cholesterol feeding.

When cholesterol feeding was carried on beyond 4–6 months, the atheromatous plaques of the aorta and pulmonary artery were so extensive (Fig. 11) that relatively normal intima was only seen in small skip areas (Wang et al., 1955b). Marked narrowing and not infrequently occlusion of the coronary arteries was seen with lipid deposition as well as considerable accumulation of acid mucopolysaccharides (Figs. 12 and 13).

It is well established that concentrations of plasma cholesterol and duration of hypercholesteremia are the two main determining factors in the development of experimental atherosclerosis. The observation that cholesterol-fed rabbits treated with cortisone or hydrocortisone exhibited, despite higher plasma cholesterol levels, less atherosclerosis than rabbits fed similar amounts of cholesterol alone, suggested that factors other than those of hypercholesteremia and its duration exert influence on atherogenesis. Such factors as phospholipid:cholesterol ratio, concentration of "giant" lipoprotein molecules, and concentration of neutral fat and chylomicrons in the plasma have been thought to be additional factors. Our observations and those of others indicated that tissue permeability and other factors might also play an important role in atherogenesis (Duff and McMillan, 1951; Kellner et al., 1951; Oppenheim and Bruger, 1952; Seifter et al., 1954; Stumpf and Wilens, 1954; Wang et al., 1955a, b; Adlersberg et al., 1957). Tables XI and XII show that cortisone enhanced hypercholesteremia but had a retarding effect upon the development of atherosclerosis. The retardation of atherogenesis produced by cortisone was prevented by the simultaneous use of hyaluronidase. Hyaluronidase intensified atherosclerosis and deposition of cholesterol in the tissues. These studies reaffirmed the importance of the ground substance in atherogenesis.

FIG. 10. Rabbit 364 fed cholesterol for 2 months (1 gm. daily). Note irregularly shaped plaques of atheroma in the ascending aorta and tiny plaques near the orifices of the branching arteries in the thoracic part of the aorta.

FIG. 11. Rabbit 520 fed cholesterol for 5 months (1 gm. daily). Note very extensive atheroma formation in the pulmonary arteries. The inner surface of the aorta is also covered by extensive atheroma formation.

FIG. 12. Experimental atherosclerosis. Rabbit 59. Note marked thickening of the intima of coronary arteries with occlusion of lumen (hematoxylin-eosin, × 76).

FIG. 13. Coronary artery of the same rabbit as in Fig. 12. Note considerable accumulation of acid mucopolysaccharides in intima (colloidal iron stain, × 76).

FIG. 14. Skin of Rabbit 18, fed cholesterol for 2 months. Note the presence of foam cells in upper corium and nests of these cells adjacent to the hair follicles (hematoxylin-eosin, × 76).

FIG. 15. Skin of Rabbit 18. Corresponding section as in Fig. 14 stained with colloidal iron. Note accumulation of acid mucopolysaccharides in the corium (× 76).

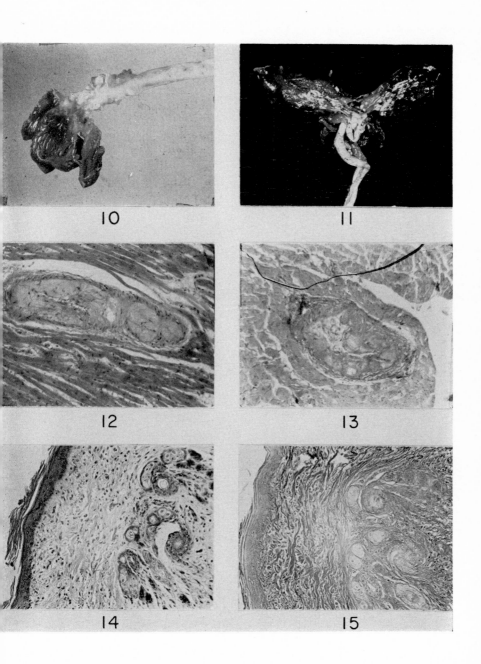

TABLE XI

Plasma Lipid Fractions of the Rabbit (mg./100 ml.) under Various Experimental Regimens[a]

(All animals received 1 gm. cholesterol per animal per day.)

Group	No. of animals	After 4 wks. cholesterol supplement[b]			Additional treatment	After 2 wks.			After 4 wks.			Degree of atherosclerosis	
		Chol. tot/est.	P-lipids	Total lipids		Chol. tot/est.	P-lipids	Total lipids	Chol. tot/est.	P-lipids	Total lipids	Aorta	Pulmonary arteries
A	9	1006/723	464	2362	None	1223/923	493	3030	1380/1060	486	3270	1.2	0.9
B	5	1098/822	398	2380	Cortisone 3.75 mg. daily	2232/1685	785	5040	3501/2392	1031	6969	0.5	0.4
C	13	1013/744	469	2171	Hyaluronidase 1000 TRU and cortisone 3.75 mg. daily	1855/1391	658	4490	2697/2004	1098	5613	1.5	0.6
D	14	1105/800	478	2543	Hyaluronidase 1000 TRU daily	1355/1000	571	3363	1376/1040	625	3258	2.0	1.8

[a] From Wang et al. (1955a).

[b] Plasma lipid values in normal rabbits in this laboratory are: Cholesterol, total/esterified (tot/est.), 50/35 mg. per 100 ml.; Phospholipids (P-lipids), 105 mg. per 100 ml.; Total lipids, 350 mg. per 100 ml.

TABLE XII
ATHEROMA FORMATION IN AORTA AND PULMONARY ARTERIES[a]
(All animals received 1 gm. of cholesterol per animal per day)

| | | Degree of atherosclerosis | |
Group and treatment	Rabbit no.	Aorta	Pulmonary arteries
A	18	0.5	0.5
None	361	1.0	1.0
	362	1.5	1.5
	364	2.0	0
	366	1.0	1.0
	367	1.0	0
	702	1.5	1.0
	705	1.0	1.5
	900	1.5	2.0
B	76	1.0	0.5
Cortisone	86	0.5	0.5
	207	0.5	0.5
	671	0.5	0.5
	672	0.5	0
C	16	2.0	0.5
Cortisone and hyal-	48	1.5	1.0
uronidase	84	3.0	2.5
	283	2.5	0.5
	350	1.5	0.5
	444	0.5	0
	529	1.0	0.5
	677	0.5	0
	717	2.0	0.5
	718	0.5	1.0
	719	0.5	1.0
	982	0.5	0
	983	3.0	0
D	21	1.0	1.5
Hyaluronidase	43	2.0	2.5
	201	1.0	3.0
	404	3.0	3.0
	501	2.0	2.0
	502	1.5	2.0
	503	2.0	2.0
	662	2.0	0.5
	680	1.5	3.0
	684	3.0	2.5
	715	3.0	0.5
	720	1.5	1.0
	980	2.5	1.5
	981	2.0	0
Group A Average		1.2	0.9
Group B Average		0.5	0.4
Group C Average		1.5	0.6
Group D Average		2.0	1.8

[a] From Wang et al. (1955a).

C. XANTHOMATOUS LESIONS

1. In the Experimental Animal

No gross xanthomata were noted in rabbits during the first month of cholesterol feeding. However, a small number of animals (2.5%) exhibited cutaneous xanthomata 2–3 months after institution of cholesterol feeding. After 3–6 months 21% of the animals, after 7–9 months 50%, and after 10–12 months, 100% of the animals showed skin xanthomata (Wang *et al.*, 1957).

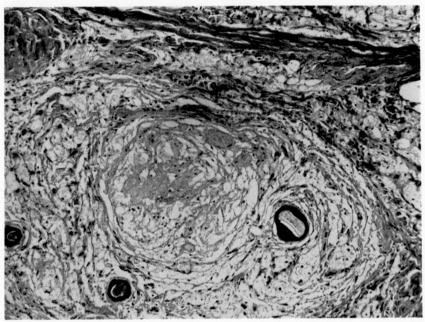

Fig. 16.   Xanthoma of skin of Rabbit 82, fed cholesterol for 187 days (1 gm. per day), showing central degeneration with collection of cholesterol crystals and cellular debris (hematoxylin-eosin stain, × 76) (from Wang *et al.*, 1957).

Xanthomata were noted first on the paws, as small reddish yellow nodules, 1–3 mm. in diameter, between the toes and over the heels. The size of these nodules slowly increased to a diameter of 1–1.5 cm. The skin of the soles became thickened and cracked. In animals fed cholesterol for longer than 3–6 months, small elevated yellowish tophi, 1–3 mm. in diameter, were seen scattered over the ears resembling eruptive xanthoma in man. Preceding traumatic injury to the ear, e.g. at the sites of puncture for blood sampling, usually predisposed the skin to the development of xanthomatous nodules. In some instances, the skin over the back and neck showed loss of hair and appeared reddish and

thickened (hyperkeratosis). In many instances, ulceration of the xanthomata and secondary infection with abscess formation complicated the
picture.

Earliest skin xanthoma, not visible to the naked eye, showed foam
cells, isolated or in nests in the upper corium and in perivascular and
perineural spaces in the deep corium. The presence of foam cells was
usually accompanied by a local bluish violet hue of the ground substance
in sections stained with hematoxylin-eosin. Accumulation of large quantities of acid mucopolysaccharides can be demonstrated with the col-

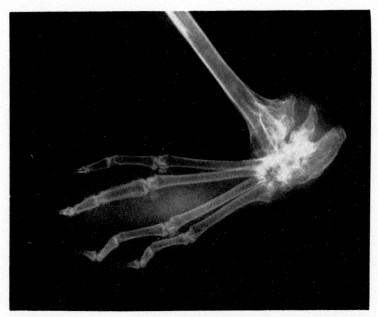

Fig. 17. Roentgenogram of left hind leg of Rabbit 171 after 180 days of cholesterol feeding (1 gm. per day). Note thinning of the cortex with fan-shaped widen-
ing and osteosclerotic changes in the lower end of the tibia and in the tarsal bones
resulting in complete destruction of the ankle joint. Also notice periosteal elevation
and soft tissue swelling (from Wang *et al.*, 1957).

loidal iron technique (Figs. 14 and 15). A typical well-developed
xanthomatous skin nodule was characterized histologically by thinning
of the epidermis, marked distention of the dermis with fat-laden foam
cells, and a central pool consisting of cholesterol crystals and cellular
debris (Fig. 16). The usual wavy contour of the epidermis became
flattened. Nests of foam cells were separated by heavy strands of collagenous fibers of the dermis. No foreign body giant cells were found.
The deposition of foam cells in the synovial membrane, periosteum, and

bone marrow was noted long before the development of any roentgeno-logical changes in the bones or joints (Fig. 17). After two months of cholesterol feeding the synovial membranes and the periosteum showed already marked thickening due to the presence of many foam cells. Isolated foam cells or clusters of them were seen in the bone marrow of the long bones and of the ribs especially in animals with active hemo-poiesis. In the adult animal with inactive bone marrow of the long bones large foam cells and cholesterol crystals were very frequently observed in the bone lacunae (Fig. 18). In the tendons and ligaments the foam

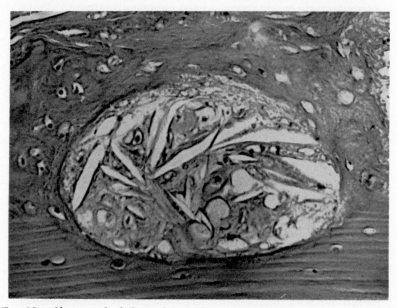

Fig. 18. Clusters of cholesterol crystals in Howship's lacuna of the femoral cortex in Rabbit 458 fed cholesterol for 270 days (hematoxylin-eosin, × 800) (from Wang *et al.*, 1957).

cells were usually confined to the fibrous sheath only. Occasionally, 1 or 2 isolated foam cells were seen at the insertion of a tendon or a ligament to the cartilaginous cap of a long bone. In bones with fractures the deposition of foam cells and cholesterol crystals was more abundant than in intact bones. The deposition of cholesterol was particularly heavy at the site of the fracture. Callus formation occurred in tissues loaded with cholesterol crystals and large numbers of foam cells. It seemed as if the heavy deposition of cholesterol crystals precipitated pathological fracture of the bone. On the other hand, it has been well known that any injury to the tissues invited the deposition of cholesterol

(Fig. 19). Figure 20 illustrates two ulcerated xanthomas found in some of the animals after prolonged cholesterol feeding.

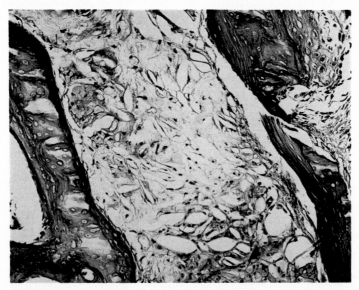

FIG. 19. Clusters of cholesterol crystals in vicinity of a pathological bone fracture (hematoxylin-eosin, × 800).

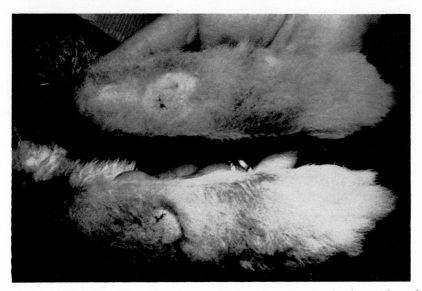

FIG. 20. Ulceration of xanthomas was sometimes seen in animals after prolonged cholesterol feeding.

2. In Man

Among the lipid storage diseases, the xanthomatoses are characterized by one common factor, namely, the deposition of cholesterol and cholesterol esters in various tissues. The xanthomatoses are usually subdivided into those associated with hypercholesteremia and/or hyperlipemia in contrast to those that are not associated with abnormal serum lipids (Thannhauser and Schmidt, 1946; Thannhauser, 1950).

Essential or primary hypercholesteremia may be associated with xanthomatosis, usually of the tendinosum variety. Xanthelasmas of the eyelids as well as xanthomas in the tendons are more often encountered in this variety than tuberous xanthomas of the skin.

The genetic transmission of this disorder has been the topic of many studies. Investigators who used skin lesions as the basis for study arrived at somewhat different results from those who studied the basic blood disturbance, i.e. hypercholesteremia or the corresponding changes of serum lipoproteins. Evidence is accumulating that this disorder is transmitted as a dominant gene with incomplete penetrance (see above).

The mechanism of the lesion is obscure. It must be assumed that some genetically controlled enzymatic pathways are basically disturbed in this condition (Adlersberg, 1951). Whether this disturbance, manifesting itself in abnormal accumulation of cholesterol in the serum, is the result of abnormal synthesis of cholesterol from its precursors (endogenous cholesterol), of abnormal absorption of exogenous cholesterol, or of impaired excretion of cholesterol through the gut, or of decreased degradation in the tissues cannot even be guessed at present. Our knowledge of the intermediary metabolism of lipids, especially of cholesterol, and of the involved enzymatic mechanisms is so inadequate that no definite statement is permissible at present as to the nature of the abnormalities of serum cholesterol. They may even represent abnormal shifts between the tissues and the blood, in other words, may represent some abnormalities of cholesterol distribution. Xanthomata of the tendons resemble histologically those of the skin. They consist of nests of cholesterol-loaded foam cells surrounded by foreign body giant cells.

Secondary hypercholesteremic xanthomatosis may be encountered in chronic biliary obstruction and especially in a comparatively rare condition, primary biliary cirrhosis. In the latter condition, the concentration of serum cholesterol may be extremely high, associated with corresponding elevations of serum phospholipids but with minimal increase in serum triglycerides. The serum is usually clear in its appearance. Histologically, the so-called xanthomatous biliary cirrhosis is indistinguishable from the usual pericholangiolitic form of cirrhosis. The development of skin xanthomata in this disorder parallels the elevation of serum lipids and the duration of these changes.

Primary hyperlipemic xanthomatosis is a familial condition, the clinical and chemical aspects of which were discussed above. The xanthomatous lesions involve mainly the skin in the form of xanthoma tuberosum. Excessive elevation of serum lipids, especially of triglycerides, in these patients may give rise to the appearance of eruptive xanthoma of the skin which again may subside or disappear with the lowering of serum lipids. Xanthelasmas of the eyelids and tendon xanthomatosis are rarely seen in this lipid disorder. It may be repeated that in the families of patients with idiopathic hyperlipemia, this disorder as well as idiopathic hypercholesteremia may be encountered (see above). At least genetically, both disorders seem to be closely related and may represent variants of the same metabolic disturbance.

Symptomatic hyperlipemic xanthomatosis has been described formerly in diabetes mellitus as xanthoma diabeticorum. Since the time of Addison this form of xanthoma has been considered to be a rare symptom of untreated diabetes mellitus in predisposed individuals. Recent observations suggest, however, that patients with diabetes exhibiting xanthoma diabeticorum (eruptive xanthoma) present clinical and chemical stigmata of idiopathic hyperlipemia (Adlersberg and Wang, 1955). The xanthoma diabeticorum may represent under these conditions a manifestation of idiopathic hyperlipemia in a patient with uncontrolled diabetes. It is of interest that clinical and chemical control of diabetes results usually in marked lowering of serum lipids, especially triglycerides, and a concomitant disappearance of eruptive xanthoma. Case histories illustrating these changes have been published previously (Adlersberg and Wang, 1955).

Corneal arcus is an opaque, white crescentic deposit in the cornea occurring with increasing frequency with advancing age. It consists of refractile lipid globules deposited first in Bowman's membrane and later in Descemet's membrane and finally involving all layers of the peripheral cornea. The lipid consists mainly of cholesterol. A correlation has been observed between coronary artery disease and corneal arcus and xanthomatosis (Boas, 1945). Because corneal arcus may occur in certain persons in young age, the descriptive term "corneal arcus" is preferable to "arcus senilis," frequently used in the literature (Adlersberg et al., 1949).

D.   OTHER LIPIDOSES; HAND-SCHÜLLER-CHRISTIAN DISEASE

The lipidoses comprise a number of rather infrequent conditions in which one or the other member of the lipids accumulates in liver, spleen, brain, or other organs. The tissue reacts with the formation of giant "foam" cells, which display characteristic differences in these various diseases. We have come to believe that these errors of metabolism are due to enzymatic disturbances.

TABLE XIII
INTERRELATIONSHIP OF TISSUE LIPIDS

Lipid	Components	Accumulated in
Free cholesterol	Cholesterol	Hand-Schüller-Christian
Cholesterol esters	{ Cholesterol { Fatty acid	Hand-Schüller-Christian
Neutral fat	{ Fatty acid { Glycerol + 2 mol. fatty acid	
Lecithin	{ Glycerol + 2 mol. fatty acid { Phosphoric acid + choline	
Sphingomyelin	{ Phosphoric acid + choline { Sphingosine + lignoceric acid	Niemann-Pick
Kerasin or cerebro- glucoside	{ Sphingosine + lignoceric acid { Galactose or glucose	Gaucher
Gangliosides	{ Sphingosine + lignoceric acid { Galactose { Neuraminic acid	Tay-Sachs, Niemann- Pick

If we list the complex lipids as in Table XIII, we find that each of the diseases appearing in the table is characterized by the prevalence of one of them (Sobotka, 1930, 1941b; Sobotka et al., 1930). It has been observed that esterase is diminished on Niemann-Pick's disease (Sobotka et al., 1933) and that a specific phosphatase is present in Gaucher's (Tuchman et al., 1956) and in Niemann-Pick's disease (Hastrup and Videbaek, 1954). The enzymes in the rather rare Hand-Schüller-Christian disease, with which we are here concerned, have not been studied. In this disease one observes deposits of cholesterol and its esters, together with carotenoids, at various sites of the body, especially in the skull. The level of cholesterol and other lipids in the serum remains within the normal range (Thannhauser and Magendantz, 1938). This disorder may be associated with diabetes insipidus, sometimes with infantilism, and frequently with exophthalmus, implicating the pituitary gland which is often invaded by lipid tumors. Hand-Schüller-Christian disease is generally not considered a primary metabolic disorder, but rather a granuloma, consisting of a proliferation of histiocytes which, later on, become infiltrated with cholesterol esters. This view is supported by the occurrence of similar lesions without cholesterol deposits in the related Letterer-Siwe's reticuloendotheliosis (Snapper, 1949).

E. Various Conditions with Cholesterol Deposits

Deposition of cholesterol crystals in the iris and the rear interface of the cornea also within the aqueous humor of the eye has been described as cholesterinosis bulbi. It is ascribed to trauma and to hyperemia or to irritation of the corpus ciliare. The lipoproteins of the serum are subject to local alterations which reduce their carrying ability for cholesterol (Georgariou, 1938).

Cholesterol is found in pleural effusions, which may contain cholesterol in excess of 1%. These are probably secondary to tuberculous infections, although as a rule no tubercle bacilli are found in them (Frew and Campbell-Fowler, 1956).

F. Gallstones

An entirely different aspect of cholesterol metabolism concerns the presence of cholesterol in the bile, which contains 50–100 mg. of non-esterified cholesterol. Under certain abnormal conditions (especially when the bile because of infection or for reasons of metabolic origin becomes more acid than ordinarily) the bile loses its dissolving power for cholesterol. The cholesterol which is thus precipitated forms either a viscous deposit, or crystallizes and gives rise to calculi.

Biliary calculi can be classified as follows (see Horn, 1956):

(1) Pure gallstones occur as large, yellow or white, ovoid stones with smooth surface. The individual crystals are often large enough to be seen with the naked eye. They are arranged in a radial manner. They form in gallbladders without inflammatory symptoms.

(2) Cholesterol-calcium-bilirubinate stones containing about 70–96% cholesterol; the balance consists of bilirubin, calcium, and of minor amounts of other metal ions, also of carbonate. These dark yellow to brown stones are the size of peas or beans; their shape is often tetrahedral or cubic, since they occur in large quantities in the gallbladder where they are subject to mutual pressure. Instructive model experiments have been carried out by Kleeberg (1953a, b, 1956). The cross-section usually shows alternation of concentric cholesterol and calcium-bilirubinate layers and one may discern the polyhedric structure in concentric layers throughout the calculus. The shape may also be influenced by gradual dehydration in a direction perpendicular to the facets. Similar stones of earthy consistence and ovoid or cylindrical shape occur in the ductus choledochus.

The formation of gallstones is favored by metabolic states with increased cholesterol production, such as diabetes, obesity, and pregnancy. No stones are found in dogs and other animals, whose bile contains little cholesterol. The bile from the dog's gallbladder is known to dissolve human gallstones; its cholesterol content increases upon addition of human gallstones, whereas the cholesterol content of human bile hardly rises under these conditions as the cholesterol-carrying capacity of man's bile is saturated; the stones remain undissolved (Stary, 1956).

Hepatic bile, a colloidal solution, becomes concentrated in the gallbladder. During this process, the pH of the bile is lowered from values around 7.5 to values averaging less than 6. This factor decreases the stability of the cholesterol-bile acids complex. During stasis the bile acids are preferentially absorbed through the gallbladder wall, thus, the ratio of bile acids:cholesterol, averaging 25:1, is reduced to, say, 12:1, which diminishes the stability of the complex. Both processes, acidification and increased absorption of bile acids, are enhanced when the bile becomes infected.

The phospholipids in the bile may also contribute to the solubilization of cholesterol; their concentration would gradually decrease under the influence of the phosphatase in bile.

Once the cholesterol has been precipitated, the formation of macroscopic concrements is favored by the incompleteness of evacuation of the gallbladder and by the increase of mucins during inflammation, which act as cement.

(3) Calcium-bilirubinate stones, containing only minor amounts of cholesterol, are very rare in man, but they are the only biliary concrements found in hogs and cattle.

Gallstones, consisting to over 50% of cholesterol, have been produced in hamsters by certain diets with great regularity by Dam and his associates (e.g. Christensen et al., 1956). The addition of certain soybean or yeast extracts, also of relatively large amounts of copper sulfate, prevents lithogenesis and even makes cholesterol stones disappear, leaving behind the pigment and protein part of the concrements. Since lithogenesis, in this case, is accompanied by cessation of growth and other abnormal symptoms, it must be considered part of a general deficiency of an alimentary factor yet to be determined.

Concrements consisting of glycocholic and glycodeoxycholic acid have been obtained in the gallbladder of rabbits after feeding of cholestanol (Bevans and Mosbach, 1956). These experimentally produced bile acid concrements in the gallbladder have a natural counterpart in the extremely rare enteroliths, found in the upper intestine. A group of a dozen stones, studied by K. A. H. Moerner and Sjoeqvist (in Sjoeqvist, 1908) consisted of 60% deoxycholic acid and smaller amounts of free fatty acids, cholesterol, bilirubin, and ash. C. Th. Moerner (1923) analyzed a solitary enterolith in the shape of a hen's egg, weighing 45 gm. It consisted of 76% of stearic acid-choleic acid, a complex of stearic acid with deoxycholic acid in the molecular proportion 1:8. A third such stone was analyzed by Raper (1921) containing 72.5% of choleic acid. Schenck (1925) described a 160 gm. concrement consisting mostly of 75% cholic acid in the abomasum of a goat.

While these stones consist of bile acids, precipitated during intestinal obstruction from the acidic contents of the upper intestinal tract, the biliary origin and the composition of the more frequent bezoar stones is doubtful; bezoar stones should be analyzed for the presence of choleic acids of plant sterols (Sobotka, 1937).

Another relative of gallstones, as it were illegitimate, is produced by the so-called oil cure. The ingestion of excessive amounts of olive oil, up to 500 ml., is followed by the passage of numerous concrements in the stool, which at the same time is rich in bile. This experiment, when performed on individuals suffering from, or suspected of gallstones, will furnish an enterprising quack with a marvelous setting for a dramatic cure, which automatically corroborates the diagnosis. Such heroic choleretic treatment may alleviate existing pain, but its ephemeral success is founded on the chimeric "removal" of stones, which on analysis prove to be pseudo-stones, consisting of triolein and tripalmitin.

The problem of gallstone formation may be summarized in the words of Salkowski (1922): "It is not quite clear to me why the problem of gallstone formation should cause so much concern to pathologists and clinicians. The complicated composition of bile offers precisely the conditions for the formation of concrements. . . . It is only necessary that one of the components is present in too high a concentration or another one in too low a concentration, and the equilibrium is disturbed with ensuing concrement formation. Inflammatory processes . . . are certainly factors favoring the precipitation of a component, but they are not an indispensable condition for it."

VI. Cholesterol and Cancer

An interesting aspect of the pathology of cholesterol is its possible association with carcinogenesis. Cholesterol has been shown by Hieger and Orr (1954) to be a carcinogen in certain strains of mice. Bischoff, Fieser, and their colleagues (e.g. Bischoff et al., 1955; Fieser et al., 1955) found that certain degradation products of cholesterol such as 6β-hydroperoxy-Δ^4-cholest–3-one produced fibrosarcomas in mice. The subject of the carcinogenic effects of cholesterol and related compounds is reviewed by Haven and Bloor (1956) and by Kennaway (1957). Developments in this field, especially in respect to cholesterogenesis from acetic or mevalonic acids in cancerous hosts at various stages of development are awaited with interest.

Summary

The deviations from normal values of the cholesterol level in the body, primarily in the blood serum, are considered as symptoms and as etiologic factors of disease. Present knowledge is not enough advanced to ascribe to cholesterol a primary role in atherosclerosis, but its experimental administration to animals results in pathological conditions resembling those found in human vascular disease.

The level of cholesterol and the percentage of its esterification are important parameters in the diagnosis of hepatic and thyroid disease.

Hypercholesteremia is also a symptom in nephrosis and diabetes.

Depositions of cholesterol are found in spontaneous and experimental atheromata, also in sundry rare diseases. Cholesterol is the main constituent of human gallstones. Its significance in malignant growth is a moot question.

The fluctuations of the cholesterol level in serum are rather easily ascertained and more frequently determined than those of any other steroid. The study of its association with the various serum proteins in recent years has added much to the existing knowledge, but its physiological functions await elucidation.

REFERENCES

(Asterisk indicates review article.)

Ackermann, P. G., Toro, G., and Korentz, W. B. (1954). *J. Lab. Clin. Med.* **44**, 517-530.

Adlersberg, D. (1949). *Bull. N.Y. Acad. Med.* **25**, 651.

Adlersberg, D. (1951). *Am. J. Med.* **11**, 600-614.

Adlersberg, D. (1955). *A.M.A. Arch. Pathol.* **60**, 481-492.

Adlersberg, D. (1957). *Am. J. Med.* **23**, 765-789.

Adlersberg, D., and Wang, C. I. (1955)). *Diabetes* **4**, 210-218.

Adlersberg, D., Parets, A. D., and Boas, E. P. (1949). *J. Am. Med. Assoc.* **141**, 246-254.

Adlersberg, D., Schaefer, L. E., and Drachman, S. R. (1950a). *J. Am. Med. Assoc.* **144**, 909-914.

Adlersberg, D., Schaefer, L. E., and Dritch, R. (1950b). *Proc. Soc. Exptl. Biol. Med.* **74**, 877-879.

Adlersberg, D., Schaefer, L. E., and Drachman, S. R. (1951). *J. Clin. Endocrinol.* **11**, 67-83.

Adlersberg, D., Schaefer, L. E., and Drachman, S. R. (1952). *J. Lab. Clin. Med.* **39**, 237-245.

Adlersberg, D., Schaefer, L. E., Steinberg, A. G., and Wang, C. I. (1954a). *Circulation* **10**, 600-601.

Adlersberg, D., Schaefer, L. E., and Wang, C. I. (1954b). *Science* **120**, 319-320.

Adlersberg, D., Bossak, E. T., Sher, I. H., and Sobotka, H. (1955). *Clin. Chem.* **1**, 18-33.

Adlersberg, D., Schaefer, L. E., and Steinberg, A. G. (1956a). *J. Am. Med. Assoc.* **162**, 619-622.

Adlersberg, D., Wang, C. I., Rifkin, H., Berkman, J., Ross, G., and Weinstein, C. (1956b). *Diabetes* **5**, 116.
Adlersberg, D., Wang, C. I., and Strauss, L. (1957). *J. Mt. Sinai Hosp. N.Y.* **24**, 655-668.
Altschul, R. (1950a). *Am. Heart J.* **40**, 401-409.
Altschul, R. (1950b). "Selected Studies on Arteriosclerosis." Blackwell, Oxford, England.
Anfinsen, C. B., Jr. (1955). *In* "Arteriosclerosis," Symposium, pp. 37-44. Univ. Minnesota, Minneapolis, Minnesota.
Anitschkow, N. (1933). *In* "Arteriosclerosis: A Survey of the Problem" (Cowdry, ed.), p. 309. Macmillan, New York.
Barker, N. W. (1939). *Ann. Internal Med.* **13**, 685-692.
Barr, D. P. (1953). *Circulation* **8**, 641-654.
Barr, D. P. (1955). *In* "Arteriosclerosis," Symposium, pp. 58-63. Univ. Minnesota, Minneapolis, Minnesota.
Barr, D. P., Russ, E. M., and Eder, H. A. (1951). *Am. J. Med.* **11**, 480-493.
Bevans, M., and Mosbach, E. H. (1956). *Circulation* **14**, 484-485.
Bischoff, F., Lopez, G., Rupp, J. J., and Gray, C. L. (1955). *Federation Proc.* **14**, 183-184.
Bloom, D., Kaufman, S. R., and Stevens, R. A. (1942). *Arch. Dermatol. and Syphilol.* **45**, 1-18.
Boas, E. P. (1945). *J. Mt. Sinai Hosp. N.Y.* **12**, 79-83.
Boas, E. P., and Adlersberg, D. (1945). *J. Mt. Sinai Hosp. N.Y.* **12**, 84-86.
Boas, E. P., Parets, A. D., and Adlersberg, D. (1948). *Am. Heart J.* **35**, 611-622.
Brock, J. F., and Bronte-Stewart, B. (1955). *In* "Arteriosclerosis," Symposium, pp. 102-113. Univ. Minnesota, Minneapolis, Minnesota.
Byers, S. O., and Friedman, M. (1956). *J. Clin. Invest.* **35**, 405-410.
Christensen, F., Dam, H., and Kristensen, G. (1956). *Acta Physiol. Scand.* **36**, 329-336.
Cook, R. P., and McCullagh, G. P. (1939). *Quart. J. Exptl. Physiol.* **29**, 283-302.
Dauber, D. V., and Katz, L. N. (1942). *A.M.A. Arch. Pathol.* **34**, 937-950.
Davidson, J. D. (1951). *Am. J. Med.* **11**, 736-748.
*Duff, G. L., and McMillan, G. C. (1951). *Am. J. Med.* **11**, 92-108. A review on the pathology of atherosclerosis.
Eilert, M. L. (1949). *Am. Heart J.* **38**, 472; (1953). *Metabolism, Clin. and Exptl.* **2**, 137-145.
Epstein, E. Z. (1931). *A.M.A. Arch. Internal Med.* **47**, 82-93; (1932). **50**, 203-222.
Epstein, F. H., and Boas, E. P. (1955). *J. Gerontol.* **10**, 331-337.
Epstein, E. Z., and Greenspan, E. B. (1936). *A.MA.. Arch. Internal Med.* **58**, 860-890.
Feigl, J. (1918). *Biochem. Z.* **86**, 171-187; **90**, 126-134.
Fieser, L. F., Greene, T. W., Bischoff, F., Lopez, G., and Rupp, J. J. (1955). *J. Am. Chem. Soc.* **77**, 3928-3929.
Fishberg, A., and Fishberg, E. H. (1927). *Proc. Soc. Exptl. Biol. Med.* **25**, 296-297; (1928). *Biochem. Z.* **195**, 20-27.
Fishberg, E. H. (1929). *J. Biol. Chem.* **81**, 205-214.
Fleischmann, W., Shumacher, H. B., and Wilkins, L. (1940). *J. Physiol.* (*London*) **131**, 317-324.
Foldes, F. F., and Murphy, A. J. (1946). *Proc. Soc. Exptl. Biol. Med.* **62**, 215-218.

Frew, H. W. O., and Campbell-Fowler, C. (1956). *Practitioner* **176**, 416-419.

Friedman, M., and Byers, S. O. (1954). *Am. J. Physiol.* **179**, 201-215.

Fry, E. G. (1937). *Endocrinology* **21**, 283.

Georgariou, P. M. (1938). *Graefe's Arch. Ophthalmol.* **139**, 32-49.

Glavind, J., Hartmann, S., Clemmesen, J., Jessen, K. E., and Dam, H. (1952). *Acta Pathol. Microbiol. Scand.* **30**, 1-6.

Gofman, J. W., Jones, H. B., Lindgren, F. T., Lyon, T. P., Elliott, H. A., and Strisower, B. (1950). *Circulation* **2**, 161-178.

Gofman, J. W., Honig, M., Jones, H. B., Laufer, M. A., Lawry, E. Y., Lewis, L. A., Mann, G. V., Moore, F. E., Ohnsted, F., and Yeager, J. F. (1956). *Circulation* **14**, 691-741.

Gould, R. G. (1951). *Am. J. Med.* **11**, 209-227.

*Gubner, R., and Ungerleider, H. E. (1949). *Am. J. Med.* **6**, 60-83. (Review.)

Hardegger, E., Ruzicka, L., and Tagmann, E. (1943). *Helv. Chim. Acta* **26**, 2205-2221.

Hastrup, B., and Videbaek, A. A. (1954). *Acta Med. Scand.* **149**, 287-290.

Haven, F. L., and Bloor, W. R. (1956). *Advances in Cancer Research* **4**, 238-314.

Henderson, A. E. (1956). *J. Histochem. and Cytochem.* **4**, 153-158.

Hieger, I., and Orr, S. F. D. (1954). *Brit. J. Cancer* **8**, 274-290.

Higginson, J. (1956). *In* "Cardiovascular Epidemiology" (A. Keys and P. D. White, eds.), pp. 34-31. Hoeber-Harper, New York.

Horlick, L., and Katz, L. N. (1948). *J. Lab. Clin. Med.* **33**, 733-742.

Horn, G. (1956). *Brit. Med. J.* **II**, 732-737.

Hueper, W. C. (1945). *A.M.A. Arch. Pathol.* **39**, 51, 117, 187.

Hurxthal, L. M. (1933). *A.M.A. Arch. Internal Med.* **51**, 22-32; **52**, 86-95.

Hurxthal, L. M. (1934). *A.M.A. Arch. Internal Med.* **53**, 762-781.

Kantiengar, N. L., and Morton, R. A. (1955). *Biochem. J.* **60**, 25-28.

Katz, L. N. (1952). *Circulation* **5**, 101-114.

*Katz, L. N., and Dauber, D. V. (1945). *J. Mt. Sinai Hosp. N.Y.* **12**, 382-410. (A review.)

Katz, L. N., and Stamler, J. (1953). "Experimental Atherosclerosis." C. C Thomas, Springfield, Illinois.

Kellner, A., Correll, J. W., and Ladd, A. T. (1951). *J. Exptl. Med.* **93**, 385-398.

Kennaway, E. L. (Sir). (1957). *In* "Cancer" (Raven, ed.), Vol. 1. Butterworths, London.

Keys, A. (1953). *J. Mt. Sinai Hosp. N.Y.* **20**, 118-139.

Keys, A. (1955). *In* "Arteriosclerosis," Symposium, pp. 28-36. Univ. Minnesota, Minneapolis, Minnesota.

Keys, A. (1956). *In* "Cardiovascular Epidemiology" (A. Keys and P. D. White, eds.), pp. 135-149. Hoeber-Harper, New York.

Keys, A., and Keys, M. H. (1954). *Brit. J. Nutrition* **8**, 138-147.

Keys, A., and White, P. D., eds. (1956). "Cardiovascular Epidemiology." Hoeber-Harper, New York.

Keys, A., Mickelsen, O., Meller, E. V. O., Hayes, E. R., and Todd, R. L. (1950). *J. Clin. Invest.* **29**, 1347-1353.

Keys, A., Fidanza, F., Scardi, V., Bergami, G., Keys, M. H., and Di Lorenzo, F. (1954a). *A.M.A. Arch. Internal Med.* **93**, 328-336.

Keys, A., Vivanco, F., Rodriguez, Miñon J. L., Keys, M. H., and Castro Mendoza, H. C. (1954b). *Clin. and Exptl. Metabolism* **3**, 195-212.

Klatskin, G., and Gordon, M. (1952). *Am. J. Med.* **12**, 3-23.

Kleeberg, J. (1953a). *Med. Radiography (Kodak)* **29**, 47-61.

Kleeberg, J. (1953b). *Gastroenterologia* **80**, 313.

Kleeberg, J. (1956). *Gastroenterologia* **85**, 271-280.

Kornerup, V. (1950). *A.M.A. Arch. Internal Med.* **85**, 398-415.

Kunkel, H. G., and Slater, R. J. (1952). *Proc. Soc. Exptl. Biol. Med.* **80**, 42-44.

Kusakawa, A. (1956). *In* "Cardiovascular Epidemiology" (A. Keys and P. D. White, eds.), pp. 159-163. Hoeber-Harper, New York.

Lerman, J., and White, P. D. (1946). *J. Clin. Invest.* **25**, 914.

Lever, W. F., Smith, P. A., and Hurley, N. A. (1954). *J. Invest. Dermatol.* **22**, 33-51; **22**, 53-69; 71-87.

Lever, W. F., Herbst, F. S. M., and Hurley, N. A. (1955). *A.M.A. Arch. Dermatol.* **71**, 150-157; **71**, 158-171.

Lew, E. A. (1957). Conference Atherosclerosis and Coronary Heart Disease, New York Heart Assoc., New York, Jan. 15, 1957.

Lindsay, S., Nichols, C. W., Jr., and Chaikoff, I. L. (1955). *A.M.A. Arch. Pathol.* **59**, 173-184.

Luetscher, J. A., Jr., Hall, A. D., and Kramer, V. L. (1956). *J. Clin. Invest.* **29**, 896-907.

McArthur, C. S. (1942). *Biochem. J.* **36**, 559-570.

MacKay, E. M., and Barnes, R. S. (1937). *Am. J. Physiol.* **118**, 525-527.

McMahon, A., Allen, H. N., Weber, C. J., and Missey, W. C., Jr. (1951). *Southern Med. J.* **44**, 993-1002.

Mann, G. V. (1956). *In* "Cardiovascular Epidemiology" (A. Keys and P. D. White, eds.), pp. 150-158. Hoeber-Harper, New York.

Mann, G. V., and Andrus, S. B. (1956). *J. Lab. Clin. Med.* **48**, 533-550.

Mann, G. V., Andrus, S. B., McNally, A., and Stare, F. J. (1953). *J. Exptl. Med.* **98**, 195-218.

Moerner, C. Th. (1923). *Z. physiol. Chem.* **130**, 24-33.

Morrison, L. M., Hall, L., and Chaney, A. L. (1948). *Am. J. Med. Sci.* **216**, 32-38.

Müller, C. (1938). *Acta Med. Scand. Suppl.* **89**, 75-84.

Mushett, C. H., and Emerson, G. H. (1956). *Federation Proc.* **15**, 526.

Nikkilä, E. A. (1953). *Scand. J. Clin. & Lab. Invest.* **5**, Suppl. 8, 5.

Novak, J., and Lustig, B. (1947). *J. Mt. Sinai Hosp. N.Y.* **14**, 534-539.

Oliver, M. F., and Boyd, G. S. (1954). *Am. Heart J.* **47**, 349-359.

Oliver, M. F., and Boyd, G. S. (1955a). *Brit. Heart. J.* **17**, 299-302.

Oliver, M. F., and Boyd, G. S. (1955b). *In* "Arteriosclerosis," Symposium, pp. 6-64. Univ. Minnesota, Minneapolis, Minnesota.

Oppenheim, E., and Bruger, M. (1952). *Circulation* **6**, 470-471.

Page, I. H. (1954). *Circulation* **10**, 1-27.

Page, I. H., Kirk, E., Lewis, W. H., Jr., Thompson, W. R., and Van Slyke, D. D. (1935). *J. Biol. Chem.* **111**, 613-639.

Paronetto, F., Wang, C. I., and Adlersberg, D. (1956). *Science* **124**, 1148.

Peifer, J. J., and Lundberg, W. O. (1957). *Federation Proc.* **16**, 232.

Peters, J. P., and Man, E. B. (1943). *J. Clin. Invest.* **22**, 715-720.

Pick, R., Stamler, J., Rodbard, S., and Katz, L. N. (1951). *Circulation* **4**, 468.

Pick, R., Rodbard, S., Stamler, J., and Katz, L. N. (1952a). *Circulation* **6**, 476-477.

Pick, R., Stamler, J., Rodbard, S., and Katz, L. N. (1952b). *Circulation* **6**, 858-862.

Poulsen, H. M. (1950). *Acta Med. Scand.* **138**, 413-420.

Raper, H. S. (1921). *Biochem. J.* **15**, 49-52.

Rinehart, J. F., and Greenberg, L. D. (1949). *Am. J. Pathol.* **25**, 481-491.

Russ, E. M., Eder, H. A., and Barr, D. P. (1951). *Am. J. Med.* **11**, 468-479.

Salkowski, E. (1922). *Klin. Wochschr.* **1**, 1368-　.

Schaefer, L. E., Drachman, S. R., Steinberg, A. G., and Adlersberg, D. (1953). *Am. Heart J.* **46**, 99-116.

Schaefer, L. E., Adlersberg, D., and Steinberg, A. G. (1957). Scientific Exhibit, Ann. Meeting, Am. Med. Assoc., New York.

Schenk, M. (1925). *Z. physiol. Chem.* **145**, 1-17; 95-100.

Schettler, G. (1955). *In* "Handbuch der Inneren Medizin" (G. von Bergmann, W. Frey, and H. Schwiegk, eds.), Vol. 7, Part 2, pp. 713-741. Springer, Berlin.

Schoenheimer, R. (1928). *Z. physiol. Chem.* **177**, 143-157.

Schoenheimer, R., von Behring, H., and Hummel, R. (1930). *Z. physiol. Chem.* **192**, 93-96.

Seifter, J., Baeder, D. H., Beckfield, W. J., Sharmer, G. P., and Ehrich, W. E. (1954). *Proc. Soc. Exptl. Biol. Med.* **83**, 468-473.

Shull, K. H., and Mann, G. V. (1957). *Am. J. Physiol.* **188**, 81-85.

Sidis, B. (1939). Quoted in "Essays in Philosophical Biology" by W. M. Wheeler, p. 67. Harvard Univ. Press, Cambridge, Massachusetts.

Sjoeqvist, J. (1908). *Hyg. Festberichte* **2**, No. 48.

Snapper, I. (1949). "Medical Clinics on Bone Diseases," 2nd ed., p. 185ff. Interscience, New York.

Sobotka, H. (1930). *Nature* **18**, 619-620.

Sobotka, H. (1937). "The Physiological Chemistry of the Bile." Williams and Wilkins, Baltimore, and Ballière, London.

Sobotka, H. (1941a). *J. Mt. Sinai Hosp. N.Y.* **8**, 255-268.

Sobotka, H. (1941b). *J. Mt. Sinai Hosp. N.Y.* **9**, 795-798.

Sobotka, H., Epstein, E. Z., and Lichtenstein, L. (1930). *A.M.A. Arch. Pathol.* **10**, 677-686.

Sobotka, H., Glick, D., Reiner, M., and Tuchman, L. R. (1933). *Biochem. J.* **27**, 2031-2034.

Soffer, A., and Murray, M. (1954). *Circulation* **10**, 611.

Soffer, L. J. (1951). "Diseases of the Endocrine Glands." Lea & Fiebiger, Philadelphia.

Soffer, L. J., Eisenberg, J., Iannaccone, A., and Gabrilove, J. L. (1955). *Ciba Colloquia Endocrinol.*

Stary, Z. (1956). Leber und Galle. *In* "Physiologische Chemie" (L. B. Flaschenträger and E. Lehnartz, eds.), especially pp. 565-569. Springer, Berlin.

Stecher, R. M., and Hersh, A. H. (1949). *Science* **109**, 61-62.

Steiner, A., and Domanski, B. (1943). *A.M.A. Arch. Internal Med.* **71**, 397-402.

Steiner, A., and Kendall, F. E. (1946). *A.M.A. Arch. Pathol.* **42**, 433-444.

Steiner, A., Kendall, F. E., and Mathers, J. A. L. (1952). *Circulation* **5**, 605-608.

Stumpf, H. H., and Wilens, S. L. (1954). *Proc. Soc. Exptl. Biol. Med.* **86**, 219-223.

Thannhauser, S. J. (1950). "Lipidoses: Diseases of the Cellular Lipid Metabolism." Oxford Univ. Press, London and New York.

Thannhauser, S. J., and Schaber, H. (1926). *Klin. Wochschr.* **5**, 252.

Thannhauser, S. J., and Magendantz, H. (1938). *Ann. Internal Med.* **11**, 1662-1669.

Thannhauser, S. J., and Schmidt, G. (1946). *Physiol. Revs.* **26**, 275-317.

Tuchman, L. R., and Sobotka, H. (1932). *J. Biol. Chem.* **98**, 35-41.

Tuchman, L. R., Suna, H., and Carr, J. J. (1956). *J. Mt. Sinai Hosp. N.Y.* **23**, 227-229; See also *Clin. Chem.* **2**, 249.

Walker, A. R. P., and Arvidsson, U. B. (1954). *J. Clin. Invest.* **33**, 1358-1365.

Wang, C. I., Schaefer, L. E., and Adlersberg, D. (1954). *J. Mt. Sinai Hosp. N.Y.* **21**, 19-25.

Wang, C. I., Schaefer, L. E., and Adlersberg, D. (1955a). *Endocrinology* **56**, 628-638.

Wang, C. I., Schaefer, L. E., and Adlersberg, D. (1955b). *Circulation* **3**, 293-296.

Wang, C. I., Strauss, L., and Adlersberg, D. (1957). *A.M.A. Arch. Pathol.* **63**, 416-422.

*Weinhouse, S., and Hirsch, E. F. (1940). *A.M.A. Arch. Pathol.* **30**, 856-867. A review.

Wilens, S. L. (1947). *A.M.A. Arch. Internal Med.* **79**, 129-147.

Wilkinson, C. F., Jr., Hand, C. A., and Fliegelman, M. T. (1948). *Ann. Internal Med.* **29**, 671-686.

Windaus, A. (1910). *Z. physiol. Chem.* **67**, 174-176.

Wissler, R. W., Eilert, M. L., Schroeder, M. A., and Cohen, L. (1952). *Federation Proc.* **11**, 434.

Wolffe, J. B., Hyman, A. S., Plungian, M. B., Dale, A.D., McGinnis, G. E., and Walkov, M. B. (1952). *J. Gerontol.* **7**, 13-23.

Chapter 11

TREATMENT OF DISORDERS OF CHOLESTEROL METABOLISM

Irvine H. Page

It is not my purpose to document exhaustively and exhaustingly the problem of treating disturbances of cholesterol metabolism. Rather, I shall present certain trends with only enough literature reference so the reader may develop his knowledge if he wishes.

"Treatment" is much more high-sounding than the facts justify. All the current methods are under investigation, hence no firm conclusions of their value are as yet justified. The very recent interest in the problem of atherosclerosis and the slightly older interest in physiologically active steroids have done much to point up the vast medical and economic importance of this field. Unfortunately time has not yet matured the fundamental intellectual concepts on which sound treatment can be based. But this is now occurring under our very noses if we will but look. Fortunately, many good investigators are now looking.

The most effective treatment now available for a variety of hyperlipemias is the low-fat, high-protein diet. The total amount of fat *consumed* in such diets should not be greater than 10 to 15% of the total calories; consumed is emphasized because in most cases what is *offered* is measured instead.

I. Diet

Most patients at first lose weight on such diets and along with weight loss there is an associated fall in plasma cholesterol. But after a few months the weight levels off and the lipids tend to return, but not reach, their original level.

If diets less than 10% of the total calories as fat are used, the response may be even more dramatic but the clinical condition of the patient may be anything but satisfactory (Page, 1954). Marked gastro-intestinal disturbance with loose, watery stools and much gas occur. The patient becomes depressed, apathetic, and muscle tone is poor. With extremely low-fat content, the bulk in the diet and the carbohydrate content are increased greatly and doubtless are responsible for some of its undesirable features.

Some physicians (e.g. Wilkinson, 1956) believe that best results are achieved by administering all the fat in one meal. In this way, the blood is cleared of fat once and for all during the 24 hours and does not show the peaks which occur after each individual fat feeding. This may also be a practical device to insure more rigid observance of the diet.

In practice most diets are higher in fat content than they seem to be on the basis of calculations from standard tables. We have ground up and analyzed such diets and find a hospital diet calculated as containing 20 gm. of fat actually contained 39 gm. The chief reason for the discrepancy is omission in the calculation of those foods containing only small amounts but which are eaten in large quantities.

The rice-fruit juice diet has been used by some as a treatment both for hypertension and atherosclerosis, the former because of its low-salt content and the latter because of the diet's low-lipid content. Plasma cholesterol fell sharply and tended to remain reduced. Recent work of Hatch *et al.*, 1955 shows that restriction of dietary fat to 3 gm./day and elimination of cholesterol intake did not reduce serum lipids or lipoproteins below normal in any of the hypertensive patients studied. Carbohydrate and protein appear to be ready sources for endogenous synthesis of plasma lipid. They subscribe to the thesis that the total caloric intake is of greater significance in the control of plasma lipid levels than the quantity of cholesterol or fat ingested.

I have repeatedly pointed out (Page, 1954) the wide variability of responses of different patients to long time administration of high- and low-fat diets. Some respond to high fat intake by an almost immediate sharp increase in both plasma lipids and lipoproteins. Others are able to consume almost unbelievable amounts of fat with little or no response of the plasma lipids.

Most observers agree that plasma cholesterol is affected by fat restriction in the diet and little at all by cholesterol restriction. This fact seems to cause investigators some concern because in animals deposition of cholesterol with formation of atherosclerosis is elicited only when cholesterol is administered. Recently, it has been shown that feeding of high-vegetable fat diets to rabbits increased serum cholesterol levels and β-lipoprotein; early atherosclerosis was noted (Steiner and Dayton, 1956).

Much has been made of the differences in effect of blood cholesterol between, on the one hand, animal and vegetable and, on the other, saturated and unsaturated fatty acids. There seems to be no doubt that differences exist between animal and vegetable fats but the explanation of this is still obscure. It may be that there is a factor in animal fat which raises blood cholesterol levels (Beveridge and associates, 1956). On the other hand it may be that the degree of unsaturation of the fatty acids in the glycerides is of importance (see Ahrens *et al.*, 1954; Kinsell and colleagues, 1956 and Bronte-Stewart and collaborators, 1956). The recent publication by Ahrens and his associates (1957) on the administration of glycerides rich in "essential fatty acids" over periods of 4 to 6 months is indicative of a positive role of these compounds in the lowering of plasma cholesterol levels. There may well be, however, factors in the chemical make up of fatty acids other than the degree of saturation which are equally, if not more important. In our view the problem is still open. Harman (1957) has indeed suggested that the administration of fats rich in highly unsaturated fatty acids may lead to adverse effects.

The total calories in the diet seem also to be of importance in regard to hyperlipemia. When they are sufficiently low (about 1000 calories) and the individual is losing weight, plasma cholesterol falls. When weight loss ceases, due to increase in calories, it stabilizes at a higher level.

II. β-Sitosterol

The use of plant sterols as competitors for the intestinal absorption transfer-mechanism has received wide interest in the past ten years. The literature is discussed in Chapter 7. Most investigators agree that a reduction of from 10 to 15% of the level of plasma cholesterol may be expected if suspensions of sitosterol up to 5 gm. are taken before each meal (e.g. Pollak, 1952; Best *et al.*, 1954).

Some data suggest that certain of the plant sterols are absorbed and converted to cholic acid like cholesterol itself (Swell *et al.*, 1956). Absorption was shown for ergosterol a number of years ago by Menschick and Page (1932). While it is still a possibility that the feeding of these large amounts of plant sterol might have a deleterious effect of its own, there is not much evidence in favor of this view.

III.   Nicotinic Acid

When very large quantities (3 to 6 gm./day) of nicotinic acid are fed to hypercholesterolemic patients, a marked decrease in cholesterol levels occurs along with reduction in the plasma β/α_1 ratio in about two-thirds of patients, according to Parsons *et al.* (1956).

IV.   Exercise

Exercise as such has been little studied in its relationship to cholesterol metabolism and level in blood. In rats, Drs. Lewis, Brown, and I have quite convincing evidence that on high cholesterol diets the plasma cholesterol is somewhat lower in rats exercised regularly for months than in their sedentary controls. Much more striking is the low content of the lipid in the liver of the exercised animals.

Exercise temporarily raises blood lipids, due to increased demand, just as it does plasma glucose. But possibly its more important function is the massage of the blood vessels and tissues to increase the clearing of fat from the vessel wall by the lymph apparatus. It has repeatedly been noticed that atherosclerosis occurs much more severely in places where the blood vessels are not subjected to the massaging action of muscles.

Against this view is the work of Keys and his group (1956) showing that physical activity in a variety of populations seems to have little influence on serum cholesterol. They attribute the differences in the level among different peoples entirely to the habitual fat content of the diet. A recent study is by Taylor *et al.* (1957).

V.   Reduction of Abnormal Arterial Pressure Levels

One of the important factors in atherogenesis as I pointed out years ago (Page, 1941) is arterial blood pressure, especially when the blood cholesterol is also elevated. When arterial pressure is elevated, it accordingly increases the severity of atherosclerosis. Evidently, then, its reduction to normal levels is most desirable. Fortunately in about one-half of patients with hypertension this is possible with modern antihypertensive therapy. There is some evidence that such treatment has a retarding effect on atherogenesis though it will be evident how difficult it is to secure rigid proof for this supposition (Corcoran *et al.*, 1956).

VI.   Endocrine Therapy

Estrogens have been shown to cause a shift of cholesterol from the large, potentially unstable β-lipoproteins to the more stable α-lipoproteins. Further, estrogens appear to decrease the degree of experimental coronary atherosclerosis in chicks fed cholesterol (Katz and Stamler,

1953). Finally, femaleness is known as one of the potent forces determining the incidence of atherosclerosis among the human population. On these bases, several studies are now under way to determine whether administration of estrogens will decrease the incidence and mortality of myocardial infarction. While the very preliminary results look promising, it is much too early to predict the outcome. A search has also been initiated for non-feminizing estrogens that will be anti-atherogenic.

A second hormone, thyroxine, as well as potassium iodide, has been used in a desultory fashion for sometime. Iodide was used for centuries in the treatment of gummas and lesions of connective tissue and to "dissolve" atheromatous lesions. It was later found that it lowered blood cholesterol and, in rabbits fed cholesterol, retarded plaque formation. Subsequently, it has been suggested that its anti-atherogenic properties are associated with the appearance in the blood of a butanol-insoluble organically bound iodine fraction (Brown and Page, 1952). This whole field needs much more careful and penetrating study and only reflects the general lack of interest which has prevailed up until the past several years (see Dauber et al., 1949; Strisower et al., 1957; Oliver and Boyd, 1957a). Such a lead in the field of cancer would not have lain dormant for a century or more!

VII. Anti-biosynthetic Compounds

Substances which block the synthesis of cholesterol by the body would in theory be most valuable agents in treatment. Several have been found which block synthesis in vitro but only two in vivo; Cottet and collaborators (1953) noted decrease in serum cholesterol in rats fed α-phenylbutyric acid. This was shown by Steinberg and Frederickson (1955) to be due most probably to inhibition of the formation of acetoacetate from acetyl-coenzyme A in the biosynthesis. In vitro studies show α-phenylbutyric acid inhibited incorporation of 1-C^{14}-acetate into cholesterol; sodium β-phenylvalerate behaved similarly.

Studies on patients with these materials have yielded conflicting results. On the whole they do not look promising. Oliver and Boyd (1957b) have reported unfavorably on the effects of phenylacetic acid and its amide.

Tomkins et al. (1953) observed that feeding large quantities of Δ^4-cholestenone to rats suppresses incorporation of acetate into cholesterol of the liver. Δ^7-cholestenol, 7-dehydrocholesterol, and dehydroisoandrosterone behave similarly. There is a dramatic inhibition of cholesterol synthesis without effect on CO_2 production. The inhibition seems to occur somewhere between the squalene step and cholesterol. Steinberg and Frederickson (1956) showed a remarkable hypertrophy of the adrenal glands and death of the animals after 8 weeks of feeding the cholestenone. Serum cholesterol levels were on the average 40% lower than the controls. Fed at levels of 0.1% it was possible to affect blood cholesterol levels without impairing normal growth and causing adrenal hypertrophy.

Clearly these are interesting approaches to the problem of reducing the cholesterol content of the body but currently are purely experimental.

VIII. Primary Hyperlipemias

The relatively rare primary hyperlipemias are usually followed by atherosclerosis with myocardial infarction and angina pectoris. Both neutral fat and cholesterol are increased along with β-globulin. The response of the plasma lipids to low-fat diet is very satisfactory in essential hyperlipemia and, if persisted in, the skin lesions may clear (Malmros et al., 1954). The occurrence of xanthomas seems largely dependent on the level of plasma cholesterol.

IX. Secondary Hyperlipemias

Lipemia occurs in the association with a variety of diseases and may of itself be responsible in part for the course of the disease. For example, the persistent hyperlipemia of diabetes or nephrosis usually results in widespread atherosclerosis, including coronary disease with angina pectoris.

Treatment of these lipemias is the treatment of the causative disease itself (Page, 1945). Hyperlipemia disappears when diabetes is effectively controlled by insulin and the same is true of the treatment of hypothyroidism and myxedema with thyroid substance. When nephrosis spontaneously clears, or is aided in doing so by cortisone, hyperlipemia also is abolished. Elevating the greatly depressed plasma albumin level so as to provide enough fatty acids acceptor for the fatty acids liberated from lipoprotein, seems to aid in preventing the occurrence of hyperlipemia.

Sometimes the fear exists that despite clearing of the abnormal blood fat, the liver and spleen may still be the repository of harmful amounts of fats with resulting cirrhosis. This has led to the largely uncontrolled use of lipotropic substances as drugs. Much more likely to be successful is the use of adequate amounts of protein in the diet. Many proteins are excellent lipotropes themselves, are much cheaper than the pharmaceutical variety, and moreover, are palatable and accessible. In the cockerel, Pick et al. (1957) have shown that a high-vitamin, high-protein diet has a protective effect on cholesterol atherogenesis.

To summarize, the aim of any therapy is "primum non nocere," and in our present state of knowledge a high-protein, low-fat diet is the best available treatment for disorders of cholesterol metabolism in man.

REFERENCES

Ahrens, E. H., Jr., Blankenhorn, D. H., and Tsaltas, T. T. (1954). *Proc. Soc. Exptl. Biol. Med.* **86**, 872.

Ahrens, E. H., Jr., Hirsch, J., Insull, W., Jr., Tsaltas, T. T., Blomstrand, R., and Peterson, M. L. (1957). *Lancet* i, 943-953.

Best, M. M., Duncan, C. H., Van Loon, E. J., and Wathen, J. D. (1954). *Circulation* **10**, 201.

Beveridge, J. M. R., Connell, W. F., and Mayer, G. A. (1956). *Can. J. Biochem and Physiol.* **34**, 441.

Bronte-Stewart, B., Antonis, A., Eales, L., and Brock, J. F. (1956). *Lancet* i, 521.

Brown, H. B., and Page, I. H. (1952). *Circulation* **5**, 647.

Corcoran, A. C., Page, I. H., Dustan, H. P., and Lewis, L. A. (1956). *Cleveland Clinic Quart.* **23**, 115.

Cottet, J., Redel, J., Krumm-Heller, C., and Tricaud, M. B. (1953). *Bull. acad. natl. méd. (Paris)* **137**, 441.

Dauber, D. V., Horlick, L., and Katz, L. N. (1949). *Am. Heart J.* **38**, 25.

Harman, D. (1957). *Lancet* ii, 1116-1117.

Hatch, F. T., Abell, L. L., and Kendall, F. E. (1955). *Am. J. Med.* **19**, 48.

Katz, L. N., and Stamler, J. (1953). "Experimental Atherosclerosis." C. C Thomas, Springfield, Illinois.

Keys, A., Anderson, J. T., Aresu, M., Biorck, G., Brock, J. F., Bronte-Stewart, B., Fidanza, F., Keys, M. H., Malmros, H., Poppi, A., Posteli, T., Swahn, B., and Del Vecchio, A. (1956). *J. Clin. Invest.* **35**, 1173.

Kinsell, L. W., Michaels, G. D., Friskey, R. W., Brown, F. R., Jr., and Maruyama, F. (1956). *Circulation* **14**, 484.

Malmros, H., Swahn, B., and Truedsson, E. (1954). *Acta Med. Scand.* **149**, 91.

Menschick, W., and Page, I. H. (1932). *Z. physiol. Chem.* **211**, 246.

Oliver, M. F., and Boyd, G. S. (1957a). *Lancet* i, 124-125.

Oliver, M. F., and Boyd, G. S. (1957b). *Lancet* ii, 829-830.

Page, I. H. (1941). *Ann. Internal. Med.* **14**, 1741.

Page, I. H. (1945). *Biol. Symposia* **11**, 43.

Page, I. H. (1954). *Circulation* **10**, 1.

Parsons, W. B., Achor, R. W. P., Berge, K. G., McKenzie, B. F., and Barker, N. W. (1956). *Proc. Staff Meetings Mayo Clinic* **31**, 377.

Pick, R., Stamler, J., and Katz, L. N. (1957). *Federation Proc.* **16**, 101.

Pollak, O. J. (1952). *Circulation* **6**, 459.

Steinberg, D., and Fredrickson, D. S. (1955). *Circulation* **12**, 493.

Steinberg, D., and Fredrickson, D. S. (1956). *Ann. N.Y. Acad. Sci.* **64**, 579.

Steiner, A., and Dayton, S. (1956). *Circulation Research* **4**, 62.

Strisower, B., Gofman, J. W., Galioni, E. F., Rubinger, J. H., Pouteau, J., and Guzvich, P. (1957). *Lancet* i, 120-123.

Swell, L., Boiter, T. A., Field, H., Jr., and Treadwell, C. R. (1956). *J. Nutrition* **58**, 385.

Taylor, H. L., Anderson, J. T., and Keys, A. (1957). *Proc. Soc. Exptl. Biol. Med.* **95**, 383-386.

Tomkins, G. M., Sheppard, H., and Chaikoff, I. L. (1953). *J. Biol. Chem.* **203**, 781.

Wilkinson, C. F., Jr. (1956). *Circulation* **14**, 494.

CHAPTER 12

EVOLUTIONARY ASPECTS OF THE STEROLS

Werner Bergmann

I. Introduction

Early this century, Henze (1904, 1908) isolated a sterol from a sponge which proved to be quite different from cholesterol, the only animal sterol then known. This first demonstration of variety among animal sterols was soon followed by Dorée's (1908) comprehensive study, which is one of the great early classics in comparative biochemistry. In the introductory paragraph of his report Dorée has clearly stated the object of his investigations: "If cholesterol is a body which is one of the primary constituents of animal protoplasm, we should expect to find it not only in the highly organized animals, but throughout the series from Chordata to Protozoa; or if cholesterol itself were not present, its place should be filled by other and closely related forms. In the latter case it might be found that each of the great classes of the animal kingdom was characterized by the presence of a different member of the cholesterol family. On the other hand, if cholesterol is not of primary importance to all forms of life, it is not impossible that animals might be found into the composition of whose protoplasm it did not enter."

Dorée's studies dealt with animals representing the more common phyla, and he found sterols in all of them. He showed cholesterol to be present not only in vertebrates, but also in several invertebrates including such primitive forms as sea anemones. In addition two invertebrates, a sponge and a starfish, each afforded a new sterol. About the same time, the presence in insects of sterols other than cholesterol had also been reported (Welsch, 1909; Menozzi and Moreschi, 1910).

Fifty years ago, therefore, it had already been recognized, but not fully appreciated, that cholesterol is not the only animal sterol but merely a representative, albeit the best known, of a group of closely related compounds. The diversity of sterols in invertebrates when contrasted with the ubiquity in vertebrates of cholesterol suggested that the latter is the end-product of some evolutionary or selective process. A study of this interesting possibility became profitable only after the establishment of the structure of cholesterol in 1932.

Since then invertebrate sterols have been investigated systematically in the laboratories of Tsujimoto, of Toyama, and of Matsumoto in Japan, by the writer and his associates, and more recently also by Idler and Fagerlund (1957).

A schematic representation of the structural relation between the main naturally occurring sterols is shown in Fig. 1. Most of the invertebrate sterols are reminiscent of or identical with sterols formerly believed to be typical constituents of plants. They differ from cholesterol in one or another, or a combination of two structural features. They may be identical with cholesterol in the ring system and hence belong to the Δ^5-sterols of type I. Their difference from cholesterol is situated in the side chain which may be substituted at C-24 by a one- or two-carbon unit as in structures V to X. In addition both C-24 epimers of V, VI, VIII, and IX have been met with among natural sterols.

Another, and probably more significant difference from cholesterol is associated with the ring system. This may be saturated as in cholestanol (III) or its derivatives with substituents at C-24 (V–X). Such stanols in contrast to the Δ^5-sterols are significantly dextrorotatory, and they do not give many of the common sterol color reactions. This is an important point, often overlooked in histochemical studies. Another and somewhat more common variation of the ring system is shown by the Δ^7-stenols (II). Their physical and chemical properties are quite different from those of sterols of types I and III, and hence are readily recognized. They also may carry either the side chain of cholesterol (IV) or one or another of the substituted side chains V–X.

II. Sterols of Animals

A. Protozoa

Sterols in the accepted sense of the word do not seem to be necessary for all forms of life. Their presence could not be demonstrated in several species of bacteria (Anderson et al., 1935) and in some primitive, asexual algae of the class Myxophyceae, also known as Cyanophyceae, the blue-green algae (Carter et al., 1939). As yet no animal has been found which is entirely devoid of sterols. Even Protozoa have been shown either to contain sterols or at least to require them. The familiar pelagic flagellate, *Noctiluca miliaris,* contains significant quantities of an unfortunately unidentified sterol (Pratje, 1921), and cholesterol has been found in the fish parasite, *Eimeria gadi* (Panzer, 1913). In the latter case, the sterol may well be of exogenous origin as it appears to

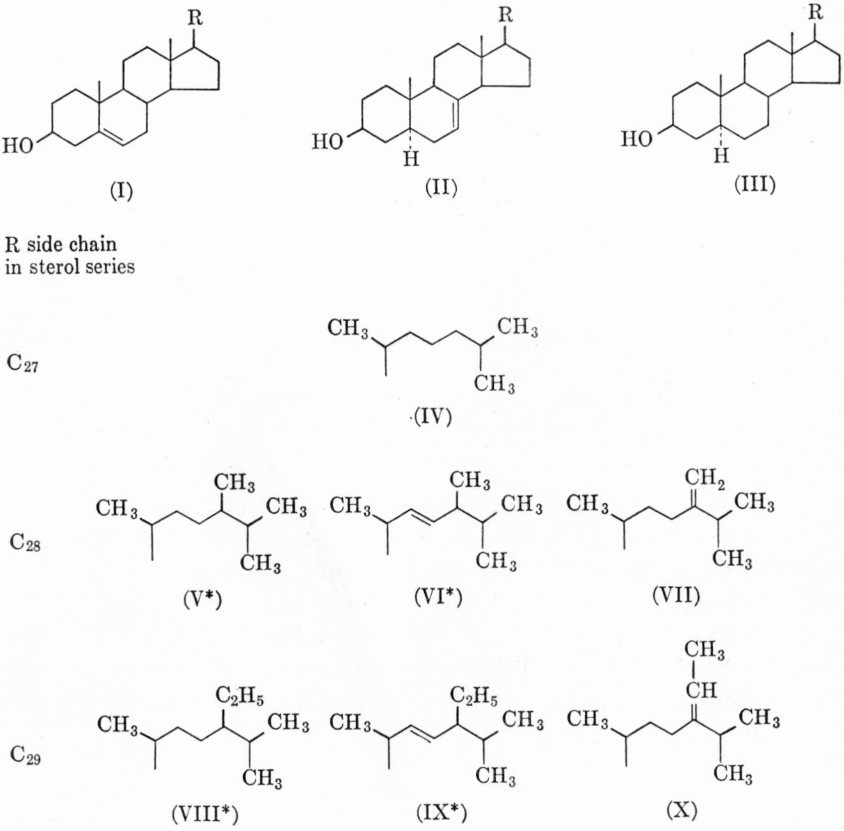

(I)   (II)   (III)

R side chain
in sterol series

C_{27}

·(IV)

C_{28}

(V*)   (VI*)   (VII)

C_{29}

(VIII*)   (IX*)   (X)

FIG. 1. The structural relation of the main naturally occurring sterols. *, the b epimer is represented but the a epimer (. . .) is also found (see text and Chapter 2, pp. 18-19).

be in Protozoa which show a growth response to sterols in their culture medium. Such responses are dependent on the ring and side chain structures of the sterols. Thus *Paramecium aurelia* responds only to Δ^5-sterols with C-24 alkyl substituents, while *Trichomonas columbae* is less selective. This intriguing and promising field has recently been reviewed by Van Wagtendonk (1955).

B. Porifera

The sterols of the Porifera are among the best known of any phylum. They have been isolated from more than fifty species of sponges, often as mixtures of bewildering complexity. Sterols of practically all the types and variations listed above are represented. The majority of them belong to the Δ^5-sterols (I), and among them cholesterol has been found in sponges of several classes and orders. The most common sponge sterols, however, are the C-24 ethyl derivatives of cholesterol, such as clionasterol (I and VIII) and poriferasterol (I and IX) (Bergmann, 1949). As yet only one sponge, *Chondrilla nucula*, has yielded a Δ^7-sterol, chondrillasterol (II and IX), in substantial amounts (Bergmann and McTigue, 1948). It is probably significant that this deviation from the norm is observed in a species of Carnosa, an order which includes sponges of rather unspongelike appearance and consistency.

Another exception to the predominant occurrence of Δ^5-sterols is found in sponges of families distributed between the orders of Hadromerina and Halichondrina. All of twelve species belonging to these families contain substantial quantities of ring-saturated sterols (III), the presence of which is so typical as to set these families apart from others assigned to the same orders. Among these sterols one finds cholestanol (III and IV) and its derivatives substituted at C-24 and also with unsaturation in the side chain, such as in spongosterol (III and VI) (Bergmann, 1949; Bergmann *et al.*, 1950). In these sponges, therefore, the ring structure of the sterols appears to be a more significant feature than the arrangement of the side chain. No noticeable relationships exist between the sterol content of these sponges and their geographic origin. Closely related species obtained from distant parts of the world, from shallow waters and the Atlantic depths, have always given sterol mixtures of very similar composition.

C. Coelenterata

It is generally held at present that the sponges are an early and probably polyphyletic branch off the main stem of evolution and hence not ancestral to higher animals. There is some validity, therefore, to the argument, that the great diversity of sponge sterols, while interesting per se, is of no significant value in tracing the biochemical history of sterols. A similar, if somewhat less spectacular variety of sterols, however, is also observed among the Coelenterata, which embraces animals more representative of the main stream of evolution. As yet our knowledge concerning this phylum is quite fragmentary and does not include any of the Hydrozoa and only one Scyphozoan, the jelly-fish, *Velella*, which contains cholesterol (Haurowitz and Waelsch, 1926). Better known are the sterols of Anthozoa which include the sea anemones, corals, and gorgonias. So far they have all been found to be of the Δ^5-type and they include cholesterol (Dorée, 1908; Bergmann et al., 1956), 24-methylenecholesterol (Bergmann and Dusza, 1957), brassicasterol, and palysterol (Bergmann et al., 1951).

D. ARTHROPODA

Only a few isolated data have become known on the sterols from animals assigned to the six or seven phyla generally listed between the Coelenterates and the Arthropods. Cholesterol has been isolated from a number of parasitic flatworms, in which it might well be of exogenous origin, and from the common earthworm, Lumbricus terrestris (for review see Bergmann, 1949). Of the multitude of animals comprising the phylum Arthropoda barely a dozen have been subjected to a more than casual sterol analysis. No comprehensive studies have yet been done on the class of Crustacea with its numerous and rather accessible species. All that is known is the occurrence of cholesterol in copepod oil in an ostracod, Cypridina, the isopod, Ligia exotica, and decapods, such as crabs and shrimps (for review see Bergmann, 1949). The presence in the latter could become of some economic importance, for as has been pointed out some time ago, shrimp waste is a potential source of quite large quantities of cholesterol (Vilbrandt and Abernethy, 1931). Quite recently, 24-dehydrocholesterol has been found to be a major constituent of the sterol mixture from the barnacle, Balanus glandula (Idler and Fagerlund, 1957). This sterol is identical with desmosterol which had previously been found to accompany cholesterol (Stokes et al., 1956).

Even less is known about the other classes of Arthropoda. No specific data are available on the sterols of spiders, Arachnoida, and centipedes, Myriapoda, beyond the fact that cholesterol is present in the horseshoe crab, Limulus (Bergmann et al., 1943), and a Δ^5-sterol mixture in a millipede (Ueno and Yamasaki, 1934). There is also a dearth of information on the sterol components of insects. A few phytophagous species, such as the silk worm and the locust contain Δ^5-sterol mixtures with cholesterol a major component (for review see Bergmann, 1949). Of great interest are the observations that many insects, if not all, require a dietary source of sterol for growth. The species thus far examined may be roughly divided into two groups on the basis of their natural food and their sterol requirement. The phytophagous species are less specific and respond to cholesterol and its C-24 homologs, while the carnivorous larvae can only utilize sterols with the carbon skeleton of cholesterol (for review see Trager, 1947; see also Fraenkel and Blewett, 1943; Noland, 1954 and Chapter 13).

E. Mollusca

An intensive, systematic study of mollusk sterols has been most rewarding, for it has brought out interesting relations between the sterols and the conventional taxonomy of this phylum. Thus the most primitive mollusks of the class Amphineura differ from the more advanced species of other classes in that they alone contain Δ^7-sterols (II) in substantial quantities. Recent, independent studies on chitons from the Pacific (Toyama and Tanaka, 1953), and the Atlantic (Kind and Meigs, 1955) have shown convincingly that these mollusks contain Δ^7-cholestenol as their principal sterol.

It has been found in many studies on thirty or more species of Pelecypoda, that these bivalves contain mainly Δ^5-sterols, often in form of mixtures of considerable complexity (for review see Bergmann, 1949; Toyama et al., 1955). Among them cholesterol is generally, if not always present, but as a rule only in association with larger amounts of its side chain derivatives, among which brassicasterol (I and VI) and the recently discovered 24-methylenecholesterol (I and VII) (Idler and Fagerlund, 1955) are the more conspicuous.

The situation is reversed among the Gastropoda, the snails, in which cholesterol is the most prominent sterol in a Δ^5-sterol mixture. Among the many species representing all the orders which have so far been investigated (for review see Bergmann, 1949; Toyama et al., 1955), only two were found to be exceptions to this rule. They are from different families of the order Pteropoda, and as Baalsrud (1950) has shown, they do not contain cholesterol in demonstrable amounts but instead another Δ^5-sterol, provisionally named pteropodasterol. This is of interest because these pelagic, free-swimming snails had been considered by older zoologists as belonging to a class of equivalent value to the Gastropoda, and even as the ancestors of the Cephalopoda. While their unusual sterol indeed sets the Pteropods apart from other Gastropods, it does not point to their relation to the Cephalopods. At least two species of squids and one of octopus have been found to contain mainly cholesterol (for review see Bergmann, 1949).

F. Echinodermata

If the various species belonging to the phylum Echinodermata were to be divided on the basis of the sterols they contain, they would form two groups. One of them containing the characteristic Δ^7-stenols would include the starfish, Asteroidea, and the sea-cucumbers, Holothuroidea. The other, containing Δ^5-sterols would embrace the sea-lilies, Crinoidea, the brittle-stars, Ophiuroidea, and the sea-urchins, Echinoidea. In a considerable measure at least this chemical classification supports the one derived from biological evidence, but the reliability of which had been questioned. (For a discussion see: Bergmann, 1949; Hyman, 1955).

The data on starfish are particularly well substantiated through studies on many species from various parts of the world. (Bergmann, 1949; Toyama et al., 1955; Toyama and Takagi, 1955). The Δ^7-sterols from starfish differ in the structure of their side chains which may be unaltered as in Δ^7-cholestenol (II and IV) (Toyama and Takagi, 1954) or substituted at C-24 and with an additional double bond at C-22, 23 (Matsumoso and Wainai, 1955). Here also the structure of the ring system appears to be a feature of greater importance than that of the side chain. It is probable that a more intimate study of the side chain differences will lead to the discovery of additional relations between sterol structure and taxonomy. The sterol content of sea-cucumbers is extraordinarily small, but has been sufficient clearly to establish the presence of Δ^7-sterols as the principal components in several species (Bergmann, 1949; Toyama et al., 1955; Toyama and Takagi, 1955; Toyama and Tanaka, 1956).

G. VERTEBRATA

Unfortunately, almost nothing is known about the sterols of Protochordata, animals belonging to the interesting twilight zone between vertebrates and invertebrates. The principal sterol of one of the Tunicata has been shown to be cholesterol (Bergmann et al., 1943), but it is by no means certain that this is true for all species of this class. In the vertebrates no exception has been found to the rule of the predominance of cholesterol. "Phytosterol-like" sterols, however, have been shown to constitute as much as one-fifth of the skin sterols of certain toads (Hüttel and Behringer, 1937) which belong to the more primitive vertebrates.

III. Conclusions

As a survey of animal sterols shows, the greatest diversity among the principal components of a sterol mixture is met with among the more primitive animals. Cholesterol appears already among the most primitive invertebrates but only as one of many sterols. At higher levels of evolution it rises to an increasingly dominant position until it has become the sole principal sterol of the vertebrate animal. It is quite probable that such a "reduction of a multitude of closely related compounds which seemingly perform closely related functions, to a few compounds if not only one, is a general phenomenon of bio-chemical evolution" (Bergmann, 1949). It would appear that in cholesterol we witness the survival of the "fittest" sterol.

In recent years the theory of the biochemical formation of triterpenoids and sterols from squalene has been shown to be in complete accord with experimental facts. The cyclization of squalene and the subsequent re-arrangements and demethylations afford a tetra-cyclic triterpenoid such as lanosterol, or a sterol with the cholesterol side chain (IV). Unless one assumes a different biosynthesis of sterols, substituted at C-24, one must conclude that they were formed by C-24 methylation and ethylation at or near the end of the formation of lanosterol or cholesterol from squalene. Indeed it has quite recently been demonstrated convincingly by Danielsson and Bloch (1957) that the addition of a single carbon unit to C-24 constitutes the final step in the biosynthesis of the carbon skele-ton of ergosterol by yeast. It is probable, therefore, that the synthesis of C-24 ethyl sterols proceeds in an analogous manner. The 24-methylene (VII) and ethylene (X) derivatives may represent intermediate steps which upon subsequent hydrogenation would afford either one or both of the C-24 methyl and ethyl epimers of which many have been en-countered among natural sterols.

There remains little doubt today that cholesterol is the primary and hence simpler sterol and that the alkyl groups at C-24 are secondary features of unknown significance. In the primitive invertebrates sterols with such additional features are encountered as often as the simpler cholesterol, but in the vertebrates the latter prevails. It appears, there-fore, that in animals C-24 substituents did not prove to be of lasting advantage and were abandoned in favor of the unaltered side chain of sterols as derived directly from squalene.

In plants evolution did not move in the direction of the simpler mole-cule. With but few exceptions, such as zymosterol, one of the minor yeast sterols, plant sterols carry the one- or two-carbon substituents at C-24. Among the more primitive plants, fungi, lichens, and some algae, the C-24 methyl- or methylene-sterols or the corresponding tetra-cyclic triterpenoids are the most conspicuous, but among higher plants C-24-ethyl derivatives of cholesterol are the most common (for review see Bergmann, 1953). On the other hand, the multitude of sapogenins (spirostans) and steroid alkaloids encountered in higher plants are derived from an unaltered cholesterol-type carbon skeleton. In addition cholesterol itself has recently been shown to occur in significant quanti-ties in a number of red algae (Tsuda et al., 1957).

As yet obscure is the significance of the striking predominance of Δ^7-sterols in animals of one order of sponges, of the most primitive class of mollusks, and of two classes of echinoderms. Such sterols are also encountered in plants, but in higher plants their occurrence is rather sporadic and not as intimately associated with taxonomic features as in animals. Only plants from in the family of Cucurbitaceae have been found with regularity to contain Δ^7-sterols in major amounts (Bergmann, 1953). A link structurally connecting Δ^5- and Δ^7-sterols are the $\Delta^{5,7}$-dienols of the type of provitamin D. These sterols which are subject to important photochemical reactions are present in small amounts in most sterol mixtures from plants and animals, and may amount to as much as one-fifth of the total sterols in invertebrates, such as mollusks. Saturation of either one of the conjugated double bonds would afford the Δ^5- or Δ^7-sterol, respectively, and conversely either one of the two sterols could yield the conjugated diene by allylic dehydrogenation.

REFERENCES

(Asterisk indicates review article)

Anderson, R. J., Schoenheimer, R., Crowder, J. S., and Stodola, F. H. (1935). Z. physiol. Chem. **237**, 40-45.

Baalsrud, K. (1950). Acta Chem. Scand. **4**, 512-517.

*Bergmann, W. (1949). J. Marine Research (Sears Foundation) **8**, 137-176. (Invertebrate sterols.)

*Bergmann, W. (1953). Ann. Rev. Plant Physiol. **4**, 383-426. (Plant sterols.)

Bergmann, W., and Dusza, J. P. (1957). Ann. Chem. Justus Liebig. **103**, 36-43 (1957).

Bergmann, W., and McTigue, F. H. (1948). J. Org. Chem. **13**, 738-741.

Bergmann, W., McLean, M. J., and Lester, D. (1943). J. Org. Chem. **8**, 271-282.

Bergmann, W., McTigue, F. H., Low, E. M., Stokes, W. M., and Feeney, R. J. (1950). J. Org. Chem. **15**, 96-105.

Bergmann, W., Feeney, R. J., and Swift, A. N. (1951). J. Org. Chem. **16**, 1337-1344.

Bergmann, W., Creighton, S. M., and Stokes, W. M. (1956). J. Org. Chem. **21**, 721-728.

Carter, P. W., Heilbron, I. M., and Lythgoe, B. (1939). Proc. Roy. Soc. (London) **B128**, 82-109.

Danielsson, H., and Bloch, K. (1957). J. Am. Chem. Soc. **79**, 500-501.

Dorée, C. (1908). Biochem. J. **4**, 72-106.

Fraenkel, G., and Blewett, M. (1943). Biochem. J. **37**, 692-695.

Haurowitz, F., and Waelsch, H. (1926). Z. physiol. Chem. **161**, 300-317.

Henze, M. (1904). Z. physiol. Chem. **41**, 109-124; (1908); ibid. **55**, 427-432.

Hüttel, R., and Behringer, H. (1937). Z. physiol. Chem. **245**, 175-180.

Hyman, L. H. (1955). In "The Invertebrates: Echinodermata," pp. 691-705. McGraw-Hill, New York.

Idler, D. R., and Fagerlund, U. H. M. (1955). J. Am. Chem. Soc. **77**, 4142-4144.

Idler, D. R., and Fagerlund, U. H. M. (1957). Abstr. Papers 132nd Meeting Am. Chem. Soc., New York, Sept. 1957, p. 46C.

Kind, C. A., and Meigs, R. A. (1955). J. Org. Chem. **20**, 1116-1118.

Matsumoto, T., and Wainai, T. (1955). Bull. Chem. Soc. Japan **28**, 448-450.

Menozzi, A., and Moreschi, A. (1910). Atti. accad. naz. Lincei Rend. Cl. sci. fis. mat. e nat. (5) **19**, 126-129.

Noland, J. L. (1954). Arch. Biochem. Biophys. **52**, 323-330.

Panzer, T. (1913). Z. physiol. Chem. **86**, 33-42.

Pratje, A. (1921). Biol. Zentr. **41**, 433-446.

Stokes, W. M., Fish, W. A., and Hickey, F. C. (1956). *J. Biol. Chem.* **220**, 415-430.

Toyama, Y., and Takagi, T. (1954). *Bull. Chem. Soc. Japan* **27**, 421-423.

Toyama, Y., and Takagi, T. (1955). *Mem. Fac. Eng. Nagoya Univ.* **7**, 151-155.

Toyama, Y., and Tanaka, T. (1953). *Bull. Chem. Soc. Japan* **26**, 497.

Toyama, Y., and Tanaka, T. (1956). *Mem. Fac. Eng. Nagoya Univ.* **8**, 29-44.

Toyama, Y., Takagi, T., and Tanaka, T. (1955). *Mem. Fac. Eng. Nagoya Univ.* **7**, 1-35. (Invertebrate sterols.)

*Trager, W. (1947). *Biol. Revs. Cambridge Phil. Soc.* **22**, 148-177. (Sterol requirement of insects.)

Tsuda, K., Akagi, S., and Kishida, Y. (1957). *Science* **126**, 927-928.

Ueno, S., and Yamasaki, R. (1934). *J. Soc. Chem. Ind. Japan Suppl.* **37**, 507B-510B.

*Van Wagtendonk, W. J. (1955). *Biochemistry and Physiol. Protozoa* **2**, 57-84. (Nutrition of ciliates.)

Vilbrandt, F. C., and Abernethy, R. F. (1931). *J. Am. Chem. Soc.* **53**, 2796-2797.

Welsch, A. (1909). Dissertation, Freiburg. 58 pp.

CHAPTER 13

THE STEROL REQUIREMENTS OF INSECTS AND OF PROTOZOA*

Marjorie G. Horning

I. Insects

A. INTRODUCTION

Although members of the Insecta have a diversity of habit and structure which includes some rather bizarre features, all species that have been studied have in common a requirement for an exogenous source of steroids for normal growth of the larvae and for metamorphosis to the adult form. Most of these studies have been carried out through a nutritional approach, with the aim of establishing a requirement for cholesterol or other steroids during some or all of the life of the insect. The steroid of choice for supporting growth has usually been cholesterol, although other steroids may be substituted for cholesterol with varying degrees of effectiveness, depending on the species under study. It is possible that the steroid requirement is related to hormonal functions necessary for growth and for metamorphosis, but this field is relatively unexplored and the reasons for the steroid requirement are still largely a matter for speculation.

Very few studies have been made of enzyme systems in the Insecta which are capable of effecting the transformation of cholesterol into metabolic products. In view of the large array of experimental subjects presented by the Insecta, it is strange that this approach has not been explored more fully.

---

* Chemical nomenclature in this chapter follows the Ciba Foundation rules.

This survey covers a period starting with the work of Hobson (1935a) on the cholesterol requirements of the larvae of *Lucilia sericata,* and it includes the most recent studies. Review articles are given in the References (Lipke and Fraenkel, 1956; Trager, 1947, 1953). A glossary of the species studied is appended.

B. METABOLIC REQUIREMENTS

Research activities over the past twenty years on steroid metabolism in insects have been concerned almost entirely with the determination of the nutritional requirements of a variety of species for normal growth of the larvae and for metamorphosis. Hobson (1935a) introduced the use of a partially purified diet in the study of insect steroid metabolism, and in his studies of the growth of the larvae of the flesh fly, *Lucilia sericata,* it was found that cholesterol was a necessary dietary component. Ergosterol and sitosterol were reported to be less effective than cholesterol when used under the same dietary conditions. The use of purified or synthetic diets has since been successful with a number of other species. Early diets generally consisted of casein (vitamin-free, lipid-free) salts, starch, yeast fractions (extracted to remove lipids and steroids), and an added steroid. An essentially synthetic diet, using amino acids in place of casein, was developed by Hinton *et al.* (1951) for *Drosophila melanogaster.* Normal development of the larvae was prolonged by one or two days when this diet was used, but adjustment of the amino acids levels may remedy this deficiency. The larvae of *Tribolium confusum* (Lemonde and Bernard, 1951), *Aedes aegypti* (Goldberg and De Meillon, 1948), and of *Pseudosarcophaga affinis,* an entomophagous insect (House, 1954), have been maintained on a synthetic diet consisting of amino acids, dextrose, salts, B vitamins, ribonucleic acid, and cholesterol.

The concentration of cholesterol in these diets has usually been set at 1% of the dry weight (Brust and Fraenkel, 1955). Optimum and minimum levels have been determined in only a few cases, and there is a considerable degree of species variation. For the blow fly, *Phormia regina,* the optimum concentration was found to be 0.25% of the dry weight of the diet (Brust and Fraenkel, 1955). The minimum level for *Dermestes vulpinus* was found to be 0.07% of the dry weight of the diet (Fraenkel *et al.,* 1941). The latter concentration was also the minimum effective level reported by Hobson (1935a) in his initial observations on *Lucilia sericata* and is comparable to the level of 0.05% reported for *Blatella germanica* (Noland, 1954a). A level of 0.007% of cholesterol was found adequate for normal growth of the black carpet beetle, *Attagenus piceus*

(McKennis, 1947). In the synthetic diet (Hinton et al., 1951) a concentration of 0.5% cholesterol was employed.

Most larvae exhibit only moderate specificity with respect to their requirement for dietary steroids. Cholesterol fills the requirement for all the larvae studied except the sawtooth grain beetle, *Oryzaephilus surinamensis* (Frobrich, 1940); this species requires ergosterol. The naturally occurring sterols, sitosterol, stigmasterol, and ergosterol, can be substituted with one exception for cholesterol, but they must be used at a higher concentration in the diet (1% at least). The beetle *Dermestes vulpinus* (Fraenkel et al., 1941), which normally feeds on dry products of animal origin, cannot utilize plant steroids. Zymosterol (cholesta-8,24,-diene-3β-ol) has not been utilized when tested (Goldberg and DeMeillon, 1948; Fraenkel *et al.*, 1941; Brust and Fraenkel, 1955).

The structural requirements for activity of the steroid molecule have been studied by several investigators and in considerable detail by Noland (1954a). He concluded that for *Blatella germanica*, the C-3 hydroxyl group, either free or esterified, was an essential structural feature; the double bond at carbon 5–carbon 6 was not essential and alterations in the nucleus or side chain had only slight effect. However, since cholestan-3β-ol, epicholesterol (cholest-5-en-3α-ol), coprostanol, and cholest-4-en-3-one were not tested, these conclusions may not be entirely justified.

Several esters of cholesterol have been tested in various genera and found effective in supporting normal growth. The acetyl ester is more effective than the free steroid as a growth factor for larvae of *Aedes aegypti* (Goldberg and DeMeillon, 1948) and it is fully as effective as cholesterol for *Attagenus piceus* (McKennis, 1947), *Blatella germanica* (Noland, 1954a), *Callosobruchus chinensis* (Ishii, 1951), and for six grain-feeding insects (Fraenkel, 1943). Other esters tested and found effective include the formate, butyrate, palmitate, diethylacetate, and benzoate of cholesterol (Noland, 1954a); the propionate and *p*-toluene-sulfonate of cholesterol (McKennis, 1954); 7-dehydrocholesterol benzoate (Fraenkel *et al.*, 1941), and the acetate and propionate of stigmasterol (Ishii, 1955).

A 3β-hydroxyl group is not an essential functional group for all larvae. Cholest-4-en-3-one can be utilized by *Musca vicina* (Bergmann and Levinson, 1954) and *Drosophila* (Van't Hoog, 1935, 1936). This ketone, however, not only is not utilized by *Aedes aegypti*, but is inhibitory (Goldberg and DeMeillon, 1948). In one instance the 3β-structure was replaced by a compound with a 3α-configuration. Larvae of *Callosobruchus chinensis* used epicholesterol without isomerization in the larval body, according to Ishii (1955).

A double bond at carbon 5–carbon 6 is not essential for several species. Cholestan-3β-ol can be used as a dietary steroid by *Aedes aegypti* (Goldberg and DeMeillon, 1948), by *Drosophila melanogaster* (Van't Hoog, 1936) *Tribolium confusum, Silvanus surinamensis, Lasioderma serricorni, Sitodrepa panicia, Ptinus tectus,* and *Ephestia kuehniella* (Fraenkel and Blewett, 1943). Cholesterol dibromide can be utilized by *Aedes aegypti* (Goldberg and DeMeillon, 1948) and *Attagenus piceus* (McKennis, 1947); tetrahydrostigmasterol by *Callosobruchus chinensis* (Ishii, 1955). The saturated steroids cholestan-3β-ol and cholestan-3-one are inhibitory for *Musca vicina* (Bergmann and Levinson, 1954). Cholestan-3β-ol-6-one can be utilized by *Aedes aegypti.* It is interesting to note that Goldberg and DeMeillon (1948) tested an isomer of this compound, cholest-4-en-3β,6-diol, and also found it to be effective in supporting growth.

It is not surprising that 7-dehydrocholesterol will also serve as a dietary supplement since it has the same structure for rings A and B as ergosterol, but its effectiveness varies with the genera. It was found active at one-fourth the concentration of cholesterol for *Dermestes vulpinus* (Fraenkel *et al.,* 1941); at the same concentration as cholesterol for *Aedes aegypti* (Goldberg and DeMeillon, 1948) and the six flour-feeding insects (Fraenkel and Blewett, 1943), and less effective than cholesterol for *Attagenus piceus* (McKennis, 1947). Calciferol, which may be considered a further oxidation product of 7-dehydrocholesterol, cannot be substituted for cholesterol in *Phormia regina* (Brust and Fraenkel, 1955) or *Dermestes vulpinus* (Fraenkel *et al.,* 1941).

From these examples it can be seen that a number of larvae vary in their ability to utilize closely related steroids. The important part of the molecule, in a structural sense, seems to be the region of C-3 to C-7 of rings A and B. Side chain variations for naturally occurring steroids are of minor importance.

C. Enzymatic Studies

Clément and Frisch were the first to report on enzyme systems involved in the steroid metabolism of insects. In 1946 these workers described an active "esterase" in the intestines of the larvae of the wax moth, *Galleria mellonella.* This esterase readily esterified cholesterol at pH 7.2. It was later suggested by Noland (1954b) that the enzymatic esterification of cholesterol in the German cockroach, *Blatella germanica,* was required to permit absorption of the sterol from the digestive tract. Accordingly, a 3-hydroxyl group, either free or esterified, was considered necessary for the sterol supplement. Inhibition studies were carried out with thirty-one nonutilizable steroids, and four of these were found to have an inhibitory action. Thiocholesterol and its acetate, cholesteryl chloride, and cholesterol methyl ether were not toxic per se, but when included in the diet (at a 1% level) with a normally satisfactory level of cholesterol (0.05%), inhibition of growth was observed. These results were interpreted as indicating a blocking action by competitive inhibition on a cholesterol esterase system by these compounds. In another study cholesteryl chloride was found to have an inhibitory action on the growth of *Attagenus piceus,* but the effect was overcome by increasing the level of cholesterol in the diet from 0.07 mg./gm. to 1 mg./gm. of diet (McKennis, 1947).

Casida *et al.* (1957) recently studied the enzymatic synthesis of cholesterol esters in the American cockroach, *Periplaneta americana.* With supplied oleic acid (8 moles per mole of steroid), esterification was carried on quite effectively by homogenates of the gastric ceca, mid-intestines, and Malpighian tubules. Cholesterol was esterified to the extent of 27%; Δ^7-cholestenol, 16%; and 7-dehydrocholesterol, 15%. Coprostanol, β-sitosterol, ergosterol, and stigmasterol were not esterified under these conditions. The phytosteroids apparently are not suitable substrates for this esterase, yet they are generally adequate for supporting growth of larval forms.

Experiments with radioactive acetate by Casida *et al.* (1957) demonstrated that the steroid molecule was subjected to reactions beyond that of esterification. Although acetate will not replace cholesterol in the diet of *Attagenus piceus* (McKennis, 1954) or *Tenebrio molitor* (Le-clercq, 1948), acetate-1-C^{14} was found to be incorporated into the steroid fraction precipitated by digitonin for *Periplaneta americana.* The extent of incorporation was comparable to that found for the mouse. These results are interpreted as indicating that the steroid side chain was cleaved, and that further reaction perhaps involving resynthesis of the isooctyl group, utilized radioactive acetate. Other observations on side chain oxidation support the belief that this mode of reaction occurs fairly readily in insects. The Australian ant, *Iridomyrmex detectus,* has been found to contain cholesterol in the body lipids, and it is known that methylheptenone is released by the metabolic processes of the ant (Cavill *et al.,* 1956). Clearly, an economical way of obtaining methyl-heptenone would be by oxidative cleavage of the cholesterol side chain. Experiments by Horning (1957) with an acetone powder of saw fly larvae, *Neodiprion pratti pratti* indicate that up to 30% of the radioactivity of cholesterol-26-C^{14} is lost by enzymatic oxidation.

D. Possible Role of Cholesterol

The precise function of cholesterol in insect metabolism has not been defined. The evidence for cholesterol as a growth factor is based on dietary studies. In a study by Leclercq (1948) of the larvae of *Tenebrio molitor,* it was established that acetate could not replace cholesterol during the early life of the larvae, and that cholesterol was required for normal growth. However, the need for cholesterol decreased with increasing age of the larvae, and after reaching approximately the halfway stage of growth it was possible to remove cholesterol from the diet without affecting further growth. The duration of the larval stage in *Tenebrio* is quite long (150–200 days, Finkel, 1948), and it is possible that the larva developed a system for the synthesis of cholesterol, or simply that the larva stored sufficient cholesterol to meet its needs. Cholesterol also seems to serve primarily as a growth factor for *Phaenicia sericata* (Kadner and LaFleur, 1952), since if the sterol is omitted from the diet death occurs within 12 days.

There is also evidence to indicate that cholesterol is required throughout the life of at least some insects, and that it may be a source of steroidal hormones during metamorphosis and in the adult life of the insect. For example, in *Musca vicina* the sterol is required both for growth and pupation (Bergmann and Levinson, 1954); in *Pyrausta nubilalis* it is required as a molting factor (Beck, 1950); and in *Blatella germanica* it is required for reproduction (Chauvin, 1949). In the mosquito *Aedes aegypti* the entire process of growth and metamorphosis is affected by the absence of cholesterol. On a cholesterol-free diet the larvae grow at a reduced rate to the fourth instar. If pupation occurs, it is only after a considerable delay and very few adults result from the pupae that are formed (Goldberg and DeMeillon, 1948).

Cholesterol is a component of the blood (hemolymph) of insects (Hopf, 1940; Levenbook, 1950), and it has been found in all tissues that were examined of the American cockroach (Casida *et al.,* 1957). The concentration in the cockroach was found to vary from 0.15 to 1.06 μg./mg. of fresh tissue; the amount in esterified form was 12 to 48% of the total cholesterol. The amount of "fast-acting" sterol, assumed to be 7-dehydrocholesterol, was as high as 53% of the sterol content in some tissues.

The chrysalis oil of the silkworm moth, *Bombyx mori,* was analyzed by W. Bergmann (1934) and was found to contain both cholesterol and sitosterol. These two sterols, in 85:15 proportion, were found to make up 33% of the unsaponifiable fraction of the oil. In fact, Leggieri (1949) has proposed that the oil be used as a commercial source of cholesterol.

In an attempt to throw additional light on this problem, the cholesterol content of the larvae of *Tenebrio molitor* was followed through growth and pupation (Finkel, 1948). The amount of cholesterol increased during larval growth, but it remained a nearly constant proportion of the total body weight. In contrast with this effect, the neutral fats and fatty acids increased markedly during this period. During pupation there was no significant change in the sterol content. The same effect was noted for *Musca vicina* (Silverman and Levinson, 1954; Levinson and Bergmann, 1957).

While it is not possible from this data to draw any firm conclusions about the precise function of cholesterol in insect metabolism, it seems likely that the sterol acts as a source of steroidal substances which probably fill hormonal functions in insects. If this is the case, it would seem that studies on the enzymatic transformations of cholesterol in insect larvae might well be useful in providing information about cholesterol metabolism in vertebrates as well as invertebrates.

II. Protozoa

A. Introduction

Very little is known about the metabolism of steroids in protozoa. This is due in part to the difficulty of maintaining protozoa in pure (axenic) culture; a symbiotic relationship with bacteria or other protozoa exists for many of these unicellular organisms, and the symbiont is not easily replaced by dietary supplements. Most of the studies that have been reported are nutritional in nature and are somewhat similar in design to those carried out with insect larvae.

B. Steroid Requirements and Reactions

Two years after Hobson (1935b) reported that cholesterol was a growth factor for insect larvae, Cailleau (1937) succeeded in obtaining a pure culture of *Trichomonas columbae,* and in demonstrating that cholesterol was also required for normal growth of this organism. A number of steroids and steroid derivatives were investigated by Cailleau (1937) for their effectiveness in replacing cholesterol. A 3β-hydroxyl group, either free or esterified was found to be essential; the acetate and palmitate esters were active in supporting growth, but 3-keto compounds, epicholesterol, cholesteryl chloride, and cholesterol methyl ether were inactive. The Δ^5 double bond was not essential, since cholestanol, ergostanol, and sitostanol were also active. Ergosterol, 7-dehydrocholesterol, and α-sitosterol were active, indicating that a Δ^7 double bond and modifications in the side chain did not affect the ability of the compound to support growth. However, partial or total loss of the side chain resulted in loss of activity. Cholesterol was also found to be a growth factor for *Trichomonas* species, *T. foetus* and *Trichomastix colubrorum* (Cailleau, 1938) and for *T. batrachorum* (Cailleau, 1939).

The influence of dietary cholesterol on the growth of *Entamoeba histolytica* has been defined less directly. When this organism was grown in a mixed culture, containing mainly diplobacillus, it was found that cholesterol was required for growth. (Snyder and Meleney, 1942, 1943). Later Rees *et al.* (1944) were able to grow the amoeba in the presence of a pure bacterial culture of "organism t." This bacterium did not require cholesterol and, by using a mixed culture of the two organisms, it was possible to demonstrate a requirement for cholesterol. The experiments of Griffin and McCartin (1949) confirmed the cholesterol requirement for *E. histolytica* and *E. terrapina*. In most of this work rather complex culture media were employed, but Hansen and Anderson (1948) were able to grow *E. histolytica* in combination with "organism t" on an essentially synthetic diet which included amino acids, salts, vitamins, nucleic acid, *Lactobacillus casei* factor, and cholesterol.

More recently (Lesser, 1953) *E. invadens* was grown on a purified diet in a bacteria-free environment. Under these circumstances it was found that all steroids, and particularly Δ^4,3-ketosteroids, were inhibitory to growth. In contrast to this effect, these steroids had no inhibitory effect on the growth of *Acanthamoeba castellani* and *Hartmanella rhysoides* in a bacteria-free culture.

The growth requirements of paramecia deserve special mention. These organisms can be grown in axenic culture on a partially purified diet when supplemented with a steroid. *Paramecium multimicronucleatum* (Johnson, 1956) grew very well when stigmasterol was included in the diet and *P. aurelia* was found to utilize C_{28} and C_{29} sterols, such as β- and γ-sitosterols, fucosterol, and brassicasterol, but not cholesterol. (Conner and van Wagtendonk, 1955). Stigmasterol, poriferasterol, and stigmasta-4,22-dienone yielded ten times the population density provided by sitosterol. Paramecia evidently cannot utilize cholesterol, and have instead a requirement which may best be filled by sterols of marine origin. The nature of the side chain is important in this case.

Peranema trichophorum, a unicellular flagellate closely related to *Euglena*, but containing no chlorophyll, also requires an exogenous steroid for growth (Storm and Hutner, 1953). Very little specificity is shown here; the organism has been grown with cholesterol, β-sitosterol, stigmasterol, poriferasterol, brassicasterol, and ergosterol.

Labyrinthula vitellina var. *pacifica* (a Myxomycetes or mycetozoa) requires an exogenous source of steroid for growth but *Labyrinthula minuta* var. *atlantica* can synthesize a sterol which has been identified as cholesterol (Vishniac, 1957).

It is well established that *Tetrahymena* can be grown on a synthetic diet without added steroids (Dewey *et al.*, 1950). Since the organism is reported to contain 0.32–0.42 μg. of steroid per milligram of dry weight (Seaman, 1950), it is apparent that steroid synthesis occurs in this case (Conner, 1957). It may also be inferred that *Plasmodium knowlesi* is able to synthesize steroids since about 25% of the lipid fraction of this organism is nonsaponifiable, mainly cholesterol (Morrison and Jeskey, 1947, 1948).

A study of steroid transformations by *Trichomonas gallinae* has been reported (Sebek *et al.*, 1957). 3-Ketosteroids of the pregnane allopregnane series are reduced at the C-3 position; Δ^4, 3-keto structures are not affected.

From these examples, it may be concluded that an exogenous source of steroids is required by some but not all protozoa. There is some degree of specificity in the requirement, where it exists, and in this respect there is a resemblance to insect growth requirements. Nothing is known of the metabolic function of steroids in protozoa. The recent work of Sebek *et al.* (1957) demonstrates that it is possible to study the transformation metabolism of steroids by protozoa at the enzyme level.

Glossary of Insect Species

Aedes aegypti	Mosquito
Attagenus piceus	Black carpet beetle
Blatella germanica	German cockroach
Bombyx mori	Silkworm moth
Callosobruchus chinensis	A grain beetle
Dermestes vulpinus	Hide beetle
Drosophila melanogaster	Fruit fly
Ephestia kuehniella	Flour moth
Galleria mellonella	Wax moth
Iridomyrmex detectus	Australian ant
Lasioderma serricorni	Cigarette beetle
Lucilia sericata	Flesh fly, blow fly
Musca vicina	House fly
Neodiprion pratti pratti	Pine saw fly
Oryzaephilus surinamensis	Sawtooth grain beetle
Periplaneta americana	American cockroach
Phormia regina	Sheep maggot fly (Australia)
Pseudosarcophaga affinis	An entomophagous fly
Ptinus tectus	Spider beetle (flour-eating)
Pyrausta nubilalis	European cornborer (moth)
Silvanus surinamensis	Sawtooth grain beetle
Sitodrepa panicis	Drugstore or biscuit weevil
Tenebrio molitor	Meal worm
Tribolium confusum	Flour beetle

REFERENCES

(Asterisk indicates review article)

Beck, S. D. (1950). *Physiol. Zöol.* **23**, 353-361.
Bergmann, E. D., and Levinson, Z. H. (1954). *Nature* **173**, 211-212.
Bergmann, W. (1934). *J. Biol. Chem.* **107**, 527-532.
Brust, M., and Fraenkel, G. (1955). *Physiol. Zoöl.* **28**, 186-204.
Cailleau, R. (1937). *Ann. inst. Pasteur* **59**, 137-172, 293-328.
Cailleau, R. (1938). *Compt. rend. soc. biol.* **127**, 861-863, 1421-1423.
Cailleau, R. (1939). *Compt. rend. soc. biol.* **131**, 964-966.
Casida, J. E., Beck, S. D., and Cole, M. J. (1957). *J. Biol. Chem.* **224**, 365-371.
Cavill, G. W. K., Ford, D. L., and Locksley, H. D. (1956). *Australian J. Chem.* **9**, 288-293.
Chauvin, R. (1949). *Compt. rend.* **229**, 902-903.
Clément, G., and Frisch, A. M. (1946). *Compt. rend. soc. biol.* **140**, 472-473.
Conner, R. L. (1957). *Science* **126**, 698.
Conner, R. L., and Van Wagtendonk, W. J. (1955). *J. Gen. Microbiol.* **12**, 31-36.
Dewey, V. C., Parks, R. E., Jr., and Kidder, G. W (1950). *Arch. Biochem.* **29**, 281-290.
Finkel, A. J. (1948). *Physiol. Zoöl.* **21**, 111-133.
Fraenkel, G., and Blewett, M. (1943). *Biochem. J.* **37**, 692-695.
Fraenkel, G., and Blewett, M. (1946). *J. Exptl. Biol.* **22**, 162-171, 172-190.
Fraenkel, G., Reid, J. A., and Blewett, M. (1941). *Biochem. J.* **35**, 712-720.
Frobrich, G. (1940). *Z. vergleich. Physiol.* **27**, 335-483.
Goldberg, L., and DeMeillon, B. (1948). *Biochem. J.* **43**, 372-378; 379-387.
Griffin, A. M., and McCartin, W. G. (1949). *Proc. Soc. Exptl. Biol. Med.* **72**, 645-648.
Hansen, E. L., and Anderson, H. H. (1948). *Parasitology* **39**, 69-72.
Hinton, T., Noyes, D. T., and Ellis, J. (1951). *Physiol. Zoöl.* **24**, 335-353.
Hobson, R. P. (1935a). *Biochem. J.* **29**, 1292-1296.
Hobson, R. P. (1935b). *Biochem. J.* **29**, 2023-2026.
Hopf, H. S. (1940). *Biochem. J.* **34**, 1396-1403.
Horning, M. G. Presented at the American Chemical Society Meeting, Miami, Fla., April 7, 1957. See Abstracts of Papers, p. 60C.
House, H. L. (1954). *Can. J. Zool.* **32**, 331-341.
Ishii, S. (1951). *Botyu-Kagaku* **16**, 83.
Ishii, S. (1955). *Bull. Natl. Inst. Agr. Sci. (Japan)* **C5**, 29.
*Johnson, W. H. (1956). *Ann. Rev. Microbiol.* **10**, 193-212.
Kadner, C. G., and LaFleur, F. M. (1952). *Wasmann J. Biol.* **9**, 129-136.
Leclercq, J. (1948). *Biochim. et Biophys. Acta* **2**, 614-617.
Leggieri, G. (1949). *Quaderni nutriz.* **10**, 371-377.
Lemonde, A., and Bernard, R. (1951). *Can. J. Zool.* **29**, 71-79.
Lesser, E. (1953). *Can. J. Zool.* **31**, 511-518.
Levenbook, L. (1950). *Biochem. J.* **47**, 336-346.
Levinson, Z. H., and Bergmann, E. D. (1957). *Biochem. J.* **65**, 254-260.
*Lipke, H., and Fraenkel, G. (1956). *Ann. Rev. Entomol.* **1**, 17-44.
McKennis, H. (1947). *J. Biol. Chem.* **167**, 645-654.
McKennis, H. (1954). *Proc. Soc. Exptl. Biol. Med.* **87**, 289-291.
Morrison, D. B., and Jeskey, H. A. (1947). *Federation Proc.* **6**, 279.
Morrison, D. B., and Jeskey, H. A. (1948). *J. Natl. Malaria Soc.* **7**,   .

Rees, C. W., Bozichevich, J., Reardon, L. V., and Daft, F. S. (1944). *Am. J. Trop. Med.* **24**, 189-193.

Noland, J. L. (1954a). *Arch. Biochem. Biophys.* **48**, 370-379.

Noland, J. L. (1954b). *Arch. Biochem. Biophys.* **52**, 323-330.

Seaman, G. R. (1950). *J. Cellular Comp. Physiol.* **36**, 129-131.

Sebek, O., Rosselet, J. P., and Michaels, R. M. (1957). *Proc. Soc. Am. Bacteriol.* in press.

Silverman, P. H., and Levinson, Z. H. (1954). *Biochem. J.* **58**, 291-294, 294-297.

Snyder, T. L., and Meleney, H. E. (1942). *J. Parasitol.* **28**, (suppl.), II.

Snyder, T. L., and Meleney, H. E. (1943). *J. Parisitol.* **29**, 278-284.

Storm, J., and Hutner, S. H. (1953). *Ann. N.Y. Acad. Sci.* **56**, 901-909.

*Trager, W. (1947). *Biol. Revs. Cambridge Phil. Soc.* **22**, 148-177.

*Trager, W. (1953). *In* "Insect Physiology" (K. D. Roeder, ed.) pp. 350-386. Wiley, New York.

Van't Hoog, E. G. (1935). *Z. Vitaminforsch.* **4**, 300-324.

Van't Hoog, E. G. (1936). *Z. Vitaminforsch.* **5**, 118-126.

Vishniac, H. S. (1957). *Biochim. et Biophys. Acta* **26**, 430-431.

CHAPTER 14

THE MICROBIAL METABOLISM OF STEROIDS

Thressa C. Stadtman

I. Introduction

Although it has long been recognized that microorganisms serve as powerful tools for the carrying out of many complex chemical processes, it is only of recent years that the microbial metabolism of steroids* has attracted particular attention. This is principally due to the interest in the production of cortisone and of other hormones, the purely chemical manufacture of which can be elaborate and expensive. The feasibility of such an approach seemed apparent from a number of earlier studies showing that a wide variety of bacteria and fungi are able to carry out limited oxidation of steroids (Arnaudi, 1951). Elaboration and application of these observations has led to the very successful large-scale production of numerous steroids of medical and commercial importance.

The complete degradation of steroids by soil microorganisms is, unfortunately, an example of an important process about which there is still only meager information. Considerably greater success has attended recent studies undertaken to elucidate the mechanism of sterol synthesis by fungi. From these experiments it would apear that fungal and mammalian synthetic pathways employed for the formation of these complex molecules from simple carbon units have much in common. Any conclusions concerning the possible similarity of synthetic and degradative pathways employed by microorganisms for the metabolism of steroids, however, must await more detailed information.

II. Oxidation of Nuclear Positions in the Steroid Molecule

In the hormone series, Ercoli (1940) showed that 3-hydroxy compounds such as dehydroandrosterone, and pregnenolone were oxidized

---

* The formulas of sterols are given in Chapter 2, and those of steroid hormones in Chapter 8.

by *Flavobacterium dehydrogenans* to the corresponding 3-keto derivatives; androstenedione and progesterone. Of the 3,17-dihydroxy compounds investigated, androstenediol was oxidized only at position 3
yielding testosterone and estradiol only at carbon 17 to give estrone,
whereas both carbons 3 and 17 of androstanediol were oxidized yielding
androstanedione. In the bile acid series Hoehn *et al.* (1944) found that
a number of the hydroxy acids were oxidized to the corresponding keto
acids by *Alcaligenes faecalis*. The order of ease of oxidation ($7 > 12 > 3$)
paralleled that observed for chromate oxidations. Carbon 3 of cholesterol
also proved to be readily oxidized by a number of bacteria resulting in
the formation of the corresponding 3-ketosteroid, cholestenone (Turfitt,
1944; Horváth and Krámli, 1947; Arnaudi and Colla, 1949; Stadtman
et al., 1954). Related sterols such as stigmasterol, β-sitosterol, and
coprostanol were oxidized to the corresponding ketones (Turfitt, 1946).

The introduction of a nuclear hydroxyl group into a steroid molecule
by microbial action was first reported by Krámli and Horváth (1949).
They observed the formation of 7-hydroxycholesterol from cholesterol
by a *Proactinomyces*.

This served as precedent for the concerted efforts of a number of
investigators to find an analogous hydroxylation reaction at carbon 11;
a reaction much sought after when clinical studies showed that cortisone
and hydrocortisone owed their biological activity to the presence in their
molecules of an oxygen atom at this position.

Microorganisms really came into their own as "steroid chemists" with
the dramatic report by Peterson *et al.* (1952) that progesterone, a relatively available steroid, could be oxygenated to 11α-hydroxyprogesterone
in essentially quantitative yields by *Rhizopus nigricans*. Previously such
a conversion had been accomplished only in low yields by a series of
rather difficult organic chemical reactions. Thus, by a relatively simple
industrial fermentation process, a compound became available in large
amounts that could be readily converted to the desired derivatives with
therapeutic value. The more recent investigations by the research groups
at Upjohn and Co., Chas. Pfizer and Co., Squibb, and Ciba have shown
that microorganisms are capable of hydroxylating a number of other
positions of the cyclopentenophenanthrene nucleus of steroids (Fig. 1).
For details concerning the specific compounds that have been hydroxylated and the microorganisms effecting these transformations, the
reader is referred to the comprehensive reviews of Peterson (1955, 1956)
and Shull (1956).

The origin of the oxygen of the hydroxy function introduced into the
steroid molecule was shown by Hayano *et al.* (1956) to be almost en-

tirely atmospheric oxygen. This was determined by growing cultures of a number of species of fungi effecting hydroxylations at positions 6, 11, 17, and 21 in the presence of O_2[18].

The mechanism of hydrogenation and dehydrogenation reactions as effected by certain microorganisms has been investigated in considerable detail. Particularly noteworthy are the studies of Talalay and associates (Talalay *et al.*, 1952; Talalay and Marcus, 1956; Marcus and Talalay, 1956) with enzyme systems derived from *Pseudomonas testosteroni*, an organism able to grow on certain C_{19} steroids as its sole carbon source. An induced, DPN-linked* dehydrogenase specific for 3α-hydroxysteroids and another induced, DPN-linked enzyme acting on 3β- and 17β-hydroxy-steroids have been isolated from the bacterium. In both cases the products are the corresponding ketosteroids. C_{27} compounds of the

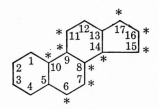

Fig. 1. Positions of the cyclopentenophenanthrene nucleus that have been shown to undergo biological hydroxylation: 6–β; 7–α, β; 8–β (or 9–α); 10—configuration not established; 11–α, β; 14–α; 15–α, β; 16–α; 17–α.

cholesterol series are not metabolized by these enzymes. The reactions are freely reversible and, like that catalyzed by yeast alcohol dehydrogenase, involve the direct transfer of hydrogen from substrate to DPN. (Talalay *et al.*, 1955). The β-hydroxysteroid dehydrogenase differs, however, in that it transfers hydrogen to and from the opposite side of the nicotinamide ring from that used by yeast alcohol, heart muscle lactic, and wheat germ malic dehydrogenases.

A DPN-linked dehydrogenase specific for compounds in the bile acid series has been obtained from *Escherichia freundii* by Hayaishi *et al.* (1955). It appears to be distinct from those of *Pseudomonas testosteroni* and also differs from the mammalian steroid dehydrogenase described by Tomkins (1956).

Another enzyme system of some interest, namely one catalyzing the isomerization of Δ^5-3-ketosteroids to Δ^4-3-ketosteroids has been found to be widely distributed in bacterial and animal cells (Talalay and Wang, 1955). As contrasted to the nonenzymatic reaction, the enzyme-

---

* DPN, diphosphopyridine nucleotide.

catalyzed transformation involves almost no incorporation of deuterium from D_2O into the molecule. A direct intramolecular transfer is thus suggested.

A number of other interesting type reactions have been observed to occur during biological transformations of steroids (Peterson, 1956; Shull, 1956) but, as yet, the detailed mechanisms of such reactions have not been investigated. Among these are oxidations involving introduction of a ring double bond, epoxide formation, and oxidative cleavage of the 2-carbon side chain of C_{21} steroids to yield C_{19} steroids. The latter reaction is associated in some cases with lactone formation in ring D. It has also been reported (Fried et al., 1952) that Aspergillus niger catalyzed the enlargement of ring D of 17α-hydroxyprogesterone to a compound with 6 carbon atoms in ring D.

III. Degradation of Steroids

In addition to the above-mentioned types of limited oxidations of steroids, a number of microorganisms are known to degrade these compounds much more extensively. This is evident from the fact that, in spite of the huge quantities of plant and animal sterols constantly returned to the soil, these compounds do not accumulate there, but, like all other organic compounds of biological origin, are converted back to their simpler elements by the soil microorganisms. Söhngen (1913) showed that there are bacteria in the soil capable of living on cholesterol as a sole carbon source. Later studies by Tak (1942) and by Turfitt (1944) further demonstrated that microorganisms which actively decompose cholesterol could be isolated by the enrichment culture technique. Additional evidence that the cyclopentenophenanthrene nucleus is actually degraded by microorganisms was provided by studies with some Pseudomonads that utilized as sole carbon source steroids lacking a C_{17} side chain. Manometric data obtained with cell suspensions of these bacteria showed, for example, that testosterone could be extensively oxidized (Santer and Ajl, 1952; Santer et al., 1952). Balance experiments and isotopic data also demonstrated that growing cultures and cell suspensions of a Nocardia oxidize cholesterol and related steroids completely to carbon dioxide (Stadtman et al., 1954). Aside from a keto acid (Windaus' keto acid), resulting from the oxidative cleavage of ring A of cholesterol, that was isolated by Turfitt (1948), there is, however, no information concerning intermediates in the microbial degradation of the steroid nucleus to CO_2. The mechanism whereby the side chain carbons of a compound such as cholesterol are converted to CO_2 is almost equally obscure. Since the intermediates in these oxidative processes seem to accumulate in only trace amounts, if at all, when intact cells are employed, further information as to the nature of such steroid degradation reactions undoubtedly awaits the preparation of active soluble enzyme systems.

IV. Biosynthesis in Yeasts and Fungi

In the synthetic direction, it has been found that yeasts and fungi, as well as higher plants and animals, build up their characteristic complex sterol molecules from simple components such as acetate and formate. A number of bacteria are known to synthesize acetate from one-carbon compounds, such as CO_2 or formate, thereby furnishing the link in the over-all cycle of synthesis of steroids from CO_2 followed by their eventual complete degradation in the soil to this simple building block. It should be pointed out that although a number of true bacteria have been shown to grow on steroids as sole carbon sources or to require various members of this class of compounds as growth factors (Gaines et al., 1950, 1951; Edward and Fitzgerald, 1951) they have not been demonstrated to possess steroids as normal cellular constituents. At present it is uncertain as to whether the true bacteria (i.e. the Schizomycetes) really do not contain steroids or the methods employed for their detection have been too insensitive and nonspecific.

Although the pathway of biosynthesis of sterols has been principally investigated in animal tissues, a few experiments have been carried out recently with yeasts and fungi (see Chapter 6). Employing an acetate-requiring strain of *Neurospora*, it was shown that at least 26 of the 28 carbon atoms of the ergosterol synthesized were derived from acetate (Ottke et al., 1951). The investigations of Hanahan and Wakil (1952) and Klein and Lipmann (1953) with CoA-deficient yeast implicated acetyl-coenzyme A as the C_2-condensing unit which eventually is converted to ergosterol. More recently, Dauben and Richards (1956) and Dauben et al. (1957a) have carried out degradation studies on radioactive eburicoic acid (4,4,14,24-tetramethyl-$\Delta^{8,24:28}$-cholestadienol-carboxylic acid-21) a C_{31} steroid synthesized by the fungus, *Polyporus sulfureus*, from $CH_3C^{14}OOH$ and $C^{14}H_3COOH$. This sterol is structurally related to lanosterol (C_{30}) which in turn is related to cholesterol (C_{27}) and ergosterol (C_{28}) (Fig. 2). Carbons 4 and 11, and 12 of eburicoic acid were found to be derived from the carboxyl carbon of acetate whereas 21, 30, and 31 were derived from the methyl carbon of acetate. This is in accord with the squalene cyclization theory of the origin of the steroid nucleus as proposed by Woodward and Bloch (1953) and parallels the findings of Bloch and co-workers regarding the origin of the corresponding carbons of lanosterol and cholesterol. The methyl substituent in the ergosterol side chain (C-28), earlier found not to be derived from acetate carboxyl carbon (Hanahan and Wakil, 1953), has recently been reported by Danielson and Bloch (1957) to be derived from formate carbon. Furthermore, cell suspensions of Fleischmann's bakers' yeast appeared to incorporate formate carbon only into the side chain of ergosterol and only in the C-28 carbon atom. The hydrocarbon fraction (i.e. squalene) contained no radioactive formate carbon suggesting the addition of C-28 after cyclization of squalene had occurred. These results are in accord with the experiments of Dauben and collaborators (1956, 1957b) wherein the corresponding atom (C-28) of

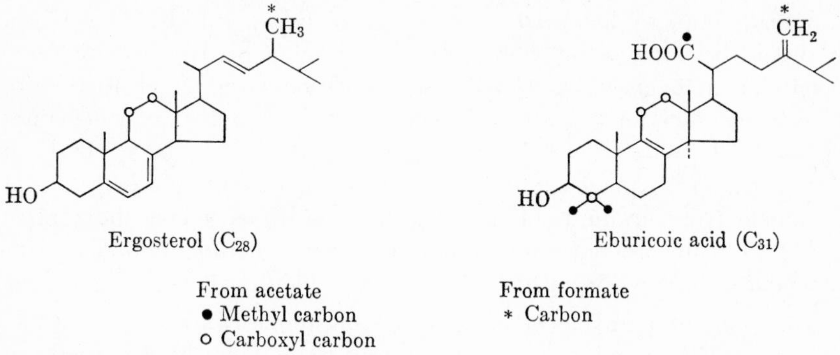

Ergosterol (C_{28})   Eburicoic acid (C_{31})

From acetate   From formate
● Methyl carbon   * Carbon
○ Carboxyl carbon

FIG. 2. The origin of carbon atoms in the biosynthesis of ergosterol and of eburicoic acid. (See also Figs. 1 and 5, Chapter 6.)

eburicoic acid was derived neither from acetate methyl nor from acetate carboxyl carbon. Moreover, recent experiments reported by Dauben et al. (1957b) show that P. sulfureus also forms the C-28 methylenic carbon from formate.

REFERENCES

(Asterisk indicates review article)

*Arnaudi, C. (1951). Experientia 7, 81-89.
Arnaudi, C., and Colla, C. (1949). Experientia 5, 120-122.
Danielsson, H., and Bloch, K. (1957). J. Am. Chem. Soc. 79, 500-501.
Dauben, W. G., and Richards, J. H. (1956). J. Am. Chem. Soc. 78, 5329-5335.
Dauben, W. G., Ban, Y., and Richards, J. H. (1957a). J. Am. Chem. Soc. 79, 968-970.
Dauben, W. G., Fonken, G. J., and Boswell, G. A. (1957b). J. Am. Chem. Soc. 79, 1000-1001.
Edward, D. G., and Fitzgerald, W. A. (1951). J. Gen. Microbiol. 5, 576-586.
Ercoli, A. (1940). Boll. sci. fac. chim. ind. univ. Bologna 10.
Fried, J., Thoma, R. W., Gerke, J. R., Herz, J. E., Donin, M. N., and Perlman, D. (1952). J. Am. Chem. Soc. 74, 3962-3963.

Gaines, D. S., and Totter, J. R. (1950). *Proc. Soc. Exptl. Biol. Med.* **74**, 558-561.

Gaines, D. S., Broquist, H. P., and Williams, W. L. (1951). *Proc. Soc. Exptl. Biol. Med.* **77**, 247-249.

Hanahan, D. J., and Wakil, S. J. (1952). *Arch. Biochem. Biophys.* **37**, 167-171.

Hanahan, D. J., and Wakil, S. J. (1953). *J. Am. Chem. Soc.* **75**, 273-275.

Hayaishi, O., Sato, Y., Jakoby, W. B., and Stohlman, E. F. (1955). *Arch. Biochem. Biophys.* **56**, 554-555.

Hayano, M., Saito, A., Stone, D., and Dorfman, R. I. (1956). *Biochim. et Biophys. Acta* **21**, 380-381.

Hoehn, W. M., Schmidt, L. H., and Hughes, H. B. (1944). *J. Biol. Chem.* **152**, 59-66.

Horváth, J., and Krámli, A. (1947). *Nature* **160**, 639.

Klein, H. P., and Lipmann, F. (1953). *J. Biol. Chem.* **203**, 95-99.

Krámli, A., and Horváth, J. (1949). *Nature* **163**, 219.

Marcus, P. I., and Talalay, P. (1956). *J. Biol. Chem.* **218**, 661-674.

Ottke, R. C., Tatum, E. L., Zabin, I., and Bloch, K. (1951). *J. Biol. Chem.* **189**, 429-433.

*Peterson, D. H. (1955). *In* "Perspectives and Horizons in Microbiology" (S. A. Waksman, ed.), Vol. 9, pp. 121-137. Rutgers Univ. Press, New Brunswick, New Jersey.

*Peterson, D. H. (1956). *Record Chem. Progr.* **17**, 211-240.

Peterson, D. H., Murray, H. C., Eppstein, S. H., Reineke, L. M., Weintraub, A., Meister, P. D., and Leigh, H. M. (1952). *J. Am. Chem. Soc.* **74**, 5933-5936.

Santer, M., and Ajl, S. J. (1952). *J. Biol. Chem.* **199**, 85-90.

Santer, M., Ajl, S. J., and Turner, R. A. (1952). *J. Biol. Chem.* **198**, 397-404.

*Shull, G. M. (1956). *Trans. N.Y. Acad. Sci.* [2] **19**, 147-172.

Söhngen, N. L. (1913). *Centr. Bakteriol. Parasitenk.* **37**, 595-609.

Stadtman, T. C., Cherkes, A., and Anfinsen, C. B., Jr. (1954). *J. Biol. Chem.* **206**, 511-523.

Tak, J. D. (1942). *Antonie van Leeuwenhoek. J. Microbiol. Serol.* **8**, 32-40.

Talalay, P., and Marcus, P. I. (1956). *J. Biol. Chem.* **218**, 675-691.

Talalay, P., and Wang, V. S. (1955). *Biochim. et Biophys. Acta* **18**, 300-301.

Talalay, P., Dobson, M. M., and Tapley, D. F. (1952). *Nature* **170**, 620-623.

Talalay, P., Loewus, F. A., and Vennesland, B. (1955). *J. Biol. Chem.* **212**, 801-809.

Tomkins, G. M. (1956). *J. Biol. Chem.* **218**, 437-447.

Turfitt, G. E. (1944). *Biochem. J.* **38**, 492-496.

Turfitt, G. E. (1946). *Biochem. J.* **40**, 79-80.

Turfitt, G. E. (1948). *Biochem. J.* **42**, 376-383.

Woodward, R. B., and Bloch, K. (1953). *J. Am. Chem. Soc.* **75**, 2023-2024.

CHAPTER 15

SOME RELATIONS OF CHOLESTEROL TO OTHER LIPIDS

Robert P. Cook

I. Introduction

While the main theme of this book permits an arbitrary division into chapters dealing with specific topics, it is inevitable that other important aspects of cholesterol metabolism and/or function remain to be discussed. This is because the metabolic pathways and apparent functions of cholesterol are so diverse that some aspects did not "fit in" with the chapter headings. These remaining subjects must not be regarded as a miscellany but rather as indicating the potentialities and imperfectly explored fields in cholesterol research.

II. Interrelations with Other Lipids
A. GENERAL

The level of cholesterol in blood plasma and some of the factors influencing it are discussed in Chapters 5 and 10. On account of the ready accessibility of material and because of the apparent ease of estimation, plasma cholesterol has been studied more extensively than have the other lipid components; or even the total lipid.

465

The close relation between cholesterol and the phospholipids is
seen from analyses of the plasma lipoproteins. Analyses of the tissues
show also that the lipid is complex in composition (Chapter 4). The
concept of the *"élément constant"* or "essential lipid" consisting chemically of cholesterol, its esters, phospholipids, and glycolipids, which form
the "structural" part of cells, is generally accepted (cf. Terroine and
Belin, 1927; Deuel, 1955, p. 597ff.). The metabolic interrelation between
the classes of lipids still remains speculative.

B. In the Tissues

1. Phospholipids

The evidence on the interrelations between phospholipids and cholesterol in liver is contradictory. Cholesterol depresses the rate of incorporation of labeled phosphorus into the hepatic phospholipids of
rats (Perlman and Chaikoff, 1939; Clément *et al.*, 1953). In rabbit liver,
McCandless and Zilversmit (1956) observed no such depression and
the phospholipid turnover in the aorta was actually increased. Mc-
Candless and Zilversmit have an interesting discussion on the species
response to the administration of cholesterol to the phospholipid turnover in various tissues. For review see Zilversmit (1957).

2. Fat-Soluble Vitamins

There is little information on this subject. The feeding of cholesterol
lowers the level of vitamin A in livers of male rats but not in females
(Green *et al.*, 1957). The relation of vitamin E (tocopherol) to cholesterol in the liver is unknown; oral administration does not lower the
plasma level in humans (Beveridge *et al.*, 1957; Malmros and Wigand,
1957).

3. Fatty Livers

The liver normally contains about one-fifth of its cholesterol content
as ester but when cholesterol is fed in a fatty medium to experimental
animals there is a large increase in the esterified cholesterol (e.g., Ridout
et al., 1954a). This enlarged and fatty infiltrated liver is commonly
known as the cholesterol fatty liver (CFL). It is of interest as demonstrating an example of the homeostatic activity of the liver in regulating
the level of cholesterol in the plasma (Chapter 7). The condition has
been studied mostly in the rat but fatty infiltrated livers are produced
in a variety of animals (Chapter 10). The hepatic cholesterol content
is increased with the level of dietary cholesterol (Fig. 1).

Another type, the fat fatty liver (FFL), is produced when diets rich
in fat but deficient in lipotropic factors are fed (see below). In Table I

are shown values for the lipid content and distribution in the two types of fatty liver; considerable variations are reported but those given may be regarded as typical. In both types the amounts of neutral fat are greatly increased; in the CFL in rats there is a large increase in the

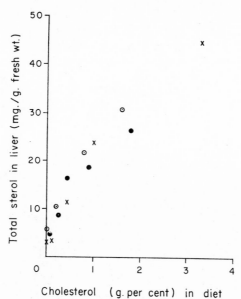

FIG. 1. The effect of increasing dosage of dietary cholesterol on the total sterol deposited in rat and chicken livers. Rat feeding experiments: ●, the diet contained 15% beet fat and was fed for 22 days (from Cook and Jenkins, unpublished observations). ⊙, the diet contained 10% beef fat and was fed for 21 days (from Ridout *et al.*, 1954a). Chicken feeding experiments: X, the diet contained 10% arachis oil and was fed for 28 days (from Dam *et al.*, 1955).

TABLE I

TYPICAL VALUES FOR THE COMPOSITION OF THE NORMAL, THE CHOLESTEROL FATTY LIVER (CFL), AND THE FAT FATTY LIVER (FFL) IN RATS[a, b]

	Normal	CFL	FFL
Wt. of liver	8.0	12.8	8.8
Total lipid extract	0.5[c]	2.3[c]	1.5[c]
Total sterol	0.02	0.5	0.03
Steryl esters	0.008	0.6	0.02
Phospholipids	0.25	0.25	0.25
Glycerides	0.2	1.5	1.2

[a] Values as grams per 250 gm. rat.

[b] Data from Cook's laboratory and results of Ridout *et al.* (1954a).

[c] Ether and ethanol extract.

amount of steryl esters which consist mainly of cholesteryl linoleate and oleate (Rattray *et al.*, 1956). Although the percentage of phospholipid is less in both types of fatty liver the *absolute* amount is unchanged.

The excess lipid in fatty livers has been shown by differential centrifugation to be present in the floating layer and supernatant fractions of the cell (Alfin-Slater *et al.*, 1954; Spiro and McKibbin, 1956; Clément *et al.*, 1954, 1956). Histological examination shows it to be present as cellular cytoplasmic inclusions (Clément *et al.*, 1954).

4. The Effect of Lipotropic and Other Factors

The general term lipotropic factors is used for agents which either prevent or remove the lipid from fatty livers. Ridout *et al.* (1954b, c) in a study on the effect of various lipotropic factors at various levels of dietary cholesterol found that, at a 0.2% intake of cholesterol, dietary *choline* or *betaine* prevented the excessive deposition of both glycerides and of cholesteryl esters. When diets rich in cholesterol were fed, even 1.28% choline in the diet did not prevent the excessive deposition of cholesteryl esters in the liver. *Inositol* was without appreciable lipotropic effect on either fraction. *Vitamin B_{12}* exerted a lipotropic action on the glycerides but much less on the cholesteryl esters. Deficiency of this vitamin in the diet of experimental animals induces hypercholesterolemia (Hsu and Chow, 1957).

In *pantothenic acid*-deficient rats where there is a fall in the levels of plasma, liver, and adrenal cholesterol, the feeding of dietary cholesterol produces small increases only in the levels of plasma and of liver cholesterol (Guehring *et al.*, 1952). These observations have been confirmed by Swell *et al.* (1955, review) who showed further that deposition of liver cholesterol occurred in the deficient animals on a low-fat cholesterol diet, and that on a fat-containing diet the increase in cholesterol and its esters in the liver was about one-sixth that of the control animals. Although coenzyme A or an associated compound is considered essential for the early stages of cholesterol biosynthesis (Chapter 6) animals deficient in pantothenic acid still have some ability to synthesize cholesterol (Smith and Mefferd, 1955). The effects produced in the deficient animals may be assigned tentatively to a disturbance of the transesterification occurring with the other cellular lipids, but this is questioned by Boyd (1953).

Okey *et al.* (1951) in an interesting study on the effect of eggs in the diet of rats showed that *biotin*-deficient rats do not store excess cholesterol esters in the liver, biotin being apparently necessary for the esterification process.

Channon and Wilkinson (1935) found that the level of dietary *protein* influenced the deposition of cholesteryl esters in rat liver. Okey and Lyman (1956) in an extensive study of rats fed control and cholesterol-containing diets showed that protein was less effective as a lipotropic agent in adults than in rapidly growing adolescents. In 1957 they extended their studies to the effects of cystine and methionine on cholesterol storage. Methionine was found to have a somewhat smaller lipotropic effect than the equivalent amount of protein.

Rats fed excess methionine showed an increase in serum and carcass cholesterol and a decreased carcass total lipid. The incorporation of labeled acetate into hepatic cholesterol was greater in the methionine-fed animals (Roth and Milstein, 1957).

The effect of a *cold environment* on liver fat and cholesterol deposition has been investigated by Treadwell *et al.* (1955a, b); whereas cold has a pseudolipotropic effect on the FFL (Sellers and You, 1952) it has no effect or actually increases the lipid content of the CFL.

Although there is an impressive amount of factual information on the lipid composition of normal, and of fatty livers (e.g. Clément, 1953), and of the effect of various lipotropic factors, it is difficult to assess the implications of these studies. The liver of the newly hatched chick is of the CFL type (see Chapter 4) and it probably occurs in the young of other birds. In the newly born guinea pig the liver is of the FFL type. In disease in humans the liver is of the FFL type (e.g. Popper and Schaffner, 1957, pp. 249-254) but there is some evidence that livers of children with Kwashiorkor (a disease associated with protein deficiency) contain more cholesterol than do those of normal children (Ramalingaswami *et al.*, 1952).

5. Ethyl Alcohol (Ethanol)

Of some interest is the effect of ethyl alcohol, a constituent of the dietary of variety of humans, on cholesterol metabolism and deposition. Ethanol is a potential precursor of cholesterol (Chapter 6). Feller and Huff (1955) found that it had no effect, neither inhibiting nor accelerating the deposition of cholesterol in rabbit aortas. Morgan *et al.* (1957, review) found in experimental animals that ethanol was available as calories for growth and that when additional dietary cholesterol was fed the effect on deposition in the livers of the animals was least in wine-fed animals. A curious observation of Ratnoff *et al.* (1956) is that rats fed spaghetti, olive oil, and wine develop fatty livers.

The incidence of atherosclerosis in 519 chronic alcoholics was studied by Wilens (1947) who found that there was a lessened deposition of cholesterol and associated lesions as compared with 600 control subjects.

It may be concluded that in those of temperate habits alcohol has no appreciable effect on cholesterol metabolism nor on its abnormal deposition. In chronic alcoholics the low incidence of atherosclerosis is probably related to the relatively young age at which they die and the lack of association with conditions favoring development of the disease (see Wilens, 1947).

C. RELATION TO FATTY ACIDS

1. The Essential Fatty Acids

Most attention has been given to the effect of fats containing the "essential fatty acids" (EFA), i.e. the di- and tri-ethenoid acids such as linoleic and linolenic acids (for review see Deuel and Reiser, 1955). The relation of the EFA to the transport and metabolism of cholesterol has

TABLE II

SOME STUDIES ON FAT DEFICIENCY AND ON THE EFFECT OF VARIOUS DIETARY FATS
ON PLASMA AND TISSUE CHOLESTEROL LEVELS

Species	References
Mouse	Schettler (1949); Mead et al. (1956)
Rat	Mead and Fillerup (1954); Alfin-Slater et al. (1954); Aftergood et al. (1956);[a] Grunbaum et al. (1957); Okey et al. (1957)[a]
Rabbit	Putignano (1952)
Dog	Wiese and Hansen (1951)
Swine	Hill et al. (1957)
Chicken	Opdyke and Ott (1954); Dam et al. (1956a, b); Dam and Nielsen (1956); Jones et al. (1956)
Comparative study on adrenal cholesterol	Carroll (1957)

[a] Sex differences studied.

for long invited speculation (review Holman, 1956) and recent developments indicate that esterification of cholesterol with these acids occurs in the liver, they are also present in the blood plasma ester fraction (Chapter 7 and below).

A variety of glycerides (poor or rich in EFA) have been fed to experimental animals and their effect on the levels of cholesterol in the plasma and/or liver and other tissues studied (Table II). It is difficult to summarize the various workers' results which are often discordant but in experimental animals it would seem on feeding EFA-deficient diets that there is a lowering in the level of plasma cholesterol and increases in the cholesterol content in liver and in adrenals. The feeding of cholesterol to deficient animals hastens the symptoms of deficiency (Peifer and Holman, 1955) and high levels of cholesterol are found in the plasma. Mead *et al.* (1956) found no impairment of cholesterol biosynthesis in EFA-deficient mice. Shapiro and Freedman (1955) studied the effect of various fats on plasma cholesterol levels in rats on a methionine-deficient, cholesterol-containing diet. The hypercholesterolemic response was largely prevented by the use of fats rich in EFA and supplementation with methionine.

In human subjects Ahrens and his associates (1957)* have shown clearly that the composition of dietary fat, particularly the degree of unsaturation of the fatty acids, has a marked effect on lowering the level of plasma cholesterol. This conclusion has been substantiated by Malmros and Wigand (1957). A contrasting view is that of Beveridge and his colleagues (1957) who, while agreeing that certain natural fats lower the plasma cholesterol level, and that others raise it, consider that an anticholesterogenic factor, possibly a vegetable sterol, is the active agent. Keys *et al.* (1957) give a formula based on the composition of the glycerides (saturated and polyethenoid acids) from which the serum cholesterol responses can be predicted. Regarding the mechanism of action, Gordon *et al.* (1957) suggest that the unsaturated oils promote the catabolism of cholesterol, causing its excretion in the form of fecal bile acids. In rodents this is undoubtedly a major pathway of excretion (Chapter 7), but its importance in humans (under normal circumstances) has been questioned by Frantz and Carey (1957).

2. *Lipid Partition of the Fatty Acids*

An account was given in Chapter 7 of the fatty acid component of cholesteryl esters. More information is now becoming available on the fatty acid composition in the several lipid components of human plasma and tissues. Keegan and Gould (1953) isolated a cholesteryl ester from human (and dog) plasma which consisted mainly of cholesteryl oleate, the iodine value indicated that a more unsaturated acid was also present. James *et al.* (1957) have studied the fatty acid composition of the acetone-soluble fraction (i.e. the mixture of glycerides and of cholesteryl esters) and of the phospholipid fraction of sera from control subjects and from a group suffering from coronary disease. The composition of the fatty acids from the two groups was very similar. There was no significant difference in the content of diethenoid acids but the fatty

---

* The preparation of the human diets is described by Ahrens *et al.* (1954).

acids from the coronary group contained a significantly greater proportion of stearic acid at the expense of oleic acid than did the control group. A summary of the fatty acid composition is shown in Table III.

TABLE III
FATTY ACID COMPONENTS OF HUMAN SERUM LIPID FRACTIONS[a, b]

	Acetone soluble[c]	Phospholipids
Saturated acids		
C_{14}–C_{20}	35	40
Monoethenoid acids		
C_{16}–C_{20}	40	25
Diethenoid acids		
C_{18}–C_{20}	15	30

[a] Values are as per cent total fatty acids.
[b] From the results of James et al. (1957).
[c] The acetone soluble fraction contains a mixture of glycerides and cholesteryl esters.

Hirsch et al. (1957) in a chromatographic study of the fractions from human serum lipids found that the feeding of corn oil doubled the linoleic acid content of the cholesteryl esters and of the phospholipids, but the amount of linoleic acid in the triglycerides was increased elevenfold.

The fatty acid composition of the fractions from rat plasma after the administration of labeled methyl stearate, methyl oleate, and methyl linoleate was investigated by Mead and Fillerup (1957). The partition of the fatty acids was influenced by the particular ester; linoleate appeared largely as phospholipid and significantly as cholesteryl ester. We have found in the rat that the feeding of olive oil results in an ester fraction rich in oleic and palmitic acids (Rattray et al., 1958). Values for the plasma lipid partition in rats are given by Mukherjee et al. (1957). In plasma of the lactating cow Lough and Garton (1957) report a sterol ester fraction rich in di- and tri-ethenoid acids.

Analyses of the cholesteryl ester fractions of human adrenal gland by Sim and Cook (unpublished observations) gave values (as per cent total fatty acids) of saturated acids, mainly palmitic 25–37, monoethenoid acids, mainly oleic 62–81, diethenoid acids about 1. Values of 8% for di- and tri-ethenoid acids were found for the glyceride fraction.

The fatty acid composition of the lipid fractions of livers of rats fed olive oil-containing diets show a complex pattern. In all fractions, even those containing cholesteryl esters, oleic and palmitic acids are predominant, but there are present also other fatty acids, even or odd numbered, straight or branched chain, saturated or unsaturated (Rattray et al., 1958).

The writer is puzzled as to which fatty acids should be regarded as "essential." The summary given below reflects his personal opinions.

3. Summary

The interrelations of the lipids in liver and plasma are complex. Factors which influence the amount and nature of the lipid fractions are the types of dietary fatty acid fed and the nature of the compounds forming part of the phospholipids such as choline, inositol, etc. (see articles in "Biochemical Problems of Lipids," Popják and Le Breton, eds.,

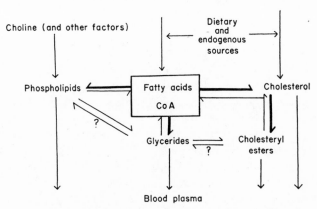

FIG. 2.   The suggested interrelations of lipids in the liver.

1956). The system will be governed by the enzyme content a::d distribution in the tissues. This in its turn is dependent on the dietary sources of protein and vitamins. Moreover, endocrine factors are concerned in the processes.

In Fig. 2 is given a scheme of some of the possible interchanges. The fatty acids, as their coenzyme A compounds, are considered as the center piece of lipid interrelations. The fatty acids may be transferred to phospholipids, glycerides, or cholesteryl esters. Interesterification reactions occur between these compounds but the role of the phospholipids is still uncertain. In the plasma of human subjects it has been suggested that the "nonphospholipid" fraction may function as the major vehicle for the transport of fatty acids (Lipsky et al., 1955). The scheme should be compared with Table XIII, Chapter 10. It may be that a close study of the lipidoses will clarify the normal interrelations. With regard to atherosclerosis, a fair conclusion is that it is a manifestation of lipid imbalance. Of interest in this respect is the observation of Stetten and his colleagues (Stetten and Salcedo, 1945; Kesten *et al.*, 1945) that choline-deficient rats develop a fatal myocarditis when fed ethyl laurate. The importance of choline for the well-being of the tissues of the body has been demonstrated by Best and his colleagues (for review see Best, 1956).

Recent reviews on the metabolic and dietary factors concerned in lipid regulation are given by Brock and Gordon (1957); Man and Albrink (1957), discussing the interrelation with carbohydrate metabolism; and Mann (1957).

III. Results from Balance Experiments

The balance method as applied to absorption and to metabolism studies was described in Chapter 7. The conclusion reached there was that the main pathway of cholesterol catabolism is via the bile acids whose end-products are excreted in the feces. The possibility of alternative pathways in cholesterol metabolism, as with that of other constituents of the animal body, must be considered. When rats are fed large amounts of cholesterol there is an apparent balance with the fecal excretion of fatty acids (Cook *et al.*, 1955). The administration of smaller amounts of labeled cholesterol leads to the appearance of the label in the long-chain fatty acid fraction in the feces and in the tissues (Van Bruggen *et al.*, 1951; Kritchevsky *et al.*, 1952).

It is tempting to agree with Robinson (1946-47) that the acid metabolic products may be long branched chain fatty acids produced by opening of the ring system. This type of fatty acid has now been found to have a wide distribution in animal tissues (review Shorland, 1956).

IV. The D Vitamins

The biological formation and functions of the D group of vitamins are still obscure. The best known members of the group, cholecalciferol (D_3) and ergocalciferol (D_2), are the only authenticated steroidal compounds that are accessory food factors for higher animals (History, Chapter 1; see also Bills, 1954).

The vitamins are readily formed by ultraviolet irradiation of precursors such as 7-dehydrocholesterol and ergosterol (i.e. compounds with a conjugate double bond system in ring B). The chemical changes involved in the transformation and the nature of the compounds are known (for review see Inhoffen and Bruckner, 1954). It is possible to transform cholesterol to antirachitic compounds by a variety of natural earth, floridin (Raoul *et al.,* 1956). The "activating" process is thus not specific for light irradiation.

It has been shown that 7-dehydrocholesterol is produced in quantity in guinea pig intestinal mucosa but in other species the amounts are small (Chapter 4). It is uncertain whether this potential precursor is converted into vitamin D in the animal. Species differences in the requirement and nature of the D vitamins adds a complication to the study. Chickens require cholecalciferol, but in man vitamins D_2 and D_3 are apparently interchangeable (for review see Dam, 1955). In experimental animals such as the rat, dog, and chicken, and in man, the deprivation effects are well recognized. It is generally agreed that the vitamin is necessary for calcium absorption and for the deposition of calcium phosphate in bone (for review see Nicolaysen and Eeg-Larsen, 1953). Recent observations by De Luca *et al.* (1957), suggest that the vitamin is concerned with citrate oxidation. It is known that citrate is an important constituent of bone.

To speculate, it would seem perhaps that the evolutionary need for dietary sterols is still manifest to some extent in the higher animals (cf. Chapter 13).

V. General Conclusions

The complex metabolic relations of cholesterol have been described in various chapters. Some speculations as to the role of cholesterol in the cell membrane particularly that of the red blood cell, and of myelin, were made in Chapter 9. The shape of the free sterol would apparently fit it for this function but it is only one part of the *élément constant*. The phospholipids are attractive components because of their zwitterion character whereby they can combine with the dominant cellular proteins. Anfinsen (1954) has suggested "that cholesterol may provide van der Waals and hydrogen bonding centers in the evolution of protein molecules which have specific functions in the transportation of triglycerides and phospholipids, and that cholesterol may be merely incidental to the transport."

The current aim of therapy of disorders of cholesterol metabolism is to lower the plasma level. It is perhaps worth recalling that the older French clinicians tried to raise the plasma cholesterol level, particularly in infective disease (e.g. Leuret and Dutrenit, 1934). Cholesterol (*in vitro* at any rate) has an antihemolytic action and might be considered as being protective against hemolytic agents, e.g. of microbial or of endogenous origin such as bile salts (Chapter 10). The reader is referred to the fine study by Berliner and Schoenheimer (1938) relating the structure of bile acids and of sterols to hemolytic and antihemolytic properties.

We have been presented to a molecule which can be synthesized from small units, metabolized to a variety of compounds, is interrelated structurally and metabolically with other constituents, and which in the myelin sheath remains apparently static. What can we conclude? Perhaps a free translation of the quotation from Goethe which opened Chapter I is not amiss.

> Life so varied and world so wide,
> Honest striving on every side,
> Ever searching and reasons well founded,
> Never ending but arguments rounded.
> The oldest you must preserve true,
> And gladly welcome the new.
> With spirit serene and purpose pure,
> Of progress you may soon be sure.

REFERENCES

(Asterisk indicates review article.)

Aftergood, L., Alfin-Slater, R. B., and Deuel, H. J., Jr. (1956). *Federation Proc.* **15**, 541.

Ahrens, E. H., Jr., Dole, V. P., and Blankenhorn, D. H. (1954). *Am. J. Clin. Nutrition* **2**, 336-342.

Ahrens, E. H., Jr., Hirsch, J., Insull, W., Jr., Tsaltas, T. T., Blomstrand, R., and Peterson, M. L. (1957). *Lancet* i, 943-953.

Alfin-Slater, R. B., Aftergood, L., Wells, G. F., and Deuel, H. J., Jr. (1954). *Arch. Biochem. Biophys.* **52**, 180-185.

Anfinsen, C. B., Jr. (1954). *In* Symposium on Atherosclerosis, Discussion pp. 167-168. National Research Council, Washington, D. C. (See Chapter 7.)

Berliner, F., and Schoenheimer, R. (1938). *J. Biol. Chem.* **124**, 525-541.

*Best, C. H. (1956). *Proc. Roy. Soc.* **B145**, 151-169. Lipotropic agents.

Beveridge, J. M. R., Connell, W. F., and Mayer, G. A. (1957). *Can. J. Biochem. and Physiol.* **35**, 257-270; *Federation Proc.* **16**, 11.

*Bills, C. E. (1954). *In* "The Vitamins" (W. H. Sebrell, Jr., and R. S. Harris, eds.), Vol. 2, pp. 131-223. Academic Press, New York. Vitamin D.

Boyd, G. S. (1953). *Biochem. J.* **55**, 892-895.

*Brock, J. F., and Gordon, H. (1957). *S. African Med. J.* **31**, 663-671.

Carroll, K. (1957). *Proc. Soc. Exptl. Biol. Med.* **94**, 202-205.

Channon, H. J., and Wilkinson, H. (1935). *Biochem. J.* **29**, 350-356.

Clément, G. (1953). *Ann. nutrition aliment.* **7**, C267-282.

Clément, G., Le Breton, E., Pascaud, M., and Tubiana, M. (1953). *Compt. rend.* **236**, 412-415.

Clément, G., Clément, J., and Le Breton, E. (1954). *Arch. sci. physiol.* **8**, 259-278.

Clément, G., Clément, J., and Le Breton, E. (1956). *In* "Biochemical Problems of Lipids" (G. Popják and E. Le Breton, eds.), pp. 385-394. Butterworths, London.

Cook, R. P., Edwards, D. C., Riddell, C., and Thomson, R. O. (1955). *Biochem. J.* **61**, 676-681.

*Dam, H. (1955). *Progr. in Chem. Fats Lipids* **3**, 153-211. Fat-Soluble Vitamins.

Dam, H., and Nielsen, G. K. (1956). *Acta Physiol. Scand.* **37**, 359-362.

Dam, H., Prange, I., and Søndergaard, E. (1955). *Acta Physiol. Scand.* **34**, 141-146.

Dam, H., Kristensen, G., Nielsen, G. K., Prange, I., and Søndergaard, E. (1956a). *Acta Physiol. Scand.* **36**, 319-328.

Dam, H., Engel, P. F., and Nielsen, G. K. (1956b). *Acta Physiol. Scand.* **37**, 142-149.

De Luca, H. F., Gran, F. C., and Steenbock, H. (1957). *J. Biol. Chem.* **224**, 201-208.

*Deuel, H. J., Jr. (1955). "The Lipids," Vol. 2. Interscience, New York.

*Deuel, H. J., Jr., and Reiser, R. (1955). *Vitamins and Hormones* **13**, 29-70. Essential fatty acids.

Feller, D. D., and Huff, R. L. (1955). *Am. J. Physiol.* **182**, 237-242.

Frantz, I. D., Jr., and Carey, J. B., Jr. (1957). *J. Lab. Clin. Med.* **50**, 814-815.

Gordon, H., Lewis, B., Eales, L., and Brock, J. F. (1957). *Lancet* ii, 1299-1306.

Green, B., Horner, A. A., Lowe, J. S., and Morton, R. A. (1957). *Biochem. J.* **65**, P33.

Grunbaum, B. W., Geary, J. R., Jr., Grande, F., Anderson, J. T., and Glick, D. (1957). *Proc. Soc. Exptl. Biol. Med.* **94**, 613-617.

Guehring, R. R., Hurley, L. S., and Morgan, A. F. (1952). *J. Biol. Chem.* **197**, 485-493.

Hill, E. G., Marmanen, E. L., Hayes, H., and Holman, R. T. (1957). *Proc. Soc. Exptl. Biol. Med.* **95**, 274-278.

Hirsch, J., Insull, W., Jr., and Ahrens, E. H., Jr. (1957). *J. Lab. Clin. Med.* **50**, 826.

*Holman, R. T. (1956). *In* "Biochemical Problems of Lipids" (G. Popják and E. Le Breton, eds.), pp. 463,471. Butterworths, London. Essential fatty acids.

Hsu, J. M., and Chow, B. F. (1957). *Federation Proc.* **16**, 63.

*Inhoffen, H. H., and Bruckner, K. (1954). *Fortschr. Chem. org. Naturstoffe* **11**, 83-123. Chemistry of vitamin D.

James, A. T., Lovelock, J. E., Webb, J., and Trotter, W. R. (1957). *Lancet* i, 705-708.

Jones, R. J., Reiss, O. K., and Huffman, S. (1956). *Proc. Soc. Exptl. Biol. Med.* **93**, 88-91.

Keegan, P., and Gould, R. G. (1953). *Federation Proc.* **12**, 228-229.

Kesten, H. D., Salcedo, J., Jr., and Stetten, D., Jr. (1945). *J. Nutrition* **29**, 171-177.

Keys, A., Anderson, J. T., and Grande, F. (1957). *Lancet* ii, 959-966.

Kritchevsky, D., Kirk, M. R., and Biggs, M. W. (1952). *Metabolism, Clin. and. Exptl.* **1**, 254-258.

*Leuret, F., and Dutrenit, J. (1934). "Le Cholestérol." Baillière, Paris.

Lipsky, S. R., McGuire, J. S., Jr., Bondy, P. K., and Man, E. B. (1955). *J. Clin. Invest.* **34**, 1760-1765.

Lough, A. K., and Garton, G. A. (1957). *Biochem. J.* **67**, 345-351.

McCandless, E. L., and Zilversmit, D. B. (1956). *Arch. Biochem. Biophys.* **62**, 402-410.

Malmros, H., and Wigand, G. (1957). *Lancet* ii, 1-7.
*Man, E. B., and Albrink, M. J. (1957). *In* "Essays in Metabolism" (L. G. Welt, ed.), pp. 316-334. Little, Brown, Boston.
*Mann, G. V. (1957). *A.M.A. Arch. Internal. Med.* **100**, 77-84.
Mead, J. F., and Fillerup, D. L. (1954). *Proc. Soc. Exptl. Biol. Med.* **86**, 449-451.
Mead, J. F., Salton, W. H., Jr., and Decker, A. B. (1956). *J. Biol. Chem.* **218**, 401-407.
Mead, J. F., and Fillerup, D. L. (1957). *J. Biol. Chem.* **227**, 1009-1023.
Morgan, A. F., Brinner, L., Plaa, C. B., and Stone, M. M. (1957). *Am. J. Physiol.* **189**, 290-296.
Mukherjee, S., Achaya, K. T., Deuel, H. J., Jr., and Alfin-Slater, R. B. (1957). *J. Biol. Chem.* **226**, 845-849.
*Nicolaysen, R., and Eeg-Larsen, N. (1953). *Vitamins and Hormones* **11**, 29-60. Biochemistry and physiology vitamin D.
Okey, R., and Lyman, M. M. (1956). *J. Nutrition* **58**, 471-482.
Okey, R., and Lyman, M. M. (1957). *J. Nutrition* **61**, 103-112.
Okey, R., Pencharz, R., Lepkovsky, S., and Vernon, E. R. (1951). *J. Nutrition* **44**, 83-99.
Okey, R., Lyman, M. M., and Einset, B. M. (1957). *Federation Proc.* **16**, 394-395.
Opdyke, D. F., and Ott, W. H. (1954). *Proc. Soc. Exptl. Biol. Med.* **85**, 414-415.
Peifer, J. J., and Holman, R. T. (1955). *Arch. Biochem. Biophys.* **57**, 520-521.
Perlman, I., and Chaikoff, I. L. (1939). *J. Biol. Chem.* **128**, 735-743.
*Popják, G., and Le Breton, E., eds. (1956). "Biochemical Problems of Lipids." Butterworths, London.
Popper, H., and Schaffner, F. (1957). "Liver: Structure and Function." McGraw-Hill, New York.
Putignano, T. 1952). *Boll. soc. ital. biol. sper.* **28**, 1154; *Chem. Abstr.* **48**, 236.
Ramalingaswami, V., Sriramachari, S., and Tulpule, P. G. (1952). *Lancet* ii, 661-662.
Raoul, Y., Le Boulch, N., Baron, C., Bazier, R., and Guérrilot-Vinet, A. (1956). *Bull. soc. chim. biol.* **38**, 495-503.
Ratnoff, O. D., Koletsky, S., and Patek, A. J., Jr. (1956). *Proc. Soc. Exptl. Biol. Med.* **90**, 620-623.
Rattray, J. B. M., Cook, R. P., and James, A T. (1956). *Biochem. J.* **64**, P10.
Rattray, J. B. M., James, A. T., and Cook, R. P. (1958). *Biochem. J.* To be published.
Ridout, J. H., Lucas, C. C., Patterson, J. M., and Best, C. H. (1954a). *Biochem. J.* **58**, 297-301.
Ridout, J. H., Lucas, C. C., Patterson, J. M., and Best, C. H. (1954b). *Biochem. J.* **58**, 301-306.
Ridout, J. H., Patterson, J. M., Lucas, C. C., and Best, C. H. (1954c). *Biochem. J.* **58**, 306-312.
Robinson, R. (1946-47). *Proc. Roy. Soc.* **A188**, 143.
Roth, J. S., and Milstein, S. W. (1957). *Arch. Biochem. Biophys.* **70**, 392-400.
Schettler, G. (1949). *Biochem. Z.* **319**, 349-358; 444-452.
Sellers, E. A., and You, R. W. (1952). *Biochem. J.* **51**, 573-576.
Shapiro, S. L., and Freedman, L. (1955). *Am. J. Physiol.* **181**, 441-445.
Shorland, F. B. (1956). *Ann. Rev. Biochem.* **25**, 108-109.
Smith, L. L., and Mefferd, R. B., Jr. (1955). *Texas Repts. Biol. and Med.* **13**, 362-374.

Spiro, M. J., and McKibbin, J. M. (1956). *J. Biol. Chem.* **219**, 643-651.

Stetten, D., Jr., and Salcedo, J., Jr. (1945). *J. Nutrition* **29**, 167-170.

Swell, L., Boiter, T. A., Feld, H., Jr., and Treadwell, C. R. (1955). *J. Nutrition* **57**, 121-132.

*Terroine, E. F., and Belin, P. (1927). *Bull. soc. chim. biol.* **9**, 12-48. L'élément constant.

Treadwell, C. R., Flick, D. F., and Vahouny, G. V. (1955a). *Federation Proc.* **14**, 452-453.

Treadwell, C. R., Vahouny, G. V., and Flick, D. F. (1955b). *Federation Proc.* **14**, 453.

Van Bruggen, J. T., Hutchens, T. T., and West, E. S. (1951). *Federation Proc.* **10**, 263.

Wiese, H. F., and Hansen, A. E. (1951). *Texas Repts. Biol. and Med.* **9**, 516-544.

Wilens, S. L. (1947). *J. Am. Med. Assoc.* **135**, 1136-1139.

*Zilversmit, D. B. (1957). *Am. J. Med.* **23**, 120-133.

ADDITIONAL REFERENCES

The relation of dietary fat to human nutrition, and the importance of cholesterol, particularly with regard to the development of atheroma (myocardial infarction, coronary disease) is discussed in three recent symposia. These are: "Fats in Human Nutrition," Council on Foods and Nutrition, *J. Am. Med. Assoc.* **164**, 1890-1925 (1957); "Atherosclerosis and the Fat Content of the Diet," Page, I. H., Stare, F. J., Corcoran, A. C., Pollak, H., and Wilkinson, C. F., Jr. (1957). *Circulation* **16**, 163-178 (see also *J. Am. Med. Assoc.* **164**, 2048-2051); "Coronary Diseases," *Practitioner*, **180**, 159-210.

The third volume of "The Lipids," Deuel, H. J., Jr., Interscience, New York and London, 1957, contains much interesting information.

APPENDIX OF PRACTICAL METHODS

Abbreviations. Apart from those abbreviations in current use the following will be found in the text:

Measurements of time are given as sec., second; min., minute; and hr., hour.

The word volume has been abbreviated to vol. and v/v represents volume per volume; w/v is weight per volume and w/w is weight per weight. All temperatures are recorded in °C.

I. General

The modification of the existing methods given here are our personal suggestion. The descriptions have been made in the hope that they may be of value to workers *starting* in this field and with experience will undoubtedly be altered to suit particular requirements. We have not given any example of rapid, "direct" methods but references to these are given in Chapter 3.

A. Choice of Method

The choice of method is dependent largely on the amount of material available. For the semi-microgravimetric methods described at least 5 ml. of blood plasma or serum, or from 5 to 10 gm. of tissue should be available; larger amounts will lessen the experimental error. The colorimetric methods need less material, 1 ml. of plasma or 1 gm. of tissue being commonly used, but these may be scaled down to one-tenth of these amounts (i.e., 0.1 ml. or 0.1 gm.). The importance of *correct sampling* is stressed.

B. Apparatus

The following special apparatus should be available:

Chemical Balance. For the gravimetric estimations and the preparation of standard solutions a good analytical balance is essential (sensitivity at least 0.2 mg.).

Centrifuge. The most convenient type is one with an interchangeable head of the multitube swing out type so that the precipitate collects in the base of the tube. The machine should be capable of giving about $700 \times g$, i.e. about 2000 r.p.m. for a swing out distance of 15 cm. [The relative centrifugal force (R.C.F.) or the gravitational force acting on 1-gm. mass at a distance R (in cm.) from the center of the spindle to the extreme end of the tube is derived from $1.118 \times 10^{-5} \times R \times (\text{r.p.m})^2$.]

Photometer (absorptiometer or spectrophotometer). A number of good models are available commercially. Adaptors for using photometer tubes of 1 ml. capacity or suitable cuvettes are required. The tubes or cuvettes should be standardized optically. The use of the correct wavelength for the measurement of light absorbance is important and for this either the monochromator type of instrument may be used or filters inserted to give the correct wavelength.

Thermostatically controlled baths (*or incubators*). The temperatures used are 0°, 25°, 38°, and 50°. Separate baths at these temperatures are more convenient but an adjustable control bath for the higher temperatures may be used. The bath at 25° is fitted conveniently with a cover with apertures to hold the centrifuge tubes.

A *water* or *steam bath* should be available and also a *drying oven* for drying to constant weight, and for use in paper chromatography.

Pipettes. Transferring (Pasteur) pipettes are constructed by drawing out a piece of glass tube to a short capillary, a rubber bulb being used for drawing up the fluid. Standardized pipettes of known capacities should always be used, attention being paid to environmental temperature.

Apparatus generally. All apparatus with which the material under investigation comes into actual contact, and bottles in which the reagents to be used are kept, must be rinsed before use with ethanol and then with ethyl ether to render them lipid free.

C. Chemicals and Reagents

All chemicals used must be of CP or AR grade and where doubt exists about purity they must be purified; this is of particular importance with the solvents.

Solvents. All solvents, and this includes water, should be completely volatile and free from substances which might interfere with the reactions used. Methods for the purification of organic solvents are given by L. F. Fieser, "Experiments in Organic Chemistry," 3rd ed., Heath, Boston, 1955 and by A. I. Vogel, "A Text-Book of Practical Organic Chemistry," 3rd ed., Longmans, Green, New York, 1956. For the estimation of ketosteroids specially purified ethanol must be used and its preparation is described on p. 492.

Reagents. The preparation of the reagents used for the different techniques is given below. As a general rule reagents should be prepared fresh before use, but unless stated otherwise, may be stored safely for approximately two months in the absence of light at a low temperature.

Sterols. The sterols used as standard reference compounds must contain no contaminant and are best recrystallized before use. A useful crystallizing medium for cholesterol is ethyl acetate with the drop-wise addition of methanol to incipient precipitation; the crystallized product after drying at 100° *in vacuo* should be stored in a dark bottle in an evacuated desiccator. Crystallization of cholesterol from acetic acid gives a pure product but the process is more laborious.

Δ^7-Cholestenol (lathosterol) the standard for "fast acting" sterol determinations (see below) may be prepared simply from 7-dehydrocholesterol by the method described by L. F. Fieser and J. E. Herz, *J. Am. Chem. Soc.* **75**, 121-124 (1953).

II.   Extraction Procedures

A.   TOTAL LIPID

Apparatus

Cellulose powder and thimbles.

Extractor. The Soxhlet type of apparatus or a continuous extractor may be used.

Filter paper, Whatman No. 1.

Homogenizer. A glass homogenizer of the Potter-Elvehjem type.

Volumetric flasks accurately standardized.

Chemicals

Acetone. For solvent mixture.

Ethanol. As such and as a solvent mixture.

Ethyl ether. As such and as a solvent mixture.

Solvent mixtures. The following mixtures of solvents are commonly used; the measures are v/v:

   No. 1.   Acetone–ethanol (1:1)

   No. 2.   Acetone–ethyl ether (1:1)

   No. 3.   Ethanol–ethyl ether (3:1)

Petroleum ether (40–60°) or pentane.

1. Dry Extraction

A weighed amount (1–5 gm.) of coarsely chopped tissue is placed in a cellulose thimble (previously extracted with boiling ethanol) and dried *in vacuo* at 80°. With plasma or serum, place cellulose powder in the thimble to absorb the fluid before drying. The water content may be determined but is preferably made on a separate sample. The dried material is extracted in a suitable apparatus with solvent mixture 3 for 2 hr. with 1-gm. quantities and for 8 hr. for 5-gm. amounts. The volume of solvent should half fill the extracting receiver. The extract is made up to a convenient volume; with small amounts of material a calibrated tube attached to the extractor is convenient. The total extract may be used as such or, after removal of solvent, treated with petroleum ether which dissolves sterols and their esters leaving behind the more polar compounds.

For large amounts of material, e.g. dried feces, an ethanol extraction is first made until minimal color is present in the extracting fluid, the feces are then removed, ground, and reextracted with ethyl ether for 6–8 hr.

2. Wet Extraction

For plasma or serum (use solvent mixture in ratio 25 to 1 of plasma); depending on the amount of plasma available a convenient sized volumetric flask is taken and half filled with solvent mixture. The plasma (1 vol.) is added from a pipette slowly and with constant agitation. The flask and its contents are shaken in a water bath to ebullition, removed, cooled and made up to volume (25 vol.) with the solvent mixture. The precipitate of protein is allowed to settle and the extract is filtered through a solvent-extracted filter paper; a sample of the filtrate being taken for analysis.

Tissues. A weighed amount of the coarsely chopped tissue is transferred to a homogenizer tube which is calibrated at a suitable volume, e.g. 25 ml. For a good extraction, tissue (1 part) to solvent mixture 1 or 3 (25 parts) is used, sufficient of the mixture being added at first to cover the plunger. The mixture is then finely dispersed, the tube removed, the plunger rinsed with solvent, and the tube and its contents heated in a water bath to ebullition. The tube is then cooled, made up to volume with the solvent, mixed, the proteins allowed to settle and filtered, a sample of the filtrate being used for analysis.

B.   Microgravimetric Determination

Apparatus

Centrifuge tubes, strong-walled glass tubes, conical in shape, of 12–15 ml. capacity and calibrated at 2 ml. intervals.

Stirring rods. Solid glass rods about 13 cm. in length and tapered to a fine bulb point.

Separating funnels. Glass separating funnels of approximate capacity of 100 ml. equipped with *glass* stoppers. No lubricant other than water is used for the stopcock.

Chemicals

Acetone. For solvent mixture.

Aluminum chloride solution. A 30% solution is prepared by dissolving aluminum chloride hexahydrate (30 gm.) in water (70 ml.).

Benzene.

Digitonin solution. A 1% solution is prepared by dissolving digitonin (1 gm.) in 95% ethanol (55 ml.) and water (45 ml.) at 60°.

Ethanol. For solvent mixture.

Ethyl ether. As such and for solvent mixture.

Potassium hydroxide. An approximately normal solution is prepared
by dissolving potassium hydroxide (56 gm.) in a minimal volume
of water and making up to 1000 ml. with ethanol. The solution is
allowed to stand for 24 hr. and any precipitate is removed by filtration. The solution should be discarded when a slight color is
apparent.

Solvent mixtures. 1 and 2 (as above) are used.

Ethyl acetate, chloroform, pentane or petroleum ether may be needed
(see below).

1. Unsaponifiable Matter

We use this procedure for the hydrolysis of lipid extracts of not less
than 50 mg. in weight to determine total unsaponifiable matter. To a
weighed amount of the extract (0.05 to 2 gm.) is added the ethanolic
potassium hydroxide solution using the ratio of 5 ml. of solution per
1 gm. of lipid. To ensure complete solubilization of the lipid, the saponification medium is increased in volume tenfold with the addition of
ethanol or benzene. The hydrolysis is carried out at the ebullition temperature for 2 hr. under an atmosphere of nitrogen. On its completion
the solution is reduced in volume by distillation, cooled, and transferred
to a separating funnel using water (2 vol.) divided into 4 portions and
ethyl ether (1 vol.) divided into 4 portions. The mixture is partitioned
and the ether layer is washed with water (2 vol.) divided into 4 portions
or until no more alkali is present, the water washings being added to
the soap solution. The ethereal extract is concentrated by distillation and
the final traces of water removed by the addition of benzene and dried
in vacuo to constant weight, the resulting unsaponifiable matter being
weighed. The aqueous extract of soaps may be used for the determination of acids (steam-volatile, etc.) or for glycerol.

Variant solvents for extracting unsaponifiable matter are petroleum
ether or pentane which removes the less polar monohydroxy sterols, or
ethyl acetate or chloroform for extracting in addition the more polar
dihydroxysterols.

2. Total Sterol as Digitonide

A centrifuge tube together with its stirring rod is weighed and the unsaponifiable matter is transferred with solvent mixture 1. The total
volume should not exceed 5 ml. for 10 mg. of material, larger tubes
being used for greater amounts. The 1% digitonin solution is added in
amount dependent on the weight of unsaponifiable matter—for each mg.
add 0.5 ml. digitonin solution. The contents of the tube are well mixed,

and allowed to stand for 18 hr. at 20° or the process may be speeded by the addition of aluminum chloride solution (see p. 489). The stirring rod is carefully drained, removed, and placed upside down in the rack so that any adherent particles are not dislodged and the tube and its contents are then centrifuged at 700 $\times$ g for 15 min. If particles are present on the surface, centrifugation is repeated. The clear supernatant is removed carefully so as not to disturb the precipitate. The precipitate is washed with solvent mixture 2 (5 ml.), thoroughly stirred, recentrifuged, the supernatant removed and washed finally with ether (5 ml.). The tube, stirring rod, and its contents are dried to constant weight. The content of 3β-ol sterols is by weight 100 digitonide = 23.9 sterols.

The values obtained for cholesterol and cholestanol are accurate but that for coprostanol, due to its greater solubility (about 30 times), is low. The digitonide may be analyzed by the colorimetric method described below for its sterol content; those not reacting which consist mainly of cholestanol are obtained by difference.

III.   Colorimetric Determinations

A.   The Liebermann-Burchard Method*

Apparatus

Baths or incubators. The temperature of these are 0°, 25°, 38°, and 50°.

Burettes. With a good scale to allow accurate delivery of 1 or 2 ml.

Centrifuge. See above.

Centrifuge tubes. See above.

Drying oven. Maintained at 100–110°.

Photometer. As described above.

Photometer tubes. Optically standardized glass tubes of approximately 4 ml. capacity.

Rack.

Stirring rods. See above.

Wide mouth jars. Jars of 1–2 lb. capacity with screw tops and layered with sand (3 cm. deep). These are used in the alkali hydrolysis of the steryl esters.

Chemicals and Reagents

Acetic anhydride. For preparation of the color reagents see below.

Acetic acid. (1) Glacial acetic acid; (2) 10% acetic acid prepared by diluting glacial acetic acid (10 ml.) with water (90 ml.).

Acetone. For solvent mixtures.

---

* Based on the method of Sperry and Webb, see Chapter 3.

Aluminum chloride solution. A 30% solution is prepared by dissolving aluminum chloride hexahydrate (30 gm.) in water (70 ml.).

Benzene. For preparation of color reagent 2.

Color reagent. (1) To chilled acetic anhydride (19 ml.) is added concentrated sulfuric acid (1 ml.). (2) To chilled acetic anhydride (19 ml.) is added benzene (20 ml.) and concentrated sulfuric acid (1 ml.). Both reagents are prepared fresh before use and for the addition of the reagent a burette *must be used.* Carefully discard the excess reagent after use.

Digitonin solution. A 1% solution is prepared by dissolving digitonin (1 gm.) in 95% ethanol (55 ml.) and water (45 ml.) at 60°.

Ethanol. For solvent mixtures.

Ethyl ether. As such and for solvent mixtures.

Phenolphthalein solution. A 1% solution is prepared by dissolving phenolphthalein (1 gm.) in ethanol (100 ml.).

Potassium hydroxide. An approximately 50% solution is prepared by dissolving potassium hydroxide (10 gm.) in water (20 ml.). Any sediment is removed by filtration.

Solvent mixtures. 1, 2, and 3 (see above) are used.

Standard sterol solutions.

(1) Cholesterol (100 mg.) is dissolved in glacial acetic acid and made up to a volume of 100 ml. From this stock solution (1 mg. cholesterol/ml.) suitable dilutions are made for working standards, e.g. 0.5 mg./ml. and 0.1 mg./ml.

(2) Δ^7-Cholestenol (10 mg.) is dissolved in glacial acetic acid and made up to a volume of 100 ml. From this stock solution (0.1 mg. Δ^7-cholestenol/ml.) suitable working standards are 0.1 mg./ml. and 0.05 mg./ml.

Sulfuric acid. Concentrated sulfuric acid for the preparation of the color reagents.

1. Preliminary Determination of Total Sterol

The Liebermann-Burchard method is most convenient in the range of from 0.1 to 0.5 mg. of sterol. The total sterol content for plasma and most animal tissues is in the range 50 to 300 mg./100 gm. fresh weight (see Chapters 4 and 5) so that in theory 0.05 to 0.5 gm. of tissue is needed to provide the necessary amount of sterol for estimation. For brain and nervous tissue (approximately 2% sterol) only about 0.01 gm. is needed and for adrenal glands of most animals (approximately 5% sterol) about half this amount is sufficient. There are, however, two important factors: (1) The volume of extract affects the estimation by dilution. Dry extraction is useful in that a small final volume is obtained and thus smaller amounts of tissue can be used. Wet extraction is more convenient but the volume of extractant is large (1 tissue to 25 solvent) and the aliquot taken (normally one-tenth) must contain the necessary amount of sterol. The amounts used must therefore be scaled up. (2) The size of photometer tube available affects the amount determined. The larger tubes of 3–6 ml. capacity are used when there is sufficient material available but smaller tubes or cuvettes (0.5 to 1 ml.) are used to scale down the amounts of material.

A generalized procedure allowing for amounts of tissue varying from 0.2 to 1 gm. and for differences in the size of photometer tube is to take plasma or tissue (1 part) and add solvent to make a volume of 25 parts and follow the extraction procedure described in Section II, A, 2. The filtered extract is then used in aliquots of the total volume (25) of 1/5, 1/10, and 1/20. These pipetted aliquots are placed in small flasks and heated gently on a steam bath until all solvent is removed. To each flask is then added glacial acetic acid (1 vol.) which is gently warmed, the flask and its contents are then cooled, color reagent 1 (2 vol.) is added and mixed. The colors are developed for 30 min. at 25° and transferred to the appropriate photometer tube and compared with those obtained with cholesterol standards of 0.1, 0.25 and 0.5 mg. in volumes selected for the size of the photometer tubes. From the results found a suitable aliquot of the extract can then be chosen for the accurate estimation described in the next section.

2. Determination of Free and Total Sterol ("Fast" and "Slow Acting")

This description is for the colorimetric determination of the "fast" and "slow acting" sterols in a sample containing 0.1 to 0.5 mg. of total sterol in a 2-ml. volume of acetone–ethanol extract from the wet extraction of 1 ml. plasma (or 1 gm. tissue) in 25 ml. of solvent.

a. Free sterol. Pipette the extract into a centrifuge tube, add aluminum trichloride solution (2 drops), and stir. The digitonin solution (1 ml.) is then added, mixed well, and the solution warmed at 50° for 5 min. in a water bath. The stirring rods are drained, removed, and placed upside down in a rack so that any adherent particles are not rubbed off. The solution is then centrifuged at $700 \times g$ for 15 min. If particles are floating on the surface the process is repeated for a longer time at increased speed. The clear supernatant is removed through a finely drawn-out tube under water pump vacuum, care being taken not to disturb the precipitate.

The stirring rods are returned to their respective tubes, to each of which is added solvent mixture 2 (2 ml.), the contents are well stirred, the rod returned to the rack, the tubes centrifuged, and the supernatant removed as described before. The precipitate is washed twice more in the same manner with *ether*. The rod is then returned to the tube, the ether removed carefully by placing in a warm water bath and dried at 100° for 30 min. (If necessary tubes may be stored for several days at this stage.)

b. Total sterol. The potassium hydroxide solution (1 drop) is placed in a dry centrifuge tube, the acetone–ethanol extract (2 ml.) added and the mixture stirred with a vigorous up and down motion of the stirring rod until no droplets of the alkali solution are seen at the tip of the tube. The tube is placed in the sand of the previously warmed jar which is covered tightly and placed in a 38° incubator for 30 min.

The tube is removed, cooled, the rod is raised, acetone–ethanol is added to the 2 ml. mark, phenolphthalein solution (1 drop) is added, and the pink color just discharged with 10% acetic acid added carefully, any cloudiness being discharged by the addition of a further drop of the acetic acid solution. The resulting solution is then treated as described under free sterol precipitation except that the precipitate is washed only once with *ether*.

3. Color Development

The tubes containing the digitonide are equilibrated in the 25° water bath. To each tube is added glacial acetic acid (1 ml.) and the digitonide dissolved by gentle stirring, the rod being left in the tube.

To each of the tubes, which should be arranged in order, the color reagent 1 (2 ml.) is added from a burette at $\frac{1}{2}$ min. intervals. The solutions are mixed and allowed to develop for $1\frac{1}{2}$ min. for "fast acting" sterols and 35 min. for Δ^5-stenols. The contents of the centrifuge tubes are transferred to suitable vessels (tubes or cuvettes) for the color determination.

The photometer blank is made containing acetic acid (1 ml.) and the reagent (2 ml.). The sterol standards, to which is added the reagent (2 ml.), are set up at the beginning and end of a series of determinations; for accurate work a predetermined calibration curve is unsuitable. In estimations where a different final volume is required, the ratio of color reagent to glacial acetic acid of 2:1 by volume must be observed.

4. Color Determination

The absorbancy, or color density, is measured at a wavelength of 620 mμ or using the appropriate color filter.

Amount of sterol present in unknown (as mg./2 ml. of extract) =

$$\frac{\text{Reading of unknown} \times \text{amount present in standard (as mg.)}}{\text{Reading of standard}}$$

The values per unit weight or as per cent of a fraction are obtained by simple proportion from the dilution and volume or weight used.

"*Fast acting*" *Sterols.* P. R. Moore and C. A. Baumann (*J. Biol. Chem.* **195**, 615, 1952) correct for the color development of both "slow" and "fast acting" sterols using the same sample and measuring the color intensity after 1½ min. and again after 35 min. A comparison is made with reference standards of 0.1 mg. Δ^7-cholestenol for "fast acting" and 0.5 mg. cholesterol for "slow acting."

$$\text{Fast acting sterol (mg.)} = \frac{R_1 y - R_2 a}{xy - ab}$$

$$\text{Slow acting sterol (mg.)} = \frac{R_2 x - R_1 b}{xy - ab}$$

Where: R_1 = reading of unknown at 1½ min.

R_2 = reading of unknown at 35 min.

x = reading for 1 mg. of Δ^7-cholestenol at 1½ min. (reading of 0.1 standard × 10).

b = as for x but after 35 min.

y = reading for 1 mg. of cholesterol at 35 min. (reading of 0.5 standard × 2).

a = as for y but after 1½ min.

An alternative procedure in which the "fast acting" sterols alone are determined is to develop the color with the ice-cold reagent 2 (p. 488). No color is apparent due to the "slow acting" sterols. The digitonide is dissolved in glacial acetic acid (1 ml.) to which is added the thoroughly chilled color reagent 2 (2 ml.) and the color intensity is measured at 620 mμ after a development period of 10 minutes at 0°. The "fast acting" sterol standard is treated in a similar manner.

B. Ketosteroids by the Zimmermann Method[*]

Apparatus

Photometer as described above.

Photometer tubes. Optically standardized tubes of approximately 1-ml. capacity. In order that the final volume of reactants may be

---

[*] Based on method of H. Wilson (see Chapter 3) who describes a more sensitive method.

measured accurately it is necessary to cover such tubes with a dark opaque paper shield to the meniscus of the solution.

Bath or cold room at 0°

Chemicals and Reagents

Aldehyde-free ethanol. Ethanol (1000 ml.) is heated under reflux for 1 hr. with zinc dust (20 gm.) and potassium hydroxide (20 gm.). The purified aldehyde-free ethanol is distilled, the head and tail fractions being discarded.

m-Dinitrobenzene reagent. *m*-Dinitrobenzene (20 gm.) in 95% ethanol (750 ml.) is warmed to 40° and 2 N sodium hydroxide (100 ml.) is added. After 5 min. the solution is cooled, water (2500 ml.) is added, the precipitated material collected on a Buchner filter, well washed with water, then recrystallized twice from 85% (v/v) ethanol and dried *in vacuo*. The material should be almost colorless and be stored in a dark container in a cool place.

The reagent solution is a 2% (w/v) solution of the purified compound in pure ethanol; if kept in the dark it may be used for 10 days.

2.5 N Potassium hydroxide. Potassium hydroxide (18 gm.) is dissolved by constant shaking in 100 ml. of ethanol. Any precipitate is removed by filtration through a sintered glass filter. The concentration should be adjusted to 2.5 N ($\pm$ 2%). The solution is stable if kept in the cold but should be discarded when it becomes colored.

Standard ketone solutions.

(1) Δ^5-Cholesten-3-one (10 mg.) is dissolved in ethanol and made up to a volume of 10 ml. From this stock solution (1 mg./ml.) suitable aliquots are taken.

(2) Cholestan-3-one (10 mg.) is dissolved in ethanol and made up to a volume of 10 ml. From this stock solution (1 mg./ml.) suitable standards are prepared.

Procedure. As the reaction is light sensitive it is carried out in the complete exclusion of direct radiation. To the test sample containing about 100 µg. of the ketosteroid in ethanol (0.4 ml.), the ketosteroid standards (100 µg. in 0.4 ml. ethanol) and a photometer blank of ethanol (0.4 ml.) is added the *m*-dinitrobenzene solution (0.4 ml.) and the mixtures equilibrated at 0°; the potassium hydroxide solution (0.4 ml.) is then added and the contents of the tubes mixed. After a development time of 15 min. the optical density at various wave lengths (490, 540, 560, 580, and 600 mµ are suggested) is measured. The optical density is similarly determined after a color development time of 3 hr. From the rate of reaching maximum color intensity and the absorbance at specific wavelengths the type and amount of the ketosteroid may be determined (see Table III, Chapter III).

N.B. Care must be taken that no acetone or other ketone is present.

IV. Chromatography

A. Paper Partition Chromatography[*]

Apparatus

Chromatographic chamber consisting of (1) glass tank (approximately 38 × 25 × 25 cm.) lined with blotting paper, (2) dish of aluminum, or other suitable material (approximately 20 × 8 × 2.5 cm.), supported on glass rods fastened to the chamber sides by suckers, (3) heavy glass lid to cover the tank. The chamber is made airtight by sealing the lid with starch paste prepared by mixing soluble starch (9 parts) and glycerol (33 parts), heating with stirring to 140° and cooling before use and (4) glass plates for holding the chromatograms. The chamber is kept at 25°.

Drying cabinet. The cabinet is maintained at a temperature of 100° and must allow convectional circulation of the atmosphere.

Incubator. An incubator maintained at 25° is necessary for consistent results.

Paper. Whatman No. 7 chromatography paper.

Pipettes. Accurate pipettes (0.1-ml. capacity) with a drop-like flow.

Roller and glass plate.

Sprayer. A glass sprayer with a capillary nozzle to allow a very fine spray and worked under compressed air.

Chemicals and Reagents

Antimony pentachloride. For preparation of the spraying reagent see below.

Chloroform. For preparation of spraying reagent.

Heptane. For preparation of solvent systems.

Phenylcellosolve (2-phenoxyethanol). For preparation of solvent systems.

Solvent systems. (1) Stationary phase: phenyl cellosolve. (2) Mobile phase: heptane saturated with phenyl cellosolve.

Spraying reagent. Antimony pentachloride (20 gm.) is dissolved in chloroform (100 ml.). The reagent is prepared before use and the excess should be discarded immediately after use.

---

[*] Based on the method of Neher and Wettstein (see Chapter 3).

Standard sterol solution.

(1) Cholesterol (5 mg.) in chloroform (10 ml.).

(2) 7α-Hydroxycholesterol (5 mg.) in chloroform (10 ml.).

Solutions of other reference sterols and of the sterol to be chromatographed are made to contain about 50 μg. in 0.1 ml.

Method. The blotting paper lining the tank is wet thoroughly with the mobile phase and the excess solvent placed at the bottom of the tank. A starting line is ruled 12 cm. from the top of strips of paper 42 cm. long. These are then impregnated with phenyl cellosolve, placed between blotting paper and well rolled to remove excess solvent. The impregnated papers are suspended over glass plates in the reservoir trough and equilibrated for 1 hr. The steroid solutions (0.1 ml. = 50 μg.) are applied to the starting line and the mobile phase (300 ml.) added to the trough. The chamber is made gas-tight. Development period of 4–5 hr. is necessary for mono-hydroxysterols and 20 hr. for di- and tri-hydroxysterols. The papers are dried thoroughly at 100° until all solvent is removed. The paper is sprayed with the spraying reagent and the steroids detected by the specific color reaction and their movement with respect to that of a known compound (see Table I).

TABLE I

THE COLOR PRODUCTION WITH ANTIMONY PENTACHLORIDE OF CERTAIN CHROMATO-
GRAPHED STEROLS AND THEIR RELATIVE MOBILITY IN THE SYSTEM PHENYL
CELLOSOLVE AND HEPTANE

			Movement relative to	
				7α-Hydroxy-
	Δ-	Color with anti-mony pentachloride	Cholesterol	cholesterol
Sterol	Position	reagent[a]	(after 5 hr.)	(after 20 hr.)
Cholesterol	5	Pink	1.0	—
Δ⁷-Cholestenol	7	Reddish-purple	0.9	—
7-Dehydrocholesterol	5,7	Blue-green (I)	0.7	—
Cholestanol	—	Pink (S)	1.1	—
Coprostanol	—	Salmon pink (S)	1.3	—
7α-Hydroxycholesterol	5	Blue-green (I)	—	1.0
7β-Hydroxycholesterol	5	Blue-green (I)	—	0.7
Cholest-4-ene-3β,6-diol	4	Faint brown	—	0.6
25-Hydroxycholesterol	5	Maroon (I)	—	0.4
Cholestane-3β,5α,6β-triol	—	Yellow-brown (S)	—	0.5

[a] (I) indicates immediate color on spraying; (S) indicates color development on heating. See note on p. 59 for configurations of 7-hydroxy compounds.

B. ADSORPTION CHROMATOGRAPHY

This simple and pleasing technique can be varied in its details so that it is difficult to describe a standardized account. The following general suggestions may be of value; the method is learned by experience.

1. Chromatographic Columns

These are glass tubes, convenient sizes being (diameter × height in cm.) 1 × 15, 1.5 × 40, 2.5 × 60; the dimensions are not critical and smaller or larger columns may be used. The lower end of the tube is fitted with a porous sintered glass filter, or it may be packed lightly with cotton or glass wool on which is placed a layer (about 5 mm.) of coarse sand. The lower end of the tube should be tapered slightly to allow collection of the effluent, i.e. the issuing solvent.

2. Adsorbents

Good general adsorbents are:

Alumina. That supplied by Merck and Co., Inc., Rahway, New Jersey, is acid washed. Savory and Moore Ltd., London, supply a good grade but if necessary (e.g. with methyl esters) it is washed with dilute acetic acid, followed by methanol, and reactivated by heating at 200°. The alumina should be standardized by the method of H. Brockmann and H. Schodder (*Ber.* **74**, 73, 1941) and its activity stated; we find grade II useful for the preliminary separation of unsaponifiable matter. For the resolution of subfractions it is sometimes necessary to use "weakened" alumina which is prepared by adding a small amount of water.

Silicic acid. That supplied by Mallinckrodt Chemical Works, St. Louis (Agents Savory and Moore, London) we find consistent in behavior for separating lipid extracts.

"Celite." Celite 545 from Johns-Manville, New York and London, is mixed with the silicic acid. Before use a mixture is made of (parts by weight) silicic acid (2) and celite (1) and the material dried in an air oven at 100°. This mixture gives a more rapid flow and without impairment of the resolving power of the silicic acid (J. B. Wilkes, *Ind. Eng. Chem. Anal. Ed.* **18**, 329, 1946).

3. Selecting and packing the column

The size of column and amounts of adsorbent necessary will depend on the amounts of material available. The ratio of adsorbent to material to be chromatographed can be varied considerably. We use (w/w) for lipid extract (1) the silicic acid-celite mixture (15); for unsaponifiable matter (1) we use alumina (50). In Table II are given the amounts of adsorbent used for the specimen columns. The columns are filled by adding the adsorbent from a spatula shaking down the material evenly by gentle tapping. The even filling of a column is of the utmost importance. A small filter paper is placed on top of the adsorbent to prevent channeling when the solvent is added.

TABLE II
CHROMATOGRAPHIC COLUMNS AND ADSORBENT

Column			Amount of adsorbent (gm.)	Amount to be chromatographed	
Diameter (cm.)	Height (cm.)	Approximate capacity (ml.)		Lipid	Unsaponifiable matter
1	15	10–15	About 1	50 mg.	20 mg.
1.5	40	75	About 5	250 mg.	100 mg.
2.5	60	300	30–50	1.5–2.5 gm.	1 gm.

4. Eluting or developing the column

To ensure even running the first solvent is added gently to the column and allowed to run through. In a properly packed column the solvent runs uniformly; if it does not prepare a fresh column.

The material to be chromatographed is dissolved in a *small* amount of the least polar solvent and run gently on to the top of the column. When it has soaked in, the process of elution is started. We used the following sequence of solvents for lipid extracts and for unsaponifiable matter. (1) Petroleum ether (b.p. 40–60°) *or* pentane, (2) benzene, (3) ethyl ether, (4) methanol *or* ethanol. The change from one solvent to another is made by adding a small amount of the more polar solvent, e.g. a change from benzene to ethyl ether by adding a mixture of (v/v) benzene 90: ethyl ether 10. The solvents used and the mixtures thereof may be varied considerably to suit particular purposes.

The volume of effluent collected depends on the amount and nature of material to be chromatographed—10, 50, or 100 ml. fractions may be taken. The effluents are collected conveniently in round-bottomed flasks and evaporated to dryness soon after collection. If little or no material has been eluted a change is made to the next solvent. Re-chromatography of the separated fractions may be necessary for fine resolutions.

If it is necessary to stop the flow temporarily the column is placed in a measuring cylinder containing the same solvent used for eluting, keeping the level in the cylinder the same as that above the column. Never let a column run dry during development and for smooth running keep a head of solvent of about the same height as that of the packed adsorbent.

On the completion of a run the contents of the column are extruded into a flask, treated with boiling ethanol, filtered, and the extracted material recovered.

V. Estimation of Serum Lipoproteins by Zone Electrophoresis and Estimation of Cholesterol*

Apparatus (Dimensions in inches)

(1) Heavy brass cooling plate (8 × 5 × ¼) with an optically flat upper surface and a coil of ¼ inch copper tubing soldered to the lower surface to permit circulation of tap water.

(2) Two glass plates (9 × 6).

(3) Four clear plastic distance pieces (6 × ¼ × ¼).

(4) Screw clamping device.

(5) Electrode vessels of perspex, about 500-ml. capacity to contain the buffer solution.

(6) Platinum electrodes (strips 4 × ½).

(7) The apparatus should be covered by, e.g. a glass jar, to prevent evaporation.

(8) DC regulated power supply variable between 150–450 v. with a maximum current up to 25 mA.

Filter Paper. Sheets of Whatman 3 MM paper (14 × 5).

Buffer Solution. A mixture of (as gm./l.) diethylbarbituric acid (1.22) and sodium diethylbarbiturate (6.86) gives a solution of 0.04 μ and pH 8.6.

The filter paper is clamped taut between the two glass plates but prevented from touching them by the distance pieces. The screw clamping device allows the lower glass plate to press on the upper surface of the cooling plate. The hydrostatic pressure in the vessels is equilibrated before each run by means of a glass bridge placed temporarily between them.

Procedure. A pencil line is drawn across the filter paper about 4 inches from one end. Buffer is sprayed on to this line producing a damp band about 1 inch wide. Using a drawn-out capillary pipette, 0.15 ml. serum is evenly applied to the line to within ¼ inch from either end. The remainder of the paper is then sprayed with the buffer solution, with the exception of about 2 inches at each end which are left dry in the meantime to facilitate the insertion of the paper in the apparatus. After clamping tightly in the apparatus with the thumb screws, the ends of the paper are dipped in the buffer solutions. At this stage, with cooling water running through the apparatus, a period of 30 min. is allowed for temperature and hydrostatic equilibration.

A potential difference of 300 v. is then applied across the paper, the

* Contributed by George S. Boyd and Michael F. Oliver.

current carried by the paper being about 6 mA. The air temperature within the case is controlled to $12 \pm 1°$ the period of each run being 8 hr. Upon completion of the run, the paper is removed, and allowed to dry slowly in air. Segments 1 cm. apart are marked out on the paper, parallel to the line of origin, and the paper is then cut into 1 cm. pieces. One filter paper strip is inserted into each centrifuge tube and 7 ml. acetone–ethanol (1:1 v/v) added. The tubes are placed in a water bath at about 30° and the temperature is gradually raised until it reaches 66° where it is maintained for 10 min. and then allowed to cool to 40°.

The filter paper strips are removed from the solvent by stainless steel forceps and each strip washed with a fine jet of acetone–ethanol, adding the wash liquid to the extract. The centrifuge tubes are placed in a water bath at 60° and the solvent is completely removed by a gentle stream of air. A thin glass rod is placed in each tube, and all the tubes are set in a beaker of sand in an oven at 110° for 30 min.

Cholesterol estimation. Each tube is then treated with 0.5 ml. glacial acetic acid, followed by 1.0 ml. freshly prepared ice-cold acetic anhydride–sulfuric acid reagent (19:1 v/v). The contents of each tube are thoroughly stirred and incubated at 25° in the dark for exactly 30 min. The resultant colored solutions are transferred by dry Pasteur pipettes to a glass cell of capacity 1 ml. and the optical density of each solution is read in a photometer. The cholesterol contained in each sample may be determined from a calibration graph prepared from standard cholesterol solutions. A plot of the amount of cholesterol found per segment against the migration distance from the origin yields the lipoprotein pattern.

Calculation of α-:β-lipoprotein ratio. A line is drawn on the graph of each lipoprotein pattern parallel to the baseline in such a manner that both the cholesterol (lipoprotein) peaks are isolated from as much "background" material as possible. From this datum line, the area under each component is calculated, and the cholesterol on the α-lipoprotein expressed as a percentage of the total cholesterol on both the α- and β-lipoproteins.

An adaptation of this method is the detection on a parallel strip of paper of the α- and β-lipoproteins using a lipophilic dye (see page 351 for references). By employing the stained paper as a guide, the unstained paper may be cut into two major fractions from which the cholesterol can be eluted and estimated, yielding the α- : β-lipoprotein ratio.

Author Index

A

Subject Index

Compiled by P. BLADON and R. P. COOK

At the head of each chapter in this book there is a summary of the main topics discussed. It is hoped that readers will consult these. Moreover, in each chapter condensed information is given in tabular and/or diagrammatic form.

To save index space we have omitted the names of some cholesterol derivatives, which are mentioned only in the Charts (pp. 34-75) and/or Tables of Physical Constants (pp. 89-103) in Chapter 2. The occurrence of the main types of compounds such as cholestadienones, cholestenols, in these tables is given in this index. Cross references from the Tables to the Charts allow the location of individual compounds. The pages marked in *italics* indicate where physical constants are given of cholesterol derivatives, and of natural sterols.

In the index the *chemical* nomenclature is, in general, similar to that of Chemical Abstracts. Trivial names are used for certain compounds, particularly steroid hormones, the systematic nomenclature and synonyms being given in parenthesis. Where compounds have two or more names, cross references are given.

For *biological* nomenclature the common names of the animals and plants studied are given with an indication of the genus. The systematic names of bacteria are included, as are the protozoa but the insect genera appear as a text glossary.

Cross references are also given for the different nomenclatures for pathological conditions and diseases.

A

Absorption, intestinal, 7, 240 ff
  of cholesterol, 241 ff
  of squalene, 246
  of sterols, 244 ff
Absorption spectrophotometry, 135
  infrared, 79
  ultraviolet, 79
Acetaldehyde, 212
Acetate, as sterol precursor, 211 ff, 337 ff
Acetoacetate, 212 ff
Acetone, 212
Acid I, Acid II, 264, 267
ACTH (adrenocorticotrop(h)ic hormone
  of anterior pituitary, corticotropin)
  adrenal gland and, 227, 282, 326, 343,
    362, 363
  androgen production, 333
  corticosteroids and, 314
  plasma level and, 195, 197, 398
Addison's disease, 398
Adenosine triphosphate (ATP), 213, 225,
  226, 269
Adipocire, 1
Adipose tissue, 166, 167

Adrenal cortex,
  composition, 165, 166
  histology, 360
  hormones, 317 ff
Adrenal cortical hormones,
  biosynthesis of, 317 ff
  effect on plasma level, 196 ff
  formulas, 317
Adrenal gland, (see also species)
  biosynthesis in, 227
  turnover in, 282
Adrenal medulla, 165, 363
Adrenalectomy, 282
Adrenalin, 200
Adrenogenital syndrome, 311, 326, 328
Adrenosterone, 332
Age, effect of, on sterol in blood plasma,
  192-194, 377 ff
  aorta, 156
  tissues, 152, 158, 161, 167, 369
Agnosterol, 3, *19*
Alcaligenes faecalis, 458
Alcohol, 212, 469
Alcohols, equilibration, 29, 35
  oxidation, 29

529

I M